Statistics for Business and Economics

Custom Edition

Anderson | Sweeney | Williams | Camm | Cochran

Australia • Brazil • Japan • Korea • Mexico • Singapore • Spain • United Kingdom • United States

**Statistics for Business and Economics:
Custom Edition**

Statistics for Business & Economics, 12th Edition
David R. Anderson | Dennis J. Sweeney | Thomas A. Williams |
Jeffrey D. Camm | James J. Cochran

Senior Manager, Student Engagement:

Linda deStefano

Janey Moeller

Manager, Student Engagement:

Julie Dierig

Marketing Manager:

Rachael Kloos

Manager, Production Editorial:

Kim Fry

Manager, Intellectual Property Project Manager:

Brian Methe

Senior Manager, Production and Manufacturing:

Donna M. Brown

Manager, Production:

Terri Daley

For product information and technology assistance, contact us at
Cengage Learning Customer & Sales Support, 1-800-354-9706
For permission to use material from this text or product,
submit all requests online at **cengage.com/permissions**
Further permissions questions can be emailed to
permissionrequest@cengage.com

This book contains select works from existing Cengage Learning resources and
was produced by Cengage Learning Custom Solutions for collegiate use. As such,
those adopting and/or contributing to this work are responsible for editorial
content accuracy, continuity and completeness.

Compilation © 2014 Cengage Learning

ISBN-13: 978-1-305-29988-7

ISBN-10: 1-305-29988-4

WCN: 01-100-101

Cengage Learning

5191 Natorp Boulevard
Mason, Ohio 45040
USA

Cengage Learning is a leading provider of customized learning solutions with
office locations around the globe, including Singapore, the United Kingdom,
Australia, Mexico, Brazil, and Japan. Locate your local office at:
international.cengage.com/region.

Cengage Learning products are represented in Canada by Nelson Education, Ltd.
For your lifelong learning solutions, visit **www.cengage.com/custom.**
Visit our corporate website at **www.cengage.com.**

Printed in the United States of America

Brief Contents

Chapter 8   Interval Estimation.. 342

Chapter 9   Hypothesis Tests. 382

Chapter 14   Simple Linear Regression 598

Chapter 15   Multiple Regression 682

Chapter 16   Regression Analysis: Model Building 751

Chapter 17   Time Series Analysis and Forecasting 800

             Appendix B Tables 974

             Appendix D Self-Test Solutions and Answers to Even Numbered

             Exercises...1026

CHAPTER 8

Interval Estimation

CONTENTS

STATISTICS IN PRACTICE:
FOOD LION

8.1 POPULATION MEAN:
σ KNOWN
Margin of Error and the Interval
Estimate
Practical Advice

8.2 POPULATION MEAN:
σ UNKNOWN
Margin of Error and the Interval
Estimate

Practical Advice
Using a Small Sample
Summary of Interval
Estimation Procedures

8.3 DETERMINING THE
SAMPLE SIZE

8.4 POPULATION PROPORTION
Determining the Sample Size

STATISTICS *in* PRACTICE

FOOD LION*
SALISBURY, NORTH CAROLINA

Founded in 1957 as Food Town, Food Lion is one of the largest supermarket chains in the United States, with 1300 stores in 11 Southeastern and Mid-Atlantic states. The company sells more than 24,000 different products and offers nationally and regionally advertised brand-name merchandise, as well as a growing number of high-quality private label products manufactured especially for Food Lion. The company maintains its low price leadership and quality assurance through operating efficiencies such as standard store formats, innovative warehouse design, energy-efficient facilities, and data synchronization with suppliers. Food Lion looks to a future of continued innovation, growth, price leadership, and service to its customers.

Being in an inventory-intense business, Food Lion made the decision to adopt the LIFO (last-in, first-out) method of inventory valuation. This method matches current costs against current revenues, which minimizes the effect of radical price changes on profit and loss results. In addition, the LIFO method reduces net income thereby reducing income taxes during periods of inflation.

Food Lion establishes a LIFO index for each of seven inventory pools: Grocery, Paper/Household, Pet Supplies, Health & Beauty Aids, Dairy, Cigarette/Tobacco, and Beer/Wine. For example, a LIFO index of 1.008 for the Grocery pool would indicate that the company's grocery inventory value at current costs reflects a 0.8% increase due to inflation over the most recent one-year period.

A LIFO index for each inventory pool requires that the year-end inventory count for each product be valued at the current year-end cost and at the preceding year-end

As an inventory-intense business, Food Lion adopted the LIFO method of inventory valuation. © Bloomberg/Getty Images.

cost. To avoid excessive time and expense associated with counting the inventory in all 1200 store locations, Food Lion selects a random sample of 50 stores. Year-end physical inventories are taken in each of the sample stores. The current-year and preceding-year costs for each item are then used to construct the required LIFO indexes for each inventory pool.

For a recent year, the sample estimate of the LIFO index for the Health & Beauty Aids inventory pool was 1.015. Using a 95% confidence level, Food Lion computed a margin of error of .006 for the sample estimate. Thus, the interval from 1.009 to 1.021 provided a 95% confidence interval estimate of the population LIFO index. This level of precision was judged to be very good.

In this chapter you will learn how to compute the margin of error associated with sample estimates. You will also learn how to use this information to construct and interpret interval estimates of a population mean and a population proportion.

---

*The authors are indebted to Keith Cunningham, Tax Director, and Bobby Harkey, Staff Tax Accountant, at Food Lion for providing this Statistics in Practice.

In Chapter 7, we stated that a point estimator is a sample statistic used to estimate a population parameter. For instance, the sample mean $\bar{x}$ is a point estimator of the population mean μ and the sample proportion $\bar{p}$ is a point estimator of the population proportion p. Because a point estimator cannot be expected to provide the exact value of the population parameter, an **interval estimate** is often computed by adding and subtracting a value, called the **margin of error**, to the point estimate. The general form of an interval estimate is as follows:

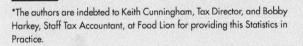

Point estimate $\pm$ Margin of error

The purpose of an interval estimate is to provide information about how close the point estimate, provided by the sample, is to the value of the population parameter.

In this chapter we show how to compute interval estimates of a population mean μ and a population proportion p. The general form of an interval estimate of a population mean is

$$\bar{x} \pm \text{Margin of error}$$

Similarly, the general form of an interval estimate of a population proportion is

$$\bar{p} \pm \text{Margin of error}$$

The sampling distributions of $\bar{x}$ and $\bar{p}$ play key roles in computing these interval estimates.

8.1 Population Mean: σ Known

In order to develop an interval estimate of a population mean, either the population standard deviation σ or the sample standard deviation s must be used to compute the margin of error. In most applications σ is not known, and s is used to compute the margin of error. In some applications, large amounts of relevant historical data are available and can be used to estimate the population standard deviation prior to sampling. Also, in quality control applications where a process is assumed to be operating correctly, or "in control," it is appropriate to treat the population standard deviation as known. We refer to such cases as the **σ known** case. In this section we introduce an example in which it is reasonable to treat σ as known and show how to construct an interval estimate for this case.

Each week Lloyd's Department Store selects a simple random sample of 100 customers in order to learn about the amount spent per shopping trip. With x representing the amount spent per shopping trip, the sample mean $\bar{x}$ provides a point estimate of μ, the mean amount spent per shopping trip for the population of all Lloyd's customers. Lloyd's has been using the weekly survey for several years. Based on the historical data, Lloyd's now assumes a known value of $\sigma = \$20$ for the population standard deviation. The historical data also indicate that the population follows a normal distribution.

Lloyd's

During the most recent week, Lloyd's surveyed 100 customers ($n = 100$) and obtained a sample mean of $\bar{x} = \$82$. The sample mean amount spent provides a point estimate of the population mean amount spent per shopping trip, μ. In the discussion that follows, we show how to compute the margin of error for this estimate and develop an interval estimate of the population mean.

Margin of Error and the Interval Estimate

In Chapter 7 we showed that the sampling distribution of $\bar{x}$ can be used to compute the probability that $\bar{x}$ will be within a given distance of μ. In the Lloyd's example, the historical data show that the population of amounts spent is normally distributed with a standard deviation of $\sigma = 20$. So, using what we learned in Chapter 7, we can conclude that the sampling distribution of $\bar{x}$ follows a normal distribution with a standard error of $\sigma_{\bar{x}} = \sigma/\sqrt{n} = 20/\sqrt{100} = 2$. This sampling distribution is shown in Figure 8.1.[1] Because

---

[1]We use the fact that the population of amounts spent has a normal distribution to conclude that the sampling distribution of $\bar{x}$ has a normal distribution. If the population did not have a normal distribution, we could rely on the central limit theorem and the sample size of $n = 100$ to conclude that the sampling distribution of $\bar{x}$ is approximately normal. In either case, the sampling distribution of $\bar{x}$ would appear as shown in Figure 8.1.

FIGURE 8.1 SAMPLING DISTRIBUTION OF THE SAMPLE MEAN AMOUNT SPENT FROM SIMPLE RANDOM SAMPLES OF 100 CUSTOMERS

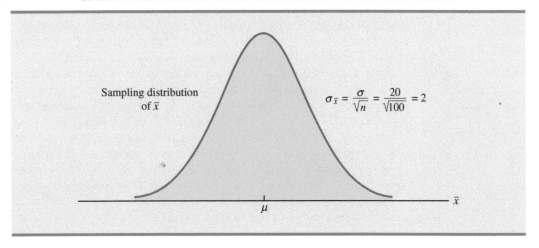

the sampling distribution shows how values of $\bar{x}$ are distributed around the population mean μ, the sampling distribution of $\bar{x}$ provides information about the possible differences between $\bar{x}$ and μ.

Using the standard normal probability table, we find that 95% of the values of any normally distributed random variable are within ± 1.96 standard deviations of the mean. Thus, when the sampling distribution of $\bar{x}$ is normally distributed, 95% of the $\bar{x}$ values must be within $\pm 1.96\sigma_{\bar{x}}$ of the mean μ. In the Lloyd's example we know that the sampling distribution of $\bar{x}$ is normally distributed with a standard error of $\sigma_{\bar{x}} = 2$. Because $\pm 1.96\sigma_{\bar{x}} = 1.96(2) = 3.92$, we can conclude that 95% of all $\bar{x}$ values obtained using a sample size of $n = 100$ will be within ± 3.92 of the population mean μ. See Figure 8.2.

FIGURE 8.2 SAMPLING DISTRIBUTION OF $\bar{x}$ SHOWING THE LOCATION OF SAMPLE MEANS THAT ARE WITHIN 3.92 OF μ

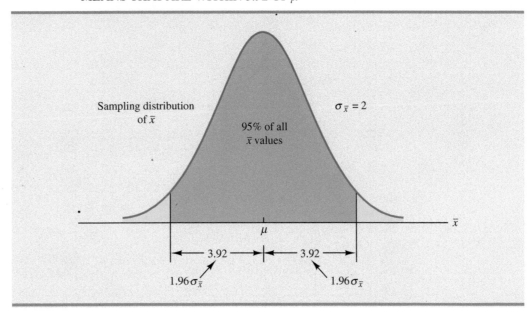

In the introduction to this chapter we said that the general form of an interval estimate of the population mean μ is $\bar{x} \pm$ margin of error. For the Lloyd's example, suppose we set the margin of error equal to 3.92 and compute the interval estimate of μ using $\bar{x} \pm 3.92$. To provide an interpretation for this interval estimate, let us consider the values of $\bar{x}$ that could be obtained if we took three *different* simple random samples, each consisting of 100 Lloyd's customers. The first sample mean might turn out to have the value shown as $\bar{x}_1$ in Figure 8.3. In this case, Figure 8.3 shows that the interval formed by subtracting 3.92 from $\bar{x}_1$ and adding 3.92 to $\bar{x}_1$ includes the population mean μ. Now consider what happens if the second sample mean turns out to have the value shown as $\bar{x}_2$ in Figure 8.3. Although this sample mean differs from the first sample mean, we see that the interval formed by subtracting 3.92 from $\bar{x}_2$ and adding 3.92 to $\bar{x}_2$ also includes the population mean μ. However, consider what happens if the third sample mean turns out to have the value shown as $\bar{x}_3$ in Figure 8.3. In this case, the interval formed by subtracting 3.92 from $\bar{x}_3$ and adding 3.92 to $\bar{x}_3$ does not include the population mean μ. Because $\bar{x}_3$ falls in the upper tail of the sampling distribution and is farther than 3.92 from μ, subtracting and adding 3.92 to $\bar{x}_3$ forms an interval that does not include μ.

Any sample mean $\bar{x}$ that is within the darkly shaded region of Figure 8.3 will provide an interval that contains the population mean μ. Because 95% of all possible sample means are in the darkly shaded region, 95% of all intervals formed by subtracting 3.92 from $\bar{x}$ and adding 3.92 to $\bar{x}$ will include the population mean μ.

Recall that during the most recent week, the quality assurance team at Lloyd's surveyed 100 customers and obtained a sample mean amount spent of $\bar{x} = 82$. Using $\bar{x} \pm 3.92$ to

FIGURE 8.3   INTERVALS FORMED FROM SELECTED SAMPLE MEANS AT LOCATIONS $\bar{x}_1$, $\bar{x}_2$, AND $\bar{x}_3$

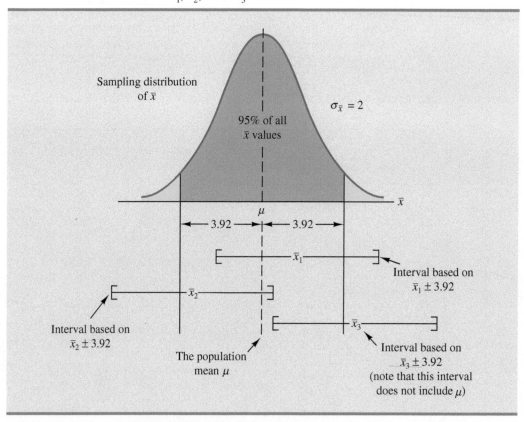

construct the interval estimate, we obtain 82 ± 3.92. Thus, the specific interval estimate of μ based on the data from the most recent week is $82 - 3.92 = 78.08$ to $82 + 3.92 = 85.92$. Because 95% of all the intervals constructed using $\bar{x} \pm 3.92$ will contain the population mean, we say that we are 95% confident that the interval 78.08 to 85.92 includes the population mean μ. We say that this interval has been established at the 95% **confidence level**. The value .95 is referred to as the **confidence coefficient**, and the interval 78.08 to 85.92 is called the 95% **confidence interval**.

This discussion provides insight as to why the interval is called a 95% confidence interval.

With the margin of error given by $z_{\alpha/2}(\sigma/\sqrt{n})$, the general form of an interval estimate of a population mean for the σ known case follows.

> **INTERVAL ESTIMATE OF A POPULATION MEAN: σ KNOWN**
>
> $$\bar{x} \pm z_{\alpha/2}\frac{\sigma}{\sqrt{n}} \qquad (8.1)$$
>
> where $(1 - \alpha)$ is the confidence coefficient and $z_{\alpha/2}$ is the z value providing an area of $\alpha/2$ in the upper tail of the standard normal probability distribution.

Let us use expression (8.1) to construct a 95% confidence interval for the Lloyd's example. For a 95% confidence interval, the confidence coefficient is $(1 - \alpha) = .95$ and thus, $\alpha = .05$. Using the standard normal probability table, an area of $\alpha/2 = .05/2 = .025$ in the upper tail provides $z_{.025} = 1.96$. With the Lloyd's sample mean $\bar{x} = 82$, $\sigma = 20$, and a sample size $n = 100$, we obtain

$$82 \pm 1.96\frac{20}{\sqrt{100}}$$

$$82 \pm 3.92$$

Thus, using expression (8.1), the margin of error is 3.92 and the 95% confidence interval is $82 - 3.92 = 78.08$ to $82 + 3.92 = 85.92$.

Although a 95% confidence level is frequently used, other confidence levels such as 90% and 99% may be considered. Values of $z_{\alpha/2}$ for the most commonly used confidence levels are shown in Table 8.1. Using these values and expression (8.1), the 90% confidence interval for the Lloyd's example is

$$82 \pm 1.645\frac{20}{\sqrt{100}}$$

$$82 \pm 3.29$$

TABLE 8.1   VALUES OF $z_{\alpha/2}$ FOR THE MOST COMMONLY USED CONFIDENCE LEVELS

Confidence Level	α	$\alpha/2$	$z_{\alpha/2}$
90%	.10	.05	1.645
95%	.05	.025	1.960
99%	.01	.005	2.576

Thus, at 90% confidence, the margin of error is 3.29 and the confidence interval is $82 - 3.29 = 78.71$ to $82 + 3.29 = 85.29$. Similarly, the 99% confidence interval is

$$82 \pm 2.576 \frac{20}{\sqrt{100}}$$

$$82 \pm 5.15$$

Thus, at 99% confidence, the margin of error is 5.15 and the confidence interval is $82 - 5.15 = 76.85$ to $82 + 5.15 = 87.15$.

Comparing the results for the 90%, 95%, and 99% confidence levels, we see that in order to have a higher degree of confidence, the margin of error and thus the width of the confidence interval must be larger.

Practical Advice

If the population follows a normal distribution, the confidence interval provided by expression (8.1) is exact. In other words, if expression (8.1) were used repeatedly to generate 95% confidence intervals, exactly 95% of the intervals generated would contain the population mean. If the population does not follow a normal distribution, the confidence interval provided by expression (8.1) will be approximate. In this case, the quality of the approximation depends on both the distribution of the population and the sample size.

In most applications, a sample size of $n \geq 30$ is adequate when using expression (8.1) to develop an interval estimate of a population mean. If the population is not normally distributed but is roughly symmetric, sample sizes as small as 15 can be expected to provide good approximate confidence intervals. With smaller sample sizes, expression (8.1) should only be used if the analyst believes, or is willing to assume, that the population distribution is at least approximately normal.

NOTES AND COMMENTS

1. The interval estimation procedure discussed in this section is based on the assumption that the population standard deviation σ is known. By σ known we mean that historical data or other information are available that permit us to obtain a good estimate of the population standard deviation prior to taking the sample that will be used to develop an estimate of the population mean. So technically we don't mean that σ is actually known with certainty. We just mean that we obtained a good estimate of the standard deviation prior to sampling and thus we won't be using the same sample to estimate both the population mean and the population standard deviation.

2. The sample size n appears in the denominator of the interval estimation expression (8.1). Thus, if a particular sample size provides too wide an interval to be of any practical use, we may want to consider increasing the sample size. With n in the denominator, a larger sample size will provide a smaller margin of error, a narrower interval, and greater precision. The procedure for determining the size of a simple random sample necessary to obtain a desired precision is discussed in Section 8.3.

Exercises

Methods

1. A simple random sample of 40 items resulted in a sample mean of 25. The population standard deviation is $\sigma = 5$.
   a. What is the standard error of the mean, $\sigma_{\bar{x}}$?
   b. At 95% confidence, what is the margin of error?

2. A simple random sample of 50 items from a population with $\sigma = 6$ resulted in a sample mean of 32.
   a. Provide a 90% confidence interval for the population mean.
   b. Provide a 95% confidence interval for the population mean.
   c. Provide a 99% confidence interval for the population mean.

3. A simple random sample of 60 items resulted in a sample mean of 80. The population standard deviation is $\sigma = 15$.
   a. Compute the 95% confidence interval for the population mean.
   b. Assume that the same sample mean was obtained from a sample of 120 items. Provide a 95% confidence interval for the population mean.
   c. What is the effect of a larger sample size on the interval estimate?

4. A 95% confidence interval for a population mean was reported to be 152 to 160. If $\sigma = 15$, what sample size was used in this study?

Applications

5. Data were collected on the amount spent by 64 customers for lunch at a major Houston restaurant. These data are contained in the file named Houston. Based upon past studies the population standard deviation is known with $\sigma = \$6$.
   a. At 99% confidence, what is the margin of error?
   b. Develop a 99% confidence interval estimate of the mean amount spent for lunch.

Houston

6. Nielsen Media Research conducted a study of household television viewing times during the 8 P.M. to 11 P.M. time period. The data contained in the file named Nielsen are consistent with the findings reported (*The World Almanac,* 2003). Based upon past studies the population standard deviation is assumed known with $\sigma = 3.5$ hours. Develop a 95% confidence interval estimate of the mean television viewing time per week during the 8 P.M. to 11 P.M. time period.

Nielsen

7. *The Wall Street Journal* reported that automobile crashes cost the United States $162 billion annually (*The Wall Street Journal,* March 5, 2008). The average cost per person for crashes in the Tampa, Florida, area was reported to be $1599. Suppose this average cost was based on a sample of 50 persons who had been involved in car crashes and that the population standard deviation is $\sigma = \$600$. What is the margin of error for a 95% confidence interval? What would you recommend if the study required a margin of error of $150 or less?

8. Studies show that massage therapy has a variety of health benefits and it is not too expensive (*The Wall Street Journal,* March 13, 2012). A sample of 10 typical one-hour massage therapy sessions showed an average charge of $59. The population standard deviation for a one-hour session is $\sigma = \$5.50$.
   a. What assumptions about the population should we be willing to make if a margin of error is desired?
   b. Using 95% confidence, what is the margin of error?
   c. Using 99% confidence, what is the margin of error?

TaxReturn

9. AARP reported on a study conducted to learn how long it takes individuals to prepare their federal income tax return (*AARP Bulletin,* April 2008). The data contained in the file named TaxReturn are consistent with the study results. These data provide the time in hours required for 40 individuals to complete their federal income tax returns. Using past years' data, the population standard deviation can be assumed known with $\sigma = 9$ hours. What is the 95% confidence interval estimate of the mean time it takes an individual to complete a federal income tax return?

10. *Playbill* magazine reported that the mean annual household income of its readers is $119,155 (*Playbill,* January 2006). Assume this estimate of the mean annual household income is based on a sample of 80 households, and based on past studies, the population standard deviation is known to be $\sigma = \$30,000$.

a. Develop a 90% confidence interval estimate of the population mean.
b. Develop a 95% confidence interval estimate of the population mean.
c. Develop a 99% confidence interval estimate of the population mean.
d. Discuss what happens to the width of the confidence interval as the confidence level is increased. Does this result seem reasonable? Explain.

8.2 Population Mean: σ Unknown

When developing an interval estimate of a population mean we usually do not have a good estimate of the population standard deviation either. In these cases, we must use the same sample to estimate both μ and σ. This situation represents the *σ unknown* case. When s is used to estimate σ, the margin of error and the interval estimate for the population mean are based on a probability distribution known as the *t distribution*. Although the mathematical development of the *t* distribution is based on the assumption of a normal distribution for the population we are sampling from, research shows that the *t* distribution can be successfully applied in many situations where the population deviates significantly from normal. Later in this section we provide guidelines for using the *t* distribution if the population is not normally distributed.

William Sealy Gosset, writing under the name "Student," is the founder of the t distribution. Gosset, an Oxford graduate in mathematics, worked for the Guinness Brewery in Dublin, Ireland. He developed the t distribution while working on small-scale materials and temperature experiments.

The *t* distribution is a family of similar probability distributions, with a specific *t* distribution depending on a parameter known as the **degrees of freedom**. The *t* distribution with one degree of freedom is unique, as is the *t* distribution with two degrees of freedom, with three degrees of freedom, and so on. As the number of degrees of freedom increases, the difference between the *t* distribution and the standard normal distribution becomes smaller and smaller. Figure 8.4 shows *t* distributions with 10 and 20 degrees of freedom and their relationship to the standard normal probability distribution. Note that a *t* distribution with more degrees of freedom exhibits less variability and more

FIGURE 8.4   COMPARISON OF THE STANDARD NORMAL DISTRIBUTION WITH *t* DISTRIBUTIONS HAVING 10 AND 20 DEGREES OF FREEDOM

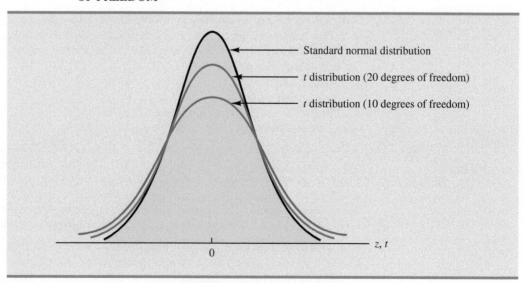

closely resembles the standard normal distribution. Note also that the mean of the t distribution is zero.

We place a subscript on t to indicate the area in the upper tail of the t distribution. For example, just as we used $z_{.025}$ to indicate the z value providing a .025 area in the upper tail of a standard normal distribution, we will use $t_{.025}$ to indicate a .025 area in the upper tail of a t distribution. In general, we will use the notation $t_{\alpha/2}$ to represent a t value with an area of $\alpha/2$ in the upper tail of the t distribution. See Figure 8.5.

As the degrees of freedom increase, the t distribution approaches the standard normal distribution.

Table 2 in Appendix B contains a table for the t distribution. A portion of this table is shown in Table 8.2. Each row in the table corresponds to a separate t distribution with the degrees of freedom shown. For example, for a t distribution with 9 degrees of freedom, $t_{.025} = 2.262$. Similarly, for a t distribution with 60 degrees of freedom, $t_{.025} = 2.000$. As the degrees of freedom continue to increase, $t_{.025}$ approaches $z_{.025} = 1.96$. In fact, the standard normal distribution z values can be found in the infinite degrees of freedom row (labeled ∞) of the t distribution table. If the degrees of freedom exceed 100, the infinite degrees of freedom row can be used to approximate the actual t value; in other words, for more than 100 degrees of freedom, the standard normal z value provides a good approximation to the t value.

Margin of Error and the Interval Estimate

In Section 8.1 we showed that an interval estimate of a population mean for the σ known case is

$$\bar{x} \pm z_{\alpha/2}\frac{\sigma}{\sqrt{n}}$$

To compute an interval estimate of μ for the σ unknown case, the sample standard deviation s is used to estimate σ, and $z_{\alpha/2}$ is replaced by the t distribution value $t_{\alpha/2}$. The margin

FIGURE 8.5 t DISTRIBUTION WITH $\alpha/2$ AREA OR PROBABILITY IN THE UPPER TAIL

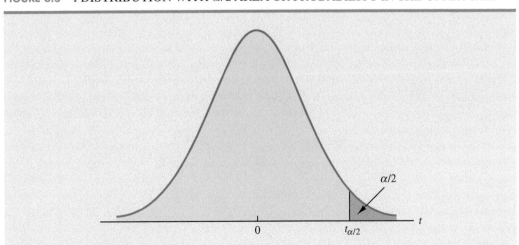

TABLE 8.2   SELECTED VALUES FROM THE *t* DISTRIBUTION TABLE*

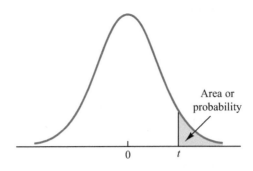

Degrees of Freedom	Area in Upper Tail					
	.20	.10	.05	.025	.01	.005
1	1.376	3.078	6.314	12.706	31.821	63.656
2	1.061	1.886	2.920	4.303	6.965	9.925
3	.978	1.638	2.353	3.182	4.541	5.841
4	.941	1.533	2.132	2.776	3.747	4.604
5	.920	1.476	2.015	2.571	3.365	4.032
6	.906	1.440	1.943	2.447	3.143	3.707
7	.896	1.415	1.895	2.365	2.998	3.499
8	.889	1.397	1.860	2.306	2.896	3.355
9	.883	1.383	1.833	2.262	2.821	3.250
⋮	⋮	⋮	⋮	⋮	⋮	⋮
60	.848	1.296	1.671	2.000	2.390	2.660
61	.848	1.296	1.670	2.000	2.389	2.659
62	.847	1.295	1.670	1.999	2.388	2.657
63	.847	1.295	1.669	1.998	2.387	2.656
64	.847	1.295	1.669	1.998	2.386	2.655
65	.847	1.295	1.669	1.997	2.385	2.654
66	.847	1.295	1.668	1.997	2.384	2.652
67	.847	1.294	1.668	1.996	2.383	2.651
68	.847	1.294	1.668	1.995	2.382	2.650
69	.847	1.294	1.667	1.995	2.382	2.649
⋮	⋮	⋮	⋮	⋮	⋮	⋮
90	.846	1.291	1.662	1.987	2.368	2.632
91	.846	1.291	1.662	1.986	2.368	2.631
92	.846	1.291	1.662	1.986	2.368	2.630
93	.846	1.291	1.661	1.986	2.367	2.630
94	.845	1.291	1.661	1.986	2.367	2.629
95	.845	1.291	1.661	1.985	2.366	2.629
96	.845	1.290	1.661	1.985	2.366	2.628
97	.845	1.290	1.661	1.985	2.365	2.627
98	.845	1.290	1.661	1.984	2.365	2.627
99	.845	1.290	1.660	1.984	2.364	2.626
100	.845	1.290	1.660	1.984	2.364	2.626
∞	.842	1.282	1.645	1.960	2.326	2.576

Note: A more extensive table is provided as Table 2 of Appendix B.

of error is then given by $t_{\alpha/2}s/\sqrt{n}$. With this margin of error, the general expression for an interval estimate of a population mean when σ is unknown follows.

INTERVAL ESTIMATE OF A POPULATION MEAN: σ UNKNOWN

$$\bar{x} \pm t_{\alpha/2}\frac{s}{\sqrt{n}} \tag{8.2}$$

where s is the sample standard deviation, $(1 - \alpha)$ is the confidence coefficient, and $t_{\alpha/2}$ is the t value providing an area of $\alpha/2$ in the upper tail of the t distribution with $n - 1$ degrees of freedom.

The reason the number of degrees of freedom associated with the t value in expression (8.2) is $n - 1$ concerns the use of s as an estimate of the population standard deviation σ. The expression for the sample standard deviation is

$$s = \sqrt{\frac{\Sigma(x_i - \bar{x})^2}{n - 1}}$$

Degrees of freedom refer to the number of independent pieces of information that go into the computation of $\Sigma(x_i - \bar{x})^2$. The n pieces of information involved in computing $\Sigma(x_i - \bar{x})^2$ are as follows: $x_1 - \bar{x}, x_2 - \bar{x}, \ldots, x_n - \bar{x}$. In Section 3.2 we indicated that $\Sigma(x_i - \bar{x}) = 0$ for any data set. Thus, only $n - 1$ of the $x_i - \bar{x}$ values are independent; that is, if we know $n - 1$ of the values, the remaining value can be determined exactly by using the condition that the sum of the $x_i - \bar{x}$ values must be 0. Thus, $n - 1$ is the number of degrees of freedom associated with $\Sigma(x_i - \bar{x})^2$ and hence the number of degrees of freedom for the t distribution in expression (8.2).

To illustrate the interval estimation procedure for the σ unknown case, we will consider a study designed to estimate the mean credit card debt for the population of U.S. households. A sample of $n = 70$ households provided the credit card balances shown in Table 8.3. For this situation, no previous estimate of the population standard deviation σ is available. Thus, the sample data must be used to estimate both the population mean and the population standard deviation. Using the data in Table 8.3, we compute the sample mean $\bar{x} = \$9312$ and the sample standard deviation $s = \$4007$. With 95% confidence and $n - 1 = 69$ degrees of

TABLE 8.3 CREDIT CARD BALANCES FOR A SAMPLE OF 70 HOUSEHOLDS

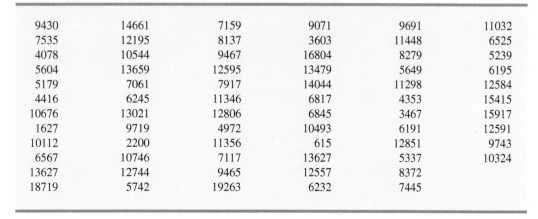

9430	14661	7159	9071	9691	11032
7535	12195	8137	3603	11448	6525
4078	10544	9467	16804	8279	5239
5604	13659	12595	13479	5649	6195
5179	7061	7917	14044	11298	12584
4416	6245	11346	6817	4353	15415
10676	13021	12806	6845	3467	15917
1627	9719	4972	10493	6191	12591
10112	2200	11356	615	12851	9743
6567	10746	7117	13627	5337	10324
13627	12744	9465	12557	8372	
18719	5742	19263	6232	7445	

freedom, Table 8.2 can be used to obtain the appropriate value for $t_{.025}$. We want the t value in the row with 69 degrees of freedom, and the column corresponding to .025 in the upper tail. The value shown is $t_{.025} = 1.995$.

We use expression (8.2) to compute an interval estimate of the population mean credit card balance.

$$9312 \pm 1.995 \frac{4007}{\sqrt{70}}$$

$$9312 \pm 955$$

The point estimate of the population mean is \$9312, the margin of error is \$955, and the 95% confidence interval is $9312 - 955 = \$8357$ to $9312 + 955 = \$10,267$. Thus, we are 95% confident that the mean credit card balance for the population of all households is between \$8357 and \$10,267.

The procedures used by Minitab, Excel and StatTools to develop confidence intervals for a population mean are described in Appendixes 8.1, 8.2 and 8.3. For the household credit card balances study, the results of the Minitab interval estimation procedure are shown in Figure 8.6. The sample of 70 households provides a sample mean credit card balance of \$9312, a sample standard deviation of \$4007, a standard error of the mean of \$479, and a 95% confidence interval of \$8357 to \$10,267.

Practical Advice

If the population follows a normal distribution, the confidence interval provided by expression (8.2) is exact and can be used for any sample size. If the population does not follow a normal distribution, the confidence interval provided by expression (8.2) will be approximate. In this case, the quality of the approximation depends on both the distribution of the population and the sample size.

Larger sample sizes are needed if the distribution of the population is highly skewed or includes outliers.

In most applications, a sample size of $n \geq 30$ is adequate when using expression (8.2) to develop an interval estimate of a population mean. However, if the population distribution is highly skewed or contains outliers, most statisticians would recommend increasing the sample size to 50 or more. If the population is not normally distributed but is roughly symmetric, sample sizes as small as 15 can be expected to provide good approximate confidence intervals. With smaller sample sizes, expression (8.2) should only be used if the analyst believes, or is willing to assume, that the population distribution is at least approximately normal.

Using a Small Sample

In the following example we develop an interval estimate for a population mean when the sample size is small. As we already noted, an understanding of the distribution of the population becomes a factor in deciding whether the interval estimation procedure provides acceptable results.

Scheer Industries is considering a new computer-assisted program to train maintenance employees to do machine repairs. In order to fully evaluate the program, the director of

FIGURE 8.6   MINITAB CONFIDENCE INTERVAL FOR THE CREDIT CARD BALANCE SURVEY

Variable	N	Mean	StDev	SE Mean	95% CI
NewBalance	70	9312	4007	479	(8357, 10267)

TABLE 8.4 TRAINING TIME IN DAYS FOR A SAMPLE OF 20 SCHEER INDUSTRIES EMPLOYEES

WEB file

Scheer

52	59	54	42
44	50	42	48
55	54	60	55
44	62	62	57
45	46	43	56

manufacturing requested an estimate of the population mean time required for maintenance employees to complete the computer-assisted training.

A sample of 20 employees is selected, with each employee in the sample completing the training program. Data on the training time in days for the 20 employees are shown in Table 8.4. A histogram of the sample data appears in Figure 8.7. What can we say about the distribution of the population based on this histogram? First, the sample data do not support the conclusion that the distribution of the population is normal, yet we do not see any evidence of skewness or outliers. Therefore, using the guidelines in the previous subsection, we conclude that an interval estimate based on the t distribution appears acceptable for the sample of 20 employees.

We continue by computing the sample mean and sample standard deviation as follows.

$$\bar{x} = \frac{\Sigma x_i}{n} = \frac{1030}{20} = 51.5 \text{ days}$$

$$s = \sqrt{\frac{\Sigma(x_i - \bar{x})^2}{n - 1}} = \sqrt{\frac{889}{20 - 1}} = 6.84 \text{ days}$$

FIGURE 8.7 HISTOGRAM OF TRAINING TIMES FOR THE SCHEER INDUSTRIES SAMPLE

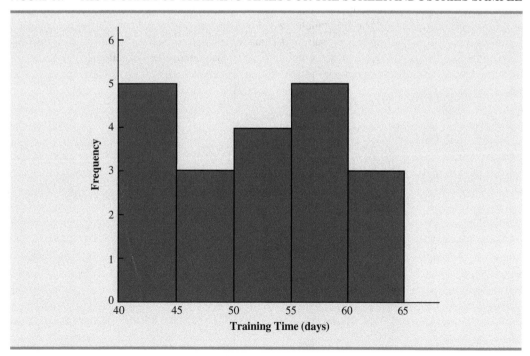

For a 95% confidence interval, we use Table 2 of Appendix B and $n - 1 = 19$ degrees of freedom to obtain $t_{.025} = 2.093$. Expression (8.2) provides the interval estimate of the population mean.

$$51.5 \pm 2.093\left(\frac{6.84}{\sqrt{20}}\right)$$

$$51.5 \pm 3.2$$

The point estimate of the population mean is 51.5 days. The margin of error is 3.2 days and the 95% confidence interval is $51.5 - 3.2 = 48.3$ days to $51.5 + 3.2 = 54.7$ days.

Using a histogram of the sample data to learn about the distribution of a population is not always conclusive, but in many cases it provides the only information available. The histogram, along with judgment on the part of the analyst, can often be used to decide whether expression (8.2) can be used to develop the interval estimate.

Summary of Interval Estimation Procedures

We provided two approaches to developing an interval estimate of a population mean. For the σ known case, σ and the standard normal distribution are used in expression (8.1) to compute the margin of error and to develop the interval estimate. For the σ unknown case, the sample standard deviation s and the t distribution are used in expression (8.2) to compute the margin of error and to develop the interval estimate.

A summary of the interval estimation procedures for the two cases is shown in Figure 8.8. In most applications, a sample size of $n \geq 30$ is adequate. If the population has a normal or approximately normal distribution, however, smaller sample sizes may be used.

FIGURE 8.8   SUMMARY OF INTERVAL ESTIMATION PROCEDURES
FOR A POPULATION MEAN

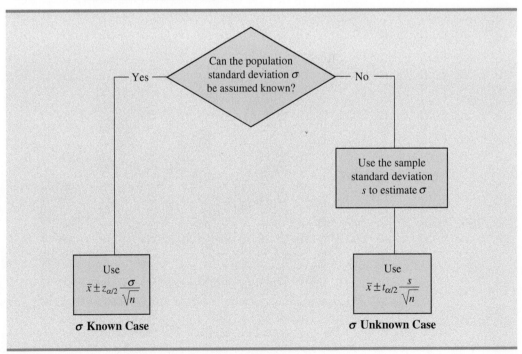

For the σ unknown case a sample size of $n \geq 50$ is recommended if the population distribution is believed to be highly skewed or has outliers.

NOTES AND COMMENTS

1. When σ is known, the margin of error, $z_{\alpha/2}(\sigma/\sqrt{n})$, is fixed and is the same for all samples of size n. When σ is unknown, the margin of error, $t_{\alpha/2}(s/\sqrt{n})$, varies from sample to sample. This variation occurs because the sample standard deviation s varies depending upon the sample selected. A large value for s provides a larger margin of error, while a small value for s provides a smaller margin of error.

2. What happens to confidence interval estimates when the population is skewed? Consider a population that is skewed to the right with large data values stretching the distribution to the right. When such skewness exists, the sample mean $\bar{x}$ and the sample standard deviation s are positively correlated. Larger values of s tend to be associated with larger values of $\bar{x}$. Thus, when $\bar{x}$ is larger than the population mean, s tends to be larger than σ. This skewness causes the margin of error, $t_{\alpha/2}(s/\sqrt{n})$, to be larger than it would be with σ known. The confidence interval with the larger margin of error tends to include the population mean μ more often than it would if the true value of σ were used. But when $\bar{x}$ is smaller than the population mean, the correlation between $\bar{x}$ and s causes the margin of error to be small. In this case, the confidence interval with the smaller margin of error tends to miss the population mean more than it would if we knew σ and used it. For this reason, we recommend using larger sample sizes with highly skewed population distributions.

Exercises

Methods

11. For a t distribution with 16 degrees of freedom, find the area, or probability, in each region.
    a. To the right of 2.120
    b. To the left of 1.337
    c. To the left of -1.746
    d. To the right of 2.583
    e. Between -2.120 and 2.120
    f. Between -1.746 and 1.746

12. Find the t value(s) for each of the following cases.
    a. Upper tail area of .025 with 12 degrees of freedom
    b. Lower tail area of .05 with 50 degrees of freedom
    c. Upper tail area of .01 with 30 degrees of freedom
    d. Where 90% of the area falls between these two t values with 25 degrees of freedom
    e. Where 95% of the area falls between these two t values with 45 degrees of freedom

13. The following sample data are from a normal population: 10, 8, 12, 15, 13, 11, 6, 5.
    a. What is the point estimate of the population mean?
    b. What is the point estimate of the population standard deviation?
    c. With 95% confidence, what is the margin of error for the estimation of the population mean?
    d. What is the 95% confidence interval for the population mean?

14. A simple random sample with $n = 54$ provided a sample mean of 22.5 and a sample standard deviation of 4.4.
    a. Develop a 90% confidence interval for the population mean.
    b. Develop a 95% confidence interval for the population mean.

c.   Develop a 99% confidence interval for the population mean.
d.   What happens to the margin of error and the confidence interval as the confidence level is increased?

Applications

15. Sales personnel for Skillings Distributors submit weekly reports listing the customer contacts made during the week. A sample of 65 weekly reports showed a sample mean of 19.5 customer contacts per week. The sample standard deviation was 5.2. Provide 90% and 95% confidence intervals for the population mean number of weekly customer contacts for the sales personnel.

CorporateBonds

16. A sample containing years to maturity and yield for 40 corporate bonds are contained in the data file named CorporateBonds (*Barron's,* April 2, 2012).
a.   What is the sample mean years to maturity for corporate bonds and what is the sample standard deviation?
b.   Develop a 95% confidence interval for the population mean years to maturity.
c.   What is the sample mean yield on corporate bonds and what is the sample standard deviation?
d.   Develop a 95% confidence interval for the population mean yield on corporate bonds.

17. The International Air Transport Association surveys business travelers to develop quality ratings for transatlantic gateway airports. The maximum possible rating is 10. Suppose a simple random sample of 50 business travelers is selected and each traveler is asked to provide a rating for the Miami International Airport. The ratings obtained from the sample of 50 business travelers follow.

Miami

6	4	6	8	7	7	6	3	3	8	10	4	8
7	8	7	5	9	5	8	4	3	8	5	5	4
4	4	8	4	5	6	2	5	9	9	8	4	8
9	9	5	9	7	8	3	10	8	9	6		

Develop a 95% confidence interval estimate of the population mean rating for Miami.

JobSearch

18. Older people often have a hard time finding work. AARP reported on the number of weeks it takes a worker aged 55 plus to find a job. The data on number of weeks spent searching for a job contained in the file JobSearch are consistent with the AARP findings (*AARP Bulletin,* April 2008).
a.   Provide a point estimate of the population mean number of weeks it takes a worker aged 55 plus to find a job.
b.   At 95% confidence, what is the margin of error?
c.   What is the 95% confidence interval estimate of the mean?
d.   Discuss the degree of skewness found in the sample data. What suggestion would you make for a repeat of this study?

19. The average cost per night of a hotel room in New York City is $273 (*SmartMoney,* March 2009). Assume this estimate is based on a sample of 45 hotels and that the sample standard deviation is $65.
a.   With 95% confidence, what is the margin of error?
b.   What is the 95% confidence interval estimate of the population mean?
c.   Two years ago the average cost of a hotel room in New York City was $229. Discuss the change in cost over the two-year period.

Program

20. Is your favorite TV program often interrupted by advertising? CNBC presented statistics on the average number of programming minutes in a half-hour sitcom (CNBC, February 23, 2006). The following data (in minutes) are representative of their findings.

21.06	22.24	20.62
21.66	21.23	23.86
23.82	20.30	21.52
21.52	21.91	23.14
20.02	22.20	21.20
22.37	22.19	22.34
23.36	23.44	

Assume the population is approximately normal. Provide a point estimate and a 95% confidence interval for the mean number of programming minutes during a half-hour television sitcom.

Alcohol

21. Consumption of alcoholic beverages by young women of drinking age in the United Kingdom, the United States, and Europe was reported (*The Wall Street Journal,* February 15, 2006). Data (annual consumption in liters) consistent with the findings reported in *The Wall Street Journal* article are shown for a sample of 20 European young women.

266	82	199	174	97
170	222	115	130	169
164	102	113	171	0
93	0	93	110	130

Assuming the population is roughly symmetric, construct a 95% confidence interval for the mean annual consumption of alcoholic beverages by European young women.

22. Disney's *Hannah Montana: The Movie* opened on Easter weekend in April 2009. Over the three-day weekend, the movie became the number-one box office attraction (*The Wall Street Journal,* April 13, 2009). The ticket sales revenue in dollars for a sample of 25 theaters is as follows.

TicketSales

20,200	10,150	13,000	11,320	9700
8350	7300	14,000	9940	11,200
10,750	6240	12,700	7430	13,500
13,900	4200	6750	6700	9330
13,185	9200	21,400	11,380	10,800

a. What is the 95% confidence interval estimate for the mean ticket sales revenue per theater? Interpret this result.
b. Using the movie ticket price of $7.16 per ticket, what is the estimate of the mean number of customers per theater?
c. The movie was shown in 3118 theaters. Estimate the total number of customers who saw *Hannah Montana: The Movie* and the total box office ticket sales for the three-day weekend.

8.3 Determining the Sample Size

If a desired margin of error is selected prior to sampling, the procedures in this section can be used to determine the sample size necessary to satisfy the margin of error requirement.

In providing practical advice in the two preceding sections, we commented on the role of the sample size in providing good approximate confidence intervals when the population is not normally distributed. In this section, we focus on another aspect of the sample size issue. We describe how to choose a sample size large enough to provide a desired margin of error. To understand how this process works, we return to the σ known case presented in Section 8.1. Using expression (8.1), the interval estimate is

$$\bar{x} \pm z_{\alpha/2}\frac{\sigma}{\sqrt{n}}$$

The quantity $z_{\alpha/2}(\sigma/\sqrt{n})$ is the margin of error. Thus, we see that $z_{\alpha/2}$, the population standard deviation σ, and the sample size n combine to determine the margin of error. Once we select a confidence coefficient $1 - \alpha$, $z_{\alpha/2}$ can be determined. Then, if we have a value for σ, we can determine the sample size n needed to provide any desired margin of error. Development of the formula used to compute the required sample size n follows.

Let E = the desired margin of error:

$$E = z_{\alpha/2} \frac{\sigma}{\sqrt{n}}$$

Solving for $\sqrt{n}$, we have

$$\sqrt{n} = \frac{z_{\alpha/2}\sigma}{E}$$

Squaring both sides of this equation, we obtain the following expression for the sample size.

Equation (8.3) can be used to provide a good sample size recommendation. However, judgment on the part of the analyst should be used to determine whether the final sample size should be adjusted upward.

SAMPLE SIZE FOR AN INTERVAL ESTIMATE OF A POPULATION MEAN

$$n = \frac{(z_{\alpha/2})^2 \sigma^2}{E^2} \tag{8.3}$$

This sample size provides the desired margin of error at the chosen confidence level.

In equation (8.3), E is the margin of error that the user is willing to accept, and the value of $z_{\alpha/2}$ follows directly from the confidence level to be used in developing the interval estimate. Although user preference must be considered, 95% confidence is the most frequently chosen value ($z_{.025} = 1.96$).

Finally, use of equation (8.3) requires a value for the population standard deviation σ. However, even if σ is unknown, we can use equation (8.3) provided we have a preliminary or *planning value* for σ. In practice, one of the following procedures can be chosen.

A planning value for the population standard deviation σ must be specified before the sample size can be determined. Three methods of obtaining a planning value for σ are discussed here.

1. Use the estimate of the population standard deviation computed from data of previous studies as the planning value for σ.
2. Use a pilot study to select a preliminary sample. The sample standard deviation from the preliminary sample can be used as the planning value for σ.
3. Use judgment or a "best guess" for the value of σ. For example, we might begin by estimating the largest and smallest data values in the population. The difference between the largest and smallest values provides an estimate of the range for the data. Finally, the range divided by 4 is often suggested as a rough approximation of the standard deviation and thus an acceptable planning value for σ.

Let us demonstrate the use of equation (8.3) to determine the sample size by considering the following example. A previous study that investigated the cost of renting automobiles in the United States found a mean cost of approximately $55 per day for renting a midsize automobile. Suppose that the organization that conducted this study would like to conduct a new study in order to estimate the population mean daily rental cost for a midsize automobile in the United States. In designing the new study, the project director specifies that the population mean daily rental cost be estimated with a margin of error of $2 and a 95% level of confidence.

The project director specified a desired margin of error of $E = 2$, and the 95% level of confidence indicates $z_{.025} = 1.96$. Thus, we only need a planning value for the population standard deviation σ in order to compute the required sample size. At this point, an analyst reviewed the sample data from the previous study and found that the sample standard deviation for the daily rental cost was $9.65. Using 9.65 as the planning value for σ, we obtain

Equation (8.3) provides the minimum sample size needed to satisfy the desired margin of error requirement. If the computed sample size is not an integer, rounding up to the next integer value will provide a margin of error slightly smaller than required.

$$n = \frac{(z_{\alpha/2})^2 \sigma^2}{E^2} = \frac{(1.96)^2 (9.65)^2}{2^2} = 89.43$$

Thus, the sample size for the new study needs to be at least 89.43 midsize automobile rentals in order to satisfy the project director's $2 margin-of-error requirement. In cases where the computed n is not an integer, we round up to the next integer value; hence, the recommended sample size is 90 midsize automobile rentals.

Exercises

Methods

23. How large a sample should be selected to provide a 95% confidence interval with a margin of error of 10? Assume that the population standard deviation is 40.

24. The range for a set of data is estimated to be 36.
    a. What is the planning value for the population standard deviation?
    b. At 95% confidence, how large a sample would provide a margin of error of 3?
    c. At 95% confidence, how large a sample would provide a margin of error of 2?

Applications

25. Refer to the Scheer Industries example in Section 8.2. Use 6.84 days as a planning value for the population standard deviation.
    a. Assuming 95% confidence, what sample size would be required to obtain a margin of error of 1.5 days?
    b. If the precision statement was made with 90% confidence, what sample size would be required to obtain a margin of error of 2 days?

26. The U.S. Energy Information Administration (US EIA) reported that the average price for a gallon of regular gasoline is $3.94 (US EIA website, April 6, 2012). The US EIA updates its estimates of average gas prices on a weekly basis. Assume the standard deviation is $.25 for the price of a gallon of regular gasoline and recommend the appropriate sample size for the US EIA to use if they wish to report each of the following margins of error at 95% confidence.
    a. The desired margin of error is $.10.
    b. The desired margin of error is $.07.
    c. The desired margin of error is $.05.

27. Annual starting salaries for college graduates with degrees in business administration are generally expected to be between $30,000 and $45,000. Assume that a 95% confidence interval estimate of the population mean annual starting salary is desired. What is the planning value for the population standard deviation? How large a sample should be taken if the desired margin of error is
    a. $500?
    b. $200?
    c. $100?
    d. Would you recommend trying to obtain the $100 margin of error? Explain.

28. An online survey by ShareBuilder, a retirement plan provider, and Harris Interactive reported that 60% of female business owners are not confident they are saving enough for retirement (*SmallBiz*, Winter 2006). Suppose we would like to do a follow-up study to determine how much female business owners are saving each year toward retirement and want to use $100 as the desired margin of error for an interval estimate of the population mean. Use $1100 as a planning value for the standard deviation and recommend a sample size for each of the following situations.
    a. A 90% confidence interval is desired for the mean amount saved.
    b. A 95% confidence interval is desired for the mean amount saved.

c. A 99% confidence interval is desired for the mean amount saved.

d. When the desired margin of error is set, what happens to the sample size as the confidence level is increased? Would you recommend using a 99% confidence interval in this case? Discuss.

29. The travel-to-work time for residents of the 15 largest cities in the United States is reported in the *2003 Information Please Almanac*. Suppose that a preliminary simple random sample of residents of San Francisco is used to develop a planning value of 6.25 minutes for the population standard deviation.

a. If we want to estimate the population mean travel-to-work time for San Francisco residents with a margin of error of 2 minutes, what sample size should be used? Assume 95% confidence.

b. If we want to estimate the population mean travel-to-work time for San Francisco residents with a margin of error of 1 minute, what sample size should be used? Assume 95% confidence.

30. There has been a trend toward less driving in the last few years, especially by young people. From 2001 to 2009 the annual vehicle miles traveled by people from 16 to 34 years of age decreased from 10,300 to 7900 miles per person (U.S. PIRG and Education Fund website, April 6, 2012). Assume the standard deviation was 2000 miles in 2009. Suppose you would like to conduct a survey to develop a 95% confidence interval estimate of the annual vehicle-miles per person for people 16 to 34 years of age at the current time. A margin of error of 100 miles is desired. How large a sample should be used for the current survey?

8.4 Population Proportion

In the introduction to this chapter we said that the general form of an interval estimate of a population proportion p is

$$\bar{p} \pm \text{Margin of error}$$

The sampling distribution of $\bar{p}$ plays a key role in computing the margin of error for this interval estimate.

In Chapter 7 we said that the sampling distribution of $\bar{p}$ can be approximated by a normal distribution whenever $np \geq 5$ and $n(1 - p) \geq 5$. Figure 8.9 shows the normal approximation

FIGURE 8.9   NORMAL APPROXIMATION OF THE SAMPLING DISTRIBUTION OF $\bar{p}$

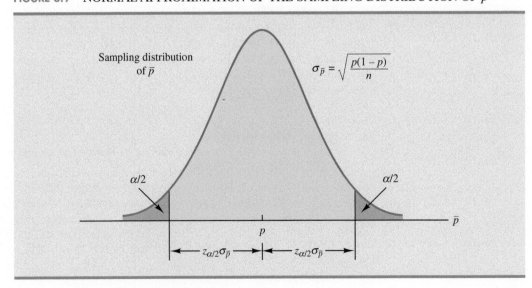

of the sampling distribution of $\bar{p}$. The mean of the sampling distribution of $\bar{p}$ is the population proportion p, and the standard error of $\bar{p}$ is

$$\sigma_{\bar{p}} = \sqrt{\frac{p(1-p)}{n}} \qquad (8.4)$$

Because the sampling distribution of $\bar{p}$ is normally distributed, if we choose $z_{\alpha/2}\sigma_{\bar{p}}$ as the margin of error in an interval estimate of a population proportion, we know that $100(1-\alpha)\%$ of the intervals generated will contain the true population proportion. But $\sigma_{\bar{p}}$ cannot be used directly in the computation of the margin of error because p will not be known; p is what we are trying to estimate. So $\bar{p}$ is substituted for p and the margin of error for an interval estimate of a population proportion is given by

$$\text{Margin of error} = z_{\alpha/2}\sqrt{\frac{\bar{p}(1-\bar{p})}{n}} \qquad (8.5)$$

With this margin of error, the general expression for an interval estimate of a population proportion is as follows.

When developing confidence intervals for proportions, the quantity $z_{\alpha/2}\sqrt{\bar{p}(1-\bar{p})/n}$ provides the margin of error.

INTERVAL ESTIMATE OF A POPULATION PROPORTION

$$\bar{p} \pm z_{\alpha/2}\sqrt{\frac{\bar{p}(1-\bar{p})}{n}} \qquad (8.6)$$

where $1-\alpha$ is the confidence coefficient and $z_{\alpha/2}$ is the z value providing an area of $\alpha/2$ in the upper tail of the standard normal distribution.

TeeTimes

The following example illustrates the computation of the margin of error and interval estimate for a population proportion. A national survey of 900 women golfers was conducted to learn how women golfers view their treatment at golf courses in the United States. The survey found that 396 of the women golfers were satisfied with the availability of tee times. Thus, the point estimate of the proportion of the population of women golfers who are satisfied with the availability of tee times is $396/900 = .44$. Using expression (8.6) and a 95% confidence level,

$$\bar{p} \pm z_{\alpha/2}\sqrt{\frac{\bar{p}(1-\bar{p})}{n}}$$

$$.44 \pm 1.96\sqrt{\frac{.44(1-.44)}{900}}$$

$$.44 \pm .0324$$

Thus, the margin of error is .0324 and the 95% confidence interval estimate of the population proportion is .4076 to .4724. Using percentages, the survey results enable us to state with 95% confidence that between 40.76% and 47.24% of all women golfers are satisfied with the availability of tee times.

Determining the Sample Size

Let us consider the question of how large the sample size should be to obtain an estimate of a population proportion at a specified level of precision. The rationale for the sample size determination in developing interval estimates of p is similar to the rationale used in Section 8.3 to determine the sample size for estimating a population mean.

Previously in this section we said that the margin of error associated with an interval estimate of a population proportion is $z_{\alpha/2}\sqrt{\bar{p}(1-\bar{p})/n}$. The margin of error is based on the value of $z_{\alpha/2}$, the sample proportion $\bar{p}$, and the sample size n. Larger sample sizes provide a smaller margin of error and better precision.

Let E denote the desired margin of error.

$$E = z_{\alpha/2}\sqrt{\frac{\bar{p}(1-\bar{p})}{n}}$$

Solving this equation for n provides a formula for the sample size that will provide a margin of error of size E.

$$n = \frac{(z_{\alpha/2})^2 \bar{p}(1-\bar{p})}{E^2}$$

Note, however, that we cannot use this formula to compute the sample size that will provide the desired margin of error because $\bar{p}$ will not be known until after we select the sample. What we need, then, is a planning value for $\bar{p}$ that can be used to make the computation. Using p^* to denote the planning value for $\bar{p}$, the following formula can be used to compute the sample size that will provide a margin of error of size E.

SAMPLE SIZE FOR AN INTERVAL ESTIMATE OF A POPULATION PROPORTION

$$n = \frac{(z_{\alpha/2})^2 p^*(1-p^*)}{E^2} \tag{8.7}$$

In practice, the planning value p^* can be chosen by one of the following procedures.

1. Use the sample proportion from a previous sample of the same or similar units.
2. Use a pilot study to select a preliminary sample. The sample proportion from this sample can be used as the planning value, p^*.
3. Use judgment or a "best guess" for the value of p^*.
4. If none of the preceding alternatives apply, use a planning value of $p^* = .50$.

Let us return to the survey of women golfers and assume that the company is interested in conducting a new survey to estimate the current proportion of the population of women golfers who are satisfied with the availability of tee times. How large should the sample be if the survey director wants to estimate the population proportion with a margin of error of .025 at 95% confidence? With $E = .025$ and $z_{\alpha/2} = 1.96$, we need a planning value p^* to answer the sample size question. Using the previous survey result of $\bar{p} = .44$ as the planning value p^*, equation (8.7) shows that

$$n = \frac{(z_{\alpha/2})^2 p^*(1-p^*)}{E^2} = \frac{(1.96)^2(.44)(1-.44)}{(.025)^2} = 1514.5$$

TABLE 8.5 SOME POSSIBLE VALUES FOR $p^*(1 - p^*)$

p^*	$p^*(1 - p^*)$	
.10	$(.10)(.90) = .09$	
.30	$(.30)(.70) = .21$	
.40	$(.40)(.60) = .24$	
.50	$(.50)(.50) = .25$	← Largest value for $p^*(1 - p^*)$
.60	$(.60)(.40) = .24$	
.70	$(.70)(.30) = .21$	
.90	$(.90)(.10) = .09$	

Thus, the sample size must be at least 1514.5 women golfers to satisfy the margin of error requirement. Rounding up to the next integer value indicates that a sample of 1515 women golfers is recommended to satisfy the margin of error requirement.

The fourth alternative suggested for selecting a planning value p^* is to use $p^* = .50$. This value of p^* is frequently used when no other information is available. To understand why, note that the numerator of equation (8.7) shows that the sample size is proportional to the quantity $p^*(1 - p^*)$. A larger value for the quantity $p^*(1 - p^*)$ will result in a larger sample size. Table 8.5 gives some possible values of $p^*(1 - p^*)$. Note that the largest value of $p^*(1 - p^*)$ occurs when $p^* = .50$. Thus, in case of any uncertainty about an appropriate planning value, we know that $p^* = .50$ will provide the largest sample size recommendation. In effect, we play it safe by recommending the largest necessary sample size. If the sample proportion turns out to be different from the .50 planning value, the margin of error will be smaller than anticipated. Thus, in using $p^* = .50$, we guarantee that the sample size will be sufficient to obtain the desired margin of error.

In the survey of women golfers example, a planning value of $p^* = .50$ would have provided the sample size

$$n = \frac{(z_{\alpha/2})^2 p^*(1 - p^*)}{E^2} = \frac{(1.96)^2(.50)(1 - .50)}{(.025)^2} = 1536.6$$

Thus, a slightly larger sample size of 1537 women golfers would be recommended.

NOTES AND COMMENTS

The desired margin of error for estimating a population proportion is almost always .10 or less. In national public opinion polls conducted by organizations such as Gallup and Harris, a .03 or .04 margin of error is common. With such margins of error, equation (8.7) will almost always provide a sample size that is large enough to satisfy the requirements of $np \geq 5$ and $n(1 - p) \geq 5$ for using a normal distribution as an approximation for the sampling distribution of $\bar{x}$.

Exercises

Methods

31. A simple random sample of 400 individuals provides 100 Yes responses.
    a. What is the point estimate of the proportion of the population that would provide Yes responses?
    b. What is your estimate of the standard error of the proportion, $\sigma_{\bar{p}}$?
    c. Compute the 95% confidence interval for the population proportion.

32. A simple random sample of 800 elements generates a sample proportion $\bar{p} = .70$.
    a. Provide a 90% confidence interval for the population proportion.
    b. Provide a 95% confidence interval for the population proportion.

33. In a survey, the planning value for the population proportion is $p^* = .35$. How large a sample should be taken to provide a 95% confidence interval with a margin of error of .05?

34. At 95% confidence, how large a sample should be taken to obtain a margin of error of .03 for the estimation of a population proportion? Assume that past data are not available for developing a planning value for p^*.

Applications

35. The Consumer Reports National Research Center conducted a telephone survey of 2000 adults to learn about the major economic concerns for the future (*Consumer Reports,* January 2009). The survey results showed that 1760 of the respondents think the future health of Social Security is a major economic concern.
    a. What is the point estimate of the population proportion of adults who think the future health of Social Security is a major economic concern.
    b. At 90% confidence, what is the margin of error?
    c. Develop a 90% confidence interval for the population proportion of adults who think the future health of Social Security is a major economic concern.
    d. Develop a 95% confidence interval for this population proportion.

36. According to statistics reported on CNBC, a surprising number of motor vehicles are not covered by insurance (CNBC, February 23, 2006). Sample results, consistent with the CNBC report, showed 46 of 200 vehicles were not covered by insurance.
    a. What is the point estimate of the proportion of vehicles not covered by insurance?
    b. Develop a 95% confidence interval for the population proportion.

37. Towers Perrin, a New York human resources consulting firm, conducted a survey of 1100 employees at medium-sized and large companies to determine how dissatisfied employees were with their jobs (*The Wall Street Journal,* January 29, 2003). Representative data are shown in the file JobSatisfaction. A response of Yes indicates the employee strongly disliked the current work experience.

JobSatisfaction

    a. What is the point estimate of the proportion of the population of employees who strongly dislike their current work experience?
    b. At 95% confidence, what is the margin of error?
    c. What is the 95% confidence interval for the proportion of the population of employees who strongly dislike their current work experience?
    d. Towers Perrin estimates that it costs employers one-third of an hourly employee's annual salary to find a successor and as much as 1.5 times the annual salary to find a successor for a highly compensated employee. What message did this survey send to employers?

38. According to Thomson Financial, through January 25, 2006, the majority of companies reported profits had beaten estimates (*BusinessWeek,* February 6, 2006). A sample of 162 companies showed 104 beat estimates, 29 matched estimates, and 29 fell short.
    a. What is the point estimate of the proportion that fell short of estimates?
    b. Determine the margin of error and provide a 95% confidence interval for the proportion that beat estimates.
    c. How large a sample is needed if the desired margin of error is .05?

39. The percentage of people not covered by health care insurance in 2003 was 15.6% (*Statistical Abstract of the United States*, 2006). A congressional committee has been charged with conducting a sample survey to obtain more current information.
    a. What sample size would you recommend if the committee's goal is to estimate the current proportion of individuals without health care insurance with a margin of error of .03? Use a 95% confidence level.
    b. Repeat part (a) using a 99% confidence level.

40. For many years businesses have struggled with the rising cost of health care. But recently, the increases have slowed due to less inflation in health care prices and employees paying for a larger portion of health care benefits. A recent Mercer survey showed that 52% of U.S. employers were likely to require higher employee contributions for health care coverage in 2009 (*BusinessWeek*, February 16, 2009). Suppose the survey was based on a sample of 800 companies. Compute the margin of error and a 95% confidence interval for the proportion of companies likely to require higher employee contributions for health care coverage in 2009.

41. Fewer young people are driving. In 1983, 87% of 19-year-olds had a driver's license. Twenty-five years later that percentage had dropped to 75% (University of Michigan Transportation Research Institute website, April 7, 2012). Suppose these results are based on a random sample of 1200 19-year-olds in 1983 and again in 2008.

   a. At 95% confidence, what is the margin of error and the interval estimate of the number of 19-year-old drivers in 1983?

   b. At 95% confidence, what is the margin of error and the interval estimate of the number of 19-year-old drivers in 2008?

   c. Is the margin of error the same in parts (a) and (b)? Why or why not?

42. A poll for the presidential campaign sampled 491 potential voters in June. A primary purpose of the poll was to obtain an estimate of the proportion of potential voters who favored each candidate. Assume a planning value of $p^* = .50$ and a 95% confidence level.

   a. For $p^* = .50$, what was the planned margin of error for the June poll?

   b. Closer to the November election, better precision and smaller margins of error are desired. Assume the following margins of error are requested for surveys to be conducted during the presidential campaign. Compute the recommended sample size for each survey.

Survey	Margin of Error
September	.04
October	.03
Early November	.02
Pre-Election Day	.01

43. A Phoenix Wealth Management/Harris Interactive survey of 1500 individuals with net worth of $1 million or more provided a variety of statistics on wealthy people (*BusinessWeek*, September 22, 2003). The previous three-year period had been bad for the stock market, which motivated some of the questions asked.

   a. The survey reported that 53% of the respondents lost 25% or more of their portfolio value over the past three years. Develop a 95% confidence interval for the proportion of wealthy people who lost 25% or more of their portfolio value over the past three years.

   b. The survey reported that 31% of the respondents feel they have to save more for retirement to make up for what they lost. Develop a 95% confidence interval for the population proportion.

   c. Five percent of the respondents gave $25,000 or more to charity over the previous year. Develop a 95% confidence interval for the proportion who gave $25,000 or more to charity.

   d. Compare the margin of error for the interval estimates in parts (a), (b), and (c). How is the margin of error related to $\bar{p}$? When the same sample is being used to estimate a variety of proportions, which of the proportions should be used to choose the planning value p^*? Why do you think $p^* = .50$ is often used in these cases?

Summary

In this chapter we presented methods for developing interval estimates of a population mean and a population proportion. A point estimator may or may not provide a good estimate of a population parameter. The use of an interval estimate provides a measure of the precision of an estimate. Both the interval estimate of the population mean and the population proportion are of the form: point estimate ± margin of error.

We presented interval estimates for a population mean for two cases. In the σ known case, historical data or other information is used to develop an estimate of σ prior to taking a sample. Analysis of new sample data then proceeds based on the assumption that σ is known. In the σ unknown case, the sample data are used to estimate both the population mean and the population standard deviation. The final choice of which interval estimation procedure to use depends upon the analyst's understanding of which method provides the best estimate of σ.

In the σ known case, the interval estimation procedure is based on the assumed value of σ and the use of the standard normal distribution. In the σ unknown case, the interval estimation procedure uses the sample standard deviation s and the t distribution. In both cases the quality of the interval estimates obtained depends on the distribution of the population and the sample size. If the population is normally distributed the interval estimates will be exact in both cases, even for small sample sizes. If the population is not normally distributed, the interval estimates obtained will be approximate. Larger sample sizes will provide better approximations, but the more highly skewed the population is, the larger the sample size needs to be to obtain a good approximation. Practical advice about the sample size necessary to obtain good approximations was included in Sections 8.1 and 8.2. In most cases a sample of size 30 or more will provide good approximate confidence intervals.

The general form of the interval estimate for a population proportion is $\bar{p}$ ± margin of error. In practice the sample sizes used for interval estimates of a population proportion are generally large. Thus, the interval estimation procedure is based on the standard normal distribution.

Often a desired margin of error is specified prior to developing a sampling plan. We showed how to choose a sample size large enough to provide the desired precision.

Glossary

Interval estimate An estimate of a population parameter that provides an interval believed to contain the value of the parameter. For the interval estimates in this chapter, it has the form: point estimate ± margin of error.

Margin of error The ± value added to and subtracted from a point estimate in order to develop an interval estimate of a population parameter.

σ known The case when historical data or other information provides a good value for the population standard deviation prior to taking a sample. The interval estimation procedure uses this known value of σ in computing the margin of error.

Confidence level The confidence associated with an interval estimate. For example, if an interval estimation procedure provides intervals such that 95% of the intervals formed using the procedure will include the population parameter, the interval estimate is said to be constructed at the 95% confidence level.

Confidence coefficient The confidence level expressed as a decimal value. For example, .95 is the confidence coefficient for a 95% confidence level.

Confidence interval Another name for an interval estimate.

σ unknown The more common case when no good basis exists for estimating the population standard deviation prior to taking the sample. The interval estimation procedure uses the sample standard deviation s in computing the margin of error.

t distribution A family of probability distributions that can be used to develop an interval estimate of a population mean whenever the population standard deviation σ is unknown and is estimated by the sample standard deviation s.

Degrees of freedom A parameter of the t distribution. When the t distribution is used in the computation of an interval estimate of a population mean, the appropriate t distribution has $n - 1$ degrees of freedom, where n is the size of the sample.

Key Formulas

Interval Estimate of a Population Mean: σ Known

$$\bar{x} \pm z_{\alpha/2} \frac{\sigma}{\sqrt{n}} \qquad (8.1)$$

Interval Estimate of a Population Mean: σ Unknown

$$\bar{x} \pm t_{\alpha/2} \frac{s}{\sqrt{n}} \qquad (8.2)$$

Sample Size for an Interval Estimate of a Population Mean

$$n = \frac{(z_{\alpha/2})^2 \sigma^2}{E^2} \qquad (8.3)$$

Interval Estimate of a Population Proportion

$$\bar{p} \pm z_{\alpha/2} \sqrt{\frac{\bar{p}(1 - \bar{p})}{n}} \qquad (8.6)$$

Sample Size for an Interval Estimate of a Population Proportion

$$n = \frac{(z_{\alpha/2})^2 p^*(1 - p^*)}{E^2} \qquad (8.7)$$

Supplementary Exercises

44. A sample survey of 54 discount brokers showed that the mean price charged for a trade of 100 shares at $50 per share was $33.77 (*AAII Journal,* February 2006). The survey is conducted annually. With the historical data available, assume a known population standard deviation of $15.
    a. Using the sample data, what is the margin of error associated with a 95% confidence interval?
    b. Develop a 95% confidence interval for the mean price charged by discount brokers for a trade of 100 shares at $50 per share.

45. A survey conducted by the American Automobile Association showed that a family of four spends an average of $215.60 per day while on vacation. Suppose a sample of 64 families of four vacationing at Niagara Falls resulted in a sample mean of $252.45 per day and a sample standard deviation of $74.50.
    a. Develop a 95% confidence interval estimate of the mean amount spent per day by a family of four visiting Niagara Falls.
    b. Based on the confidence interval from part (a), does it appear that the population mean amount spent per day by families visiting Niagara Falls differs from the mean reported by the American Automobile Association? Explain.

46. The 92 million Americans of age 50 and over control 50 percent of all discretionary income (*AARP Bulletin,* March 2008). AARP estimated that the average annual expenditure on restaurants and carryout food was $1873 for individuals in this age group. Suppose this estimate is based on a sample of 80 persons and that the sample standard deviation is $550.
    a. At 95% confidence, what is the margin of error?
    b. What is the 95% confidence interval for the population mean amount spent on restaurants and carryout food?
    c. What is your estimate of the total amount spent by Americans of age 50 and over on restaurants and carryout food?
    d. If the amount spent on restaurants and carryout food is skewed to the right, would you expect the median amount spent to be greater or less than $1873?

47. Many stock market observers say that when the P/E ratio for stocks gets over 20 the market is overvalued. The P/E ratio is the stock price divided by the most recent 12 months of earnings. Suppose you are interested in seeing whether the current market is overvalued and would also like to know what proportion of companies pay dividends. A random sample of 30 companies listed on the New York Stock Exchange (NYSE) is provided (*Barron's,* January 19, 2004).

NYSEStocks

Company	Dividend	P/E Ratio	Company	Dividend	P/E Ratio
Albertsons	Yes	14	NY Times A	Yes	25
BRE Prop	Yes	18	Omnicare	Yes	25
CityNtl	Yes	16	PallCp	Yes	23
DelMonte	No	21	PubSvcEnt	Yes	11
EnrgzHldg	No	20	SensientTch	Yes	11
Ford Motor	Yes	22	SmtProp	Yes	12
Gildan A	No	12	TJX Cos	Yes	21
HudsnUtdBcp	Yes	13	Thomson	Yes	30
IBM	Yes	22	USB Hldg	Yes	12
JeffPilot	Yes	16	US Restr	Yes	26
KingswayFin	No	6	Varian Med	No	41
Libbey	Yes	13	Visx	No	72
MasoniteIntl	No	15	Waste Mgt	No	23
Motorola	Yes	68	Wiley A	Yes	21
Ntl City	Yes	10	Yum Brands	No	18

   a. What is a point estimate of the P/E ratio for the population of stocks listed on the New York Stock Exchange? Develop a 95% confidence interval.
   b. Based on your answer to part (a), do you believe that the market is overvalued?
   c. What is a point estimate of the proportion of companies on the NYSE that pay dividends? Is the sample size large enough to justify using the normal distribution to construct a confidence interval for this proportion? Why or why not?

Flights

48. US Airways conducted a number of studies that indicated a substantial savings could be obtained by encouraging Dividend Miles frequent flyer customers to redeem miles and schedule award flights online (*US Airways Attaché,* February 2003). One study collected data on the amount of time required to redeem miles and schedule an award flight over the telephone. A sample showing the time in minutes required for each of 150 award flights scheduled by telephone is contained in the data set Flights. Use Minitab or Excel to help answer the following questions.
   a. What is the sample mean number of minutes required to schedule an award flight by telephone?
   b. What is the 95% confidence interval for the population mean time to schedule an award flight by telephone?
   c. Assume a telephone ticket agent works 7.5 hours per day. How many award flights can one ticket agent be expected to handle a day?
   d. Discuss why this information supported US Airways' plans to use an online system to reduce costs.

49. A recent article reported that there are approximately 11 minutes of actual playing time in a typical National Football League (NFL) game (*The Wall Street Journal,* January 15, 2010). The article included information about the amount of time devoted to replays, the amount of time devoted to commercials, and the amount of time the players spend standing around between plays. Data consistent with the findings published in *The Wall Street Journal* are in the file named Standing. These data provide the amount of time players spend standing around between plays for a sample of 60 NFL games.
   a. Use the Standing data set to develop a point estimate of the number of minutes during an NFL game that players are standing around between plays. Compare this to the actual playing time reported in the article. Are you surprised?
   b. What is the sample standard deviation?

    c.   Develop a 95% confidence interval for the number of minutes players spend standing around between plays.

50.   Mileage tests are conducted for a particular model of automobile. If a 98% confidence interval with a margin of error of 1 mile per gallon is desired, how many automobiles should be used in the test? Assume that preliminary mileage tests indicate the standard deviation is 2.6 miles per gallon.

51.   In developing patient appointment schedules, a medical center wants to estimate the mean time that a staff member spends with each patient. How large a sample should be taken if the desired margin of error is two minutes at a 95% level of confidence? How large a sample should be taken for a 99% level of confidence? Use a planning value for the population standard deviation of eight minutes.

52.   Annual salary plus bonus data for chief executive officers are presented in the *BusinessWeek* Annual Pay Survey. A preliminary sample showed that the standard deviation is $675 with data provided in thousands of dollars. How many chief executive officers should be in a sample if we want to estimate the population mean annual salary plus bonus with a margin of error of $100,000? (*Note:* The desired margin of error would be $E = 100$ if the data are in thousands of dollars.) Use 95% confidence.

53.   The National Center for Education Statistics reported that 47% of college students work to pay for tuition and living expenses. Assume that a sample of 450 college students was used in the study.

    a.   Provide a 95% confidence interval for the population proportion of college students who work to pay for tuition and living expenses.

    b.   Provide a 99% confidence interval for the population proportion of college students who work to pay for tuition and living expenses.

    c.   What happens to the margin of error as the confidence is increased from 95% to 99%?

54.   A *USA Today*/CNN/Gallup survey of 369 working parents found 200 who said they spend too little time with their children because of work commitments.

    a.   What is the point estimate of the proportion of the population of working parents who feel they spend too little time with their children because of work commitments?

    b.   At 95% confidence, what is the margin of error?

    c.   What is the 95% confidence interval estimate of the population proportion of working parents who feel they spend too little time with their children because of work commitments?

55.   Which would be hardest for you to give up: Your computer or your television? In a recent survey of 1677 U.S. Internet users, 74% of the young tech elite (average age of 22) say their computer would be very hard to give up (*PC Magazine,* February 3, 2004). Only 48% say their television would be very hard to give up.

    a.   Develop a 95% confidence interval for the proportion of the young tech elite that would find it very hard to give up their computer.

    b.   Develop a 99% confidence interval for the proportion of the young tech elite that would find it very hard to give up their television.

    c.   In which case, part (a) or part (b), is the margin of error larger? Explain why.

56.   Cincinnati/Northern Kentucky International Airport had the second highest on-time arrival rate for 2005 among the nation's busiest airports (*The Cincinnati Enquirer,* February 3, 2006). Assume the findings were based on 455 on-time arrivals out of a sample of 550 flights.

    a.   Develop a point estimate of the on-time arrival rate (proportion of flights arriving on time) for the airport.

    b.   Construct a 95% confidence interval for the on-time arrival rate of the population of all flights at the airport during 2005.

57.   The *2003 Statistical Abstract of the United States* reported the percentage of people 18 years of age and older who smoke. Suppose that a study designed to collect new data on smokers and nonsmokers uses a preliminary estimate of the proportion who smoke of .30.

    a.   How large a sample should be taken to estimate the proportion of smokers in the population with a margin of error of .02? Use 95% confidence.

b. Assume that the study uses your sample size recommendation in part (a) and finds 520 smokers. What is the point estimate of the proportion of smokers in the population?

c. What is the 95% confidence interval for the proportion of smokers in the population?

58. A well-known bank credit card firm wishes to estimate the proportion of credit card holders who carry a nonzero balance at the end of the month and incur an interest charge. Assume that the desired margin of error is .03 at 98% confidence.

a. How large a sample should be selected if it is anticipated that roughly 70% of the firm's card holders carry a nonzero balance at the end of the month?

b. How large a sample should be selected if no planning value for the proportion could be specified?

59. Workers in several industries were surveyed to determine the proportion of workers who feel their industry is understaffed. In the government sector, 37% of the respondents said they were understaffed, in the health care sector 33% said they were understaffed, and in the education sector 28% said they were understaffed (*USA Today,* January 11, 2010). Suppose that 200 workers were surveyed in each industry.

a. Construct a 95% confidence interval for the proportion of workers in each of these industries who feel their industry is understaffed.

b. Assuming the same sample size will be used in each industry, how large would the sample need to be to ensure that the margin of error is .05 or less for each of the three confidence intervals?

60. Although airline schedules and cost are important factors for business travelers when choosing an airline carrier, a *USA Today* survey found that business travelers list an airline's frequent flyer program as the most important factor. From a sample of $n = 1993$ business travelers who responded to the survey, 618 listed a frequent flyer program as the most important factor.

a. What is the point estimate of the proportion of the population of business travelers who believe a frequent flyer program is the most important factor when choosing an airline carrier?

b. Develop a 95% confidence interval estimate of the population proportion.

c. How large a sample would be required to report the margin of error of .01 at 95% confidence? Would you recommend that *USA Today* attempt to provide this degree of precision? Why or why not?

Case Problem 1   Young Professional Magazine

Young Professional magazine was developed for a target audience of recent college graduates who are in their first 10 years in a business/professional career. In its two years of publication, the magazine has been fairly successful. Now the publisher is interested in expanding the magazine's advertising base. Potential advertisers continually ask about the demographics and interests of subscribers to *Young Professional*. To collect this information, the magazine commissioned a survey to develop a profile of its subscribers. The survey results will be used to help the magazine choose articles of interest and provide advertisers with a profile of subscribers. As a new employee of the magazine, you have been asked to help analyze the survey results.

Some of the survey questions follow:

WEB file

Professional

1. What is your age?
2. Are you: Male_____   Female_____
3. Do you plan to make any real estate purchases in the next two years? Yes_____ No_____
4. What is the approximate total value of financial investments, exclusive of your home, owned by you or members of your household?
5. How many stock/bond/mutual fund transactions have you made in the past year?

TABLE 8.6   PARTIAL SURVEY RESULTS FOR *YOUNG PROFESSIONAL* MAGAZINE

Age	Gender	Real Estate Purchases	Value of Investments($)	Number of Transactions	Broadband Access	Household Income($)	Children
38	Female	No	12200	4	Yes	75200	Yes
30	Male	No	12400	4	Yes	70300	Yes
41	Female	No	26800	5	Yes	48200	No
28	Female	Yes	19600	6	No	95300	No
31	Female	Yes	15100	5	No	73300	Yes
⋮	⋮	⋮	⋮	⋮	⋮	⋮	⋮

6. Do you have broadband access to the Internet at home? Yes_____   No_____
7. Please indicate your total household income last year. _____
8. Do you have children? Yes_____   No_____

The file entitled Professional contains the responses to these questions. Table 8.6 shows the portion of the file pertaining to the first five survey respondents.

Managerial Report

Prepare a managerial report summarizing the results of the survey. In addition to statistical summaries, discuss how the magazine might use these results to attract advertisers. You might also comment on how the survey results could be used by the magazine's editors to identify topics that would be of interest to readers. Your report should address the following issues, but do not limit your analysis to just these areas.

1. Develop appropriate descriptive statistics to summarize the data.
2. Develop 95% confidence intervals for the mean age and household income of subscribers.
3. Develop 95% confidence intervals for the proportion of subscribers who have broadband access at home and the proportion of subscribers who have children.
4. Would *Young Professional* be a good advertising outlet for online brokers? Justify your conclusion with statistical data.
5. Would this magazine be a good place to advertise for companies selling educational software and computer games for young children?
6. Comment on the types of articles you believe would be of interest to readers of *Young Professional.*

Case Problem 2   Gulf Real Estate Properties

Gulf Real Estate Properties, Inc., is a real estate firm located in southwest Florida. The company, which advertises itself as "expert in the real estate market," monitors condominium sales by collecting data on location, list price, sale price, and number of days it takes to sell each unit. Each condominium is classified as *Gulf View* if it is located directly on the Gulf of Mexico or *No Gulf View* if it is located on the bay or a golf course, near but not on the Gulf. Sample data from the Multiple Listing Service in Naples, Florida, provided recent sales data for 40 Gulf View condominiums and 18 No Gulf View condominiums. Prices are in thousands of dollars. The data are shown in Table 8.7.

Managerial Report

1. Use appropriate descriptive statistics to summarize each of the three variables for the 40 Gulf View condominiums.

TABLE 8.7   SALES DATA FOR GULF REAL ESTATE PROPERTIES

Gulf View Condominiums			No Gulf View Condominiums		
List Price	Sale Price	Days to Sell	List Price	Sale Price	Days to Sell
495.0	475.0	130	217.0	217.0	182
379.0	350.0	71	148.0	135.5	338
529.0	519.0	85	186.5	179.0	122
552.5	534.5	95	239.0	230.0	150
334.9	334.9	119	279.0	267.5	169
550.0	505.0	92	215.0	214.0	58
169.9	165.0	197	279.0	259.0	110
210.0	210.0	56	179.9	176.5	130
975.0	945.0	73	149.9	144.9	149
314.0	314.0	126	235.0	230.0	114
315.0	305.0	88	199.8	192.0	120
885.0	800.0	282	210.0	195.0	61
975.0	975.0	100	226.0	212.0	146
469.0	445.0	56	149.9	146.5	137
329.0	305.0	49	160.0	160.0	281
365.0	330.0	48	322.0	292.5	63
332.0	312.0	88	187.5	179.0	48
520.0	495.0	161	247.0	227.0	52
425.0	405.0	149			
675.0	669.0	142			
409.0	400.0	28			
649.0	649.0	29			
319.0	305.0	140			
425.0	410.0	85			
359.0	340.0	107			
469.0	449.0	72			
895.0	875.0	129			
439.0	430.0	160			
435.0	400.0	206			
235.0	227.0	91			
638.0	618.0	100			
629.0	600.0	97			
329.0	309.0	114			
595.0	555.0	45			
339.0	315.0	150			
215.0	200.0	48			
395.0	375.0	135			
449.0	425.0	53			
499.0	465.0	86			
439.0	428.5	158			

WEB file

GulfProp

2. Use appropriate descriptive statistics to summarize each of the three variables for the 18 No Gulf View condominiums.

3. Compare your summary results. Discuss any specific statistical results that would help a real estate agent understand the condominium market.

4. Develop a 95% confidence interval estimate of the population mean sales price and population mean number of days to sell for Gulf View condominiums. Interpret your results.

5. Develop a 95% confidence interval estimate of the population mean sales price and population mean number of days to sell for No Gulf View condominiums. Interpret your results.
6. Assume the branch manager requested estimates of the mean selling price of Gulf View condominiums with a margin of error of $40,000 and the mean selling price of No Gulf View condominiums with a margin of error of $15,000. Using 95% confidence, how large should the sample sizes be?
7. Gulf Real Estate Properties just signed contracts for two new listings: a Gulf View condominium with a list price of $589,000 and a No Gulf View condominium with a list price of $285,000. What is your estimate of the final selling price and number of days required to sell each of these units?

Case Problem 3   Metropolitan Research, Inc.

Metropolitan Research, Inc., a consumer research organization, conducts surveys designed to evaluate a wide variety of products and services available to consumers. In one particular study, Metropolitan looked at consumer satisfaction with the performance of automobiles produced by a major Detroit manufacturer. A questionnaire sent to owners of one of the manufacturer's full-sized cars revealed several complaints about early transmission problems. To learn more about the transmission failures, Metropolitan used a sample of actual transmission repairs provided by a transmission repair firm in the Detroit area. The following data show the actual number of miles driven for 50 vehicles at the time of transmission failure.

85,092	32,609	59,465	77,437	32,534	64,090	32,464	59,902
39,323	89,641	94,219	116,803	92,857	63,436	65,605	85,861
64,342	61,978	67,998	59,817	101,769	95,774	121,352	69,568
74,276	66,998	40,001	72,069	25,066	77,098	69,922	35,662
74,425	67,202	118,444	53,500	79,294	64,544	86,813	116,269
37,831	89,341	73,341	85,288	138,114	53,402	85,586	82,256
77,539	88,798						

Managerial Report

1. Use appropriate descriptive statistics to summarize the transmission failure data.
2. Develop a 95% confidence interval for the mean number of miles driven until transmission failure for the population of automobiles with transmission failure. Provide a managerial interpretation of the interval estimate.
3. Discuss the implication of your statistical findings in terms of the belief that some owners of the automobiles experienced early transmission failures.
4. How many repair records should be sampled if the research firm wants the population mean number of miles driven until transmission failure to be estimated with a margin of error of 5000 miles? Use 95% confidence.
5. What other information would you like to gather to evaluate the transmission failure problem more fully?

Appendix 8.1   Interval Estimation with Minitab

We describe the use of Minitab in constructing confidence intervals for a population mean and a population proportion.

Population Mean: σ Known

Lloyd's

We illustrate interval estimation using the Lloyd's example in Section 8.1. The amounts spent per shopping trip for the sample of 100 customers are in column C1 of a Minitab worksheet. The population standard deviation $\sigma = 20$ is assumed known. The following steps can be used to compute a 95% confidence interval estimate of the population mean.

Step 1. Select the **Stat** menu
Step 2. Choose **Basic Statistics**
Step 3. Choose **1-Sample Z**
Step 4. When the 1-Sample Z dialog box appears:
　　　　　Enter C1 in the **Samples in columns** box
　　　　　Enter 20 in the **Standard deviation** box
Step 5. Click **OK**

The Minitab default is a 95% confidence level. In order to specify a different confidence level such as 90%, add the following to step 4.

　　　　Select **Options**
　　　　When the 1-Sample Z-Options dialog box appears:
　　　　　Enter 90 in the **Confidence level** box
　　　　Click **OK**

Population Mean: σ Unknown

NewBalance

We illustrate interval estimation using the data in Table 8.3 showing the credit card balances for a sample of 70 households. The data are in column C1 of a Minitab worksheet. In this case the population standard deviation σ will be estimated by the sample standard deviation s. The following steps can be used to compute a 95% confidence interval estimate of the population mean.

Step 1. Select the **Stat** menu
Step 2. Choose **Basic Statistics**
Step 3. Choose **1-Sample t**
Step 4. When the 1-Sample t dialog box appears:
　　　　　Enter C1 in the **Samples in columns** box
Step 5. Click **OK**

The Minitab default is a 95% confidence level. In order to specify a different confidence level such as 90%, add the following to step 4.

　　　　Select **Options**
　　　　When the 1-Sample t-Options dialog box appears:
　　　　　Enter 90 in the **Confidence level** box
　　　　Click **OK**

Population Proportion

TeeTimes

We illustrate interval estimation using the survey data for women golfers presented in Section 8.4. The data are in column C1 of a Minitab worksheet. Individual responses are recorded as Yes if the golfer is satisfied with the availability of tee times and No otherwise. The following steps can be used to compute a 95% confidence interval estimate of the proportion of women golfers who are satisfied with the availability of tee times.

Step 1. Select the **Stat** menu
Step 2. Choose **Basic Statistics**
Step 3. Choose **1 Proportion**

Step 4. When the 1 Proportion dialog box appears:
           Enter C1 in the **Samples in columns** box
Step 5. Select **Options**
Step 6. When the 1 Proportion-Options dialog box appears:
           Select **Use test and interval based on normal distribution**
           Click **OK**
Step 7. Click **OK**

The Minitab default is a 95% confidence level. In order to specify a different confidence level such as 90%, enter 90 in the **Confidence Level** box when the 1 Proportion-Options dialog box appears in step 6.

    Note: Minitab's 1 Proportion routine uses an alphabetical ordering of the responses and selects the *second response* for the population proportion of interest. In the women golfers example, Minitab used the alphabetical ordering No-Yes and then provided the confidence interval for the proportion of Yes responses. Because Yes was the response of interest, the Minitab output was fine. However, if Minitab's alphabetical ordering does not provide the response of interest, select any cell in the column and use the sequence: Editor > Column > Value Order. It will provide you with the option of entering a user-specified order, but you must list the response of interest second in the define-an-order box.

Appendix 8.2   Interval Estimation Using Excel

We describe the use of Excel in constructing confidence intervals for a population mean and a population proportion.

Population Mean: σ Known

WEB file

Lloyd's

We illustrate interval estimation using the Lloyd's example in Section 8.1. The population standard deviation $\sigma = 20$ is assumed known. The amounts spent for the sample of 100 customers are in column A of an Excel worksheet. Excel's AVERAGE and CONFIDENCE.NORM functions can be used to compute the point estimate and the margin of error for an estimate of the population mean.

    Step 1. Select cell C1 and enter the Excel formula =AVERAGE(A2:A101)
    Step 2. Select cell C2 and enter the Excel formula =CONFIDENCE.NORM(.05,20,100)

The three inputs of the CONFIDENCE.NORM function are

        Alpha = 1 − confidence coefficient = 1 − .95 = .05
        The population standard deviation = 20
        The sample size = 100

The point estimate of the population mean (82) in cell C1 and the margin of error (3.92) in cell C2 allow the confidence interval for the population mean to be easily computed.

Population Mean: σ Unknown

WEB file

NewBalance

We illustrate interval estimation using the data in Table 8.3, which show the credit card balances for a sample of 70 households. The data are in column A of an Excel worksheet. The following steps can be used to compute the point estimate and the margin of error for an interval estimate of a population mean. We will use Excel's Descriptive Statistics Tool described in Chapter 3.

FIGURE 8.10 INTERVAL ESTIMATION OF THE POPULATION MEAN CREDIT CARD BALANCE USING EXCEL

	A	B	C	D	E	F
1	**NewBalance**		*NewBalance*			
2	9430					Point Estimate
3	7535		Mean	9312		
4	4078		Standard Error	478.9281		
5	5604		Median	9466		
6	5179		Mode	13627		
7	4416		Standard Deviation	4007		
8	10676		Sample Variance	16056048		
9	1627		Kurtosis	-0.2960		
10	10112		Skewness	0.1879		
11	6567		Range	18648		
12	13627		Minimum	615		
13	18719		Maximum	19263		
14	14661		Sum	651840		
15	12195		Count	70		Margin of Error
16	10544		Confidence Level(95.0%)	955		
17	13659					
70	9743					
71	10324					
72						

Note: Rows 18 to 69 are hidden.

Step 1. Click the **Data** tab on the Ribbon
Step 2. In the **Analysis** group, click **Data Analysis**
Step 3. Choose **Descriptive Statistics** from the list of Analysis Tools
Step 4. When the Descriptive Statistics dialog box appears:
    Enter A1:A71 in the **Input Range** box
    Select **Grouped by Columns**
    Select **Labels in First Row**
    Select **Output Range**
    Enter C1 in the Output Range box
    Select **Summary Statistics**
    Select **Confidence Level for Mean**
      Enter 95 in the Confidence Level for Mean box
    Click **OK**

The summary statistics will appear in columns C and D. The point estimate of the population mean appears in cell D3. The margin of error, labeled "Confidence Level(95.0%)," appears in cell D16. The point estimate ($9312) and the margin of error ($955) allow the confidence interval for the population mean to be easily computed. The output from this Excel procedure is shown in Figure 8.10.

FIGURE 8.11   EXCEL TEMPLATE FOR INTERVAL ESTIMATION OF A POPULATION PROPORTION

◢	A	B	C	D	E
1	**Response**		**Interval Estimate of a Population Proportion**		
2	Yes				
3	No		Sample Size	=COUNTA(A2:A901)	
4	Yes		**Response of Interest**	Yes	
5	Yes		**Count for Response**	=COUNTIF(A2:A901,D4)	
6	No		**Sample Proportion**	=D5/D3	
7	No				
8	No		**Confidence Coefficient**	0.95	
9	Yes		**z Value**	=NORM.S.INV(0.5+D8/2)	
10	Yes				
11	Yes		**Standard Error**	=SQRT(D6*(1-D6)/D3)	
12	No		**Margin of Error**	=D9*D11	
13	No				
14	Yes		**Point Estimate**	=D6	
15	No		**Lower Limit**	=D14-D12	
16	No		**Upper Limit**	=D14+D12	
17	Yes				
18	No				
901	Yes				
902					

◢	A	B	C	D	E	F	G
1	**Response**		**Interval Estimate of a Population Proportion**				
2	Yes						
3	No		**Sample Size**	900	Enter the response of interest		
4	Yes		**Response of Interest**	Yes			
5	Yes		**Count for Response**	396			
6	No		**Sample Proportion**	0.4400			
7	No				Enter the confidence coefficient		
8	No		**Confidence Coefficient**	0.95			
9	Yes		**z Value**	1.960			
10	Yes						
11	Yes		**Standard Error**	0.0165			
12	No		**Margin of Error**	0.0324			
13	No						
14	Yes		**Point Estimate**	0.4400			
15	No		**Lower Limit**	0.4076			
16	No		**Upper Limit**	0.4724			
17	Yes						
18	No						
901	Yes						
902							

Note: Rows 19 to 900 are hidden.

Population Proportion

We illustrate interval estimation using the survey data for women golfers presented in Section 8.4. The data are in column A of an Excel worksheet. Individual responses are recorded as Yes if the golfer is satisfied with the availability of tee times and No otherwise. Excel does not offer a built-in routine to handle the estimation of a population proportion; however, it is relatively easy to develop an Excel template that can be used for this purpose. The template shown in Figure 8.11 provides the 95% confidence interval estimate of the proportion of women golfers who are satisfied with the availability of tee times. Note that the background worksheet in Figure 8.11 shows the cell formulas that provide the interval estimation results shown in the foreground worksheet. The following steps are necessary to use the template for this data set.

Step 1. Enter the data range A2:A901 into the =COUNTA cell formula in cell D3
Step 2. Enter Yes as the response of interest in cell D4
Step 3. Enter the data range A2:A901 into the =COUNTIF cell formula in cell D5
Step 4. Enter .95 as the confidence coefficient in cell D8

The template automatically provides the confidence interval in cells D15 and D16.

This template can be used to compute the confidence interval for a population proportion for other applications. For instance, to compute the interval estimate for a new data set, enter the new sample data into column A of the worksheet and then make the changes to the four cells as shown. If the new sample data have already been summarized, the sample data do not have to be entered into the worksheet. In this case, enter the sample size into cell D3 and the sample proportion into cell D6; the worksheet template will then provide the confidence interval for the population proportion. The worksheet in Figure 8.11 is available in the file Interval p on the website that accompanies this book.

Appendix 8.3   Interval Estimation with StatTools

In this appendix we show how StatTools can be used to develop an interval estimate of a population mean for the σ unknown case and determine the sample size needed to provide a desired margin of error.

Population Mean: σ Unknown Case

In this case the population standard deviation σ will be estimated by the sample standard deviation s. We use the credit card balance data in Table 8.3 to illustrate. Begin by using the Data Set Manager to create a StatTools data set for these data using the procedure described in the appendix to Chapter 1. The following steps can be used to compute a 95% confidence interval estimate of the population mean.

WEB file

NewBalance

Step 1. Click the **StatTools** tab on the Ribbon
Step 2. In the **Analyses** group, click **Statistical Inference**
Step 3. Choose the **Confidence Interval** option
Step 4. Choose Mean/Std. Deviation
Step 5. When the StatTools-Confidence Interval for Mean/Std. Deviation dialog box appears:
> For **Analysis Type** choose **One-Sample Analysis**
> In the **Variables** section, select **NewBalance**
> In the **Confidence Intervals to Calculate** section:
> > Select the **For the Mean** option
> > Select 95% for the **Confidence Level**
> Click **OK**

Some descriptive statistics and the confidence interval will appear.

Determining the Sample Size

In Section 8.3 we showed how to determine the sample size needed to provide a desired margin of error. The example used involved a study designed to estimate the population mean daily rental cost for a midsize automobile in the United States. The project director specified that the population mean daily rental cost be estimated with a margin of error of

$2 and a 95% level of confidence. Sample data from a previous study provided a sample standard deviation of $9.65; this value was used as the planning value for the population standard deviation. The following steps can be used to compute the recommended sample size required to provide a 95% confidence interval estimate of the population mean with a margin of error of $2.

Step 1. Click the **StatTools** tab on the Ribbon
Step 2. In the **Analyses** group, click **Statistical Inference**
Step 3. Choose the **Sample Size Selection** option
Step 4. When the StatTools-Sample Size Selection dialog box appears:
          In the **Parameter to Estimate** section, select **Mean**
          In the **Confidence Interval Specification** section:
              Select **95%** for the **Confidence Level**
              Enter **2** in the **Half-Length of Interval** box
              Enter **9.65** in the **Estimated Std Dev** box
          Click **OK**

The half-length of interval is the margin of error.

The output showing a recommended sample size of 90 will appear.

Population Proportion

We illustrate using the survey data for women golfers presented in Section 8.4. Begin by using the Data Set Manager to create a StatTools data set for these data using the procedure described in the appendix to Chapter 1. The following steps can be used to compute a 95% confidence interval estimate of the population mean.

Tee Times

Step 1. Click the **StatTools** tab on the Ribbon
Step 2. In the **Analyses** group, click **Statistical Inference**
Step 3. Choose **Confidence Interval**
Step 4. Choose **Proportion**
Step 5. When the StatTools-Confidence Interval for Proportion dialog box appears:
          For **Analysis Type** choose **One-Sample Analysis**
          In the **Variables** section, select **Response**
          In the **Categories to Analyze** section, select **Yes**
          In the **Options** section, enter 95% in the **Confidence Level** box
              Click **OK**

Some descriptive statistics and the confidence interval will appear.

StatTools also provides a capability for determining the appropriate sample size to provide a desired margin of error. The steps are similar to those for determining the sample size in the previous subsection.

CHAPTER 9

Hypothesis Tests

CONTENTS

STATISTICS IN PRACTICE:
JOHN MORRELL & COMPANY

9.1 DEVELOPING NULL AND
ALTERNATIVE HYPOTHESES
The Alternative Hypothesis as a
Research Hypothesis
The Null Hypothesis as an
Assumption to Be Challenged
Summary of Forms for Null and
Alternative Hypotheses

9.2 TYPE I AND TYPE II ERRORS

9.3 POPULATION MEAN:
σ KNOWN
One-Tailed Test
Two-Tailed Test
Summary and Practical Advice
Relationship Between Interval
Estimation and Hypothesis
Testing

9.4 POPULATION MEAN:
σ UNKNOWN
One-Tailed Test
Two-Tailed Test
Summary and Practical Advice

9.5 POPULATION PROPORTION
Summary

9.6 HYPOTHESIS TESTING AND
DECISION MAKING

9.7 CALCULATING THE
PROBABILITY OF TYPE II
ERRORS

9.8 DETERMINING THE SAMPLE
SIZE FOR A HYPOTHESIS
TEST ABOUT A POPULATION
MEAN

STATISTICS *in* PRACTICE

JOHN MORRELL & COMPANY*
CINCINNATI, OHIO

John Morrell & Company, which began in England in 1827, is considered the oldest continuously operating meat manufacturer in the United States. It is a wholly owned and independently managed subsidiary of Smithfield Foods, Smithfield, Virginia. John Morrell & Company offers an extensive product line of processed meats and fresh pork to consumers under 13 regional brands including John Morrell, E-Z-Cut, Tobin's First Prize, Dinner Bell, Hunter, Kretschmar, Rath, Rodeo, Shenson, Farmers Hickory Brand, Iowa Quality, and Peyton's. Each regional brand enjoys high brand recognition and loyalty among consumers.

Market research at Morrell provides management with up-to-date information on the company's various products and how the products compare with competing brands of similar products. A recent study compared a Beef Pot Roast made by Morrell to similar beef products from two major competitors. In the three-product comparison test, a sample of consumers was used to indicate how the products rated in terms of taste, appearance, aroma, and overall preference.

One research question concerned whether the Beef Pot Roast made by Morrell was the preferred choice of more than 50% of the consumer population. Letting p indicate the population proportion preferring Morrell's product, the hypothesis test for the research question is as follows:

$$H_0: p \leq .50$$
$$H_a: p > .50$$

The null hypothesis H_0 indicates the preference for Morrell's product is less than or equal to 50%. If the sample data support rejecting H_0 in favor of the

Market research at Morrell provides up-to-date information on their various products and how they compare with competing brands.
© Jeff Greenberg/Alamy Limited.

alternative hypothesis H_a, Morrell will draw the research conclusion that in a three-product comparison, their Beef Pot Roast is preferred by more than 50% of the consumer population.

In an independent taste test study using a sample of 224 consumers in Cincinnati, Milwaukee, and Los Angeles, 150 consumers selected the Beef Pot Roast made by Morrell as the preferred product. Using statistical hypothesis testing procedures, the null hypothesis H_0 was rejected. The study provided statistical evidence supporting H_a and the conclusion that the Morrell product is preferred by more than 50% of the consumer population.

The point estimate of the population proportion was $\bar{p} = 150/224 = .67$. Thus, the sample data provided support for a food magazine advertisement showing that in a three-product taste comparison, Beef Pot Roast made by Morrell was "preferred 2 to 1 over the competition."

In this chapter we will discuss how to formulate hypotheses and how to conduct tests like the one used by Morrell. Through the analysis of sample data, we will be able to determine whether a hypothesis should or should not be rejected.

---

*The authors are indebted to Marty Butler, Vice President of Marketing, John Morrell, for providing this Statistics in Practice.

In Chapters 7 and 8 we showed how a sample could be used to develop point and interval estimates of population parameters. In this chapter we continue the discussion of statistical inference by showing how hypothesis testing can be used to determine whether a statement about the value of a population parameter should or should not be rejected.

In hypothesis testing we begin by making a tentative assumption about a population parameter. This tentative assumption is called the **null hypothesis** and is denoted by H_0. We then define another hypothesis, called the **alternative hypothesis**, which is the opposite of what is stated in the null hypothesis. The alternative hypothesis is denoted by H_a.

The hypothesis testing procedure uses data from a sample to test the two competing statements indicated by H_0 and H_a.

This chapter shows how hypothesis tests can be conducted about a population mean and a population proportion. We begin by providing examples that illustrate approaches to developing null and alternative hypotheses.

9.1   Developing Null and Alternative Hypotheses

It is not always obvious how the null and alternative hypotheses should be formulated. Care must be taken to structure the hypotheses appropriately so that the hypothesis testing conclusion provides the information the researcher or decision maker wants. The context of the situation is very important in determining how the hypotheses should be stated. All hypothesis testing applications involve collecting a sample and using the sample results to provide evidence for drawing a conclusion. Good questions to consider when formulating the null and alternative hypotheses are, What is the purpose of collecting the sample? What conclusions are we hoping to make?

Learning to correctly formulate hypotheses will take some practice. Expect some initial confusion over the proper choice of the null and alternative hypotheses. The examples in this section are intended to provide guidelines.

In the chapter introduction, we stated that the null hypothesis H_0 is a tentative assumption about a population parameter such as a population mean or a population proportion. The alternative hypothesis H_a is a statement that is the opposite of what is stated in the null hypothesis. In some situations it is easier to identify the alternative hypothesis first and then develop the null hypothesis. In other situations it is easier to identify the null hypothesis first and then develop the alternative hypothesis. We will illustrate these situations in the following examples.

The Alternative Hypothesis as a Research Hypothesis

Many applications of hypothesis testing involve an attempt to gather evidence in support of a research hypothesis. In these situations, it is often best to begin with the alternative hypothesis and make it the conclusion that the researcher hopes to support. Consider a particular automobile that currently attains a fuel efficiency of 24 miles per gallon in city driving. A product research group has developed a new fuel injection system designed to increase the miles-per-gallon rating. The group will run controlled tests with the new fuel injection system looking for statistical support for the conclusion that the new fuel injection system provides more miles per gallon than the current system.

Several new fuel injection units will be manufactured, installed in test automobiles, and subjected to research-controlled driving conditions. The sample mean miles per gallon for these automobiles will be computed and used in a hypothesis test to determine if it can be concluded that the new system provides more than 24 miles per gallon. In terms of the population mean miles per gallon μ, the research hypothesis $\mu > 24$ becomes the alternative hypothesis. Since the current system provides an average or mean of 24 miles per gallon, we will make the tentative assumption that the new system is not any better than the current system and choose $\mu \leq 24$ as the null hypothesis. The null and alternative hypotheses are:

$$H_0: \mu \leq 24$$
$$H_a: \mu > 24$$

If the sample results lead to the conclusion to reject H_0, the inference can be made that $H_a: \mu > 24$ is true. The researchers have the statistical support to state that the new fuel injection system increases the mean number of miles per gallon. The production of automobiles with the new fuel injection system should be considered. However, if the sample results lead to the conclusion that H_0 cannot be rejected, the researchers cannot conclude that the new fuel injection system is better than the current system. Production of automobiles with the new fuel injection system on the basis of better gas mileage cannot be justified. Perhaps more research and further testing can be conducted.

Successful companies stay competitive by developing new products, new methods, new systems, and the like, that are better than what is currently available. Before adopting something new, it is desirable to conduct research to determine if there is statistical support for the conclusion that the new approach is indeed better. In such cases, the research hypothesis is stated as the alternative hypothesis. For example, a new teaching method is developed that is believed to be better than the current method. The alternative hypothesis is that the new method is better. The null hypothesis is that the new method is no better than the old method. A new sales force bonus plan is developed in an attempt to increase sales. The alternative hypothesis is that the new bonus plan increases sales. The null hypothesis is that the new bonus plan does not increase sales. A new drug is developed with the goal of lowering blood pressure more than an existing drug. The alternative hypothesis is that the new drug lowers blood pressure more than the existing drug. The null hypothesis is that the new drug does not provide lower blood pressure than the existing drug. In each case, rejection of the null hypothesis H_0 provides statistical support for the research hypothesis. We will see many examples of hypothesis tests in research situations such as these throughout this chapter and in the remainder of the text.

The conclusion that the research hypothesis is true is made if the sample data provide sufficient evidence to show that the null hypothesis can be rejected.

The Null Hypothesis as an Assumption to Be Challenged

Of course, not all hypothesis tests involve research hypotheses. In the following discussion we consider applications of hypothesis testing where we begin with a belief or an assumption that a statement about the value of a population parameter is true. We will then use a hypothesis test to challenge the assumption and determine if there is statistical evidence to conclude that the assumption is incorrect. In these situations, it is helpful to develop the null hypothesis first. The null hypothesis H_0 expresses the belief or assumption about the value of the population parameter. The alternative hypothesis H_a is that the belief or assumption is incorrect.

As an example, consider the situation of a manufacturer of soft drink products. The label on a soft drink bottle states that it contains 67.6 fluid ounces. We consider the label correct provided the population mean filling weight for the bottles is *at least* 67.6 fluid ounces. Without any reason to believe otherwise, we would give the manufacturer the benefit of the doubt and assume that the statement provided on the label is correct. Thus, in a hypothesis test about the population mean fluid weight per bottle, we would begin with the assumption that the label is correct and state the null hypothesis as $\mu \geq 67.6$. The challenge to this assumption would imply that the label is incorrect and the bottles are being underfilled. This challenge would be stated as the alternative hypothesis $\mu < 67.6$. Thus, the null and alternative hypotheses are:

$$H_0: \mu \geq 67.6$$
$$H_a: \mu < 67.6$$

A manufacturer's product information is usually assumed to be true and stated as the null hypothesis. The conclusion that the information is incorrect can be made if the null hypothesis is rejected.

A government agency with the responsibility for validating manufacturing labels could select a sample of soft drinks bottles, compute the sample mean filling weight, and use the sample results to test the preceding hypotheses. If the sample results lead to the conclusion to reject H_0, the inference that $H_a: \mu < 67.6$ is true can be made. With this statistical support, the agency is justified in concluding that the label is incorrect and underfilling of the bottles is occurring. Appropriate action to force the manufacturer to comply with labeling standards would be considered. However, if the sample results indicate H_0 cannot be rejected, the assumption that the manufacturer's labeling is correct cannot be rejected. With this conclusion, no action would be taken.

Let us now consider a variation of the soft drink bottle filling example by viewing the same situation from the manufacturer's point of view. The bottle-filling operation has been designed to fill soft drink bottles with 67.6 fluid ounces as stated on the label. The company does not want to underfill the containers because that could result in an underfilling complaint from customers or, perhaps, a government agency. However, the company does not want to overfill containers either because putting more soft drink than necessary into the containers would be an unnecessary cost. The company's goal would be to adjust the bottle-filling operation so that the population mean filling weight per bottle is 67.6 fluid ounces as specified on the label.

Although this is the company's goal, from time to time any production process can get out of adjustment. If this occurs in our example, underfilling or overfilling of the soft drink bottles will occur. In either case, the company would like to know about it in order to correct the situation by readjusting the bottle-filling operation to the designed 67.6 fluid ounces. In a hypothesis testing application, we would again begin with the assumption that the production process is operating correctly and state the null hypothesis as $\mu = 67.6$ fluid ounces. The alternative hypothesis that challenges this assumption is that $\mu \neq 67.6$, which indicates either overfilling or underfilling is occurring. The null and alternative hypotheses for the manufacturer's hypothesis test are:

$$H_0: \mu = 67.6$$
$$H_a: \mu \neq 67.6$$

Suppose that the soft drink manufacturer uses a quality control procedure to periodically select a sample of bottles from the filling operation and computes the sample mean filling weight per bottle. If the sample results lead to the conclusion to reject H_0, the inference is made that $H_a: \mu \neq 67.6$ is true. We conclude that the bottles are not being filled properly and the production process should be adjusted to restore the population mean to 67.6 fluid ounces per bottle. However, if the sample results indicate H_0 cannot be rejected, the assumption that the manufacturer's bottle filling operation is functioning properly cannot be rejected. In this case, no further action would be taken and the production operation would continue to run.

The two preceding forms of the soft drink manufacturing hypothesis test show that the null and alternative hypotheses may vary depending upon the point of view of the researcher or decision maker. To correctly formulate hypotheses it is important to understand the context of the situation and structure the hypotheses to provide the information the researcher or decision maker wants.

Summary of Forms for Null and Alternative Hypotheses

The hypothesis tests in this chapter involve two population parameters: the population mean and the population proportion. Depending on the situation, hypothesis tests about a population parameter may take one of three forms: two use inequalities in the null hypothesis; the third uses an equality in the null hypothesis. For hypothesis tests involving a population mean, we let μ_0 denote the hypothesized value and we must choose one of the following three forms for the hypothesis test.

The three possible forms of hypotheses H_0 and H_a are shown here. Note that the equality always *appears in the null hypothesis H_0.*

$$H_0: \mu \geq \mu_0 \qquad H_0: \mu \leq \mu_0 \qquad H_0: \mu = \mu_0$$
$$H_a: \mu < \mu_0 \qquad H_a: \mu > \mu_0 \qquad H_a: \mu \neq \mu_0$$

For reasons that will be clear later, the first two forms are called one-tailed tests. The third form is called a two-tailed test.

In many situations, the choice of H_0 and H_a is not obvious and judgment is necessary to select the proper form. However, as the preceding forms show, the equality part of the expression (either $\geq$, $\leq$, or $=$) *always* appears in the null hypothesis. In selecting the proper form of H_0 and H_a, keep in mind that the alternative hypothesis is often what the test is attempting to establish. Hence, asking whether the user is looking for evidence to support $\mu < \mu_0$, $\mu > \mu_0$, or $\mu \neq \mu_0$ will help determine H_a. The following exercises are designed to provide practice in choosing the proper form for a hypothesis test involving a population mean.

Exercises

1. The manager of the Danvers-Hilton Resort Hotel stated that the mean guest bill for a weekend is $600 or less. A member of the hotel's accounting staff noticed that the total charges for guest bills have been increasing in recent months. The accountant will use a sample of future weekend guest bills to test the manager's claim.
    a. Which form of the hypotheses should be used to test the manager's claim? Explain.

$$H_0: \mu \geq 600 \qquad H_0: \mu \leq 600 \qquad H_0: \mu = 600$$
$$H_a: \mu < 600 \qquad H_a: \mu > 600 \qquad H_a: \mu \neq 600$$

    b. What conclusion is appropriate when H_0 cannot be rejected?
    c. What conclusion is appropriate when H_0 can be rejected?

2. The manager of an automobile dealership is considering a new bonus plan designed to increase sales volume. Currently, the mean sales volume is 14 automobiles per month. The manager wants to conduct a research study to see whether the new bonus plan increases sales volume. To collect data on the plan, a sample of sales personnel will be allowed to sell under the new bonus plan for a one-month period.
    a. Develop the null and alternative hypotheses most appropriate for this situation.
    b. Comment on the conclusion when H_0 cannot be rejected.
    c. Comment on the conclusion when H_0 can be rejected.

3. A production line operation is designed to fill cartons with laundry detergent to a mean weight of 32 ounces. A sample of cartons is periodically selected and weighed to determine whether underfilling or overfilling is occurring. If the sample data lead to a conclusion of underfilling or overfilling, the production line will be shut down and adjusted to obtain proper filling.
    a. Formulate the null and alternative hypotheses that will help in deciding whether to shut down and adjust the production line.
    b. Comment on the conclusion and the decision when H_0 cannot be rejected.
    c. Comment on the conclusion and the decision when H_0 can be rejected.

4. Because of high production-changeover time and costs, a director of manufacturing must convince management that a proposed manufacturing method reduces costs before the new method can be implemented. The current production method operates with a mean cost of $220 per hour. A research study will measure the cost of the new method over a sample production period.
    a. Develop the null and alternative hypotheses most appropriate for this study.
    b. Comment on the conclusion when H_0 cannot be rejected.
    c. Comment on the conclusion when H_0 can be rejected.

9.2 Type I and Type II Errors

The null and alternative hypotheses are competing statements about the population. Either the null hypothesis H_0 is true or the alternative hypothesis H_a is true, but not both. Ideally the hypothesis testing procedure should lead to the acceptance of H_0 when H_0 is true and the

TABLE 9.1   ERRORS AND CORRECT CONCLUSIONS IN HYPOTHESIS TESTING

		Population Condition	
		H_0 **True**	H_a **True**
Conclusion	**Accept H_0**	Correct Conclusion	Type II Error
	Reject H_0	Type I Error	Correct Conclusion

rejection of H_0 when H_a is true. Unfortunately, the correct conclusions are not always possible. Because hypothesis tests are based on sample information, we must allow for the possibility of errors. Table 9.1 illustrates the two kinds of errors that can be made in hypothesis testing.

The first row of Table 9.1 shows what can happen if the conclusion is to accept H_0. If H_0 is true, this conclusion is correct. However, if H_a is true, we make a **Type II error**; that is, we accept H_0 when it is false. The second row of Table 9.1 shows what can happen if the conclusion is to reject H_0. If H_0 is true, we make a **Type I error**; that is, we reject H_0 when it is true. However, if H_a is true, rejecting H_0 is correct.

Recall the hypothesis testing illustration discussed in Section 9.1 in which an automobile product research group developed a new fuel injection system designed to increase the miles-per-gallon rating of a particular automobile. With the current model obtaining an average of 24 miles per gallon, the hypothesis test was formulated as follows.

$$H_0: \mu \leq 24$$
$$H_a: \mu > 24$$

The alternative hypothesis, $H_a: \mu > 24$, indicates that the researchers are looking for sample evidence to support the conclusion that the population mean miles per gallon with the new fuel injection system is greater than 24.

In this application, the Type I error of rejecting H_0 when it is true corresponds to the researchers claiming that the new system improves the miles-per-gallon rating ($\mu > 24$) when in fact the new system is not any better than the current system. In contrast, the Type II error of accepting H_0 when it is false corresponds to the researchers concluding that the new system is not any better than the current system ($\mu \leq 24$) when in fact the new system improves miles-per-gallon performance.

For the miles-per-gallon rating hypothesis test, the null hypothesis is $H_0: \mu \leq 24$. Suppose the null hypothesis is true as an equality; that is, $\mu = 24$. The probability of making a Type I error when the null hypothesis is true as an equality is called the **level of significance**. Thus, for the miles-per-gallon rating hypothesis test, the level of significance is the probability of rejecting $H_0: \mu \leq 24$ when $\mu = 24$. Because of the importance of this concept, we now restate the definition of level of significance.

LEVEL OF SIGNIFICANCE

The level of significance is the probability of making a Type I error when the null hypothesis is true as an equality.

The Greek symbol α (alpha) is used to denote the level of significance, and common choices for α are .05 and .01.

In practice, the person responsible for the hypothesis test specifies the level of significance. By selecting α, that person is controlling the probability of making a Type I error. If the cost of making a Type I error is high, small values of α are preferred. If the cost of making a Type I error is not too high, larger values of α are typically used. Applications of hypothesis testing that only control for the Type I error are called *significance tests*. Many applications of hypothesis testing are of this type.

If the sample data are consistent with the null hypothesis H_0, we will follow the practice of concluding "do not reject H_0." This conclusion is preferred over "accept H_0," because the conclusion to accept H_0 puts us at risk of making a Type II error.

Although most applications of hypothesis testing control for the probability of making a Type I error, they do not always control for the probability of making a Type II error. Hence, if we decide to accept H_0, we cannot determine how confident we can be with that decision. Because of the uncertainty associated with making a Type II error when conducting significance tests, statisticians usually recommend that we use the statement "do not reject H_0" instead of "accept H_0." Using the statement "do not reject H_0" carries the recommendation to withhold both judgment and action. In effect, by not directly accepting H_0, the statistician avoids the risk of making a Type II error. Whenever the probability of making a Type II error has not been determined and controlled, we will not make the statement "accept H_0." In such cases, only two conclusions are possible: *do not reject H_0* or *reject H_0*.

Although controlling for a Type II error in hypothesis testing is not common, it can be done. In Sections 9.7 and 9.8 we will illustrate procedures for determining and controlling the probability of making a Type II error. If proper controls have been established for this error, action based on the "accept H_0" conclusion can be appropriate.

NOTES AND COMMENTS

Walter Williams, syndicated columnist and professor of economics at George Mason University, points out that the possibility of making a Type I or a Type II error is always present in decision making (*The Cincinnati Enquirer,* August 14, 2005). He notes that the Food and Drug Administration (FDA) runs the risk of making these errors in its drug approval process. The FDA must either approve a new drug or not approve it. Thus the FDA runs the risk of making a Type I error by approving a new drug that is not safe and effective, or making a Type II error by failing to approve a new drug that is safe and effective. Regardless of the decision made, the possibility of making a costly error cannot be eliminated.

Exercises

5. Duke Energy reported that the cost of electricity for an efficient home in a particular neighborhood of Cincinnati, Ohio, was $104 per month (*Home Energy Report,* Duke Energy, March 2012). A researcher believes that the cost of electricity for a comparable neighborhood in Chicago, Illinois, is higher. A sample of homes in this Chicago neighborhood will be taken and the sample mean monthly cost of electricity will be used to test the following null and alternative hypotheses.

$$H_0: \mu \leq 104$$
$$H_a: \mu > 104$$

a. Assume the sample data led to rejection of the null hypothesis. What would be your conclusion about the cost of electricity in the Chicago neighborhood?

b. What is the Type I error in this situation? What are the consequences of making this error?

c. What is the Type II error in this situation? What are the consequences of making this error?

6. The label on a 3-quart container of orange juice states that the orange juice contains an average of 1 gram of fat or less. Answer the following questions for a hypothesis test that could be used to test the claim on the label.
   a. Develop the appropriate null and alternative hypotheses.
   b. What is the Type I error in this situation? What are the consequences of making this error?
   c. What is the Type II error in this situation? What are the consequences of making this error?

7. Carpetland salespersons average $8000 per week in sales. Steve Contois, the firm's vice president, proposes a compensation plan with new selling incentives. Steve hopes that the results of a trial selling period will enable him to conclude that the compensation plan increases the average sales per salesperson.
   a. Develop the appropriate null and alternative hypotheses.
   b. What is the Type I error in this situation? What are the consequences of making this error?
   c. What is the Type II error in this situation? What are the consequences of making this error?

8. Suppose a new production method will be implemented if a hypothesis test supports the conclusion that the new method reduces the mean operating cost per hour.
   a. State the appropriate null and alternative hypotheses if the mean cost for the current production method is $220 per hour.
   b. What is the Type I error in this situation? What are the consequences of making this error?
   c. What is the Type II error in this situation? What are the consequences of making this error?

9.3 Population Mean: σ Known

In Chapter 8 we said that the σ known case corresponds to applications in which historical data and/or other information are available that enable us to obtain a good estimate of the population standard deviation prior to sampling. In such cases the population standard deviation can, for all practical purposes, be considered known. In this section we show how to conduct a hypothesis test about a population mean for the σ known case.

The methods presented in this section are exact if the sample is selected from a population that is normally distributed. In cases where it is not reasonable to assume the population is normally distributed, these methods are still applicable if the sample size is large enough. We provide some practical advice concerning the population distribution and the sample size at the end of this section.

One-Tailed Test

One-tailed tests about a population mean take one of the following two forms.

Lower Tail Test	Upper Tail Test
$H_0: \mu \geq \mu_0$	$H_0: \mu \leq \mu_0$
$H_a: \mu < \mu_0$	$H_a: \mu > \mu_0$

Let us consider an example involving a lower tail test.

The Federal Trade Commission (FTC) periodically conducts statistical studies designed to test the claims that manufacturers make about their products. For example, the label on a large can of Hilltop Coffee states that the can contains 3 pounds of coffee. The FTC knows that Hilltop's production process cannot place exactly 3 pounds of coffee in each can, even if the mean filling weight for the population of all cans filled is 3 pounds per can. However, as long as the population mean filling weight is at least 3 pounds per can, the rights of consumers will be protected. Thus, the FTC interprets the label information on a large can of coffee as a claim by Hilltop that the population mean filling weight is at least 3 pounds per can. We will show how the FTC can check Hilltop's claim by conducting a lower tail hypothesis test.

The first step is to develop the null and alternative hypotheses for the test. If the population mean filling weight is at least 3 pounds per can, Hilltop's claim is correct. This establishes the null hypothesis for the test. However, if the population mean weight is less than 3 pounds per can, Hilltop's claim is incorrect. This establishes the alternative hypothesis. With μ denoting the population mean filling weight, the null and alternative hypotheses are as follows:

$$H_0: \mu \geq 3$$
$$H_a: \mu < 3$$

Note that the hypothesized value of the population mean is $\mu_0 = 3$.

If the sample data indicate that H_0 cannot be rejected, the statistical evidence does not support the conclusion that a label violation has occurred. Hence, no action should be taken against Hilltop. However, if the sample data indicate H_0 can be rejected, we will conclude that the alternative hypothesis, $H_a: \mu < 3$, is true. In this case a conclusion of underfilling and a charge of a label violation against Hilltop would be justified.

Suppose a sample of 36 cans of coffee is selected and the sample mean $\bar{x}$ is computed as an estimate of the population mean μ. If the value of the sample mean $\bar{x}$ is less than 3 pounds, the sample results will cast doubt on the null hypothesis. What we want to know is how much less than 3 pounds must $\bar{x}$ be before we would be willing to declare the difference significant and risk making a Type I error by falsely accusing Hilltop of a label violation. A key factor in addressing this issue is the value the decision maker selects for the level of significance.

As noted in the preceding section, the level of significance, denoted by α, is the probability of making a Type I error by rejecting H_0 when the null hypothesis is true as an equality. The decision maker must specify the level of significance. If the cost of making a Type I error is high, a small value should be chosen for the level of significance. If the cost is not high, a larger value is more appropriate. In the Hilltop Coffee study, the director of the FTC's testing program made the following statement: "If the company is meeting its weight specifications at $\mu = 3$, I do not want to take action against them. But, I am willing to risk a 1% chance of making such an error." From the director's statement, we set the level of significance for the hypothesis test at $\alpha = .01$. Thus, we must design the hypothesis test so that the probability of making a Type I error when $\mu = 3$ is .01.

For the Hilltop Coffee study, by developing the null and alternative hypotheses and specifying the level of significance for the test, we carry out the first two steps required in conducting every hypothesis test. We are now ready to perform the third step of hypothesis testing: collect the sample data and compute the value of what is called a test statistic.

Test statistic For the Hilltop Coffee study, previous FTC tests show that the population standard deviation can be assumed known with a value of $\sigma = .18$. In addition, these tests also show that the population of filling weights can be assumed to have a normal distribution. From the study of sampling distributions in Chapter 7 we know that if the population from which we are sampling is normally distributed, the sampling distribution of $\bar{x}$ will also be normally distributed. Thus, for the Hilltop Coffee study, the sampling distribution of $\bar{x}$ is normally distributed. With a known value of $\sigma = .18$ and a sample size of $n = 36$, Figure 9.1 shows the sampling distribution of $\bar{x}$ when the null hypothesis is true as an equality; that is, when $\mu = \mu_0 = 3$.[1] Note that the standard error of $\bar{x}$ is given by $\sigma_{\bar{x}} = \sigma/\sqrt{n} = .18/\sqrt{36} = .03$.

Because the sampling distribution of $\bar{x}$ is normally distributed, the sampling distribution of

The standard error of $\bar{x}$ is the standard deviation of the sampling distribution of $\bar{x}$.

$$z = \frac{\bar{x} - \mu_0}{\sigma_{\bar{x}}} = \frac{\bar{x} - 3}{.03}$$

---

[1]In constructing sampling distributions for hypothesis tests, it is assumed that H_0 is satisfied as an equality.

FIGURE 9.1   SAMPLING DISTRIBUTION OF $\bar{x}$ FOR THE HILLTOP COFFEE STUDY
WHEN THE NULL HYPOTHESIS IS TRUE AS AN EQUALITY ($\mu = 3$)

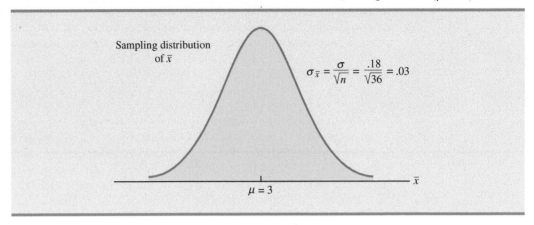

is a standard normal distribution. A value of $z = -1$ means that the value of $\bar{x}$ is one standard error below the hypothesized value of the mean, a value of $z = -2$ means that the value of $\bar{x}$ is two standard errors below the hypothesized value of the mean, and so on. We can use the standard normal probability table to find the lower tail probability corresponding to any z value. For instance, the lower tail area at $z = -3.00$ is .0013. Hence, the probability of obtaining a value of z that is three or more standard errors below the mean is .0013. As a result, the probability of obtaining a value of $\bar{x}$ that is 3 or more standard errors below the hypothesized population mean $\mu_0 = 3$ is also .0013. Such a result is unlikely if the null hypothesis is true.

For hypothesis tests about a population mean in the σ known case, we use the standard normal random variable z as a **test statistic** to determine whether $\bar{x}$ deviates from the hypothesized value of μ enough to justify rejecting the null hypothesis. With $\sigma_{\bar{x}} = \sigma/\sqrt{n}$, the test statistic is as follows.

**TEST STATISTIC FOR HYPOTHESIS TESTS ABOUT A POPULATION MEAN:
σ KNOWN**

$$z = \frac{\bar{x} - \mu_0}{\sigma/\sqrt{n}} \qquad (9.1)$$

The key question for a lower tail test is, How small must the test statistic z be before we choose to reject the null hypothesis? Two approaches can be used to answer this question: the p-value approach and the critical value approach.

***p*-value approach**   The p-value approach uses the value of the test statistic z to compute a probability called a *p*-value.

A small p-value indicates the value of the test statistic is unusual given the assumption that H_0 is true.

***p*-VALUE**

A *p*-value is a probability that provides a measure of the evidence against the null hypothesis provided by the sample. Smaller *p*-values indicate more evidence against H_0.

The p-value is used to determine whether the null hypothesis should be rejected.

Let us see how the p-value is computed and used. The value of the test statistic is used to compute the p-value. The method used depends on whether the test is a lower tail, an upper tail, or a two-tailed test. For a lower tail test, the p-value is the probability of obtaining a value for the test statistic as small as or smaller than that provided by the sample. Thus, to compute the p-value for the lower tail test in the σ known case, we use the standard normal distribution to find the probability that z is less than or equal to the value of the test statistic. After computing the p-value, we must then decide whether it is small enough to reject the null hypothesis; as we will show, this decision involves comparing the p-value to the level of significance.

WEB file

Coffee

Let us now compute the p-value for the Hilltop Coffee lower tail test. Suppose the sample of 36 Hilltop coffee cans provides a sample mean of $\bar{x} = 2.92$ pounds. Is $\bar{x} = 2.92$ small enough to cause us to reject H_0? Because this is a lower tail test, the p-value is the area under the standard normal curve for values of $z \leq$ the value of the test statistic. Using $\bar{x} = 2.92$, $\sigma = .18$, and $n = 36$, we compute the value of the test statistic z.

$$z = \frac{\bar{x} - \mu_0}{\sigma/\sqrt{n}} = \frac{2.92 - 3}{.18/\sqrt{36}} = -2.67$$

Thus, the p-value is the probability that z is less than or equal to -2.67 (the lower tail area corresponding to the value of the test statistic).

Using the standard normal probability table, we find that the lower tail area at $z = -2.67$ is .0038. Figure 9.2 shows that $\bar{x} = 2.92$ corresponds to $z = -2.67$ and a p-value $= .0038$. This p-value indicates a small probability of obtaining a sample mean of $\bar{x} = 2.92$ (and a test statistic of -2.67) or smaller when sampling from a population with $\mu = 3$. This

FIGURE 9.2 p-VALUE FOR THE HILLTOP COFFEE STUDY WHEN $\bar{x} = 2.92$ AND $z = -2.67$

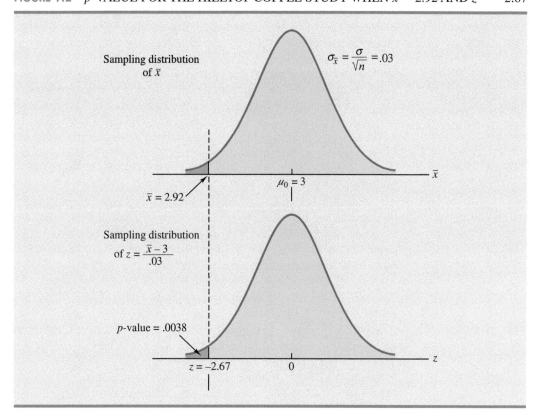

p-value does not provide much support for the null hypothesis, but is it small enough to cause us to reject H_0? The answer depends upon the level of significance for the test.

As noted previously, the director of the FTC's testing program selected a value of .01 for the level of significance. The selection of $\alpha = .01$ means that the director is willing to tolerate a probability of .01 of rejecting the null hypothesis when it is true as an equality ($\mu_0 = 3$). The sample of 36 coffee cans in the Hilltop Coffee study resulted in a p-value = .0038, which means that the probability of obtaining a value of $\bar{x} = 2.92$ or less when the null hypothesis is true as an equality is .0038. Because .0038 is less than or equal to $\alpha = .01$, we reject H_0. Therefore, we find sufficient statistical evidence to reject the null hypothesis at the .01 level of significance.

We can now state the general rule for determining whether the null hypothesis can be rejected when using the p-value approach. For a level of significance α, the rejection rule using the p-value approach is as follows:

REJECTION RULE USING p-VALUE

Reject H_0 if p-value $\leq \alpha$

In the Hilltop Coffee test, the p-value of .0038 resulted in the rejection of the null hypothesis. Although the basis for making the rejection decision involves a comparison of the p-value to the level of significance specified by the FTC director, the observed p-value of .0038 means that we would reject H_0 for any value of $\alpha \geq .0038$. For this reason, the p-value is also called the *observed level of significance.*

Different decision makers may express different opinions concerning the cost of making a Type I error and may choose a different level of significance. By providing the p-value as part of the hypothesis testing results, another decision maker can compare the reported p-value to his or her own level of significance and possibly make a different decision with respect to rejecting H_0.

Critical value approach   The critical value approach requires that we first determine a value for the test statistic called the **critical value.** For a lower tail test, the critical value serves as a benchmark for determining whether the value of the test statistic is small enough to reject the null hypothesis. It is the value of the test statistic that corresponds to an area of α (the level of significance) in the lower tail of the sampling distribution of the test statistic. In other words, the critical value is the largest value of the test statistic that will result in the rejection of the null hypothesis. Let us return to the Hilltop Coffee example and see how this approach works.

In the σ known case, the sampling distribution for the test statistic z is a standard normal distribution. Therefore, the critical value is the value of the test statistic that corresponds to an area of $\alpha = .01$ in the lower tail of a standard normal distribution. Using the standard normal probability table, we find that $z = -2.33$ provides an area of .01 in the lower tail (see Figure 9.3). Thus, if the sample results in a value of the test statistic that is less than or equal to -2.33, the corresponding p-value will be less than or equal to .01; in this case, we should reject the null hypothesis. Hence, for the Hilltop Coffee study the critical value rejection rule for a level of significance of .01 is

Reject H_0 if $z \leq -2.33$

In the Hilltop Coffee example, $\bar{x} = 2.92$ and the test statistic is $z = -2.67$. Because $z = -2.67 < -2.33$, we can reject H_0 and conclude that Hilltop Coffee is underfilling cans.

FIGURE 9.3   CRITICAL VALUE $= -2.33$ FOR THE HILLTOP COFFEE HYPOTHESIS TEST

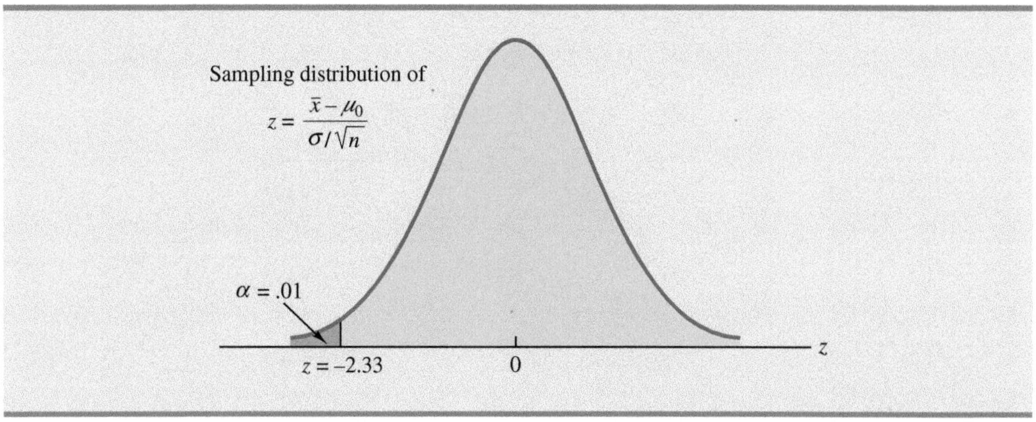

We can generalize the rejection rule for the critical value approach to handle any level of significance. The rejection rule for a lower tail test follows.

REJECTION RULE FOR A LOWER TAIL TEST: CRITICAL VALUE APPROACH

$$\text{Reject } H_0 \text{ if } z \leq -z_\alpha$$

where $-z_\alpha$ is the critical value; that is, the z value that provides an area of α in the lower tail of the standard normal distribution.

Summary   The p-value approach to hypothesis testing and the critical value approach will always lead to the same rejection decision; that is, whenever the p-value is less than or equal to α, the value of the test statistic will be less than or equal to the critical value. The advantage of the p-value approach is that the p-value tells us *how* significant the results are (the observed level of significance). If we use the critical value approach, we only know that the results are significant at the stated level of significance.

At the beginning of this section, we said that one-tailed tests about a population mean take one of the following two forms:

Lower Tail Test	Upper Tail Test
$H_0: \mu \geq \mu_0$	$H_0: \mu \leq \mu_0$
$H_a: \mu < \mu_0$	$H_a: \mu > \mu_0$

We used the Hilltop Coffee study to illustrate how to conduct a lower tail test. We can use the same general approach to conduct an upper tail test. The test statistic z is still computed using equation (9.1). But, for an upper tail test, the p-value is the probability of obtaining a value for the test statistic as large as or larger than that provided by the sample. Thus, to compute the p-value for the upper tail test in the σ known case, we must use the standard normal distribution to find the probability that z is greater than or equal to the value of the test statistic. Using the critical value approach causes us to reject the null hypothesis if the value of the test statistic is greater than or equal to the critical value z_α; in other words, we reject H_0 if $z \geq z_\alpha$.

Let us summarize the steps involved in computing p-values for one-tailed hypothesis tests.

COMPUTATION OF p-VALUES FOR ONE-TAILED TESTS

1. Compute the value of the test statistic using equation (9.1).
2. **Lower tail test:** Using the standard normal distribution, compute the probability that z is less than or equal to the value of the test statistic (area in the lower tail).
3. **Upper tail test:** Using the standard normal distribution, compute the probability that z is greater than or equal to the value of the test statistic (area in the upper tail).

Two-Tailed Test

In hypothesis testing, the general form for a **two-tailed test** about a population mean is as follows:

$$H_0: \mu = \mu_0$$
$$H_a: \mu \neq \mu_0$$

In this subsection we show how to conduct a two-tailed test about a population mean for the σ known case. As an illustration, we consider the hypothesis testing situation facing MaxFlight, Inc.

The U.S. Golf Association (USGA) establishes rules that manufacturers of golf equipment must meet if their products are to be acceptable for use in USGA events. MaxFlight uses a high-technology manufacturing process to produce golf balls with a mean driving distance of 295 yards. Sometimes, however, the process gets out of adjustment and produces golf balls with a mean driving distance different from 295 yards. When the mean distance falls below 295 yards, the company worries about losing sales because the golf balls do not provide as much distance as advertised. When the mean distance passes 295 yards, MaxFlight's golf balls may be rejected by the USGA for exceeding the overall distance standard concerning carry and roll.

MaxFlight's quality control program involves taking periodic samples of 50 golf balls to monitor the manufacturing process. For each sample, a hypothesis test is conducted to determine whether the process has fallen out of adjustment. Let us develop the null and alternative hypotheses. We begin by assuming that the process is functioning correctly; that is, the golf balls being produced have a mean distance of 295 yards. This assumption establishes the null hypothesis. The alternative hypothesis is that the mean distance is not equal to 295 yards. With a hypothesized value of $\mu_0 = 295$, the null and alternative hypotheses for the MaxFlight hypothesis test are as follows:

$$H_0: \mu = 295$$
$$H_a: \mu \neq 295$$

If the sample mean $\bar{x}$ is significantly less than 295 yards or significantly greater than 295 yards, we will reject H_0. In this case, corrective action will be taken to adjust the manufacturing process. On the other hand, if $\bar{x}$ does not deviate from the hypothesized mean $\mu_0 = 295$ by a significant amount, H_0 will not be rejected and no action will be taken to adjust the manufacturing process.

The quality control team selected $\alpha = .05$ as the level of significance for the test. Data from previous tests conducted when the process was known to be in adjustment show that

FIGURE 9.4   SAMPLING DISTRIBUTION OF $\bar{x}$ FOR THE MAXFLIGHT HYPOTHESIS TEST

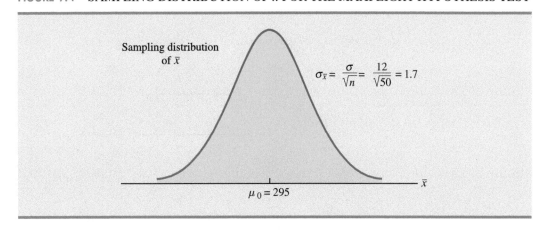

the population standard deviation can be assumed known with a value of $\sigma = 12$. Thus, with a sample size of $n = 50$, the standard error of $\bar{x}$ is

$$\sigma_{\bar{x}} = \frac{\sigma}{\sqrt{n}} = \frac{12}{\sqrt{50}} = 1.7$$

Because the sample size is large, the central limit theorem (see Chapter 7) allows us to conclude that the sampling distribution of $\bar{x}$ can be approximated by a normal distribution. Figure 9.4 shows the sampling distribution of $\bar{x}$ for the MaxFlight hypothesis test with a hypothesized population mean of $\mu_0 = 295$.

GolfTest

Suppose that a sample of 50 golf balls is selected and that the sample mean is $\bar{x} = 297.6$ yards. This sample mean provides support for the conclusion that the population mean is larger than 295 yards. Is this value of $\bar{x}$ enough larger than 295 to cause us to reject H_0 at the .05 level of significance? In the previous section we described two approaches that can be used to answer this question: the *p*-value approach and the critical value approach.

***p*-value approach** Recall that the *p*-value is a probability used to determine whether the null hypothesis should be rejected. For a two-tailed test, values of the test statistic in *either* tail provide evidence against the null hypothesis. For a two-tailed test, the *p*-value is the probability of obtaining a value for the test statistic *as unlikely as or more unlikely than* that provided by the sample. Let us see how the *p*-value is computed for the MaxFlight hypothesis test.

First we compute the value of the test statistic. For the σ known case, the test statistic z is a standard normal random variable. Using equation (9.1) with $\bar{x} = 297.6$, the value of the test statistic is

$$z = \frac{\bar{x} - \mu_0}{\sigma/\sqrt{n}} = \frac{297.6 - 295}{12/\sqrt{50}} = 1.53$$

Now to compute the *p*-value we must find the probability of obtaining a value for the test statistic *at least as unlikely as* $z = 1.53$. Clearly values of $z \geq 1.53$ are *at least as unlikely.* But, because this is a two-tailed test, values of $z \leq -1.53$ are also *at least as unlikely as* the value of the test statistic provided by the sample. In Figure 9.5, we see that the two-tailed *p*-value in this case is given by $P(z \leq -1.53) + P(z \geq 1.53)$. Because the normal curve is symmetric, we can compute this probability by finding the upper tail area at $z = 1.53$ and doubling it. The table for the standard normal distribution shows that $P(z < 1.53) = .9370$. Thus, the upper tail area is $P(z \geq 1.53) = 1.0000 - .9370 = .0630$. Doubling this, we find the *p*-value for the MaxFlight two-tailed hypothesis test is *p*-value = $2(.0630) = .1260$.

FIGURE 9.5 *p*-VALUE FOR THE MAXFLIGHT HYPOTHESIS TEST

Next we compare the *p*-value to the level of significance to see whether the null hypothesis should be rejected. With a level of significance of $\alpha = .05$, we do not reject H_0 because the *p*-value $= .1260 > .05$. Because the null hypothesis is not rejected, no action will be taken to adjust the MaxFlight manufacturing process.

The computation of the *p*-value for a two-tailed test may seem a bit confusing as compared to the computation of the *p*-value for a one-tailed test. But it can be simplified by following three steps.

COMPUTATION OF *p*-VALUES FOR TWO-TAILED TESTS

1. Compute the value of the test statistic using equation (9.1).
2. If the value of the test statistic is in the upper tail, compute the probability that z is greater than or equal to the value of the test statistic (the upper tail area). If the value of the test statistic is in the lower tail, compute the probability that z is less than or equal to the value of the test statistic (the lower tail area).
3. Double the probability (or tail area) from step 2 to obtain the *p*-value.

Critical value approach Before leaving this section, let us see how the test statistic z can be compared to a critical value to make the hypothesis testing decision for a two-tailed test. Figure 9.6 shows that the critical values for the test will occur in both the lower and upper tails of the standard normal distribution. With a level of significance of $\alpha = .05$, the area in each tail corresponding to the critical values is $\alpha/2 = .05/2 = .025$. Using the standard normal probability table, we find the critical values for the test statistic are $-z_{.025} = -1.96$ and $z_{.025} = 1.96$. Thus, using the critical value approach, the two-tailed rejection rule is

$$\text{Reject } H_0 \text{ if } z \leq -1.96 \text{ or if } z \geq 1.96$$

Because the value of the test statistic for the MaxFlight study is $z = 1.53$, the statistical evidence will not permit us to reject the null hypothesis at the .05 level of significance.

Summary and Practical Advice

We presented examples of a lower tail test and a two-tailed test about a population mean. Based upon these examples, we can now summarize the hypothesis testing procedures about a population mean for the σ known case as shown in Table 9.2. Note that μ_0 is the hypothesized value of the population mean.

FIGURE 9.6 CRITICAL VALUES FOR THE MAXFLIGHT HYPOTHESIS TEST

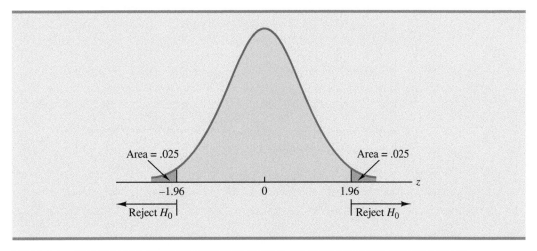

TABLE 9.2 SUMMARY OF HYPOTHESIS TESTS ABOUT A POPULATION MEAN: σ KNOWN CASE

	Lower Tail Test	**Upper Tail Test**	**Two-Tailed Test**
Hypotheses	$H_0: \mu \geq \mu_0$ $H_a: \mu < \mu_0$	$H_0: \mu \leq \mu_0$ $H_a: \mu > \mu_0$	$H_0: \mu = \mu_0$ $H_a: \mu \neq \mu_0$
Test Statistic	$z = \dfrac{\bar{x} - \mu_0}{\sigma/\sqrt{n}}$	$z = \dfrac{\bar{x} - \mu_0}{\sigma/\sqrt{n}}$	$z = \dfrac{\bar{x} - \mu_0}{\sigma/\sqrt{n}}$
Rejection Rule: **p-Value Approach**	Reject H_0 if p-value $\leq \alpha$	Reject H_0 if p-value $\leq \alpha$	Reject H_0 if p-value $\leq \alpha$
Rejection Rule: **Critical Value** **Approach**	Reject H_0 if $z \leq -z_\alpha$	Reject H_0 if $z \geq z_\alpha$	Reject H_0 if $z \leq -z_{\alpha/2}$ or if $z \geq z_{\alpha/2}$

The hypothesis testing steps followed in the two examples presented in this section are common to every hypothesis test.

STEPS OF HYPOTHESIS TESTING

Step 1. Develop the null and alternative hypotheses.
Step 2. Specify the level of significance.
Step 3. Collect the sample data and compute the value of the test statistic.

p-Value Approach

Step 4. Use the value of the test statistic to compute the p-value.
Step 5. Reject H_0 if the p-value $\leq \alpha$.
Step 6. Interpret the statistical conclusion in the context of the application.

Critical Value Approach

Step 4. Use the level of significance to determine the critical value and the rejection rule.
Step 5. Use the value of the test statistic and the rejection rule to determine whether to reject H_0.
Step 6. Interpret the statistical conclusion in the context of the application.

Practical advice about the sample size for hypothesis tests is similar to the advice we provided about the sample size for interval estimation in Chapter 8. In most applications, a sample size of $n \geq 30$ is adequate when using the hypothesis testing procedure described in this section. In cases where the sample size is less than 30, the distribution of the population from which we are sampling becomes an important consideration. If the population is normally distributed, the hypothesis testing procedure that we described is exact and can be used for any sample size. If the population is not normally distributed but is at least roughly symmetric, sample sizes as small as 15 can be expected to provide acceptable results.

Relationship Between Interval Estimation and Hypothesis Testing

In Chapter 8 we showed how to develop a confidence interval estimate of a population mean. For the σ known case, the $(1 - \alpha)\%$ confidence interval estimate of a population mean is given by

$$\bar{x} \pm z_{\alpha/2} \frac{\sigma}{\sqrt{n}}$$

In this chapter, we showed that a two-tailed hypothesis test about a population mean takes the following form:

$$H_0: \mu = \mu_0$$
$$H_a: \mu \neq \mu_0$$

where μ_0 is the hypothesized value for the population mean.

Suppose that we follow the procedure described in Chapter 8 for constructing a $100(1 - \alpha)\%$ confidence interval for the population mean. We know that $100(1 - \alpha)\%$ of the confidence intervals generated will contain the population mean and $100\alpha\%$ of the confidence intervals generated will not contain the population mean. Thus, if we reject H_0 whenever the confidence interval does not contain μ_0, we will be rejecting the null hypothesis when it is true ($\mu = \mu_0$) with probability α. Recall that the level of significance is the probability of rejecting the null hypothesis when it is true. So constructing a $100(1 - \alpha)\%$ confidence interval and rejecting H_0 whenever the interval does not contain μ_0 is equivalent to conducting a two-tailed hypothesis test with α as the level of significance. The procedure for using a confidence interval to conduct a two-tailed hypothesis test can now be summarized.

A CONFIDENCE INTERVAL APPROACH TO TESTING A HYPOTHESIS
OF THE FORM

$$H_0: \mu = \mu_0$$
$$H_a: \mu \neq \mu_0$$

1. Select a simple random sample from the population and use the value of the sample mean $\bar{x}$ to develop the confidence interval for the population mean μ.

$$\bar{x} \pm z_{\alpha/2} \frac{\sigma}{\sqrt{n}}$$

For a two-tailed hypothesis test, the null hypothesis can be rejected if the confidence interval does not include μ_0.

2. If the confidence interval contains the hypothesized value μ_0, do not reject H_0. Otherwise, reject[2] H_0.

---

[2]To be consistent with the rule for rejecting H_0 when the p-value $\leq \alpha$, we would also reject H_0 using the confidence interval approach if μ_0 happens to be equal to one of the end points of the $100(1 - \alpha)\%$ confidence interval.

Let us illustrate by conducting the MaxFlight hypothesis test using the confidence interval approach. The MaxFlight hypothesis test takes the following form:

$$H_0: \mu = 295$$
$$H_a: \mu \neq 295$$

To test these hypotheses with a level of significance of $\alpha = .05$, we sampled 50 golf balls and found a sample mean distance of $\bar{x} = 297.6$ yards. Recall that the population standard deviation is $\sigma = 12$. Using these results with $z_{.025} = 1.96$, we find that the 95% confidence interval estimate of the population mean is

$$\bar{x} \pm z_{.025}\frac{\sigma}{\sqrt{n}}$$
$$297.6 \pm 1.96\frac{12}{\sqrt{50}}$$
$$297.6 \pm 3.3$$

or

$$294.3 \text{ to } 300.9$$

This finding enables the quality control manager to conclude with 95% confidence that the mean distance for the population of golf balls is between 294.3 and 300.9 yards. Because the hypothesized value for the population mean, $\mu_0 = 295$, is in this interval, the hypothesis testing conclusion is that the null hypothesis, $H_0: \mu = 295$, cannot be rejected.

Note that this discussion and example pertain to two-tailed hypothesis tests about a population mean. However, the same confidence interval and two-tailed hypothesis testing relationship exists for other population parameters. The relationship can also be extended to one-tailed tests about population parameters. Doing so, however, requires the development of one-sided confidence intervals, which are rarely used in practice.

NOTES AND COMMENTS

We have shown how to use p-values. The smaller the p-value the greater the evidence against H_0 and the more the evidence in favor of H_a. Here are some guidelines statisticians suggest for interpreting small p-values.
- Less than .01—Overwhelming evidence to conclude H_a is true.
- Between .01 and .05—Strong evidence to conclude H_a is true.
- Between .05 and .10—Weak evidence to conclude H_a is true.
- Greater than .10—Insufficient evidence to conclude H_a is true.

Exercises

Note to Student: Some of the exercises that follow ask you to use the p-value approach and others ask you to use the critical value approach. Both methods will provide the same hypothesis testing conclusion. We provide exercises with both methods to give you practice using both. In later sections and in following chapters, we will generally emphasize the p-value approach as the preferred method, but you may select either based on personal preference.

Methods

9. Consider the following hypothesis test:

$$H_0: \mu \geq 20$$
$$H_a: \mu < 20$$

A sample of 50 provided a sample mean of 19.4. The population standard deviation is 2.
  a. Compute the value of the test statistic.
  b. What is the p-value?
  c. Using $\alpha = .05$, what is your conclusion?
  d. What is the rejection rule using the critical value? What is your conclusion?

10. Consider the following hypothesis test:

$$H_0: \mu \leq 25$$
$$H_a: \mu > 25$$

A sample of 40 provided a sample mean of 26.4. The population standard deviation is 6.
  a. Compute the value of the test statistic.
  b. What is the p-value?
  c. At $\alpha = .01$, what is your conclusion?
  d. What is the rejection rule using the critical value? What is your conclusion?

11. Consider the following hypothesis test:

$$H_0: \mu = 15$$
$$H_a: \mu \neq 15$$

A sample of 50 provided a sample mean of 14.15. The population standard deviation is 3.
  a. Compute the value of the test statistic.
  b. What is the p-value?
  c. At $\alpha = .05$, what is your conclusion?
  d. What is the rejection rule using the critical value? What is your conclusion?

12. Consider the following hypothesis test:

$$H_0: \mu \geq 80$$
$$H_a: \mu < 80$$

A sample of 100 is used and the population standard deviation is 12. Compute the p-value and state your conclusion for each of the following sample results. Use $\alpha = .01$.
  a. $\bar{x} = 78.5$
  b. $\bar{x} = 77$
  c. $\bar{x} = 75.5$
  d. $\bar{x} = 81$

13. Consider the following hypothesis test:

$$H_0: \mu \leq 50$$
$$H_a: \mu > 50$$

A sample of 60 is used and the population standard deviation is 8. Use the critical value approach to state your conclusion for each of the following sample results. Use $\alpha = .05$.
  a. $\bar{x} = 52.5$
  b. $\bar{x} = 51$
  c. $\bar{x} = 51.8$

14. Consider the following hypothesis test:

$$H_0: \mu = 22$$
$$H_a: \mu \neq 22$$

A sample of 75 is used and the population standard deviation is 10. Compute the p-value and state your conclusion for each of the following sample results. Use $\alpha = .01$.
a. $\bar{x} = 23$
b. $\bar{x} = 25.1$
c. $\bar{x} = 20$

Applications

15. Individuals filing federal income tax returns prior to March 31 received an average refund of $1056. Consider the population of "last-minute" filers who mail their tax return during the last five days of the income tax period (typically April 10 to April 15).
a. A researcher suggests that a reason individuals wait until the last five days is that on average these individuals receive lower refunds than do early filers. Develop appropriate hypotheses such that rejection of H_0 will support the researcher's contention.
b. For a sample of 400 individuals who filed a tax return between April 10 and 15, the sample mean refund was $910. Based on prior experience a population standard deviation of $\sigma = \$1600$ may be assumed. What is the p-value?
c. At $\alpha = .05$, what is your conclusion?
d. Repeat the preceding hypothesis test using the critical value approach.

16. In a study entitled How Undergraduate Students Use Credit Cards, it was reported that undergraduate students have a mean credit card balance of $3173 (*Sallie Mae*, April 2009). This figure was an all-time high and had increased 44% over the previous five years. Assume that a current study is being conducted to determine if it can be concluded that the mean credit card balance for undergraduate students has continued to increase compared to the April 2009 report. Based on previous studies, use a population standard deviation $\sigma = \$1000$.
a. State the null and alternative hypotheses.
b. What is the p-value for a sample of 180 undergraduate students with a sample mean credit card balance of $3325?
c. Using a .05 level of significance, what is your conclusion?

17. The mean hourly wage for employees in goods-producing industries is currently $24.57 (Bureau of Labor Statistics website, April, 12, 2012). Suppose we take a sample of employees from the manufacturing industry to see if the mean hourly wage differs from the reported mean of $24.57 for the goods-producing industries.
a. State the null and alternative hypotheses we should use to test whether the population mean hourly wage in the manufacturing industry differs from the population mean hourly wage in the goods-producing industries.
b. Suppose a sample of 30 employees from the manufacturing industry showed a sample mean of $23.89 per hour. Assume a population standard deviation of $2.40 per hour and compute the p-value.
c. With $\alpha = .05$ as the level of significance, what is your conclusion?
d. Repeat the preceding hypothesis test using the critical value approach.

18. The average annual total return for U.S. Diversified Equity mutual funds from 1999 to 2003 was 4.1% (*BusinessWeek*, January 26, 2004). A researcher would like to conduct a

hypothesis test to see whether the returns for mid-cap growth funds over the same period are significantly different from the average for U.S. Diversified Equity funds.

a. Formulate the hypotheses that can be used to determine whether the mean annual return for mid-cap growth funds differ from the mean for U.S. Diversified Equity funds.

b. A sample of 40 mid-cap growth funds provides a mean return of $\bar{x} = 3.4\%$. Assume the population standard deviation for mid-cap growth funds is known from previous studies to be $\sigma = 2\%$. Use the sample results to compute the test statistic and p-value for the hypothesis test.

c. At $\alpha = .05$, what is your conclusion?

19. The Internal Revenue Service (IRS) provides a toll-free help line for taxpayers to call in and get answers to questions as they prepare their tax returns. In recent years, the IRS has been inundated with taxpayer calls and has redesigned its phone service as well as posted answers to frequently asked questions on its website (*The Cincinnati Enquirer*, January 7, 2010). According to a report by a taxpayer advocate, callers using the new system can expect to wait on hold for an unreasonably long time of 12 minutes before being able to talk to an IRS employee. Suppose you select a sample of 50 callers after the new phone service has been implemented; the sample results show a mean waiting time of 10 minutes before an IRS employee comes on the line. Based upon data from past years, you decide it is reasonable to assume that the standard deviation of waiting time is 8 minutes. Using your sample results, can you conclude that the actual mean waiting time turned out to be significantly less than the 12-minute claim made by the taxpayer advocate? Use $\alpha = .05$.

20. For the United States, the mean monthly Internet bill is $32.79 per household (CNBC, January 18, 2006). A sample of 50 households in a southern state showed a sample mean of $30.63. Use a population standard deviation of $\sigma = \$5.60$.

a. Formulate hypotheses for a test to determine whether the sample data support the conclusion that the mean monthly Internet bill in the southern state is less than the national mean of $32.79.

b. What is the value of the test statistic?

c. What is the p-value?

d. At $\alpha = .01$, what is your conclusion?

Fowle

21. Fowle Marketing Research, Inc., bases charges to a client on the assumption that telephone surveys can be completed in a mean time of 15 minutes or less. If a longer mean survey time is necessary, a premium rate is charged. A sample of 35 surveys provided the survey times shown in the file named Fowle. Based upon past studies, the population standard deviation is assumed known with $\sigma = 4$ minutes. Is the premium rate justified?

a. Formulate the null and alternative hypotheses for this application.

b. Compute the value of the test statistic.

c. What is the p-value?

d. At $\alpha = .01$, what is your conclusion?

22. CCN and ActMedia provided a television channel targeted to individuals waiting in supermarket checkout lines. The channel showed news, short features, and advertisements. The length of the program was based on the assumption that the population mean time a shopper stands in a supermarket checkout line is 8 minutes. A sample of actual waiting times will be used to test this assumption and determine whether actual mean waiting time differs from this standard.

a. Formulate the hypotheses for this application.

b. A sample of 120 shoppers showed a sample mean waiting time of 8.4 minutes. Assume a population standard deviation of $\sigma = 3.2$ minutes. What is the p-value?

c. At $\alpha = .05$, what is your conclusion?

d. Compute a 95% confidence interval for the population mean. Does it support your conclusion?

9.4 Population Mean: σ Unknown

In this section we describe how to conduct hypothesis tests about a population mean for the σ unknown case. Because the σ unknown case corresponds to situations in which an estimate of the population standard deviation cannot be developed prior to sampling, the sample must be used to develop an estimate of both μ and σ. Thus, to conduct a hypothesis test about a population mean for the σ unknown case, the sample mean $\bar{x}$ is used as an estimate of μ and the sample standard deviation s is used as an estimate of σ.

The steps of the hypothesis testing procedure for the σ unknown case are the same as those for the σ known case described in Section 9.3. But, with σ unknown, the computation of the test statistic and p-value is a bit different. Recall that for the σ known case, the sampling distribution of the test statistic has a standard normal distribution. For the σ unknown case, however, the sampling distribution of the test statistic follows the t distribution; it has slightly more variability because the sample is used to develop estimates of both μ and σ.

In Section 8.2 we showed that an interval estimate of a population mean for the σ unknown case is based on a probability distribution known as the t distribution. Hypothesis tests about a population mean for the σ unknown case are also based on the t distribution. For the σ unknown case, the test statistic has a t distribution with $n - 1$ degrees of freedom.

TEST STATISTIC FOR HYPOTHESIS TESTS ABOUT A POPULATION MEAN: σ UNKNOWN

$$t = \frac{\bar{x} - \mu_0}{s/\sqrt{n}} \qquad (9.2)$$

In Chapter 8 we said that the t distribution is based on an assumption that the population from which we are sampling has a normal distribution. However, research shows that this assumption can be relaxed considerably when the sample size is large enough. We provide some practical advice concerning the population distribution and sample size at the end of the section.

One-Tailed Test

Let us consider an example of a one-tailed test about a population mean for the σ unknown case. A business travel magazine wants to classify transatlantic gateway airports according to the mean rating for the population of business travelers. A rating scale with a low score of 0 and a high score of 10 will be used, and airports with a population mean rating greater than 7 will be designated as superior service airports. The magazine staff surveyed a sample of 60 business travelers at each airport to obtain the ratings data. The sample for London's Heathrow Airport provided a sample mean rating of $\bar{x} = 7.25$ and a sample standard deviation of $s = 1.052$. Do the data indicate that Heathrow should be designated as a superior service airport?

WEB file

AirRating

We want to develop a hypothesis test for which the decision to reject H_0 will lead to the conclusion that the population mean rating for the Heathrow Airport is *greater* than 7. Thus, an upper tail test with H_a: $\mu > 7$ is required. The null and alternative hypotheses for this upper tail test are as follows:

$$H_0: \mu \leq 7$$
$$H_a: \mu > 7$$

We will use $\alpha = .05$ as the level of significance for the test.

Using equation (9.2) with $\bar{x} = 7.25, \mu_0 = 7, s = 1.052$, and $n = 60$, the value of the test statistic is

$$t = \frac{\bar{x} - \mu_0}{s/\sqrt{n}} = \frac{7.25 - 7}{1.052/\sqrt{60}} = 1.84$$

The sampling distribution of t has $n - 1 = 60 - 1 = 59$ degrees of freedom. Because the test is an upper tail test, the p-value is $P(t \geq 1.84)$, that is, the upper tail area corresponding to the value of the test statistic.

The t distribution table provided in most textbooks will not contain sufficient detail to determine the exact p-value, such as the p-value corresponding to $t = 1.84$. For instance, using Table 2 in Appendix B, the t distribution with 59 degrees of freedom provides the following information.

Area in Upper Tail	.20	.10	.05	.025	.01	.005
t Value (59 *df*)	.848	1.296	1.671	2.001	2.391	2.662

$$t = 1.84$$

We see that $t = 1.84$ is between 1.671 and 2.001. Although the table does not provide the exact p-value, the values in the "Area in Upper Tail" row show that the p-value must be less than .05 and greater than .025. With a level of significance of $\alpha = .05$, this placement is all we need to know to make the decision to reject the null hypothesis and conclude that Heathrow should be classified as a superior service airport.

Appendix F shows how to compute p-values using Excel or Minitab.

Because it is cumbersome to use a t table to compute p-values, and only approximate values are obtained, we show how to compute the exact p-value using Excel or Minitab. The directions can be found in Appendix F at the end of this text. Using Excel or Minitab with $t = 1.84$ provides the upper tail p-value of .0354 for the Heathrow Airport hypothesis test. With .0354 < .05, we reject the null hypothesis and conclude that Heathrow should be classified as a superior service airport.

The decision whether to reject the null hypothesis in the σ unknown case can also be made using the critical value approach. The critical value corresponding to an area of $\alpha = .05$ in the upper tail of a t distribution with 59 degrees of freedom is $t_{.05} = 1.671$. Thus the rejection rule using the critical value approach is to reject H_0 if $t \geq 1.671$. Because $t = 1.84 > 1.671$, H_0 is rejected. Heathrow should be classified as a superior service airport.

Two-Tailed Test

To illustrate how to conduct a two-tailed test about a population mean for the σ unknown case, let us consider the hypothesis testing situation facing Holiday Toys. The company manufactures and distributes its products through more than 1000 retail outlets. In planning production levels for the coming winter season, Holiday must decide how many units of each product to produce prior to knowing the actual demand at the retail level. For this year's most important new toy, Holiday's marketing director is expecting demand to average 40 units per retail outlet. Prior to making the final production decision based upon this estimate, Holiday decided to survey a sample of 25 retailers in order to develop more information about the demand for the new product. Each retailer was provided with information about the features of the new toy along with the cost and the suggested selling price. Then each retailer was asked to specify an anticipated order quantity.

With μ denoting the population mean order quantity per retail outlet, the sample data will be used to conduct the following two-tailed hypothesis test:

$$H_0: \mu = 40$$
$$H_a: \mu \neq 40$$

If H_0 cannot be rejected, Holiday will continue its production planning based on the marketing director's estimate that the population mean order quantity per retail outlet will be $\mu = 40$ units. However, if H_0 is rejected, Holiday will immediately reevaluate its production plan for the product. A two-tailed hypothesis test is used because Holiday wants to reevaluate the production plan if the population mean quantity per retail outlet is less than anticipated or greater than anticipated. Because no historical data are available (it's a new product), the population mean μ and the population standard deviation must both be estimated using $\bar{x}$ and s from the sample data.

Orders

The sample of 25 retailers provided a mean of $\bar{x} = 37.4$ and a standard deviation of $s = 11.79$ units. Before going ahead with the use of the t distribution, the analyst constructed a histogram of the sample data in order to check on the form of the population distribution. The histogram of the sample data showed no evidence of skewness or any extreme outliers, so the analyst concluded that the use of the t distribution with $n - 1 = 24$ degrees of freedom was appropriate. Using equation (9.2) with $\bar{x} = 37.4$, $\mu_0 = 40$, $s = 11.79$, and $n = 25$, the value of the test statistic is

$$t = \frac{\bar{x} - \mu_0}{s/\sqrt{n}} = \frac{37.4 - 40}{11.79/\sqrt{25}} = -1.10$$

Because we have a two-tailed test, the p-value is two times the area under the curve of the t distribution for $t \leq -1.10$. Using Table 2 in Appendix B, the t distribution table for 24 degrees of freedom provides the following information.

Area in Upper Tail	.20	.10	.05	.025	.01	.005
t-Value (24 *df*)	.857	1.318	1.711	2.064	2.492	2.797

$$t = 1.10$$

The t distribution table only contains positive t values. Because the t distribution is symmetric, however, the upper tail area at $t = 1.10$ is the same as the lower tail area at $t = -1.10$. We see that $t = 1.10$ is between 0.857 and 1.318. From the "Area in Upper Tail" row, we see that the area in the upper tail at $t = 1.10$ is between .20 and .10. When we double these amounts, we see that the p-value must be between .40 and .20. With a level of significance of $\alpha = .05$, we now know that the p-value is greater than α. Therefore, H_0 cannot be rejected. Sufficient evidence is not available to conclude that Holiday should change its production plan for the coming season.

Appendix F shows how the p-value for this test can be computed using Excel or Minitab. The p-value obtained is .2822. With a level of significance of $\alpha = .05$, we cannot reject H_0 because $.2822 > .05$.

The test statistic can also be compared to the critical value to make the two-tailed hypothesis testing decision. With $\alpha = .05$ and the t distribution with 24 degrees of freedom, $-t_{.025} = -2.064$ and $t_{.025} = 2.064$ are the critical values for the two-tailed test. The rejection rule using the test statistic is

Reject H_0 if $t \leq -2.064$ or if $t \geq 2.064$

TABLE 9.3   SUMMARY OF HYPOTHESIS TESTS ABOUT A POPULATION MEAN: σ UNKNOWN CASE

	Lower Tail Test	**Upper Tail Test**	**Two-Tailed Test**
Hypotheses	$H_0: \mu \geq \mu_0$ $H_a: \mu < \mu_0$	$H_0: \mu \leq \mu_0$ $H_a: \mu > \mu_0$	$H_0: \mu = \mu_0$ $H_a: \mu \neq \mu_0$
Test Statistic	$t = \dfrac{\bar{x} - \mu_0}{s/\sqrt{n}}$	$t = \dfrac{\bar{x} - \mu_0}{s/\sqrt{n}}$	$t = \dfrac{\bar{x} - \mu_0}{s/\sqrt{n}}$
Rejection Rule: *p*-**Value Approach**	Reject H_0 if p-value $\leq \alpha$	Reject H_0 if p-value $\leq \alpha$	Reject H_0 if p-value $\leq \alpha$
Rejection Rule: Critical Value Approach	Reject H_0 if $t \leq -t_\alpha$	Reject H_0 if $t \geq t_\alpha$	Reject H_0 if $t \leq -t_{\alpha/2}$ or if $t \geq t_{\alpha/2}$

Based on the test statistic $t = -1.10$, H_0 cannot be rejected. This result indicates that Holiday should continue its production planning for the coming season based on the expectation that $\mu = 40$.

Summary and Practical Advice

Table 9.3 provides a summary of the hypothesis testing procedures about a population mean for the σ unknown case. The key difference between these procedures and the ones for the σ known case is that s is used, instead of σ, in the computation of the test statistic. For this reason, the test statistic follows the t distribution.

The applicability of the hypothesis testing procedures of this section is dependent on the distribution of the population being sampled from and the sample size. When the population is normally distributed, the hypothesis tests described in this section provide exact results for any sample size. When the population is not normally distributed, the procedures are approximations. Nonetheless, we find that sample sizes of 30 or greater will provide good results in most cases. If the population is approximately normal, small sample sizes (e.g., $n < 15$) can provide acceptable results. If the population is highly skewed or contains outliers, sample sizes approaching 50 are recommended.

Exercises

Methods

23. Consider the following hypothesis test:

$$H_0: \mu \leq 12$$
$$H_a: \mu > 12$$

A sample of 25 provided a sample mean $\bar{x} = 14$ and a sample standard deviation $s = 4.32$.
   a. Compute the value of the test statistic.
   b. Use the t distribution table (Table 2 in Appendix B) to compute a range for the p-value.
   c. At $\alpha = .05$, what is your conclusion?
   d. What is the rejection rule using the critical value? What is your conclusion?

24. Consider the following hypothesis test:

$$H_0: \mu = 18$$
$$H_a: \mu \neq 18$$

A sample of 48 provided a sample mean $\bar{x} = 17$ and a sample standard deviation $s = 4.5$.
a. Compute the value of the test statistic.
b. Use the t distribution table (Table 2 in Appendix B) to compute a range for the p-value.
c. At $\alpha = .05$, what is your conclusion?
d. What is the rejection rule using the critical value? What is your conclusion?

25. Consider the following hypothesis test:

$$H_0: \mu \geq 45$$
$$H_a: \mu < 45$$

A sample of 36 is used. Identify the p-value and state your conclusion for each of the following sample results. Use $\alpha = .01$.
a. $\bar{x} = 44$ and $s = 5.2$
b. $\bar{x} = 43$ and $s = 4.6$
c. $\bar{x} = 46$ and $s = 5.0$

26. Consider the following hypothesis test:

$$H_0: \mu = 100$$
$$H_a: \mu \neq 100$$

A sample of 65 is used. Identify the p-value and state your conclusion for each of the following sample results. Use $\alpha = .05$.
a. $\bar{x} = 103$ and $s = 11.5$
b. $\bar{x} = 96.5$ and $s = 11.0$
c. $\bar{x} = 102$ and $s = 10.5$

Applications

27. The Employment and Training Administration reported that the U.S. mean unemployment insurance benefit was $238 per week (*The World Almanac,* 2003). A researcher in the state of Virginia anticipated that sample data would show evidence that the mean weekly unemployment insurance benefit in Virginia was below the national average.
a. Develop appropriate hypotheses such that rejection of H_0 will support the researcher's contention.
b. For a sample of 100 individuals, the sample mean weekly unemployment insurance benefit was $231 with a sample standard deviation of $80. What is the p-value?
c. At $\alpha = .05$, what is your conclusion?
d. Repeat the preceding hypothesis test using the critical value approach.

28. A shareholders' group, in lodging a protest, claimed that the mean tenure for a chief executive office (CEO) was at least nine years. A survey of companies reported in *The Wall Street Journal* found a sample mean tenure of $\bar{x} = 7.27$ years for CEOs with a standard deviation of $s = 6.38$ years (*The Wall Street Journal,* January 2, 2007).
a. Formulate hypotheses that can be used to challenge the validity of the claim made by the shareholders' group.
b. Assume 85 companies were included in the sample. What is the p-value for your hypothesis test?
c. At $\alpha = .01$, what is your conclusion?

Administrator

29. The national mean annual salary for a school administrator is $90,000 a year (*The Cincinnati Enquirer,* April 7, 2012). A school official took a sample of 25 school administrators in the state of Ohio to learn about salaries in that state to see if they differed from the national average.

   a. Formulate hypotheses that can be used to determine whether the population mean annual administrator salary in Ohio differs from the national mean of $90,000.

   b. The sample data for 25 Ohio administrators is contained in the file named Administrator. What is the *p*-value for your hypothesis test in part (a)?

   c. At $\alpha = .05$, can your null hypothesis be rejected? What is your conclusion?

   d. Repeat the preceding hypothesis test using the critical value approach.

ChildCare

30. The time married men with children spend on child care averages 6.4 hours per week (*Time,* March 12, 2012). You belong to a professional group on family practices that would like to do its own study to determine if the time married men in your area spend on child care per week differs from the reported mean of 6.4 hours per week. A sample of 40 married couples will be used with the data collected showing the hours per week the husband spends on child care. The sample data are contained in the file ChildCare.

   a. What are the hypotheses if your group would like to determine if the population mean number of hours married men are spending in child care differs from the mean reported by *Time* in your area?

   b. What is the sample mean and the *p*-value?

   c. Select your own level of significance. What is your conclusion?

31. The Coca-Cola Company reported that the mean per capita annual sales of its beverages in the United States was 423 eight-ounce servings (Coca-Cola Company website, February 3, 2009). Suppose you are curious whether the consumption of Coca-Cola beverages is higher in Atlanta, Georgia, the location of Coca-Cola's corporate headquarters. A sample of 36 individuals from the Atlanta area showed a sample mean annual consumption of 460.4 eight-ounce servings with a standard deviation of $s = 101.9$ ounces. Using $\alpha = .05$, do the sample results support the conclusion that mean annual consumption of Coca-Cola beverage products is higher in Atlanta?

UsedCars

32. According to the National Automobile Dealers Association, the mean price for used cars is $10,192. A manager of a Kansas City used car dealership reviewed a sample of 50 recent used car sales at the dealership in an attempt to determine whether the population mean price for used cars at this particular dealership differed from the national mean. The prices for the sample of 50 cars are shown in the file named UsedCars.

   a. Formulate the hypotheses that can be used to determine whether a difference exists in the mean price for used cars at the dealership.

   b. What is the *p*-value?

   c. At $\alpha = .05$, what is your conclusion?

33. Annual per capita consumption of milk is 21.6 gallons (*Statistical Abstract of the United States: 2006*). Being from the Midwest, you believe milk consumption is higher there and wish to support your opinion. A sample of 16 individuals from the midwestern town of Webster City showed a sample mean annual consumption of 24.1 gallons with a standard deviation of $s = 4.8$.

   a. Develop a hypothesis test that can be used to determine whether the mean annual consumption in Webster City is higher than the national mean.

   b. What is a point estimate of the difference between mean annual consumption in Webster City and the national mean?

   c. At $\alpha = .05$, test for a significant difference. What is your conclusion?

34. Joan's Nursery specializes in custom-designed landscaping for residential areas. The estimated labor cost associated with a particular landscaping proposal is based on the number of plantings of trees, shrubs, and so on to be used for the project. For cost-estimating purposes, managers use two hours of labor time for the planting of a

medium-sized tree. Actual times from a sample of 10 plantings during the past month follow (times in hours).

1.7	1.5	2.6	2.2	2.4	2.3	2.6	3.0	1.4	2.3

With a .05 level of significance, test to see whether the mean tree-planting time differs from two hours.

a. State the null and alternative hypotheses.
b. Compute the sample mean.
c. Compute the sample standard deviation.
d. What is the p-value?
e. What is your conclusion?

9.5 Population Proportion

In this section we show how to conduct a hypothesis test about a population proportion p. Using p_0 to denote the hypothesized value for the population proportion, the three forms for a hypothesis test about a population proportion are as follows.

$$
\begin{array}{ccc}
H_0\colon p \geq p_0 & H_0\colon p \leq p_0 & H_0\colon p = p_0 \\
H_a\colon p < p_0 & H_a\colon p > p_0 & H_a\colon p \neq p_0
\end{array}
$$

The first form is called a lower tail test, the second form is called an upper tail test, and the third form is called a two-tailed test.

Hypothesis tests about a population proportion are based on the difference between the sample proportion $\bar{p}$ and the hypothesized population proportion p_0. The methods used to conduct the hypothesis test are similar to those used for hypothesis tests about a population mean. The only difference is that we use the sample proportion and its standard error to compute the test statistic. The p-value approach or the critical value approach is then used to determine whether the null hypothesis should be rejected.

Let us consider an example involving a situation faced by Pine Creek golf course. Over the past year, 20% of the players at Pine Creek were women. In an effort to increase the proportion of women players, Pine Creek implemented a special promotion designed to attract women golfers. One month after the promotion was implemented, the course manager requested a statistical study to determine whether the proportion of women players at Pine Creek had increased. Because the objective of the study is to determine whether the proportion of women golfers increased, an upper tail test with $H_a\colon p > .20$ is appropriate. The null and alternative hypotheses for the Pine Creek hypothesis test are as follows:

$$
\begin{array}{c}
H_0\colon p \leq .20 \\
H_a\colon p > .20
\end{array}
$$

If H_0 can be rejected, the test results will give statistical support for the conclusion that the proportion of women golfers increased and the promotion was beneficial. The course manager specified that a level of significance of $\alpha = .05$ be used in carrying out this hypothesis test.

The next step of the hypothesis testing procedure is to select a sample and compute the value of an appropriate test statistic. To show how this step is done for the Pine Creek upper tail test, we begin with a general discussion of how to compute the value of the test statistic for any form of a hypothesis test about a population proportion. The sampling distribution of $\bar{p}$, the point estimator of the population parameter p, is the basis for developing the test statistic.

When the null hypothesis is true as an equality, the expected value of $\bar{p}$ equals the hypothesized value p_0; that is, $E(\bar{p}) = p_0$. The standard error of $\bar{p}$ is given by

$$\sigma_{\bar{p}} = \sqrt{\frac{p_0(1 - p_0)}{n}}$$

In Chapter 7 we said that if $np \geq 5$ and $n(1 - p) \geq 5$, the sampling distribution of $\bar{p}$ can be approximated by a normal distribution.[3] Under these conditions, which usually apply in practice, the quantity

$$z = \frac{\bar{p} - p_0}{\sigma_{\bar{p}}} \qquad (9.3)$$

has a standard normal probability distribution. With $\sigma_{\bar{p}} = \sqrt{p_0(1 - p_0)/n}$, the standard normal random variable z is the test statistic used to conduct hypothesis tests about a population proportion.

TEST STATISTIC FOR HYPOTHESIS TESTS ABOUT A POPULATION PROPORTION

$$z = \frac{\bar{p} - p_0}{\sqrt{\dfrac{p_0(1 - p_0)}{n}}} \qquad (9.4)$$

WEB file

WomenGolf

We can now compute the test statistic for the Pine Creek hypothesis test. Suppose a random sample of 400 players was selected, and that 100 of the players were women. The proportion of women golfers in the sample is

$$\bar{p} = \frac{100}{400} = .25$$

Using equation (9.4), the value of the test statistic is

$$z = \frac{\bar{p} - p_0}{\sqrt{\dfrac{p_0(1 - p_0)}{n}}} = \frac{.25 - .20}{\sqrt{\dfrac{.20(1 - .20)}{400}}} = \frac{.05}{.02} = 2.50$$

Because the Pine Creek hypothesis test is an upper tail test, the p-value is the probability that z is greater than or equal to $z = 2.50$; that is, it is the upper tail area corresponding to $z \geq 2.50$. Using the standard normal probability table, we find that the area to the left of $z = 2.50$ is .9938. Thus, the p-value for the Pine Creek test is $1.0000 - .9938 = .0062$. Figure 9.7 shows this p-value calculation.

Recall that the course manager specified a level of significance of $\alpha = .05$. A p-value = $.0062 < .05$ gives sufficient statistical evidence to reject H_0 at the .05 level of significance. Thus, the test provides statistical support for the conclusion that the special promotion increased the proportion of women players at the Pine Creek golf course.

---

[3]In most applications involving hypothesis tests of a population proportion, sample sizes are large enough to use the normal approximation. The exact sampling distribution of $\bar{p}$ is discrete with the probability for each value of $\bar{p}$ given by the binomial distribution. So hypothesis testing is a bit more complicated for small samples when the normal approximation cannot be used.

FIGURE 9.7   CALCULATION OF THE p-VALUE FOR THE PINE CREEK HYPOTHESIS TEST

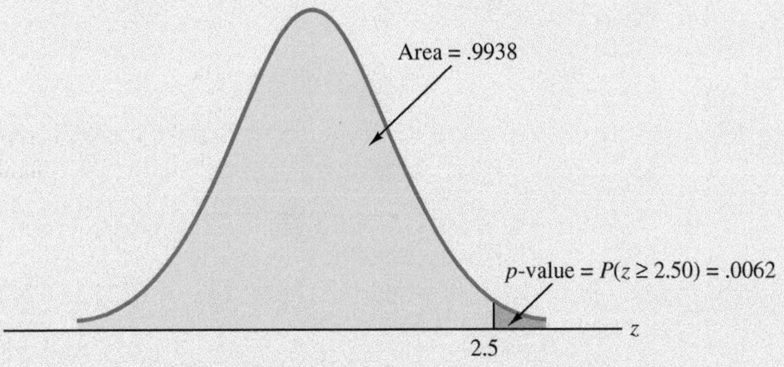

The decision whether to reject the null hypothesis can also be made using the critical value approach. The critical value corresponding to an area of .05 in the upper tail of a normal probability distribution is $z_{.05} = 1.645$. Thus, the rejection rule using the critical value approach is to reject H_0 if $z \geq 1.645$. Because $z = 2.50 > 1.645$, H_0 is rejected.

Again, we see that the p-value approach and the critical value approach lead to the same hypothesis testing conclusion, but the p-value approach provides more information. With a p-value $= .0062$, the null hypothesis would be rejected for any level of significance greater than or equal to .0062.

Summary

The procedure used to conduct a hypothesis test about a population proportion is similar to the procedure used to conduct a hypothesis test about a population mean. Although we only illustrated how to conduct a hypothesis test about a population proportion for an upper tail test, similar procedures can be used for lower tail and two-tailed tests. Table 9.4 provides a summary of the hypothesis tests about a population proportion. We assume that $np \geq 5$ and $n(1 - p) \geq 5$; thus the normal probability distribution can be used to approximate the sampling distribution of $\bar{p}$.

TABLE 9.4   SUMMARY OF HYPOTHESIS TESTS ABOUT A POPULATION PROPORTION

	Lower Tail Test	Upper Tail Test	Two-Tailed Test
Hypotheses	$H_0: p \geq p_0$ $H_a: p < p_0$	$H_0: p \leq p_0$ $H_a: p > p_0$	$H_0: p = p_0$ $H_a: p \neq p_0$
Test Statistic	$z = \dfrac{\bar{p} - p_0}{\sqrt{\dfrac{p_0(1 - p_0)}{n}}}$	$z = \dfrac{\bar{p} - p_0}{\sqrt{\dfrac{p_0(1 - p_0)}{n}}}$	$z = \dfrac{\bar{p} - p_0}{\sqrt{\dfrac{p_0(1 - p_0)}{n}}}$
Rejection Rule: **p-Value Approach**	Reject H_0 if p-value $\leq \alpha$	Reject H_0 if p-value $\leq \alpha$	Reject H_0 if p-value $\leq \alpha$

Rejection Rule:
  Critical Value
  Approach
	Reject H_0 if
	$z \leq -z_\alpha$
		Reject H_0 if
		$z \geq z_\alpha$
			Reject H_0 if
			$z \leq -z_{\alpha/2}$
			or if $z \geq z_{\alpha/2}$

Exercises

Methods

35. Consider the following hypothesis test:

$$H_0: p = .20$$
$$H_a: p \neq .20$$

A sample of 400 provided a sample proportion $\bar{p} = .175$.
    a. Compute the value of the test statistic.
    b. What is the p-value?
    c. At $\alpha = .05$, what is your conclusion?
    d. What is the rejection rule using the critical value? What is your conclusion?

36. Consider the following hypothesis test:

$$H_0: p \geq .75$$
$$H_a: p < .75$$

A sample of 300 items was selected. Compute the p-value and state your conclusion for each of the following sample results. Use $\alpha = .05$.
    a. $\bar{p} = .68$ c. $\bar{p} = .70$
    b. $\bar{p} = .72$ d. $\bar{p} = .77$

Applications

37. A study found that, in 2005, 12.5% of U.S. workers belonged to unions (*The Wall Street Journal,* January 21, 2006). Suppose a sample of 400 U.S. workers is collected in 2006 to determine whether union efforts to organize have increased union membership.
    a. Formulate the hypotheses that can be used to determine whether union membership increased in 2006.
    b. If the sample results show that 52 of the workers belonged to unions, what is the p-value for your hypothesis test?
    c. At $\alpha = .05$, what is your conclusion?

38. A study by *Consumer Reports* showed that 64% of supermarket shoppers believe supermarket brands to be as good as national name brands. To investigate whether this result applies to its own product, the manufacturer of a national name-brand ketchup asked a sample of shoppers whether they believed that supermarket ketchup was as good as the national brand ketchup.
    a. Formulate the hypotheses that could be used to determine whether the percentage of supermarket shoppers who believe that the supermarket ketchup was as good as the national brand ketchup differed from 64%.
    b. If a sample of 100 shoppers showed 52 stating that the supermarket brand was as good as the national brand, what is the p-value?
    c. At $\alpha = .05$, what is your conclusion?
    d. Should the national brand ketchup manufacturer be pleased with this conclusion? Explain.

AgeGroup

39. According to the Pew Internet & American Life Project, 75% of American adults use the Internet (Pew Internet website, April 19, 2008). The Pew project authors also reported on the percentage of Americans who use the Internet by age group. The data in the file AgeGroup are consistent with their findings. These data were obtained from a sample of 100 Internet users in the 30–49 age group and 200 Internet users in the 50–64 age group. A Yes indicates the survey repondent had used the Internet; a No indicates the survey repondent had not.

a. Formulate hypotheses that could be used to determine whether the percentage of Internet users in the two age groups differs from the overall average of 75%

b. Estimate the proportion of Internet users in the 30–49 age group. Does this proportion differ significantly from the overall proportion of .75? Use $\alpha = .05$

c. Estimate the proportion of Internet users in the 50–64 age group. Does this proportion differ significantly from the overall proportion of .75? Use $\alpha = .05$

d. Would you expect the proportion of users in the 18–29 age group to be larger or smaller than the proportion for the 30–49 age group? Support you conclusion with the results obtained in parts (b) and (c).

40. In 2008, 46% of business owners gave a holiday gift to their employees. A 2009 survey of business owners indicated that 35% planned to provide a holiday gift to their employees (Radio WEZV, Myrtle Beach, SC, November 11, 2009). Suppose the survey results are based on a sample of 60 business owners.

a. How many business owners in the survey planned to provide a holiday gift to their employees in 2009?

b. Suppose the business owners in the sample did as they planned. Compute the *p*-value for a hypothesis test that can be used to determine if the proportion of business owners providing holiday gifts had decreased from the 2008 level.

c. Using a .05 level of significance, would you conclude that the proportion of business owners providing gifts decreased? What is the smallest level of significance for which you could draw such a conclusion?

41. Speaking to a group of analysts in January 2006, a brokerage firm executive claimed that at least 70% of investors are currently confident of meeting their investment objectives. A UBS Investor Optimism Survey, conducted over the period January 2 to January 15, found that 67% of investors were confident of meeting their investment objectives (CNBC, January 20, 2006).

a. Formulate the hypotheses that can be used to test the validity of the brokerage firm executive's claim.

b. Assume the UBS Investor Optimism Survey collected information from 300 investors. What is the *p*-value for the hypothesis test?

c. At $\alpha = .05$, should the executive's claim be rejected?

42. According to the University of Nevada Center for Logistics Management, 6% of all merchandise sold in the United States gets returned (*BusinessWeek*, January 15, 2007). A Houston department store sampled 80 items sold in January and found that 12 of the items were returned.

a. Construct a point estimate of the proportion of items returned for the population of sales transactions at the Houston store.

b. Construct a 95% confidence interval for the porportion of returns at the Houston store.

c. Is the proportion of returns at the Houston store significantly different from the returns for the nation as a whole? Provide statistical support for your answer.

Eagle

43. Eagle Outfitters is a chain of stores specializing in outdoor apparel and camping gear. They are considering a promotion that involves mailing discount coupons to all their credit card customers. This promotion will be considered a success if more than 10% of those receiving the coupons use them. Before going national with the promotion, coupons were sent to a sample of 100 credit card customers.

a. Develop hypotheses that can be used to test whether the population proportion of those who will use the coupons is sufficient to go national.

b. The file Eagle contains the sample data. Develop a point estimate of the population proportion.

c. Use $\alpha = .05$ to conduct your hypothesis test. Should Eagle go national with the promotion?

Drowsy

44. In a cover story, *BusinessWeek* published information about sleep habits of Americans (*BusinessWeek*, January 26, 2004). The article noted that sleep deprivation causes a number of problems, including highway deaths. Fifty-one percent of adult drivers admit to

driving while drowsy. A researcher hypothesized that this issue was an even bigger problem for night shift workers.

a.   Formulate the hypotheses that can be used to help determine whether more than 51% of the population of night shift workers admit to driving while drowsy.

b.   A sample of 400 night shift workers identified those who admitted to driving while drowsy. See the Drowsy file. What is the sample proportion? What is the *p*-value?

c.   At $\alpha = .01$, what is your conclusion?

45.   Many investors and financial analysts believe the Dow Jones Industrial Average (DJIA) provides a good barometer of the overall stock market. On January 31, 2006, 9 of the 30 stocks making up the DJIA increased in price (*The Wall Street Journal,* February 1, 2006). On the basis of this fact, a financial analyst claims we can assume that 30% of the stocks traded on the New York Stock Exchange (NYSE) went up the same day.

a.   Formulate null and alternative hypotheses to test the analyst's claim.

b.   A sample of 50 stocks traded on the NYSE that day showed that 24 went up. What is your point estimate of the population proportion of stocks that went up?

c.   Conduct your hypothesis test using $\alpha = .01$ as the level of significance. What is your conclusion?

9.6   Hypothesis Testing and Decision Making

In the previous sections of this chapter we have illustrated hypothesis testing applications that are considered significance tests. After formulating the null and alternative hypotheses, we selected a sample and computed the value of a test statistic and the associated *p*-value. We then compared the *p*-value to a controlled probability of a Type I error, α, which is called the level of significance for the test. If *p*-value $\leq \alpha$, we made the conclusion "reject H_0" and declared the results significant; otherwise, we made the conclusion "do not reject H_0." With a significance test, we control the probability of making the Type I error, but not the Type II error. Thus, we recommended the conclusion "do not reject H_0" rather than "accept H_0" because the latter puts us at risk of making the Type II error of accepting H_0 when it is false. With the conclusion "do not reject H_0," the statistical evidence is considered inconclusive and is usually an indication to postpone a decision or action until further research and testing can be undertaken.

However, if the purpose of a hypothesis test is to make a decision when H_0 is true and a different decision when H_a is true, the decision maker may want to, and in some cases be forced to, take action with both the conclusion *do not reject H_0* and the conclusion *reject H_0*. If this situation occurs, statisticians generally recommend controlling the probability of making a Type II error. With the probabilities of both the Type I and Type II error controlled, the conclusion from the hypothesis test is either to *accept H_0* or *reject H_0*. In the first case, H_0 is concluded to be true, while in the second case, H_a is concluded true. Thus, a decision and appropriate action can be taken when either conclusion is reached.

A good illustration of hypothesis testing for decision making is lot-acceptance sampling, a topic we will discuss in more depth in Chapter 20. For example, a quality control manager must decide to accept a shipment of batteries from a supplier or to return the shipment because of poor quality. Assume that design specifications require batteries from the supplier to have a mean useful life of at least 120 hours. To evaluate the quality of an incoming shipment, a sample of 36 batteries will be selected and tested. On the basis of the sample, a decision must be made to accept the shipment of batteries or to return it to the supplier because of poor quality. Let μ denote the mean number of hours of useful life for batteries in the shipment. The null and alternative hypotheses about the population mean follow.

$$H_0: \mu \geq 120$$
$$H_a: \mu < 120$$

If H_0 is rejected, the alternative hypothesis is concluded to be true. This conclusion indicates that the appropriate action is to return the shipment to the supplier. However, if H_0 is not rejected, the decision maker must still determine what action should be taken. Thus, without directly concluding that H_0 is true, but merely by not rejecting it, the decision maker will have made the decision to accept the shipment as being of satisfactory quality.

In such decision-making situations, it is recommended that the hypothesis testing procedure be extended to control the probability of making a Type II error. Because a decision will be made and action taken when we do not reject H_0, knowledge of the probability of making a Type II error will be helpful. In Sections 9.7 and 9.8 we explain how to compute the probability of making a Type II error and how the sample size can be adjusted to help control the probability of making a Type II error.

9.7 Calculating the Probability of Type II Errors

In this section we show how to calculate the probability of making a Type II error for a hypothesis test about a population mean. We illustrate the procedure by using the lot-acceptance example described in Section 9.6. The null and alternative hypotheses about the mean number of hours of useful life for a shipment of batteries are H_0: $\mu \geq 120$ and H_a: $\mu < 120$. If H_0 is rejected, the decision will be to return the shipment to the supplier because the mean hours of useful life are less than the specified 120 hours. If H_0 is not rejected, the decision will be to accept the shipment.

Suppose a level of significance of $\alpha = .05$ is used to conduct the hypothesis test. The test statistic in the σ known case is

$$z = \frac{\bar{x} - \mu_0}{\sigma/\sqrt{n}} = \frac{\bar{x} - 120}{\sigma/\sqrt{n}}$$

Based on the critical value approach and $z_{.05} = 1.645$, the rejection rule for the lower tail test is

$$\text{Reject } H_0 \text{ if } z \leq -1.645$$

Suppose a sample of 36 batteries will be selected and based upon previous testing the population standard deviation can be assumed known with a value of $\sigma = 12$ hours. The rejection rule indicates that we will reject H_0 if

$$z = \frac{\bar{x} - 120}{12/\sqrt{36}} \leq -1.645$$

Solving for $\bar{x}$ in the preceding expression indicates that we will reject H_0 if

$$\bar{x} \leq 120 - 1.645\left(\frac{12}{\sqrt{36}}\right) = 116.71$$

Rejecting H_0 when $\bar{x} \leq 116.71$ means that we will make the decision to accept the shipment whenever

$$\bar{x} > 116.71$$

With this information, we are ready to compute probabilities associated with making a Type II error. First, recall that we make a Type II error whenever the true shipment mean is less than 120 hours and we make the decision to accept H_0: $\mu \geq 120$. Hence, to compute the probability of making a Type II error, we must select a value of μ less than 120 hours.

FIGURE 9.8   PROBABILITY OF A TYPE II ERROR WHEN $\mu = 112$

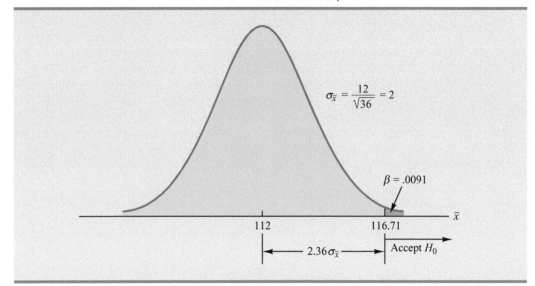

For example, suppose the shipment is considered to be of poor quality if the batteries have a mean life of $\mu = 112$ hours. If $\mu = 112$ is really true, what is the probability of accepting H_0: $\mu \geq 120$ and hence committing a Type II error? Note that this probability is the probability that the sample mean $\bar{x}$ is greater than 116.71 when $\mu = 112$.

Figure 9.8 shows the sampling distribution of $\bar{x}$ when the mean is $\mu = 112$. The shaded area in the upper tail gives the probability of obtaining $\bar{x} > 116.71$. Using the standard normal distribution, we see that at $\bar{x} = 116.71$

$$z = \frac{\bar{x} - \mu}{\sigma/\sqrt{n}} = \frac{116.71 - 112}{12/\sqrt{36}} = 2.36$$

The standard normal probability table shows that with $z = 2.36$, the area in the upper tail is $1.0000 - .9909 = .0091$. Thus, .0091 is the probability of making a Type II error when $\mu = 112$. Denoting the probability of making a Type II error as β, we see that when $\mu = 112$, $\beta = .0091$. Therefore, we can conclude that if the mean of the population is 112 hours, the probability of making a Type II error is only .0091.

We can repeat these calculations for other values of μ less than 120. Doing so will show a different probability of making a Type II error for each value of μ. For example, suppose the shipment of batteries has a mean useful life of $\mu = 115$ hours. Because we will accept H_0 whenever $\bar{x} > 116.71$, the z value for $\mu = 115$ is given by

$$z = \frac{\bar{x} - \mu}{\sigma/\sqrt{n}} = \frac{116.71 - 115}{12/\sqrt{36}} = .86$$

From the standard normal probability table, we find that the area in the upper tail of the standard normal distribution for $z = .86$ is $1.0000 - .8051 = .1949$. Thus, the probability of making a Type II error is $\beta = .1949$ when the true mean is $\mu = 115$.

In Table 9.5 we show the probability of making a Type II error for a variety of values of μ less than 120. Note that as μ increases toward 120, the probability of making a Type II error increases toward an upper bound of .95. However, as μ decreases to values farther below 120, the probability of making a Type II error diminishes. This pattern is what we

TABLE 9.5 PROBABILITY OF MAKING A TYPE II ERROR FOR THE LOT-ACCEPTANCE HYPOTHESIS TEST

Value of μ	$z = \dfrac{116.71 - \mu}{12/\sqrt{36}}$	Probability of a Type II Error (β)	Power $(1 - \beta)$
112	2.36	.0091	.9909
114	1.36	.0869	.9131
115	.86	.1949	.8051
116.71	.00	.5000	.5000
117	−.15	.5596	.4404
118	−.65	.7422	.2578
119.999	−1.645	.9500	.0500

As Table 9.5 shows, the probability of a Type II error depends on the value of the population mean μ. For values of μ near μ_0, the probability of making the Type II error can be high.

should expect. When the true population mean μ is close to the null hypothesis value of $\mu = 120$, the probability is high that we will make a Type II error. However, when the true population mean μ is far below the null hypothesis value of $\mu = 120$, the probability is low that we will make a Type II error.

The probability of correctly rejecting H_0 when it is false is called the **power** of the test. For any particular value of μ, the power is $1 - \beta$; that is, the probability of correctly rejecting the null hypothesis is 1 minus the probability of making a Type II error. Values of power are also listed in Table 9.5. On the basis of these values, the power associated with each value of μ is shown graphically in Figure 9.9. Such a graph is called a **power curve**. Note that the power curve extends over the values of μ for which the null hypothesis is false. The height of the power curve at any value of μ indicates the probability of correctly rejecting H_0 when H_0 is false.[4]

FIGURE 9.9 POWER CURVE FOR THE LOT-ACCEPTANCE HYPOTHESIS TEST

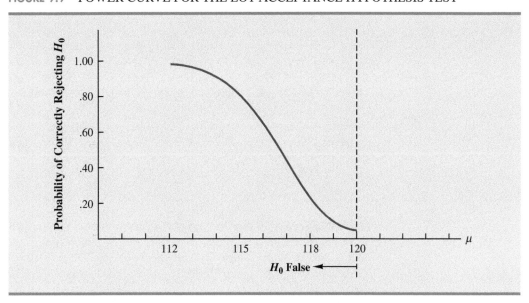

[4]Another graph, called the operating characteristic curve, is sometimes used to provide information about the probability of making a Type II error. The operating characteristic curve shows the probability of accepting H_0 and thus provides β for the values of μ where the null hypothesis is false. The probability of making a Type II error can be read directly from this graph.

In summary, the following step-by-step procedure can be used to compute the probability of making a Type II error in hypothesis tests about a population mean.

1. Formulate the null and alternative hypotheses.
2. Use the level of significance α and the critical value approach to determine the critical value and the rejection rule for the test.
3. Use the rejection rule to solve for the value of the sample mean corresponding to the critical value of the test statistic.
4. Use the results from step 3 to state the values of the sample mean that lead to the acceptance of H_0. These values define the acceptance region for the test.
5. Use the sampling distribution of $\bar{x}$ for a value of μ satisfying the alternative hypothesis, and the acceptance region from step 4, to compute the probability that the sample mean will be in the acceptance region. This probability is the probability of making a Type II error at the chosen value of μ.

Exercises

Methods

46. Consider the following hypothesis test.

$$H_0: \mu \geq 10$$
$$H_a: \mu < 10$$

The sample size is 120 and the population standard deviation is assumed known with $\sigma = 5$. Use $\alpha = .05$.
a. If the population mean is 9, what is the probability that the sample mean leads to the conclusion *do not reject H_0*?
b. What type of error would be made if the actual population mean is 9 and we conclude that $H_0: \mu \geq 10$ is true?
c. What is the probability of making a Type II error if the actual population mean is 8?

47. Consider the following hypothesis test.

$$H_0: \mu = 20$$
$$H_a: \mu \neq 20$$

A sample of 200 items will be taken and the population standard deviation is $\sigma = 10$. Use $\alpha = .05$. Compute the probability of making a Type II error if the population mean is:
a. $\mu = 18.0$
b. $\mu = 22.5$
c. $\mu = 21.0$

Applications

48. Fowle Marketing Research, Inc., bases charges to a client on the assumption that telephone surveys can be completed within 15 minutes or less. If more time is required, a premium rate is charged. With a sample of 35 surveys, a population standard deviation of 4 minutes, and a level of significance of .01, the sample mean will be used to test the null hypothesis $H_0: \mu \leq 15$.
a. What is your interpretation of the Type II error for this problem? What is its impact on the firm?
b. What is the probability of making a Type II error when the actual mean time is $\mu = 17$ minutes?

c.   What is the probability of making a Type II error when the actual mean time is $\mu = 18$ minutes?

d.   Sketch the general shape of the power curve for this test.

49.   A consumer research group is interested in testing an automobile manufacturer's claim that a new economy model will travel at least 25 miles per gallon of gasoline ($H_0: \mu \geq 25$).

a.   With a .02 level of significance and a sample of 30 cars, what is the rejection rule based on the value of $\bar{x}$ for the test to determine whether the manufacturer's claim should be rejected? Assume that σ is 3 miles per gallon.

b.   What is the probability of committing a Type II error if the actual mileage is 23 miles per gallon?

c.   What is the probability of committing a Type II error if the actual mileage is 24 miles per gallon?

d.   What is the probability of committing a Type II error if the actual mileage is 25.5 miles per gallon?

50.   *Young Adult* magazine states the following hypotheses about the mean age of its subscribers.

$$H_0: \mu = 28$$
$$H_a: \mu \neq 28$$

a.   What would it mean to make a Type II error in this situation?

b.   The population standard deviation is assumed known at $\sigma = 6$ years and the sample size is 100. With $\alpha = .05$, what is the probability of accepting H_0 for μ equal to 26, 27, 29, and 30?

c.   What is the power at $\mu = 26$? What does this result tell you?

51.   A production line operation is tested for filling weight accuracy using the following hypotheses.

Hypothesis	Conclusion and Action
$H_0: \mu = 16$	Filling okay; keep running
$H_a: \mu \neq 16$	Filling off standard; stop and adjust machine

The sample size is 30 and the population standard deviation is $\sigma = .8$. Use $\alpha = .05$.

a.   What would a Type II error mean in this situation?

b.   What is the probability of making a Type II error when the machine is overfilling by .5 ounces?

c.   What is the power of the statistical test when the machine is overfilling by .5 ounces?

d.   Show the power curve for this hypothesis test. What information does it contain for the production manager?

52.   Refer to exercise 48. Assume the firm selects a sample of 50 surveys and repeat parts (b) and (c). What observation can you make about how increasing the sample size affects the probability of making a Type II error?

53.   Sparr Investments, Inc., specializes in tax-deferred investment opportunities for its clients. Recently Sparr offered a payroll deduction investment program for the employees of a particular company. Sparr estimates that the employees are currently averaging $100 or less per month in tax-deferred investments. A sample of 40 employees will be used to test Sparr's hypothesis about the current level of investment activity among the population of employees. Assume the employee monthly tax-deferred investment amounts have a standard deviation of $75 and that a .05 level of significance will be used in the hypothesis test.

a.   What is the Type II error in this situation?

b.   What is the probability of the Type II error if the actual mean employee monthly investment is $120?

c.   What is the probability of the Type II error if the actual mean employee monthly investment is $130?

d.   Assume a sample size of 80 employees is used and repeat parts (b) and (c).

9.8   Determining the Sample Size for a Hypothesis Test About a Population Mean

Assume that a hypothesis test is to be conducted about the value of a population mean. The level of significance specified by the user determines the probability of making a Type I error for the test. By controlling the sample size, the user can also control the probability of making a Type II error. Let us show how a sample size can be determined for the following lower tail test about a population mean.

$$H_0: \mu \geq \mu_0$$
$$H_a: \mu < \mu_0$$

The upper panel of Figure 9.10 is the sampling distribution of $\bar{x}$ when H_0 is true with $\mu = \mu_0$. For a lower tail test, the critical value of the test statistic is denoted $-z_\alpha$. In the upper panel of the figure the vertical line, labeled c, is the corresponding value of $\bar{x}$. Note that, if we reject H_0 when $\bar{x} \leq c$, the probability of a Type I error will be α. With z_α representing the z value corresponding to an area of α in the upper tail of the standard normal distribution, we compute c using the following formula:

$$c = \mu_0 - z_\alpha \frac{\sigma}{\sqrt{n}} \tag{9.5}$$

FIGURE 9.10   DETERMINING THE SAMPLE SIZE FOR SPECIFIED LEVELS OF THE TYPE I (α) AND TYPE II (β) ERRORS

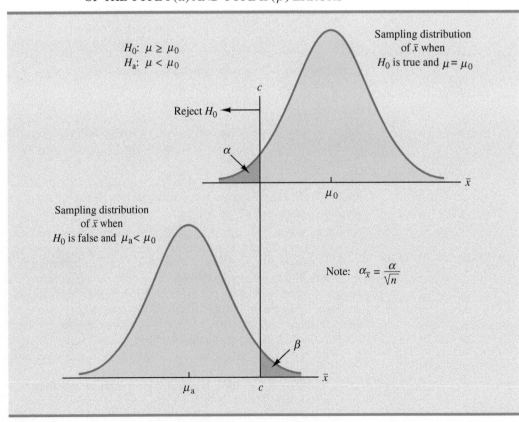

The lower panel of Figure 9.10 is the sampling distribution of $\bar{x}$ when the alternative hypothesis is true with $\mu = \mu_a < \mu_0$. The shaded region shows β, the probability of a Type II error that the decision maker will be exposed to if the null hypothesis is accepted when $\bar{x} > c$. With z_β representing the z value corresponding to an area of β in the upper tail of the standard normal distribution, we compute c using the following formula:

$$c = \mu_a + z_\beta \frac{\sigma}{\sqrt{n}} \tag{9.6}$$

Now what we want to do is to select a value for c so that when we reject H_0 and accept H_a, the probability of a Type I error is equal to the chosen value of α and the probability of a Type II error is equal to the chosen value of β. Therefore, both equations (9.5) and (9.6) must provide the same value for c, and the following equation must be true.

$$\mu_0 - z_\alpha \frac{\sigma}{\sqrt{n}} = \mu_a + z_\beta \frac{\sigma}{\sqrt{n}}$$

To determine the required sample size, we first solve for the $\sqrt{n}$ as follows.

$$\mu_0 - \mu_a = z_\alpha \frac{\sigma}{\sqrt{n}} + z_\beta \frac{\sigma}{\sqrt{n}}$$

$$\mu_0 - \mu_a = \frac{(z_\alpha + z_\beta)\sigma}{\sqrt{n}}$$

and

$$\sqrt{n} = \frac{(z_\alpha + z_\beta)\sigma}{(\mu_0 - \mu_a)}$$

Squaring both sides of the expression provides the following sample size formula for a one-tailed hypothesis test about a population mean.

SAMPLE SIZE FOR A ONE-TAILED HYPOTHESIS TEST ABOUT A POPULATION MEAN

$$n = \frac{(z_\alpha + z_\beta)^2 \sigma^2}{(\mu_0 - \mu_a)^2} \tag{9.7}$$

where

z_α = z value providing an area of α in the upper tail of a standard normal distribution

z_β = z value providing an area of β in the upper tail of a standard normal distribution

σ = the population standard deviation

μ_0 = the value of the population mean in the null hypothesis

μ_a = the value of the population mean used for the Type II error

Note: In a two-tailed hypothesis test, use (9.7) with $z_{\alpha/2}$ replacing z_α.

Although the logic of equation (9.7) was developed for the hypothesis test shown in Figure 9.10, it holds for any one-tailed test about a population mean. In a two-tailed hypothesis test about a population mean, $z_{\alpha/2}$ is used instead of z_α in equation (9.7).

Let us return to the lot-acceptance example from Sections 9.6 and 9.7. The design specification for the shipment of batteries indicated a mean useful life of at least 120 hours for the batteries. Shipments were rejected if $H_0: \mu \geq 120$ was rejected. Let us assume that the quality control manager makes the following statements about the allowable probabilities for the Type I and Type II errors.

Type I error statement: If the mean life of the batteries in the shipment is $\mu = 120$, I am willing to risk an $\alpha = .05$ probability of rejecting the shipment.

Type II error statement: If the mean life of the batteries in the shipment is 5 hours under the specification (i.e., $\mu = 115$), I am willing to risk a $\beta = .10$ probability of accepting the shipment.

These statements are based on the judgment of the manager. Someone else might specify different restrictions on the probabilities. However, statements about the allowable probabilities of both errors must be made before the sample size can be determined.

In the example, $\alpha = .05$ and $\beta = .10$. Using the standard normal probability distribution, we have $z_{.05} = 1.645$ and $z_{.10} = 1.28$. From the statements about the error probabilities, we note that $\mu_0 = 120$ and $\mu_a = 115$. Finally, the population standard deviation was assumed known at $\sigma = 12$. By using equation (9.7), we find that the recommended sample size for the lot-acceptance example is

$$n = \frac{(1.645 + 1.28)^2(12)^2}{(120 - 115)^2} = 49.3$$

Rounding up, we recommend a sample size of 50.

Because both the Type I and Type II error probabilities have been controlled at allowable levels with $n = 50$, the quality control manager is now justified in using the *accept H_0* and *reject H_0* statements for the hypothesis test. The accompanying inferences are made with allowable probabilities of making Type I and Type II errors.

We can make three observations about the relationship among α, β, and the sample size n.

1. Once two of the three values are known, the other can be computed.
2. For a given level of significance α, increasing the sample size will reduce β.
3. For a given sample size, decreasing α will increase β, whereas increasing α will decrease β.

The third observation should be kept in mind when the probability of a Type II error is not being controlled. It suggests that one should not choose unnecessarily small values for the level of significance α. For a given sample size, choosing a smaller level of significance means more exposure to a Type II error. Inexperienced users of hypothesis testing often think that smaller values of α are always better. They are better if we are concerned only about making a Type I error. However, smaller values of α have the disadvantage of increasing the probability of making a Type II error.

Exercises

Methods

54. Consider the following hypothesis test.

$$H_0: \mu \geq 10$$
$$H_a: \mu < 10$$

The sample size is 120 and the population standard deviation is 5. Use $\alpha = .05$. If the actual population mean is 9, the probability of a Type II error is .2912. Suppose the researcher wants to reduce the probability of a Type II error to .10 when the actual population mean is 9. What sample size is recommended?

55. Consider the following hypothesis test.

$$H_0: \mu = 20$$
$$H_a: \mu \neq 20$$

The population standard deviation is 10. Use $\alpha = .05$. How large a sample should be taken if the researcher is willing to accept a .05 probability of making a Type II error when the actual population mean is 22?

Applications

56. Suppose the project director for the Hilltop Coffee study (see Section 9.3) asked for a .10 probability of claiming that Hilltop was not in violation when it really was underfilling by 1 ounce ($\mu_a = 2.9375$ pounds). What sample size would have been recommended?

57. A special industrial battery must have a life of at least 400 hours. A hypothesis test is to be conducted with a .02 level of significance. If the batteries from a particular production run have an actual mean use life of 385 hours, the production manager wants a sampling procedure that only 10% of the time would show erroneously that the batch is acceptable. What sample size is recommended for the hypothesis test? Use 30 hours as an estimate of the population standard deviation.

58. *Young Adult* magazine states the following hypotheses about the mean age of its subscribers.

$$H_0: \mu = 28$$
$$H_a: \mu \neq 28$$

If the manager conducting the test will permit a .15 probability of making a Type II error when the true mean age is 29, what sample size should be selected? Assume $\sigma = 6$ and a .05 level of significance.

59. An automobile mileage study tested the following hypotheses.

Hypothesis	Conclusion
$H_0: \mu \geq 25$ mpg	Manufacturer's claim supported
$H_a: \mu < 25$ mpg	Manufacturer's claim rejected; average mileage per gallon less than stated

For $\sigma = 3$ and a .02 level of significance, what sample size would be recommended if the researcher wants an 80% chance of detecting that μ is less than 25 miles per gallon when it is actually 24?

Summary

Hypothesis testing is a statistical procedure that uses sample data to determine whether a statement about the value of a population parameter should or should not be rejected. The hypotheses are two competing statements about a population parameter. One statement is called the null hypothesis (H_0), and the other statement is called the alternative hypothesis (H_a). In Section 9.1 we provided guidelines for developing hypotheses for situations frequently encountered in practice.

Whenever historical data or other information provides a basis for assuming that the population standard deviation is known, the hypothesis testing procedure for the population mean is based on the standard normal distribution. Whenever σ is unknown, the sample standard deviation s is used to estimate σ and the hypothesis testing procedure is based on the t distribution. In both cases, the quality of results depends on both the form of the population distribution and the sample size. If the population has a normal distribution, both hypothesis testing procedures are applicable, even with small sample sizes. If the population is not normally distributed, larger sample sizes are needed. General guidelines about the sample size were provided in Sections 9.3 and 9.4. In the case of hypothesis tests about a population proportion, the hypothesis testing procedure uses a test statistic based on the standard normal distribution.

In all cases, the value of the test statistic can be used to compute a p-value for the test. A p-value is a probability used to determine whether the null hypothesis should be rejected. If the p-value is less than or equal to the level of significance α, the null hypothesis can be rejected.

Hypothesis testing conclusions can also be made by comparing the value of the test statistic to a critical value. For lower tail tests, the null hypothesis is rejected if the value of the test statistic is less than or equal to the critical value. For upper tail tests, the null hypothesis is rejected if the value of the test statistic is greater than or equal to the critical value. Two-tailed tests consist of two critical values: one in the lower tail of the sampling distribution and one in the upper tail. In this case, the null hypothesis is rejected if the value of the test statistic is less than or equal to the critical value in the lower tail or greater than or equal to the critical value in the upper tail.

Extensions of hypothesis testing procedures to include an analysis of the Type II error were also presented. In Section 9.7 we showed how to compute the probability of making a Type II error. In Section 9.8 we showed how to determine a sample size that will control for the probability of making both a Type I error and a Type II error.

Glossary

Null hypothesis The hypothesis tentatively assumed true in the hypothesis testing procedure.

Alternative hypothesis The hypothesis concluded to be true if the null hypothesis is rejected.

Type II error The error of accepting H_0 when it is false.

Type I error The error of rejecting H_0 when it is true.

Level of significance The probability of making a Type I error when the null hypothesis is true as an equality.

One-tailed test A hypothesis test in which rejection of the null hypothesis occurs for values of the test statistic in one tail of its sampling distribution.

Test statistic A statistic whose value helps determine whether a null hypothesis should be rejected.

p-value A probability that provides a measure of the evidence against the null hypothesis given by the sample. Smaller p-values indicate more evidence against H_0. For a lower tail test, the p-value is the probability of obtaining a value for the test statistic as small as or smaller than that provided by the sample. For an upper tail test, the p-value is the probability of obtaining a value for the test statistic as large as or larger than that provided by the sample. For a two-tailed test, the p-value is the probability of obtaining a value for the test statistic at least as unlikely as or more unlikely than that provided by the sample.

Critical value A value that is compared with the test statistic to determine whether H_0 should be rejected.

Two-tailed test A hypothesis test in which rejection of the null hypothesis occurs for values of the test statistic in either tail of its sampling distribution.

Power The probability of correctly rejecting H_0 when it is false.

Power curve A graph of the probability of rejecting H_0 for all possible values of the population parameter not satisfying the null hypothesis. The power curve provides the probability of correctly rejecting the null hypothesis.

Key Formulas

Test Statistic for Hypothesis Tests About a Population Mean: σ Known

$$z = \frac{\bar{x} - \mu_0}{\sigma/\sqrt{n}} \tag{9.1}$$

Test Statistic for Hypothesis Tests About a Population Mean: σ Unknown

$$t = \frac{\bar{x} - \mu_0}{s/\sqrt{n}} \tag{9.2}$$

Test Statistic for Hypothesis Tests About a Population Proportion

$$z = \frac{\bar{p} - p_0}{\sqrt{\dfrac{p_0(1 - p_0)}{n}}} \tag{9.4}$$

Sample Size for a One-Tailed Hypothesis Test About a Population Mean

$$n = \frac{(z_\alpha + z_\beta)^2 \sigma^2}{(\mu_0 - \mu_a)^2} \tag{9.7}$$

In a two-tailed test, replace z_α with $z_{\alpha/2}$.

Supplementary Exercises

60. A production line operates with a mean filling weight of 16 ounces per container. Overfilling or underfilling presents a serious problem and when detected requires the operator to shut down the production line to readjust the filling mechanism. From past data, a population standard deviation $\sigma = .8$ ounces is assumed. A quality control inspector selects a sample of 30 items every hour and at that time makes the decision of whether to shut down the line for readjustment. The level of significance is $\alpha = .05$.
    a. State the hypothesis test for this quality control application.
    b. If a sample mean of $\bar{x} = 16.32$ ounces were found, what is the p-value? What action would you recommend?
    c. If a sample mean of $\bar{x} = 15.82$ ounces were found, what is the p-value? What action would you recommend?
    d. Use the critical value approach. What is the rejection rule for the preceding hypothesis testing procedure? Repeat parts (b) and (c). Do you reach the same conclusion?

61. At Western University the historical mean of scholarship examination scores for freshman applications is 900. A historical population standard deviation $\sigma = 180$ is assumed known. Each year, the assistant dean uses a sample of applications to determine whether the mean examination score for the new freshman applications has changed.
    a. State the hypotheses.
    b. What is the 95% confidence interval estimate of the population mean examination score if a sample of 200 applications provided a sample mean $\bar{x} = 935$?
    c. Use the confidence interval to conduct a hypothesis test. Using $\alpha = .05$, what is your conclusion?
    d. What is the p-value?

62. *Playbill* is a magazine distributed around the country to people attending musicals and other theatrical productions. The mean annual household income for the population of *Playbill* readers is \$119,155 (*Playbill*, January 2006). Assume the standard deviation is

$\sigma = \$20,700$. A San Francisco civic group has asserted that the mean for theatergoers in the Bay Area is higher. A sample of 60 theater attendees in the Bay Area showed a sample mean household income of \$126,100.

a. Develop hypotheses that can be used to determine whether the sample data support the conclusion that theater attendees in the Bay Area have a higher mean household income than that for all *Playbill* readers.

b. What is the *p*-value based on the sample of 60 theater attendees in the Bay Area?

c. Use $\alpha = .01$ as the level of significance. What is your conclusion?

63. On Friday, Wall Street traders were anxiously awaiting the federal government's release of numbers on the January increase in nonfarm payrolls. The early consensus estimate among economists was for a growth of 250,000 new jobs (CNBC, February 3, 2006). However, a sample of 20 economists taken Thursday afternoon provided a sample mean of 266,000 with a sample standard deviation of 24,000. Financial analysts often call such a sample mean, based on late-breaking news, the *whisper number*. Treat the "consensus estimate" as the population mean. Conduct a hypothesis test to determine whether the whisper number justifies a conclusion of a statistically significant increase in the consensus estimate of economists. Use $\alpha = .01$ as the level of significance.

FirstBirth

64. Data released by the National Center for Health Statistics showed that the mean age at which women had their first child was 25.0 in 2006 (*The Wall Street Journal,* February 4, 2009). The reporter, Sue Shellenbarger, noted that this was the first decrease in the average age at which women had their first child in several years. A recent sample of 42 women provided the data in the website file named FirstBirth concerning the age at which these women had their first child. Do the data indicate a change from 2006 in the mean age at which women had their first child? Use $\alpha = .05$.

WeeklyPay

65. A recent issue of the *AARP Bulletin* reported that the average weekly pay for a woman with a high school school degree is \$520 (*AARP Bulletin*, January–February, 2010). Suppose you would like to determine if the average weekly pay for all working women is significantly greater than that for women with a high school degree. Data providing the weekly pay for a sample of 50 working women are available in the file named WeeklyPay. These data are consistent with the findings reported in the AARP article.

a. State the hypotheses that should be used to test whether the mean weekly pay for all women is significantly greater than the mean weekly pay for women with a high school degree.

b. Use the data in the file named WeeklyPay to compute the sample mean, the test statistic, and the *p*-value.

c. Use $\alpha = .05$. What is your conclusion?

d. Repeat the hypothesis test using the critical value approach.

66. The chamber of commerce of a Florida Gulf Coast community advertises that area residential property is available at a mean cost of \$125,000 or less per lot. Suppose a sample of 32 properties provided a sample mean of \$130,000 per lot and a sample standard deviation of \$12,500. Use a .05 level of significance to test the validity of the advertising claim.

67. In Hamilton County, Ohio, the mean number of days needed to sell a house is 86 days (Cincinnati Multiple Listing Service, April, 2012). Data for the sale of 40 houses in a nearby county showed a sample mean of 80 days with a sample standard deviation of 20 days. Conduct a hypothesis test to determine whether the mean number of days until a house is sold is different than the Hamilton County mean of 86 days in the nearby county. Use $\alpha = .05$ for the level of significance, and state your conclusion.

68. On December 25, 2009, an airline passenger was subdued while attempting to blow up a Northwest Airlines flight headed for Detroit, Michigan. The passenger had smuggled explosives hidden in his underwear past a metal detector at an airport screening facility. As a result, the Transportation Security Administration (TSA) proposed installing full-body scanners to replace the metal detectors at the nation's largest airports. This proposal resulted in strong objections from privacy advocates who considered the scanners an invasion of privacy.

On January 5–6, 2010, *USA Today* conducted a poll of 542 adults to learn what proportion of airline travelers approved of using full-body scanners (*USA Today,* January 11, 2010). The poll results showed that 455 of the respondents felt that full-body scanners would improve airline security and 423 indicated that they approved of using the devices.

a. Conduct a hypothesis test to determine if the results of the poll justify concluding that over 80% of airline travelers feel that the use of full-body scanners will improve airline security. Use $\alpha = .05$.

b. Suppose the TSA will go forward with the installation and mandatory use of full-body scanners if over 75% of airline travelers approve of using the devices. You have been told to conduct a statistical analysis using the poll results to determine if the TSA should require mandatory use of the full-body scanners. Because this is viewed as a very sensitive decision, use $\alpha = .01$. What is your recommendation?

69. An airline promotion to business travelers is based on the assumption that two-thirds of business travelers use a laptop computer on overnight business trips.

a. State the hypotheses that can be used to test the assumption.

b. What is the sample proportion from an American Express sponsored survey that found 355 of 546 business travelers use a laptop computer on overnight business trips?

c. What is the *p*-value?

d. Use $\alpha = .05$. What is your conclusion?

70. Virtual call centers are staffed by individuals working out of their homes. Most home agents earn $10 to $15 per hour without benefits versus $7 to $9 per hour with benefits at a traditional call center (*BusinessWeek,* January 23, 2006). Regional Airways is considering employing home agents, but only if a level of customer satisfaction greater than 80% can be maintained. A test was conducted with home service agents. In a sample of 300 customers, 252 reported that they were satisfied with service.

a. Develop hypotheses for a test to determine whether the sample data support the conclusion that customer service with home agents meets the Regional Airways criterion.

b. What is your point estimate of the percentage of satisfied customers?

c. What is the *p*-value provided by the sample data?

d. What is your hypothesis testing conclusion? Use $\alpha = .05$ as the level of significance.

71. During the 2004 election year, new polling results were reported daily. In an IBD/TIPP poll of 910 adults, 503 respondents reported that they were optimistic about the national outlook, and President Bush's leadership index jumped 4.7 points to 55.3 (*Investor's Business Daily,* January 14, 2004).

a. What is the sample proportion of respondents who are optimistic about the national outlook?

b. A campaign manager wants to claim that this poll indicates that the majority of adults are optimistic about the national outlook. Construct a hypothesis test so that rejection of the null hypothesis will permit the conclusion that the proportion optimistic is greater than 50%.

c. Use the polling data to compute the *p*-value for the hypothesis test in part (b). Explain to the manager what this *p*-value means about the level of significance of the results.

72. A radio station in Myrtle Beach announced that at least 90% of the hotels and motels would be full for the Memorial Day weekend. The station advised listeners to make reservations in advance if they planned to be in the resort over the weekend. On Saturday night a sample of 58 hotels and motels showed 49 with a no-vacancy sign and 9 with vacancies. What is your reaction to the radio station's claim after seeing the sample evidence? Use $\alpha = .05$ in making the statistical test. What is the *p*-value?

73. According to the federal government, 24% of workers covered by their company's health care plan were not required to contribute to the premium (*Statistical Abstract of the United*

States: 2006). A recent study found that 81 out of 400 workers sampled were not required to contribute to their company's health care plan.

a. Develop hypotheses that can be used to test whether the percent of workers not required to contribute to their company's health care plan has declined.

b. What is a point estimate of the proportion receiving free company-sponsored health care insurance?

c. Has a statistically significant decline occurred in the proportion of workers receiving free company-sponsored health care insurance? Use $\alpha = .05$.

74. Shorney Construction Company bids on projects assuming that the mean idle time per worker is 72 or fewer minutes per day. A sample of 30 construction workers will be used to test this assumption. Assume that the population standard deviation is 20 minutes.

a. State the hypotheses to be tested.

b. What is the probability of making a Type II error when the population mean idle time is 80 minutes?

c. What is the probability of making a Type II error when the population mean idle time is 75 minutes?

d. What is the probability of making a Type II error when the population mean idle time is 70 minutes?

e. Sketch the power curve for this problem.

75. A federal funding program is available to low-income neighborhoods. To qualify for the funding, a neighborhood must have a mean household income of less than $15,000 per year. Neighborhoods with mean annual household income of $15,000 or more do not qualify. Funding decisions are based on a sample of residents in the neighborhood. A hypothesis test with a .02 level of significance is conducted. If the funding guidelines call for a maximum probability of .05 of not funding a neighborhood with a mean annual household income of $14,000, what sample size should be used in the funding decision study? Use $\sigma = \$4000$ as a planning value.

76. H_0: $\mu = 120$ and H_a: $\mu \neq 120$ are used to test whether a bath soap production process is meeting the standard output of 120 bars per batch. Use a .05 level of significance for the test and a planning value of 5 for the standard deviation.

a. If the mean output drops to 117 bars per batch, the firm wants to have a 98% chance of concluding that the standard production output is not being met. How large a sample should be selected?

b. With your sample size from part (a), what is the probability of concluding that the process is operating satisfactorily for each of the following actual mean outputs: 117, 118, 119, 121, 122, and 123 bars per batch? That is, what is the probability of a Type II error in each case?

Case Problem 1   Quality Associates, Inc.

Quality Associates, Inc., a consulting firm, advises its clients about sampling and statistical procedures that can be used to control their manufacturing processes. In one particular application, a client gave Quality Associates a sample of 800 observations taken during a time in which that client's process was operating satisfactorily. The sample standard deviation for these data was .21; hence, with so much data, the population standard deviation was assumed to be .21. Quality Associates then suggested that random samples of size 30 be taken periodically to monitor the process on an ongoing basis. By analyzing the new samples, the client could quickly learn whether the process was operating satisfactorily. When the process was not operating satisfactorily, corrective action could be taken to eliminate the problem. The design specification indicated the mean for the process should be 12. The hypothesis test suggested by Quality Associates follows.

$$H_0: \mu = 12$$
$$H_a: \mu \neq 12$$

Corrective action will be taken any time H_0 is rejected.

The following samples were collected at hourly intervals during the first day of operation of the new statistical process control procedure. These data are available in the data set Quality.

WEB file

Quality

Sample 1	Sample 2	Sample 3	Sample 4
11.55	11.62	11.91	12.02
11.62	11.69	11.36	12.02
11.52	11.59	11.75	12.05
11.75	11.82	11.95	12.18
11.90	11.97	12.14	12.11
11.64	11.71	11.72	12.07
11.80	11.87	11.61	12.05
12.03	12.10	11.85	11.64
11.94	12.01	12.16	12.39
11.92	11.99	11.91	11.65
12.13	12.20	12.12	12.11
12.09	12.16	11.61	11.90
11.93	12.00	12.21	12.22
12.21	12.28	11.56	11.88
12.32	12.39	11.95	12.03
11.93	12.00	12.01	12.35
11.85	11.92	12.06	12.09
11.76	11.83	11.76	11.77
12.16	12.23	11.82	12.20
11.77	11.84	12.12	11.79
12.00	12.07	11.60	12.30
12.04	12.11	11.95	12.27
11.98	12.05	11.96	12.29
12.30	12.37	12.22	12.47
12.18	12.25	11.75	12.03
11.97	12.04	11.96	12.17
12.17	12.24	11.95	11.94
11.85	11.92	11.89	11.97
12.30	12.37	11.88	12.23
12.15	12.22	11.93	12.25

Managerial Report

1. Conduct a hypothesis test for each sample at the .01 level of significance and determine what action, if any, should be taken. Provide the test statistic and p-value for each test.
2. Compute the standard deviation for each of the four samples. Does the assumption of .21 for the population standard deviation appear reasonable?
3. Compute limits for the sample mean $\bar{x}$ around $\mu = 12$ such that, as long as a new sample mean is within those limits, the process will be considered to be operating satisfactorily. If $\bar{x}$ exceeds the upper limit or if $\bar{x}$ is below the lower limit, corrective action will be taken. These limits are referred to as upper and lower control limits for quality control purposes.
4. Discuss the implications of changing the level of significance to a larger value. What mistake or error could increase if the level of significance is increased?

Case Problem 2

Ethical Behavior of Business Students at Bayview University

During the global recession of 2008 and 2009, there were many accusations of unethical behavior by Wall Street executives, financial managers, and other corporate officers. At that time, an article appeared that suggested that part of the reason for such unethical business behavior may stem from the fact that cheating has become more prevalent among business students (*Chronicle of Higher Education,* February 10, 2009). The article reported that 56 percent of business students admitted to cheating at some time during their academic career as compared to 47 percent of nonbusiness students.

Cheating has been a concern of the dean of the College of Business at Bayview University for several years. Some faculty members in the college believe that cheating is more widespread at Bayview than at other universities, while other faculty members think that cheating is not a major problem in the college. To resolve some of these issues, the dean commissioned a study to assess the current ethical behavior of business students at Bayview. As part of this study, an anonymous exit survey was administered to a sample of 90 business students from this year's graduating class. Responses to the following questions were used to obtain data regarding three types of cheating.

During your time at Bayview, did you ever present work copied off the Internet as your own?

Yes _____   No _____

During your time at Bayview, did you ever copy answers off another student's exam?

Yes _____   No _____

During your time at Bayview, did you ever collaborate with other students on projects that were supposed to be completed individually?

Yes _____   No _____

Any student who answered Yes to one or more of these questions was considered to have been involved in some type of cheating. A portion of the data collected follows. The complete data set is in the file named Bayview.

WEB file

Bayview

Student	Copied from Internet	Copied on Exam	Collaborated on Individual Project	Gender
1	No	No	No	Female
2	No	No	No	Male
3	Yes	No	Yes	Male
4	Yes	Yes	No	Male
5	No	No	Yes	Male
6	Yes	No	No	Female
.	.	.	.	.
.	.	.	.	.
88	No	No	No	Male
89	No	Yes	Yes	Male
90	No	No	No	Female

Managerial Report

Prepare a report for the dean of the college that summarizes your assessment of the nature of cheating by business students at Bayview University. Be sure to include the following items in your report.

1. Use descriptive statistics to summarize the data and comment on your findings.
2. Develop 95% confidence intervals for the proportion of all students, the proportion of male students, and the proportion of female students who were involved in some type of cheating.
3. Conduct a hypothesis test to determine if the proportion of business students at Bayview University who were involved in some type of cheating is less than that of business students at other institutions as reported by the *Chronicle of Higher Education*.
4. Conduct a hypothesis test to determine if the proportion of business students at Bayview University who were involved in some form of cheating is less than that of nonbusiness students at other institutions as reported by the *Chronicle of Higher Education*.
5. What advice would you give to the dean based upon your analysis of the data?

Appendix 9.1   Hypothesis Testing with Minitab

We describe the use of Minitab to conduct hypothesis tests about a population mean and a population proportion.

Population Mean: σ Known

We illustrate using the MaxFlight golf ball distance example in Section 9.3. The data are in column C1 of a Minitab worksheet. The population standard deviation $\sigma = 12$ is assumed known and the level of significance is $\alpha = .05$. The following steps can be used to test the hypothesis $H_0: \mu = 295$ versus $H_a: \mu \neq 295$.

GolfTest

Step 1. Select the **Stat** menu
Step 2. Choose **Basic Statistics**
Step 3. Choose **1-Sample Z**
Step 4. When the 1-Sample Z dialog box appears:
　　　　　Enter C1 in the **Samples in columns** box
　　　　　Enter 12 in the **Standard deviation** box
　　　　　Select **Perform Hypothesis Test**
　　　　　Enter 295 in the **Hypothesized mean** box
　　　　　Select **Options**
Step 5. When the 1-Sample Z-Options dialog box appears:
　　　　　Enter 95 in the **Confidence level** box*
　　　　　Select **not equal** in the **Alternative** box
　　　　　Click **OK**
Step 6. Click **OK**

In addition to the hypothesis testing results, Minitab provides a 95% confidence interval for the population mean.

---

*Minitab provides both hypothesis testing and interval estimation results simultaneously. The user may select any confidence level for the interval estimate of the population mean: 95% confidence is suggested here.

The procedure can be easily modified for a one-tailed hypothesis test by selecting the less than or greater than option in the **Alternative** box in step 5.

Population Mean: σ Unknown

AirRating

The ratings that 60 business travelers gave for Heathrow Airport are entered in column C1 of a Minitab worksheet. The level of significance for the test is $\alpha = .05$, and the population standard deviation σ will be estimated by the sample standard deviation s. The following steps can be used to test the hypothesis $H_0: \mu \leq 7$ against $H_a: \mu > 7$.

Step 1. Select the **Stat** menu
Step 2. Choose **Basic Statistics**
Step 3. Choose **1-Sample t**
Step 4. When the 1-Sample t dialog box appears:
    Enter C1 in the **Samples in columns** box
    Select **Perform Hypothesis Test**
    Enter 7 in the **Hypothesized mean** box
    Select **Options**
Step 5. When the 1-Sample t-Options dialog box appears:
    Enter 95 in the **Confidence level** box
    Select **greater than** in the **Alternative** box
    Click **OK**
Step 6. Click **OK**

The Heathrow Airport rating study involved a greater than alternative hypothesis. The preceding steps can be easily modified for other hypothesis tests by selecting the less than or not equal options in the **Alternative** box in step 5.

Population Proportion

WomenGolf

We illustrate using the Pine Creek golf course example in Section 9.5. The data with responses Female and Male are in column C1 of a Minitab worksheet. Minitab uses an alphabetical ordering of the responses and selects the *second response* for the population proportion of interest. In this example, Minitab uses the alphabetical ordering Female-Male to provide results for the population proportion of Male responses. Because Female is the response of interest, we change Minitab's ordering as follows: Select any cell in the column and use the sequence: Editor > Column > Value Order. Then choose the option of entering a user-specified order. Enter Male-Female in the **Define-an-order** box and click OK. Minitab's 1 Proportion routine will then provide the hypothesis test results for the population proportion of female golfers. We proceed as follows:

Step 1. Select the **Stat** menu
Step 2. Choose **Basic Statistics**
Step 3. Choose **1 Proportion**
Step 4. When the 1 Proportion dialog box appears:
    Enter C1 in the **Samples in Columns** box
    Select **Perform Hypothesis Test**
    Enter .20 in the **Hypothesized proportion** box
    Select **Options**
Step 5. When the 1 Proportion-Options dialog box appears:
    Enter 95 in the **Confidence level** box
    Select greater than in the **Alternative** box
    Select **Use test and interval based on normal distribution**
    Click **OK**
Step 6. Click **OK**

Appendix 9.2 Hypothesis Testing with Excel

Excel does not provide built-in routines for the hypothesis tests presented in this chapter. To handle these situations, we present Excel worksheets that we designed to use as templates for testing hypotheses about a population mean and a population proportion. The worksheets are easy to use and can be modified to handle any sample data. The worksheets are available on the website that accompanies this book.

Population Mean: σ Known

We illustrate using the MaxFlight golf ball distance example in Section 9.3. The data are in column A of an Excel worksheet. The population standard deviation $\sigma = 12$ is assumed known and the level of significance is $\alpha = .05$. The following steps can be used to test the hypothesis $H_0: \mu = 295$ versus $H_a: \mu \neq 295$.

Refer to Figure 9.11 as we describe the procedure. The worksheet in the background shows the cell formulas used to compute the results shown in the foreground worksheet. The data are entered into cells A2:A51. The following steps are necessary to use the template for this data set.

Hyp Sigma Known

Step 1. Enter the data range A2:A51 into the =COUNT cell formula in cell D4
Step 2. Enter the data range A2:A51 into the =AVERAGE cell formula in cell D5
Step 3. Enter the population standard deviation $\sigma = 12$ into cell D7
Step 4. Enter the hypothesized value for the population mean 295 into cell D8

The remaining cell formulas automatically provide the standard error, the value of the test statistic z, and three p-values. Because the alternative hypothesis ($\mu_0 \neq 295$) indicates a two-tailed test, the p-value (Two Tail) in cell D15 is used to make the rejection decision. With p-value $= .1255 > \alpha = .05$, the null hypothesis cannot be rejected. The p-values in cells D13 or D14 would be used if the hypotheses involved a one-tailed test.

This template can be used to make hypothesis testing computations for other applications. For instance, to conduct a hypothesis test for a new data set, enter the new sample data into column A of the worksheet. Modify the formulas in cells D4 and D5 to correspond to the new data range. Enter the population standard deviation into cell D7 and the hypothesized value for the population mean into cell D8 to obtain the results. If the new sample data have already been summarized, the new sample data do not have to be entered into the worksheet. In this case, enter the sample size into cell D4, the sample mean into cell D5, the population standard deviation into cell D7, and the hypothesized value for the population mean into cell D8 to obtain the results. The worksheet in Figure 9.11 is available in the file Hyp Sigma Known on the website that accompanies this book.

Population Mean: σ Unknown

We illustrate using the Heathrow Airport rating example in Section 9.4. The data are in column A of an Excel worksheet. The population standard deviation σ is unknown and will be estimated by the sample standard deviation s. The level of significance is $\alpha = .05$. The following steps can be used to test the hypothesis $H_0: \mu \leq 7$ versus $H_a: \mu > 7$.

Refer to Figure 9.12 as we describe the procedure. The background worksheet shows the cell formulas used to compute the results shown in the foreground version of the worksheet. The data are entered into cells A2:A61. The following steps are necessary to use the template for this data set.

Hyp Sigma Unknown

Step 1. Enter the data range A2:A61 into the =COUNT cell formula in cell D4
Step 2. Enter the data range A2:A61 into the =AVERAGE cell formula in cell D5
Step 3. Enter the data range A2:A61 into the =STDEV cell formula in cell D6
Step 4. Enter the hypothesized value for the population mean 7 into cell D8

FIGURE 9.11   EXCEL WORKSHEET FOR HYPOTHESIS TESTS ABOUT A POPULATION MEAN WITH σ KNOWN

	A	B	C	D	E
1	**Yards**		**Hypothesis Test about a Population Mean:**		
2	303		σ **Known Case**		
3	282				
4	289		Sample Size	=COUNT(A2:A51)	
5	298		Sample Mean	=AVERAGE(A2:A51)	
6	283				
7	317		**Population Standard Deviation**	12	
8	297		**Hypothesized Value**	295	
9	308				
10	317		**Standard Error**	=D7/SQRT(D4)	
11	293		**Test Statistic z**	=(D5-D8)/D10	
12	284				
13	290		*p*-value (Lower Tail)	=NORM.S.DIST(D11,TRUE)	
14	304		*p*-value (Upper Tail)	=1-D13	
15	290		*p*-value (Two Tail)	=2*(MIN(D13,D14))	
16	311				
50	301				
51	292				
52					

	A	B	C	D	E
1	**Yards**		**Hypothesis Test about a Population Mean:**		
2	303		σ **Known Case**		
3	282				
4	289		**Sample Size**	50	
5	298		**Sample Mean**	297.6	
6	283				
7	317		**Population Standard Deviation**	12	
8	297		**Hypothesized Value**	295	
9	308				
10	317		**Standard Error**	1.70	
11	293		**Test Statistic z**	1.53	
12	284				
13	290		*p*-value (Lower Tail)	0.9372	
14	304		*p*-value (Upper Tail)	0.0628	
15	290		*p*-value (Two Tail)	0.1255	
16	311				
50	301				
51	292				
52					

Note: Rows 17 to 49 are hidden.

The remaining cell formulas automatically provide the standard error, the value of the test statistic t, the number of degrees of freedom, and three *p*-values. Because the alternative hypothesis ($\mu > 7$) indicates an upper tail test, the *p*-value (Upper Tail) in cell D15 is used to make the decision. With *p*-value $= .0353 < \alpha = .05$, the null hypothesis is rejected. The *p*-values in cells D14 or D16 would be used if the hypotheses involved a lower tail test or a two-tailed test.

This template can be used to make hypothesis testing computations for other applications. For instance, to conduct a hypothesis test for a new data set, enter the new sample data into column A of the worksheet and modify the formulas in cells D4, D5, and D6 to

FIGURE 9.12   EXCEL WORKSHEET FOR HYPOTHESIS TESTS ABOUT A POPULATION MEAN WITH σ UNKNOWN

	A	B	C	D	E
1	**Rating**		**Hypothesis Test About a Population Mean**		
2	5		**With σ Unknown**		
3	7				
4	8		**Sample Size**	=COUNT(A2:A61)	
5	7		**Sample Mean**	=AVERAGE(A2:A61)	
6	8		**Sample Std. Deviation**	=STDEV(A2:A61)	
7	8				
8	8		**Hypothesized Value**	7	
9	7				
10	8		**Standard Error**	=D6/SQRT(D4)	
11	10		**Test Statistic _t_**	=(D5-D8)/D10	
12	6		**Degrees of Freedom**	=D4-1	
13	7				
14	8		**_p_-value (Lower Tail)**	=T.DIST(D11,D12,TRUE)	
15	8		**_p_-value (Upper Tail)**	=1-D14	
16	9		**_p_-value (Two Tail)**	=2*(MIN(D14,D15))	
17	7				
59	7				
60	7				
61	8				
62					

	A	B	C	D	E	F
1	**Rating**		**Hypothesis Test About a Population Mean**			
2	5		**With σ Unknown**			
3	7					
4	8		**Sample Size**	60		
5	7		**Sample Mean**	7.25		
6	8		**Sample Std. Deviation**	1.05		
7	8					
8	8		**Hypothesized Value**	7		
9	7					
10	8		**Standard Error**	0.136		
11	10		**Test Statistic _t_**	1.841		
12	6		**Degrees of Freedom**	59		
13	7					
14	8		**_p_-value (Lower Tail)**	0.9647		
15	8		**_p_-value (Upper Tail)**	0.0353		
16	9		**_p_-value (Two Tail)**	0.0706		
17	7					
59	7					
60	7					
61	8					
62						

Note: Rows 18 to 58 are hidden.

correspond to the new data range. Enter the hypothesized value for the population mean into cell D8 to obtain the results. If the new sample data have already been summarized, the new sample data do not have to be entered into the worksheet. In this case, enter the sample size into cell D4, the sample mean into cell D5, the sample standard deviation into cell D6, and the hypothesized value for the population mean into cell D8 to obtain the results. The worksheet in Figure 9.12 is available in the file Hyp Sigma Unknown on the website that accompanies this book.

FIGURE 9.13   EXCEL WORKSHEET FOR HYPOTHESIS TESTS ABOUT A POPULATION PROPORTION

	A	B	C	D	E
1	**Golfer**		**Hypothesis Test about a Population Proportion**		
2	Female				
3	Male		**Sample Size**	=COUNTA(A2:A401)	
4	Female		**Response of Interest**	Female	
5	Male		**Count for Response**	=COUNTIF(A2:A903,D4)	
6	Male		**Sample Proportion**	=D5/D3	
7	Female				
8	Male		**Hypothesized Value**	0.2	
9	Male				
10	Female		**Standard Error**	=SQRT(D8*(1-D8)/D3)	
11	Male		**Test Statistic** z	=(D6-D8)/D10	
12	Male				
13	Male		p-**value (Lower Tail)**	=NORM.S.DIST(D11,TRUE)	
14	Male		p-**value (Upper Tail)**	=1-D13	
15	Male		p-**value (TwoTail)**	=2*MIN(D13,D14)	
16	Female				
400	Male				
401	Male				
402					

	A	B	C	D	E	F
1	**Golfer**		**Hypothesis Test about a Population Proportion**			
2	Female					
3	Male		**Sample Size**	400		
4	Female		**Response of Interest**	Female		
5	Male		**Count for Response**	100		
6	Male		**Sample Proportion**	0.25		
7	Female					
8	Male		**Hypothesized Value**	0.20		
9	Male					
10	Female		**Standard Error**	0.02		
11	Male		**Test Statistic** z	2.5000		
12	Male					
13	Male		p-**value (Lower Tail)**	0.9938		
14	Male		p-**value (Upper Tail)**	0.0062		
15	Male		p-**value (TwoTail)**	0.0124		
16	Female					
400	Male					
401	Male					
402						

Note: Rows 17 to 399 are hidden.

Population Proportion

Hypothesis p

We illustrate using the Pine Creek golf course survey data presented in Section 9.5. The data of Male or Female golfer are in column A of an Excel worksheet. Refer to Figure 9.13 as we describe the procedure. The background worksheet shows the cell formulas used to compute the results shown in the foreground worksheet. The data are entered into cells A2:A401. The following steps can be used to test the hypothesis H_0: $p \leq .20$ versus H_a: $p > .20$.

Step 1. Enter the data range A2:A401 into the =COUNTA cell formula in cell D3
Step 2. Enter Female as the response of interest in cell D4
Step 3. Enter the data range A2:A401 into the =COUNTIF cell formula in cell D5
Step 4. Enter the hypothesized value for the population proportion .20 into cell D8

The remaining cell formulas automatically provide the standard error, the value of the test statistic z, and three p-values. Because the alternative hypothesis ($p > .20$) indicates an upper tail test, the p-value (Upper Tail) in cell D14 is used to make the decision. With p-value $= .0062 < \alpha = .05$, the null hypothesis is rejected. The p-values in cells D13 or D15 would be used if the hypothesis involved a lower tail test or a two-tailed test.

This template can be used to make hypothesis testing computations for other applications. For instance, to conduct a hypothesis test for a new data set, enter the new sample data into column A of the worksheet. Modify the formulas in cells D3 and D5 to correspond to the new data range. Enter the response of interest into cell D4 and the hypothesized value for the population proportion into cell D8 to obtain the results. If the new sample data have already been summarized, the new sample data do not have to be entered into the worksheet. In this case, enter the sample size into cell D3, the sample proportion into cell D6, and the hypothesized value for the population proportion into cell D8 to obtain the results. The worksheet in Figure 9.13 is available in the file Hypothesis p on the website that accompanies this book.

Appendix 9.3 Hypothesis Testing with StatTools

In this appendix we show how StatTools can be used to conduct hypothesis tests about a population mean for the σ unknown case

Population Mean: σ Unknown Case

AirRating

In this case the population standard deviation σ will be estimated by the sample standard deviation s. We use the example discussed in Section 9.4 involving ratings that 60 business travelers gave for Heathrow Airport.

Begin by using the Data Set Manager to create a StatTools data set for these data using the procedure described in the appendix in Chapter 1. The following steps can be used to test the hypothesis $H_0: \mu \le 7$ against $H_a: \mu > 7$.

Step 1. Click the **StatTools** tab on the Ribbon
Step 2. In the **Analyses** group, click **Statistical Inference**
Step 3. Choose the **Hypothesis Test** option
Step 4. Choose Mean/Std. Deviation
Step 5. When the StatTools-Hypothesis Test for Mean/Std. Deviation dialog box appears:

> For **Analysis Type,** choose **One-Sample Analysis**
> In the **Variables** section, select **Rating**
> In the **Hypothesis Tests to Perform** section:
>> Select the **Mean** option
>> Enter 7 in the **Null Hypothesis Value** box
>> Select **Greater Than Null Value (One-Tailed Test)** in the **Alternative Hypothesis Type** box
> If selected, remove the check in the **Standard Deviation** box
> Click **OK**

The results from the hypothesis test will appear. They include the p-value and the value of the test statistic.

Population Proportion

We illustrate using the Pine Creek golf course example in Section 9.5. Begin by using the Data Set Manager to create a StatTools data set for these data using the procedure described in the appendix to Chapter 1. The following steps can be used to conduct a hypothesis test of the population proportion.

WomenGolf

Step 1. Click the **StatTools** tab on the Ribbon
Step 2. In the **Analyses** group, click **Statistical Inference**
Step 3. Choose **Hypothesis Test**
Step 4. Choose **Proportion**
Step 5. When the StatTools-Hypothesis Test for Proportion dialog box appears:
    For **Analysis Type** choose **One-Sample Analysis**
    In the **Variables** section, select **Golfer**
    In the **Categories to Analyze** section, select **Female**
    In the **Hypotheses About Proportion** section:
        Enter .20 in the **Null Hypothesis Value** box
        In the **Alternaive Hypothesis Type** box, choose **Greater Than Null Value (One-Tailed Test)**
Click **OK**

The results from the hypothesis test will appear. They include the *p*-value and the value of the test statistic.

CHAPTER 14

Simple Linear Regression

CONTENTS

STATISTICS IN PRACTICE:
ALLIANCE DATA SYSTEMS

14.1 SIMPLE LINEAR
REGRESSION MODEL
Regression Model
and Regression
Equation
Estimated Regression
Equation

14.2 LEAST SQUARES METHOD

14.3 COEFFICIENT OF
DETERMINATION
Correlation Coefficient

14.4 MODEL ASSUMPTIONS

14.5 TESTING FOR
SIGNIFICANCE
Estimate of σ^2
t Test
Confidence Interval for β_1
F Test
Some Cautions About
the Interpretation of
Significance Tests

14.6 USING THE ESTIMATED
REGRESSION EQUATION
FOR ESTIMATION AND
PREDICTION
Interval Estimation
Confidence Interval for the Mean
Value of y
Prediction Interval for an
Individual Value of y

14.7 COMPUTER SOLUTION

14.8 RESIDUAL ANALYSIS:
VALIDATING MODEL
ASSUMPTIONS
Residual Plot Against x
Residual Plot Against $\hat{y}$
Standardized Residuals
Normal Probability Plot

14.9 RESIDUAL ANALYSIS:
OUTLIERS AND
INFLUENTIAL
OBSERVATIONS
Detecting Outliers
Detecting Influential
Observations

ALLIANCE DATA SYSTEMS*
DALLAS, TEXAS

Alliance Data Systems (ADS) provides transaction processing, credit services, and marketing services for clients in the rapidly growing customer relationship management (CRM) industry. ADS clients are concentrated in four industries: retail, petroleum/convenience stores, utilities, and transportation. In 1983, Alliance began offering end-to-end credit processing services to the retail, petroleum, and casual dining industries; today they employ more than 6500 employees who provide services to clients around the world. Operating more than 140,000 point-of-sale terminals in the United States alone, ADS processes in excess of 2.5 billion transactions annually. The company ranks second in the United States in private label credit services by representing 49 private label programs with nearly 72 million cardholders. In 2001, ADS made an initial public offering and is now listed on the New York Stock Exchange.

As one of its marketing services, ADS designs direct mail campaigns and promotions. With its database containing information on the spending habits of more than 100 million consumers, ADS can target those consumers most likely to benefit from a direct mail promotion. The Analytical Development Group uses regression analysis to build models that measure and predict the responsiveness of consumers to direct market campaigns. Some regression models predict the probability of purchase for individuals receiving a promotion, and others predict the amount spent by those consumers making a purchase.

For one particular campaign, a retail store chain wanted to attract new customers. To predict the effect of the campaign, ADS analysts selected a sample from the consumer database, sent the sampled individuals promotional materials, and then collected transaction data on the consumers' response. Sample data were collected on the amount of purchase made by the consumers responding to the campaign, as well as a variety of consumer-specific variables thought to be useful in predicting sales. The consumer-specific variable that contributed most to predicting the amount purchased was the total amount of

*The authors are indebted to Philip Clemance, Director of Analytical Development at Alliance Data Systems, for providing this Statistics in Practice.

Alliance Data Systems analysts discuss use of a regression model to predict sales for a direct marketing campaign. © Courtesy of Alliance Data Systems.

credit purchases at related stores over the past 39 months. ADS analysts developed an estimated regression equation relating the amount of purchase to the amount spent at related stores:

$$\hat{y} = 26.7 + 0.00205x$$

where

$$\hat{y} = \text{amount of purchase}$$
$$x = \text{amount spent at related stores}$$

Using this equation, we could predict that someone spending $10,000 over the past 39 months at related stores would spend $47.20 when responding to the direct mail promotion. In this chapter, you will learn how to develop this type of estimated regression equation.

The final model developed by ADS analysts also included several other variables that increased the predictive power of the preceding equation. Some of these variables included the absence/presence of a bank credit card, estimated income, and the average amount spent per trip at a selected store. In the following chapter, we will learn how such additional variables can be incorporated into a multiple regression model.

Managerial decisions often are based on the relationship between two or more variables. For example, after considering the relationship between advertising expenditures and sales, a marketing manager might attempt to predict sales for a given level of advertising expenditures. In another case, a public utility might use the relationship between the daily high temperature and the demand for electricity to predict electricity usage on the basis of next month's anticipated daily high temperatures. Sometimes a manager will rely on intuition to judge how two variables are related. However, if data can be obtained, a statistical procedure called *regression analysis* can be used to develop an equation showing how the variables are related.

The statistical methods used in studying the relationship between two variables were first employed by Sir Francis Galton (1822–1911). Galton was interested in studying the relationship between a father's height and the son's height. Galton's disciple, Karl Pearson (1857–1936), analyzed the relationship between the father's height and the son's height for 1078 pairs of subjects.

In regression terminology, the variable being predicted is called the **dependent variable**. The variable or variables being used to predict the value of the dependent variable are called the **independent variables**. For example, in analyzing the effect of advertising expenditures on sales, a marketing manager's desire to predict sales would suggest making sales the dependent variable. Advertising expenditure would be the independent variable used to help predict sales. In statistical notation, y denotes the dependent variable and x denotes the independent variable.

In this chapter we consider the simplest type of regression analysis involving one independent variable and one dependent variable in which the relationship between the variables is approximated by a straight line. It is called **simple linear regression**. Regression analysis involving two or more independent variables is called multiple regression analysis; multiple regression and cases involving curvilinear relationships are covered in Chapters 15 and 16.

14.1 Simple Linear Regression Model

Armand's Pizza Parlors is a chain of Italian-food restaurants located in a five-state area. Armand's most successful locations are near college campuses. The managers believe that quarterly sales for these restaurants (denoted by y) are related positively to the size of the student population (denoted by x); that is, restaurants near campuses with a large student population tend to generate more sales than those located near campuses with a small student population. Using regression analysis, we can develop an equation showing how the dependent variable y is related to the independent variable x.

Regression Model and Regression Equation

In the Armand's Pizza Parlors example, the population consists of all the Armand's restaurants. For every restaurant in the population, there is a value of x (student population) and a corresponding value of y (quarterly sales). The equation that describes how y is related to x and an error term is called the **regression model**. The regression model used in simple linear regression follows.

SIMPLE LINEAR REGRESSION MODEL

$$y = \beta_0 + \beta_1 x + \epsilon \qquad (14.1)$$

β_0 and β_1 are referred to as the parameters of the model, and ϵ (the Greek letter epsilon) is a random variable referred to as the error term. The error term accounts for the variability in y that cannot be explained by the linear relationship between x and y.

The population of all Armand's restaurants can also be viewed as a collection of subpopulations, one for each distinct value of x. For example, one subpopulation consists of all Armand's restaurants located near college campuses with 8000 students; another subpopulation consists of all Armand's restaurants located near college campuses with 9000 students; and so on. Each subpopulation has a corresponding distribution of y values. Thus, a distribution of y values is associated with restaurants located near campuses with 8000 students; a distribution of y values is associated with restaurants located near campuses with 9000 students; and so on. Each distribution of y values has its own mean or expected value. The equation that describes how the expected value of y, denoted $E(y)$, is related to x is called the **regression equation**. The regression equation for simple linear regression follows.

SIMPLE LINEAR REGRESSION EQUATION

$$E(y) = \beta_0 + \beta_1 x \qquad \textbf{(14.2)}$$

The graph of the simple linear regression equation is a straight line; β_0 is the y-intercept of the regression line, β_1 is the slope, and $E(y)$ is the mean or expected value of y for a given value of x.

Examples of possible regression lines are shown in Figure 14.1. The regression line in Panel A shows that the mean value of y is related positively to x, with larger values of $E(y)$ associated with larger values of x. The regression line in Panel B shows the mean value of y is related negatively to x, with smaller values of $E(y)$ associated with larger values of x. The regression line in Panel C shows the case in which the mean value of y is not related to x; that is, the mean value of y is the same for every value of x.

Estimated Regression Equation

If the values of the population parameters β_0 and β_1 were known, we could use equation (14.2) to compute the mean value of y for a given value of x. In practice, the parameter values are not known and must be estimated using sample data. Sample statistics (denoted b_0 and b_1) are computed as estimates of the population parameters β_0 and β_1. Substituting the values of the sample statistics b_0 and b_1 for β_0 and β_1 in the regression equation, we obtain the

FIGURE 14.1 POSSIBLE REGRESSION LINES IN SIMPLE LINEAR REGRESSION

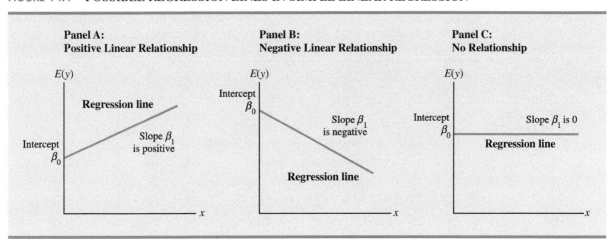

estimated regression equation. The estimated regression equation for simple linear regression follows.

ESTIMATED SIMPLE LINEAR REGRESSION EQUATION

$$\hat{y} = b_0 + b_1x \qquad\qquad \textbf{(14.3)}$$

Figure 14.2 provides a summary of the estimation process for simple linear regression.

The graph of the estimated simple linear regression equation is called the *estimated regression line*; b_0 is the y-intercept and b_1 is the slope. In the next section, we show how the least squares method can be used to compute the values of b_0 and b_1 in the estimated regression equation.

In general, $\hat{y}$ is the point estimator of $E(y)$, the mean value of y for a given value of x. Thus, to estimate the mean or expected value of quarterly sales for all restaurants located near campuses with 10,000 students, Armand's would substitute the value of 10,000 for x in equation (14.3). In some cases, however, Armand's may be more interested in predicting sales for one particular restaurant. For example, suppose Armand's would like to predict quarterly sales for the restaurant they are considering building near Talbot College, a school with 10,000 students. As it turns out, the best predictor of y for a given value of x is also provided by $\hat{y}$. Thus, to predict quarterly sales for the restaurant located near Talbot College, Armand's would also substitute the value of 10,000 for x in equation (14.3).

The value of $\hat{y}$ provides both a point estimate of $E(y)$ for a given value of x and a prediction of an individual value of y for a given value of x.

FIGURE 14.2   THE ESTIMATION PROCESS IN SIMPLE LINEAR REGRESSION

The estimation of β_0 and β_1 is a statistical process much like the estimation of μ discussed in Chapter 7. β_0 and β_1 are the unknown parameters of interest, and b_0 and b_1 are the sample statistics used to estimate the parameters.

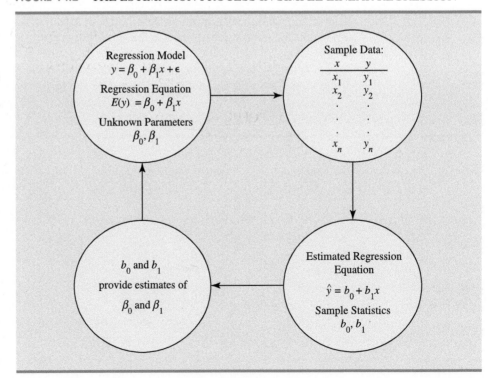

NOTES AND COMMENTS

1. Regression analysis cannot be interpreted as a procedure for establishing a cause-and-effect relationship between variables. It can only indicate how or to what extent variables are associated with each other. Any conclusions about cause and effect must be based upon the judgment of those individuals most knowledgeable about the application.

2. The regression equation in simple linear regression is $E(y) = \beta_0 + \beta_1 x$. More advanced texts in regression analysis often write the regression equation as $E(y|x) = \beta_0 + \beta_1 x$ to emphasize that the regression equation provides the mean value of y for a given value of x.

14.2   Least Squares Method

In simple linear regression, each observation consists of two values: one for the independent variable and one for the dependent variable.

The **least squares method** is a procedure for using sample data to find the estimated regression equation. To illustrate the least squares method, suppose data were collected from a sample of 10 Armand's Pizza Parlor restaurants located near college campuses. For the *i*th observation or restaurant in the sample, x_i is the size of the student population (in thousands) and y_i is the quarterly sales (in thousands of dollars). The values of x_i and y_i for the 10 restaurants in the sample are summarized in Table 14.1. We see that restaurant 1, with $x_1 = 2$ and $y_1 = 58$, is near a campus with 2000 students and has quarterly sales of $58,000. Restaurant 2, with $x_2 = 6$ and $y_2 = 105$, is near a campus with 6000 students and has quarterly sales of $105,000. The largest sales value is for restaurant 10, which is near a campus with 26,000 students and has quarterly sales of $202,000.

Figure 14.3 is a scatter diagram of the data in Table 14.1. Student population is shown on the horizontal axis and quarterly sales is shown on the vertical axis. **Scatter diagrams** for regression analysis are constructed with the independent variable x on the horizontal axis and the dependent variable y on the vertical axis. The scatter diagram enables us to observe the data graphically and to draw preliminary conclusions about the possible relationship between the variables.

What preliminary conclusions can be drawn from Figure 14.3? Quarterly sales appear to be higher at campuses with larger student populations. In addition, for these data the relationship between the size of the student population and quarterly sales appears to be approximated by a straight line; indeed, a positive linear relationship is indicated between x

TABLE 14.1   STUDENT POPULATION AND QUARTERLY SALES DATA
FOR 10 ARMAND'S PIZZA PARLORS

WEB file

Armand's

Restaurant *i*	Student Population (1000s) x_i	Quarterly Sales ($1000s) y_i
1	2	58
2	6	105
3	8	88
4	8	118
5	12	117
6	16	137
7	20	157
8	20	169
9	22	149
10	26	202

FIGURE 14.3 SCATTER DIAGRAM OF STUDENT POPULATION AND QUARTERLY SALES FOR ARMAND'S PIZZA PARLORS

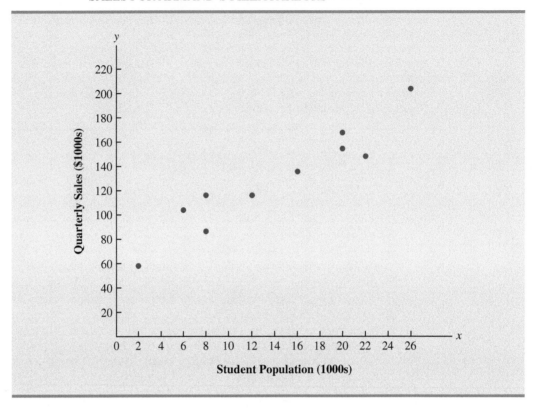

and y. We therefore choose the simple linear regression model to represent the relationship between quarterly sales and student population. Given that choice, our next task is to use the sample data in Table 14.1 to determine the values of b_0 and b_1 in the estimated simple linear regression equation. For the ith restaurant, the estimated regression equation provides

$$\hat{y}_i = b_0 + b_1 x_i \tag{14.4}$$

where

$\hat{y}_i$ = predicted value of quarterly sales ($1000s) for the ith restaurant
b_0 = the y-intercept of the estimated regression line
b_1 = the slope of the estimated regression line
x_i = size of the student population (1000s) for the ith restaurant

With y_i denoting the observed (actual) sales for restaurant i and $\hat{y}_i$ in equation (14.4) representing the predicted value of sales for restaurant i, every restaurant in the sample will have an observed value of sales y_i and a predicted value of sales $\hat{y}_i$. For the estimated regression line to provide a good fit to the data, we want the differences between the observed sales values and the predicted sales values to be small.

The least squares method uses the sample data to provide the values of b_0 and b_1 that minimize the *sum of the squares of the deviations* between the observed values of the dependent variable y_i and the predicted values of the dependent variable $\hat{y}_i$. The criterion for the least squares method is given by expression (14.5).

*Carl Friedrich Gauss
(1777–1855) proposed the
least squares method.*

LEAST SQUARES CRITERION

$$\min \Sigma(y_i - \hat{y}_i)^2 \qquad \textbf{(14.5)}$$

where

y_i = observed value of the dependent variable for the ith observation

$\hat{y}_i$ = predicted value of the dependent variable for the ith observation

---

Differential calculus can be used to show (see Appendix 14.1) that the values of b_0 and b_1 that minimize expression (14.5) can be found by using equations (14.6) and (14.7).

SLOPE AND y-INTERCEPT FOR THE ESTIMATED REGRESSION EQUATION[1]

*In computing b_1 with a
calculator, carry as many
significant digits as
possible in the intermediate
calculations. We
recommend carrying at
least four significant digits.*

$$b_1 = \frac{\Sigma(x_i - \bar{x})(y_i - \bar{y})}{\Sigma(x_i - \bar{x})^2} \qquad \textbf{(14.6)}$$

$$b_0 = \bar{y} - b_1\bar{x} \qquad \textbf{(14.7)}$$

where

x_i = value of the independent variable for the ith observation

y_i = value of the dependent variable for the ith observation

$\bar{x}$ = mean value for the independent variable

$\bar{y}$ = mean value for the dependent variable

n = total number of observations

Some of the calculations necessary to develop the least squares estimated regression equation for Armand's Pizza Parlors are shown in Table 14.2. With the sample of 10 restaurants, we have $n = 10$ observations. Because equations (14.6) and (14.7) require $\bar{x}$ and $\bar{y}$ we begin the calculations by computing $\bar{x}$ and $\bar{y}$.

$$\bar{x} = \frac{\Sigma x_i}{n} = \frac{140}{10} = 14$$

$$\bar{y} = \frac{\Sigma y_i}{n} = \frac{1300}{10} = 130$$

Using equations (14.6) and (14.7) and the information in Table 14.2, we can compute the slope and intercept of the estimated regression equation for Armand's Pizza Parlors. The calculation of the slope (b_1) proceeds as follows.

---

[1] An alternate formula for b_1 is

$$b_1 = \frac{\Sigma x_i y_i - (\Sigma x_i \Sigma y_i)/n}{\Sigma x_i^2 - (\Sigma x_i)^2/n}$$

This form of equation (14.6) is often recommended when using a calculator to compute b_1.

TABLE 14.2 CALCULATIONS FOR THE LEAST SQUARES ESTIMATED REGRESSION EQUATION FOR ARMAND'S PIZZA PARLORS

Restaurant i	x_i	y_i	$x_i - \bar{x}$	$y_i - \bar{y}$	$(x_i - \bar{x})(y_i - \bar{y})$	$(x_i - \bar{x})^2$
1	2	58	−12	−72	864	144
2	6	105	−8	−25	200	64
3	8	88	−6	−42	252	36
4	8	118	−6	−12	72	36
5	12	117	−2	−13	26	4
6	16	137	2	7	14	4
7	20	157	6	27	162	36
8	20	169	6	39	234	36
9	22	149	8	19	152	64
10	26	202	12	72	864	144
Totals	140	1300			2840	568
	Σx_i	Σy_i			$\Sigma(x_i - \bar{x})(y_i - \bar{y})$	$\Sigma(x_i - \bar{x})^2$

$$b_1 = \frac{\Sigma(x_i - \bar{x})(y_i - \bar{y})}{\Sigma(x_i - \bar{x})^2}$$

$$= \frac{2840}{568}$$

$$= 5$$

The calculation of the y intercept (b_0) follows.

$$b_0 = \bar{y} - b_1 \bar{x}$$

$$= 130 - 5(14)$$

$$= 60$$

Thus, the estimated regression equation is

$$\hat{y} = 60 + 5x$$

Figure 14.4 shows the graph of this equation on the scatter diagram.

The slope of the estimated regression equation ($b_1 = 5$) is positive, implying that as student population increases, sales increase. In fact, we can conclude (based on sales measured in $1000s and student population in 1000s) that an increase in the student population of 1000 is associated with an increase of $5000 in expected sales; that is, quarterly sales are expected to increase by $5 per student.

Using the estimated regression equation to make predictions outside the range of the values of the independent variable should be done with caution because outside that range we cannot be sure that the same relationship is valid.

If we believe the least squares estimated regression equation adequately describes the relationship between x and y, it would seem reasonable to use the estimated regression equation to predict the value of y for a given value of x. For example, if we wanted to predict quarterly sales for a restaurant to be located near a campus with 16,000 students, we would compute

$$\hat{y} = 60 + 5(16) = 140$$

Hence, we would predict quarterly sales of $140,000 for this restaurant. In the following sections we will discuss methods for assessing the appropriateness of using the estimated regression equation for estimation and prediction.

FIGURE 14.4 GRAPH OF THE ESTIMATED REGRESSION EQUATION FOR ARMAND'S PIZZA PARLORS: $\hat{y} = 60 + 5x$

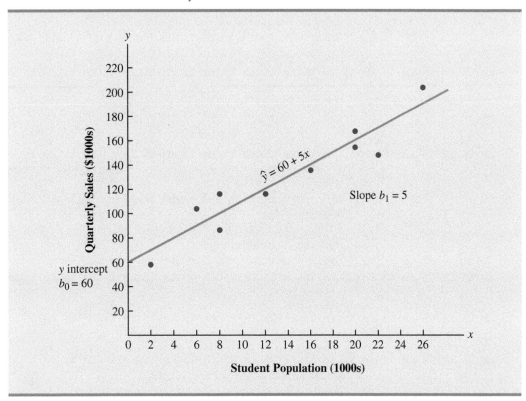

NOTES AND COMMENTS

The least squares method provides an estimated regression equation that minimizes the sum of squared deviations between the observed values of the dependent variable y_i and the predicted values of the dependent variable $\hat{y}_i$. This least squares criterion is used to choose the equation that provides the best fit. If some other criterion were used, such as minimizing the sum of the absolute deviations between y_i and $\hat{y}_i$, a different equation would be obtained. In practice, the least squares method is the most widely used.

Exercises

Methods

1. Given are five observations for two variables, x and y.

x_i	1	2	3	4	5
y_i	3	7	5	11	14

a. Develop a scatter diagram for these data.
b. What does the scatter diagram developed in part (a) indicate about the relationship between the two variables?

c. Try to approximate the relationship between x and y by drawing a straight line through the data.

d. Develop the estimated regression equation by computing the values of b_0 and b_1 using equations (14.6) and (14.7).

e. Use the estimated regression equation to predict the value of y when $x = 4$.

2. Given are five observations for two variables, x and y.

x_i	3	12	6	20	14
y_i	55	40	55	10	15

a. Develop a scatter diagram for these data.

b. What does the scatter diagram developed in part (a) indicate about the relationship between the two variables?

c. Try to approximate the relationship between x and y by drawing a straight line through the data.

d. Develop the estimated regression equation by computing the values of b_0 and b_1 using equations (14.6) and (14.7).

e. Use the estimated regression equation to predict the value of y when $x = 10$.

3. Given are five observations collected in a regression study on two variables.

x_i	2	6	9	13	20
y_i	7	18	9	26	23

a. Develop a scatter diagram for these data.

b. Develop the estimated regression equation for these data.

c. Use the estimated regression equation to predict the value of y when $x = 6$.

Applications

4. The following data give the percentage of women working in five companies in the retail and trade industry. The percentage of management jobs held by women in each company is also shown.

% Working	67	45	73	54	61
% Management	49	21	65	47	33

a. Develop a scatter diagram for these data with the percentage of women working in the company as the independent variable.

b. What does the scatter diagram developed in part (a) indicate about the relationship between the two variables?

c. Try to approximate the relationship between the percentage of women working in the company and the percentage of management jobs held by women in that company.

d. Develop the estimated regression equation by computing the values of b_0 and b_1.

e. Predict the percentage of management jobs held by women in a company that has 60% women employees.

5. Elliptical trainers are becoming one of the more popular exercise machines. Their smooth and steady low-impact motion makes them a preferred choice for individuals with knee and ankle problems. But selecting the right trainer can be a difficult process. Price and

quality are two important factors in any purchase decision. Are higher prices generally associated with higher quality elliptical trainers? *Consumer Reports* conducted extensive tests to develop an overall rating based on ease of use, ergonomics, construction, and exercise range. The following data show the price and rating for eight elliptical trainers tested (*Consumer Reports,* February 2008).

Ellipticals

Brand and Model	Price ($)	Rating
Precor 5.31	3700	87
Keys Fitness CG2	2500	84
Octane Fitness Q37e	2800	82
LifeFitness X1 Basic	1900	74
NordicTrack AudioStrider 990	1000	73
Schwinn 430	800	69
Vision Fitness X6100	1700	68
ProForm XP 520 Razor	600	55

a.   Develop a scatter diagram with price as the independent variable.
b.   An exercise equipment store that sells primarily higher priced equipment has a sign over the display area that says "Quality: You Get What You Pay For." Based upon your analysis of the data for ellipical trainers, do you think this sign fairly reflects the price-quality relationship for elliptical trainers?
c.   Use the least squares method to develop the estimated regression equation.
d.   Use the estimated regression equation to predict the rating for an ellipitical trainer with a price of $1500.

6.   The National Football League (NFL) records a variety of performance data for individuals and teams. To investigate the importance of passing on the percentage of games won by a team, the following data show the average number of passing yards per attempt (Yds/Att) and the percentage of games won (WinPct) for a random sample of 10 NFL teams for the 2011 season (NFL website, February 12, 2012).

NFLPassing

Team	Yds/Att	WinPct
Arizona Cardinals	6.5	50
Atlanta Falcons	7.1	63
Carolina Panthers	7.4	38
Chicago Bears	6.4	50
Dallas Cowboys	7.4	50
New England Patriots	8.3	81
Philadelphia Eagles	7.4	50
Seattle Seahawks	6.1	44
St. Louis Rams	5.2	13
Tampa Bay Buccaneers	6.2	25

a.   Develop a scatter diagram with the number of passing yards per attempt on the horizontal axis and the percentage of games won on the vertical axis.
b.   What does the scatter diagram developed in part (a) indicate about the relationship between the two variables?
c.   Develop the estimated regression equation that could be used to predict the percentage of games won given the average number of passing yards per attempt.
d.   Provide an interpretation for the slope of the estimated regression equation.

e. For the 2011 season, the average number of passing yards per attempt for the Kansas City Chiefs was 6.2. Use the estimated regression equation developed in part (c) to predict the percentage of games won by the Kansas City Chiefs. (*Note:* For the 2011 season the Kansas City Chiefs record was 7 wins and 9 losses.) Compare your prediction to the actual percentage of games won by the Kansas City Chiefs.

7. A sales manager collected the following data on annual sales for new customer accounts and the number of years of experience for a sample of 10 salespersons.

Sales

Salesperson	Years of Experience	Annual Sales ($1000s)
1	1	80
2	3	97
3	4	92
4	4	102
5	6	103
6	8	111
7	10	119
8	10	123
9	11	117
10	13	136

a. Develop a scatter diagram for these data with years of experience as the independent variable.
b. Develop an estimated regression equation that can be used to predict annual sales given the years of experience.
c. Use the estimated regression equation to predict annual sales for a salesperson with 9 years of experience.

8. The American Association of Individual Investors (AAII) On-Line Discount Broker Survey polls members on their experiences with discount brokers. As part of the survey, members were asked to rate the quality of the speed of execution with their broker as well as provide an overall satisfaction rating for electronic trades. Possible responses (scores) were no opinion (0), unsatisfied (1), somewhat satisfied (2), satisfied (3), and very satisfied (4). For each broker summary scores were computed by calculating a weighted average of the scores provided by each respondent. A portion of the survey results follow (AAII website, February 7, 2012).

BrokerRatings

Brokerage	Speed	Satisfaction
Scottrade, Inc.	3.4	3.5
Charles Schwab	3.3	3.4
Fidelity Brokerage Services	3.4	3.9
TD Ameritrade	3.6	3.7
E*Trade Financial	3.2	2.9
Vanguard Brokerage Services	3.8	2.8
USAA Brokerage Services	3.8	3.6
Thinkorswim	2.6	2.6
Wells Fargo Investments	2.7	2.3
Interactive Brokers	4.0	4.0
Zecco.com	2.5	2.5

a. Develop a scatter diagram for these data with the speed of execution as the independent variable.

b. What does the scatter diagram developed in part (a) indicate about the relationship between the two variables?
c. Develop the least squares estimated regression equation.
d. Provide an interpretation for the slope of the estimated regression equation.
e. Suppose Zecco.com developed new software to increase their speed of execution rating. If the new software is able to increase their speed of execution rating from the current value of 2.5 to the average speed of execution rating for the other 10 brokerage firms that were surveyed, what value would you predict for the overall satisfaction rating?

9. Using a global-positioning-system (GPS)-based navigator for your car, you enter a destination and the system will plot a route, give spoken turn-by-turn directions, and show your progress along the route. Today, even budget units include features previously available only on more expensive models. *Consumer Reports* conducted extensive tests of GPS-based navigators and developed an overall rating based on factors such as ease of use, driver information, display, and battery life. The following data show the price and rating for a sample of 20 GPS units with a 4.3-inch screen that *Consumer Reports* tested (*Consumer Reports* website, April 17, 2012).

GPS

Brand and Model	Price ($)	Rating
Garmin Nuvi 3490LMT	400	82
Garmin Nuvi 3450	330	80
Garmin Nuvi 3790T	350	77
Garmin Nuvi 3790LMT	400	77
Garmin Nuvi 3750	250	74
Garmin Nuvi 2475LT	230	74
Garmin Nuvi 2455LT	160	73
Garmin Nuvi 2370LT	270	71
Garmin Nuvi 2360LT	250	71
Garmin Nuvi 2360LMT	220	71
Garmin Nuvi 755T	260	70
Motorola Motonab TN565t	200	68
Motorola Motonab TN555	200	67
Garmin Nuvi 1350T	150	65
Garmin Nuvi 1350LMT	180	65
Garmin Nuvi 2300	160	65
Garmin Nuvi 1350	130	64
Tom Tom VIA 1435T	200	62
Garmin Nuvi 1300	140	62
Garmin Nuvi 1300LM	180	62

a. Develop a scatter diagram with price as the independent variable.
b. What does the scatter diagram developed in part (a) indicate about the relationship between the two variables?
c. Use the least squares method to develop the estimated regression equation.
d. Predict the rating for a GPS system with a 4.3-inch screen that has a price of $200.

10. On March 31, 2009, Ford Motor Company's shares were trading at a 26-year low of $2.63. Ford's board of directors gave the CEO a grant of options and restricted shares with an estimated value of $16 million. On April 26, 2011, the price of a share of Ford had increased to $15.58, and the CEO's grant was worth $202.8 million, a gain in value of $186.8 million. The following table shows the share price in 2009 and 2011 for 10 companies, the stock-option and share grants to the CEOs in late 2008 and 2009, and the value of the options and grants in 2011. Also shown are the percentage increases in the stock price and the percentage gains in the options values (*The Wall Street Journal*, April 27, 2011).

CEOGrants

Company	Stock Price 2009 ($)	Stock Price 2011 ($)	% Increase in Stock Price	Options and Grants Value 2009 ($ millions)	Options and Grants Value 2011 ($ millions)	% Gain in Options Value
Ford Motor	2.63	15.58	492	16.0	202.8	1168
Abercrombie & Fitch	23.80	70.47	196	46.2	196.1	324
Nabors Industries	9.99	32.06	221	37.2	132.2	255
Starbucks	9.99	32.06	221	12.4	75.9	512
Salesforce.com	32.73	137.61	320	7.8	67.0	759
Starwood Hotels	12.70	60.28	375	5.8	57.1	884
Caterpillar	27.96	111.94	300	4.0	47.5	1088
Oracle	18.07	34.97	94	61.9	97.5	58
Capital One	12.24	54.61	346	6.0	40.6	577
Dow Chemical	8.43	39.97	374	5.0	38.8	676

a. Develop a scatter diagram for these data with the percentage increase in the stock price as the independent variable.
b. What does the scatter diagram developed in part (a) indicate about the relationship between the two variables?
c. Develop the least squares estimated regression equation.
d. Provide an interpretation for the slope of the estimated regression equation.
e. Do the rewards for the CEO appear to be based on performance increases as measured by the stock price?

11. Sporty cars are designed to provide better handling, acceleration, and a more responsive driving experience than a typical sedan. But, even within this select group of cars, performance as well as price can vary. *Consumer Reports* provided road-test scores and prices for the following 12 sporty cars (Consumer Reports website, October 2008). Prices are in thousands of dollars and road-test scores are based on a 0–100 rating scale, with higher values indicating better performance.

SportyCars

Car	Price ($1000s)	Road-Test Score
Chevrolet Cobalt SS	24.5	78
Dodge Caliber SRT4	24.9	56
Ford Mustang GT (V8)	29.0	73
Honda Civic Si	21.7	78
Mazda RX-8	31.3	86
Mini Cooper S	26.4	74
Mitsubishi Lancer Evolution GSR	38.1	83
Nissan Sentra SE-R Spec V	23.3	66
Suburu Impreza WRX	25.2	81
Suburu Impreza WRX Sti	37.6	89
Volkswagen GTI	24.0	83
Volkswagen R32	33.6	83

a. Develop a scatter diagram with price as the independent variable.
b. What does the scatter diagram developed in part (a) indicate about the relationship between the two variables?
c. Use the least squares method to develop the estimated regression equation.
d. Provide an interpretation for the slope of the estimated regression equation.
e. Another sporty car that *Consumer Reports* tested is the BMW 135i; the price for this car was $36,700. Predict the road-test score for the BMW 135i using the estimated regression equation developed in part (c).

12. Concur Technologies, Inc., is a large expense-management company located in Redmond, Washington. *The Wall Street Journal* asked Concur to examine the data from 8.3 million expense reports to provide insights regarding business travel expenses. Their analysis of the data showed that New York was the most expensive city, with an average daily hotel room rate of $198 and an average amount spent on entertainment, including group meals and tickets for shows, sports, and other events, of $172. In comparison, the U.S. averages for these two categories were $89 for the room rate and $99 for entertainment. The following table shows the average daily hotel room rate and the amount spent on entertainment for a random sample of 9 of the 25 most visited U.S. cities (*The Wall Street Journal,* August 18, 2011).

BusinessTravel

City	Room Rate ($)	Entertainment ($)
Boston	148	161
Denver	96	105
Nashville	91	101
New Orleans	110	142
Phoenix	90	100
San Diego	102	120
San Francisco	136	167
San Jose	90	140
Tampa	82	98

a. Develop a scatter diagram for these data with the room rate as the independent variable.
b. What does the scatter diagram developed in part (a) indicate about the relationship between the two variables?
c. Develop the least squares estimated regression equation.
d. Provide an interpretation for the slope of the estimated regression equation.
e. The average room rate in Chicago is $128, considerably higher than the U.S. average. Predict the entertainment expense per day for Chicago.

13. To the Internal Revenue Service, the reasonableness of total itemized deductions depends on the taxpayer's adjusted gross income. Large deductions, which include charity and medical deductions, are more reasonable for taxpayers with large adjusted gross incomes. If a taxpayer claims larger than average itemized deductions for a given level of income, the chances of an IRS audit are increased. Data (in thousands of dollars) on adjusted gross income and the average or reasonable amount of itemized deductions follow.

Adjusted Gross Income ($1000s)	Reasonable Amount of Itemized Deductions ($1000s)
22	9.6
27	9.6
32	10.1
48	11.1
65	13.5
85	17.7
120	25.5

a. Develop a scatter diagram for these data with adjusted gross income as the independent variable.
b. Use the least squares method to develop the estimated regression equation.
c. Predict the reasonable level of total itemized deductions for a taxpayer with an adjusted gross income of $52,500. If this taxpayer claimed itemized deductions of $20,400, would the IRS agent's request for an audit appear justified? Explain.

14. *PCWorld* rated four component characteristics for 10 ultraportable laptop computers: features, performance, design, and price. Each characteristic was rated using a 0–100 point scale. An overall rating, referred to as the *PCW World* Rating, was then developed for each laptop. The following table shows the features rating and the *PCW World* Rating for the 10 laptop computers (*PC World* website, February 5, 2009).

Model	Features Rating	PCW World Rating
Thinkpad X200	87	83
VGN-Z598U	85	82
U6V	80	81
Elitebook 2530P	75	78
X360	80	78
Thinkpad X300	76	78
Ideapad U110	81	77
Micro Express JFT2500	73	75
Toughbook W7	79	73
HP Voodoo Envy133	68	72

Laptop

a. Develop a scatter diagram with the features rating as the independent variable.
b. What does the scatter diagram developed in part (a) indicate about the relationship between the two variables?
c. Use the least squares method to develop the estimated regression equation.
d. Predict the *PCW World* Rating for a new laptop computer that has a features rating of 70.

(14.3) Coefficient of Determination

For the Armand's Pizza Parlors example, we developed the estimated regression equation $\hat{y} = 60 + 5x$ to approximate the linear relationship between the size of the student population x and quarterly sales y. A question now is: How well does the estimated regression equation fit the data? In this section, we show that the **coefficient of determination** provides a measure of the goodness of fit for the estimated regression equation.

For the ith observation, the difference between the observed value of the dependent variable, y_i, and the predicted value of the dependent variable, $\hat{y}_i$, is called the ***i*th residual**. The ith residual represents the error in using $\hat{y}_i$ to estimate y_i. Thus, for the ith observation, the residual is $y_i - \hat{y}_i$. The sum of squares of these residuals or errors is the quantity that is minimized by the least squares method. This quantity, also known as the *sum of squares due to error,* is denoted by SSE.

SUM OF SQUARES DUE TO ERROR

$$SSE = \Sigma(y_i - \hat{y}_i)^2 \tag{14.8}$$

The value of SSE is a measure of the error in using the estimated regression equation to predict the values of the dependent variable in the sample.

In Table 14.3 we show the calculations required to compute the sum of squares due to error for the Armand's Pizza Parlors example. For instance, for restaurant 1 the values of the independent and dependent variables are $x_1 = 2$ and $y_1 = 58$. Using the estimated

TABLE 14.3   CALCULATION OF SSE FOR ARMAND'S PIZZA PARLORS

Restaurant i	x_i = Student Population (1000s)	y_i = Quarterly Sales ($1000s)	Predicted Sales $\hat{y}_i = 60 + 5x_i$	Error $y_i - \hat{y}_i$	Squared Error $(y_i - \hat{y}_i)^2$
1	2	58	70	−12	144
2	6	105	90	15	225
3	8	88	100	−12	144
4	8	118	100	18	324
5	12	117	120	−3	9
6	16	137	140	−3	9
7	20	157	160	−3	9
8	20	169	160	9	81
9	22	149	170	−21	441
10	26	202	190	12	144
					SSE = 1530

regression equation, we find that the predicted value of quarterly sales for restaurant 1 is $\hat{y}_1 = 60 + 5(2) = 70$. Thus, the error in using $\hat{y}_1$ to predict y_1 for restaurant 1 is $y_1 - \hat{y}_1 = 58 - 70 = -12$. The squared error, $(-12)^2 = 144$, is shown in the last column of Table 14.3. After computing and squaring the residuals for each restaurant in the sample, we sum them to obtain SSE = 1530. Thus, SSE = 1530 measures the error in using the estimated regression equation $\hat{y} = 60 + 5x$ to predict sales.

Now suppose we are asked to develop an estimate of quarterly sales without knowledge of the size of the student population. Without knowledge of any related variables, we would use the sample mean as an estimate of quarterly sales at any given restaurant. Table 14.2 showed that for the sales data, $\Sigma y_i = 1300$. Hence, the mean value of quarterly sales for the sample of 10 Armand's restaurants is $\bar{y} = \Sigma y_i / n = 1300/10 = 130$. In Table 14.4 we show the sum of squared deviations obtained by using the sample mean $\bar{y} = 130$ to predict the value of quarterly sales for each restaurant in the sample. For the ith restaurant in the sample, the difference $y_i - \bar{y}$ provides a measure of the error involved in using $\bar{y}$ to predict sales. The corresponding sum of squares, called the *total sum of squares,* is denoted SST.

TABLE 14.4   COMPUTATION OF THE TOTAL SUM OF SQUARES FOR ARMAND'S PIZZA PARLORS

Restaurant i	x_i = Student Population (1000s)	y_i = Quarterly Sales ($1000s)	Deviation $y_i - \bar{y}$	Squared Deviation $(y_i - \bar{y})^2$
1	2	58	−72	5184
2	6	105	−25	625
3	8	88	−42	1764
4	8	118	−12	144
5	12	117	−13	169
6	16	137	7	49
7	20	157	27	729
8	20	169	39	1521
9	22	149	19	361
10	26	202	72	5184
				SST = 15,730

TOTAL SUM OF SQUARES

$$SST = \Sigma(y_i - \bar{y})^2 \qquad\qquad \textbf{(14.9)}$$

The sum at the bottom of the last column in Table 14.4 is the total sum of squares for Armand's Pizza Parlors; it is SST = 15,730.

With SST = 15,730 and SSE = 1530, the estimated regression line provides a much better fit to the data than the line y = ȳ.

In Figure 14.5 we show the estimated regression line $\hat{y} = 60 + 5x$ and the line corresponding to $\bar{y} = 130$. Note that the points cluster more closely around the estimated regression line than they do about the line $\bar{y} = 130$. For example, for the 10th restaurant in the sample we see that the error is much larger when $\bar{y} = 130$ is used to predict y_{10} than when $\hat{y}_{10} = 60 + 5(26) = 190$ is used. We can think of SST as a measure of how well the observations cluster about the $\bar{y}$ line and SSE as a measure of how well the observations cluster about the $\hat{y}$ line.

To measure how much the $\hat{y}$ values on the estimated regression line deviate from $\bar{y}$, another sum of squares is computed. This sum of squares, called the *sum of squares due to regression,* is denoted SSR.

SUM OF SQUARES DUE TO REGRESSION

$$SSR = \Sigma(\hat{y}_i - \bar{y})^2 \qquad\qquad \textbf{(14.10)}$$

FIGURE 14.5   DEVIATIONS ABOUT THE ESTIMATED REGRESSION LINE AND THE LINE $y = \bar{y}$ FOR ARMAND'S PIZZA PARLORS

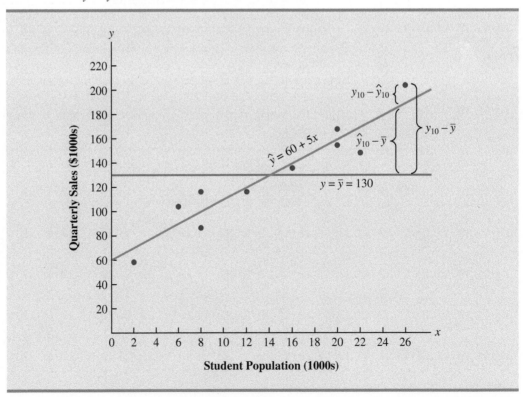

From the preceding discussion, we should expect that SST, SSR, and SSE are related. Indeed, the relationship among these three sums of squares provides one of the most important results in statistics.

SSR can be thought of as the explained portion of SST, and SSE can be thought of as the unexplained portion of SST.

RELATIONSHIP AMONG SST, SSR, AND SSE

$$SST = SSR + SSE \qquad (14.11)$$

where

$$SST = \text{total sum of squares}$$
$$SSR = \text{sum of squares due to regression}$$
$$SSE = \text{sum of squares due to error}$$

Equation (14.11) shows that the total sum of squares can be partitioned into two components, the sum of squares due to regression and the sum of squares due to error. Hence, if the values of any two of these sum of squares are known, the third sum of squares can be computed easily. For instance, in the Armand's Pizza Parlors example, we already know that SSE = 1530 and SST = 15,730; therefore, solving for SSR in equation (14.11), we find that the sum of squares due to regression is

$$SSR = SST - SSE = 15,730 - 1530 = 14,200$$

Now let us see how the three sums of squares, SST, SSR, and SSE, can be used to provide a measure of the goodness of fit for the estimated regression equation. The estimated regression equation would provide a perfect fit if every value of the dependent variable y_i happened to lie on the estimated regression line. In this case, $y_i - \hat{y}_i$ would be zero for each observation, resulting in SSE = 0. Because SST = SSR + SSE, we see that for a perfect fit SSR must equal SST, and the ratio (SSR/SST) must equal one. Poorer fits will result in larger values for SSE. Solving for SSE in equation (14.11), we see that SSE = SST - SSR. Hence, the largest value for SSE (and hence the poorest fit) occurs when SSR = 0 and SSE = SST.

The ratio SSR/SST, which will take values between zero and one, is used to evaluate the goodness of fit for the estimated regression equation. This ratio is called the *coefficient of determination* and is denoted by r^2.

COEFFICIENT OF DETERMINATION

$$r^2 = \frac{SSR}{SST} \qquad (14.12)$$

For the Armand's Pizza Parlors example, the value of the coefficient of determination is

$$r^2 = \frac{SSR}{SST} = \frac{14,200}{15,730} = .9027$$

When we express the coefficient of determination as a percentage, r^2 can be interpreted as the percentage of the total sum of squares that can be explained by using the estimated regression equation. For Armand's Pizza Parlors, we can conclude that 90.27% of the total sum of squares can be explained by using the estimated regression equation $\hat{y} = 60 + 5x$ to predict quarterly sales. In other words, 90.27% of the variability in sales can be explained by the linear relationship between the size of the student population and sales. We should be pleased to find such a good fit for the estimated regression equation.

Correlation Coefficient

In Chapter 3 we introduced the **correlation coefficient** as a descriptive measure of the strength of linear association between two variables, x and y. Values of the correlation coefficient are always between -1 and $+1$. A value of $+1$ indicates that the two variables x and y are perfectly related in a positive linear sense. That is, all data points are on a straight line that has a positive slope. A value of -1 indicates that x and y are perfectly related in a negative linear sense, with all data points on a straight line that has a negative slope. Values of the correlation coefficient close to zero indicate that x and y are not linearly related.

In Section 3.5 we presented the equation for computing the sample correlation coefficient. If a regression analysis has already been performed and the coefficient of determination r^2 computed, the sample correlation coefficient can be computed as follows.

SAMPLE CORRELATION COEFFICIENT

$$r_{xy} = (\text{sign of } b_1)\sqrt{\text{Coefficient of determination}}$$
$$= (\text{sign of } b_1)\sqrt{r^2} \tag{14.13}$$

where

$$b_1 = \text{the slope of the estimated regression equation } \hat{y} = b_0 + b_1 x$$

The sign for the sample correlation coefficient is positive if the estimated regression equation has a positive slope ($b_1 > 0$) and negative if the estimated regression equation has a negative slope ($b_1 < 0$).

For the Armand's Pizza Parlor example, the value of the coefficient of determination corresponding to the estimated regression equation $\hat{y} = 60 + 5x$ is .9027. Because the slope of the estimated regression equation is positive, equation (14.13) shows that the sample correlation coefficient is $+\sqrt{.9027} = +.9501$. With a sample correlation coefficient of $r_{xy} = +.9501$, we would conclude that a strong positive linear association exists between x and y.

In the case of a linear relationship between two variables, both the coefficient of determination and the sample correlation coefficient provide measures of the strength of the relationship. The coefficient of determination provides a measure between zero and one, whereas the sample correlation coefficient provides a measure between -1 and $+1$. Although the sample correlation coefficient is restricted to a linear relationship between two variables, the coefficient of determination can be used for nonlinear relationships and for relationships that have two or more independent variables. Thus, the coefficient of determination provides a wider range of applicability.

NOTES AND COMMENTS

1. In developing the least squares estimated regression equation and computing the coefficient of determination, we made no probabilistic assumptions about the error term ϵ, and no statistical tests for significance of the relationship between x and y were conducted. Larger values of r^2 imply that the least squares line provides a better fit to the data; that is, the observations are more closely grouped about the least squares line. But, using only r^2, we can draw no conclusion about whether the relationship between x and y is statistically significant. Such a conclusion must be based on considerations that involve the sample size and the properties of the appropriate sampling distributions of the least squares estimators.

2. As a practical matter, for typical data found in the social sciences, values of r^2 as low as .25 are often considered useful. For data in the physical and life sciences, r^2 values of .60 or greater are often found; in fact, in some cases, r^2 values greater than .90 can be found. In business applications, r^2 values vary greatly, depending on the unique characteristics of each application.

Exercises

Methods

15. The data from exercise 1 follow.

x_i	1	2	3	4	5
y_i	3	7	5	11	14

The estimated regression equation for these data is $\hat{y} = .20 + 2.60x$.
   a. Compute SSE, SST, and SSR using equations (14.8), (14.9), and (14.10).
   b. Compute the coefficient of determination r^2. Comment on the goodness of fit.
   c. Compute the sample correlation coefficient.

16. The data from exercise 2 follow.

x_i	3	12	6	20	14
y_i	55	40	55	10	15

The estimated regression equation for these data is $\hat{y} = 68 - 3x$.
   a. Compute SSE, SST, and SSR.
   b. Compute the coefficient of determination r^2. Comment on the goodness of fit.
   c. Compute the sample correlation coefficient.

17. The data from exercise 3 follow.

x_i	2	6	9	13	20
y_i	7	18	9	26	23

The estimated regression equation for these data is $\hat{y} = 7.6 + .9x$. What percentage of the total sum of squares can be accounted for by the estimated regression equation? What is the value of the sample correlation coefficient?

Applications

18. The following data show the brand, price ($), and the overall score for six stereo headphones that were tested by *Consumer Reports* (*Consumer Reports* website, March 5, 2012). The overall score is based on sound quality and effectiveness of ambient noise reduction. Scores range from 0 (lowest) to 100 (highest). The estimated regression equation for these data is $\hat{y} = 23.194 + .318x$, where x = price ($) and y = overall score.

Brand	Price ($)	Score
Bose	180	76
Skullcandy	150	71
Koss	95	61
Phillips/O'Neill	70	56
Denon	70	40
JVC	35	26

   a.   Compute SST, SSR, and SSE.
   b.   Compute the coefficient of determination r^2. Comment on the goodness of fit.
   c.   What is the value of the sample correlation coefficient?

19.   In exercise 7 a sales manager collected the following data on $x =$ annual sales and $y =$ years of experience. The estimated regression equation for these data is $\hat{y} = 80 + 4x$.

Sales

Salesperson	Years of Experience	Annual Sales ($1000s)
1	1	80
2	3	97
3	4	92
4	4	102
5	6	103
6	8	111
7	10	119
8	10	123
9	11	117
10	13	136

   a.   Compute SST, SSR, and SSE.
   b.   Compute the coefficient of determination r^2. Comment on the goodness of fit.
   c.   What is the value of the sample correlation coefficient?

20.   *Bicycling,* the world's leading cycling magazine, reviews hundreds of bicycles throughout the year. Their "Road-Race" category contains reviews of bikes used by riders primarily interested in racing. One of the most important factors in selecting a bike for racing is the weight of the bike. The following data show the weight (pounds) and price ($) for 10 racing bikes reviewed by the magazine (*Bicycling* website, March 8, 2012).

RacingBicycles

Brand	Weight	Price ($)
FELT F5	17.8	2100
PINARELLO Paris	16.1	6250
ORBEA Orca GDR	14.9	8370
EDDY MERCKX EMX-7	15.9	6200
BH RC1 Ultegra	17.2	4000
BH Ultralight 386	13.1	8600
CERVELO S5 Team	16.2	6000
GIANT TCR Advanced 2	17.1	2580
WILIER TRIESTINA Gran Turismo	17.6	3400
SPECIALIZED S-Works Amira SL4	14.1	8000

a. Use the data to develop an estimated regression equation that could be used to esti-
    mate the price for a bike given the weight.
b. Compute r^2. Did the estimated regression equation provide a good fit?
c. Predict the price for a bike that weighs 15 pounds.

21. An important application of regression analysis in accounting is in the estimation of cost.
    By collecting data on volume and cost and using the least squares method to develop an
    estimated regression equation relating volume and cost, an accountant can estimate the cost
    associated with a particular manufacturing volume. Consider the following sample of pro-
    duction volumes and total cost data for a manufacturing operation.

Production Volume (units)	Total Cost ($)
400	4000
450	5000
550	5400
600	5900
700	6400
750	7000

a. Use these data to develop an estimated regression equation that could be used to
    predict the total cost for a given production volume.
b. What is the variable cost per unit produced?
c. Compute the coefficient of determination. What percentage of the variation in total
    cost can be explained by production volume?
d. The company's production schedule shows 500 units must be produced next month.
    Predict the total cost for this operation?

22. Refer to exercise 5 where the following data were used to investigate whether higher prices
    are generally associated with higher ratings for elliptical trainers (*Consumer Reports,*
    February 2008).

WEB file

Ellipticals

Brand and Model	Price ($)	Rating
Precor 5.31	3700	87
Keys Fitness CG2	2500	84
Octane Fitness Q37e	2800	82
LifeFitness X1 Basic	1900	74
NordicTrack AudioStrider 990	1000	73
Schwinn 430	800	69
Vision Fitness X6100	1700	68
ProForm XP 520 Razor	600	55

With $x = $ price ($) and $y = $ rating, the estimated regression equation is $\hat{y} =$
$58.158 + .008449x$. For these data, SSE $= 173.88$.
a. Compute the coefficient of determination r^2.
b. Did the estimated regression equation provide a good fit? Explain.
c. What is the value of the sample correlation coefficient? Does it reflect a strong or weak
    relationship between price and rating?

14.4 Model Assumptions

In conducting a regression analysis, we begin by making an assumption about the appropriate model for the relationship between the dependent and independent variable(s). For the case of simple linear regression, the assumed regression model is

$$y = \beta_0 + \beta_1 x + \epsilon$$

Then the least squares method is used to develop values for b_0 and b_1, the estimates of the model parameters β_0 and β_1, respectively. The resulting estimated regression equation is

$$\hat{y} = b_0 + b_1 x$$

We saw that the value of the coefficient of determination (r^2) is a measure of the goodness of fit of the estimated regression equation. However, even with a large value of r^2, the estimated regression equation should not be used until further analysis of the appropriateness of the assumed model has been conducted. An important step in determining whether the assumed model is appropriate involves testing for the significance of the relationship. The tests of significance in regression analysis are based on the following assumptions about the error term ϵ.

ASSUMPTIONS ABOUT THE ERROR TERM ϵ IN THE REGRESSION MODEL

$$y = \beta_0 + \beta_1 x + \epsilon$$

1. The error term ϵ is a random variable with a mean or expected value of zero; that is, $E(\epsilon) = 0$.
   Implication: β_0 and β_1 are constants, therefore $E(\beta_0) = \beta_0$ and $E(\beta_1) = \beta_1$; thus, for a given value of x, the expected value of y is

$$E(y) = \beta_0 + \beta_1 x \qquad\qquad (14.14)$$

   As we indicated previously, equation (14.14) is referred to as the regression equation.
2. The variance of ϵ, denoted by σ^2, is the same for all values of x.
   Implication: The variance of y about the regression line equals σ^2 and is the same for all values of x.
3. The values of ϵ are independent.
   Implication: The value of ϵ for a particular value of x is not related to the value of ϵ for any other value of x; thus, the value of y for a particular value of x is not related to the value of y for any other value of x.
4. The error term ϵ is a normally distributed random variable for all values of x.
   Implication: Because y is a linear function of ϵ, y is also a normally distributed random variable for all values of x.

Figure 14.6 illustrates the model assumptions and their implications; note that in this graphical interpretation, the value of $E(y)$ changes according to the specific value of x considered. However, regardless of the x value, the probability distribution of ϵ and hence the probability distributions of y are normally distributed, each with the same variance. The specific value of the error ϵ at any particular point depends on whether the actual value of y is greater than or less than $E(y)$.

FIGURE 14.6 ASSUMPTIONS FOR THE REGRESSION MODEL

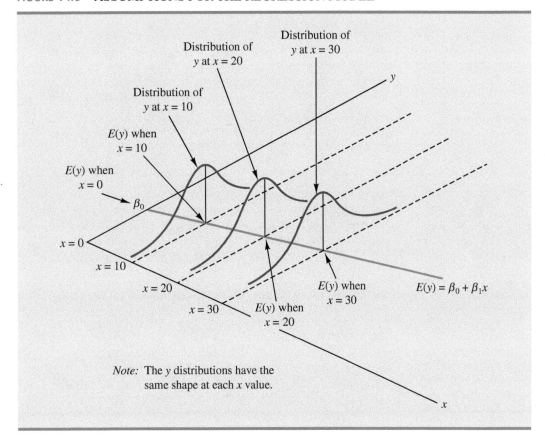

Note: The y distributions have the same shape at each x value.

At this point, we must keep in mind that we are also making an assumption or hypothesis about the form of the relationship between x and y. That is, we assume that a straight line represented by $\beta_0 + \beta_1 x$ is the basis for the relationship between the variables. We must not lose sight of the fact that some other model, for instance $y = \beta_0 + \beta_1 x^2 + \epsilon$, may turn out to be a better model for the underlying relationship.

14.5 Testing for Significance

In a simple linear regression equation, the mean or expected value of y is a linear function of x: $E(y) = \beta_0 + \beta_1 x$. If the value of β_1 is zero, $E(y) = \beta_0 + (0)x = \beta_0$. In this case, the mean value of y does not depend on the value of x and hence we would conclude that x and y are not linearly related. Alternatively, if the value of β_1 is not equal to zero, we would conclude that the two variables are related. Thus, to test for a significant regression relationship, we must conduct a hypothesis test to determine whether the value of β_1 is zero. Two tests are commonly used. Both require an estimate of σ^2, the variance of ϵ in the regression model.

Estimate of σ^2

From the regression model and its assumptions we can conclude that σ^2, the variance of ϵ, also represents the variance of the y values about the regression line. Recall that the deviations of the y values about the estimated regression line are called residuals. Thus, SSE, the sum of squared residuals, is a measure of the variability of the actual observations about the estimated regression line. The **mean square error** (MSE) provides the estimate of σ^2; it is SSE divided by its degrees of freedom.

With $\hat{y}_i = b_0 + b_1 x_i$, SSE can be written as

$$\text{SSE} = \Sigma(y_i - \hat{y}_i)^2 = \Sigma(y_i - b_0 - b_1 x_i)^2$$

Every sum of squares has associated with it a number called its degrees of freedom. Statisticians have shown that SSE has $n - 2$ degrees of freedom because two parameters (β_0 and β_1) must be estimated to compute SSE. Thus, the mean square error is computed by dividing SSE by $n - 2$. MSE provides an unbiased estimator of σ^2. Because the value of MSE provides an estimate of σ^2, the notation s^2 is also used.

MEAN SQUARE ERROR (ESTIMATE OF σ^2)

$$s^2 = \text{MSE} = \frac{\text{SSE}}{n - 2} \tag{14.15}$$

In Section 14.3 we showed that for the Armand's Pizza Parlors example, SSE = 1530; hence,

$$s^2 = \text{MSE} = \frac{1530}{8} = 191.25$$

provides an unbiased estimate of σ^2.

To estimate σ we take the square root of s^2. The resulting value, s, is referred to as the **standard error of the estimate**.

STANDARD ERROR OF THE ESTIMATE

$$s = \sqrt{\text{MSE}} = \sqrt{\frac{\text{SSE}}{n - 2}} \tag{14.16}$$

For the Armand's Pizza Parlors example, $s = \sqrt{\text{MSE}} = \sqrt{191.25} = 13.829$. In the following discussion, we use the standard error of the estimate in the tests for a significant relationship between x and y.

t **Test**

The simple linear regression model is $y = \beta_0 + \beta_1 x + \epsilon$. If x and y are linearly related, we must have $\beta_1 \neq 0$. The purpose of the t test is to see whether we can conclude that $\beta_1 \neq 0$. We will use the sample data to test the following hypotheses about the parameter β_1.

$$H_0: \beta_1 = 0$$
$$H_a: \beta_1 \neq 0$$

If H_0 is rejected, we will conclude that $\beta_1 \neq 0$ and that a statistically significant relationship exists between the two variables. However, if H_0 cannot be rejected, we will have insufficient evidence to conclude that a significant relationship exists. The properties of the sampling distribution of b_1, the least squares estimator of β_1, provide the basis for the hypothesis test.

First, let us consider what would happen if we used a different random sample for the same regression study. For example, suppose that Armand's Pizza Parlors used the sales records of a different sample of 10 restaurants. A regression analysis of this new sample might result in an estimated regression equation similar to our previous estimated regression equation $\hat{y} = 60 + 5x$. However, it is doubtful that we would obtain exactly the same equation (with an intercept of exactly 60 and a slope of exactly 5). Indeed, b_0 and b_1, the least squares estimators, are sample statistics with their own sampling distributions. The properties of the sampling distribution of b_1 follow.

SAMPLING DISTRIBUTION OF b_1

Expected Value
$$E(b_1) = \beta_1$$

Standard Deviation
$$\sigma_{b_1} = \frac{\sigma}{\sqrt{\Sigma(x_i - \bar{x})^2}} \qquad (14.17)$$

Distribution Form
Normal

Note that the expected value of b_1 is equal to β_1, so b_1 is an unbiased estimator of β_1.

Because we do not know the value of σ, we develop an estimate of σ_{b_1}, denoted s_{b_1}, by estimating σ with s in equation (14.17). Thus, we obtain the following estimate of σ_{b_1}.

The standard deviation of b_1 is also referred to as the standard error of b_1. Thus, s_{b_1} provides an estimate of the standard error of b_1.

ESTIMATED STANDARD DEVIATION OF b_1

$$s_{b_1} = \frac{s}{\sqrt{\Sigma(x_i - \bar{x})^2}} \qquad (14.18)$$

For Armand's Pizza Parlors, $s = 13.829$. Hence, using $\Sigma(x_i - \bar{x})^2 = 568$ as shown in Table 14.2, we have

$$s_{b_1} = \frac{13.829}{\sqrt{568}} = .5803$$

as the estimated standard deviation of b_1.

The t test for a significant relationship is based on the fact that the test statistic

$$\frac{b_1 - \beta_1}{s_{b_1}}$$

follows a t distribution with $n - 2$ degrees of freedom. If the null hypothesis is true, then $\beta_1 = 0$ and $t = b_1/s_{b_1}$.

Let us conduct this test of significance for Armand's Pizza Parlors at the $\alpha = .01$ level of significance. The test statistic is

$$t = \frac{b_1}{s_{b_1}} = \frac{5}{.5803} = 8.62$$

Appendixes 14.3 and 14.4 show how Minitab and Excel can be used to compute the p-value.

The t distribution table (Table 2 of Appendix D) shows that with $n - 2 = 10 - 2 = 8$ degrees of freedom, $t = 3.355$ provides an area of .005 in the upper tail. Thus, the area in the upper tail of the t distribution corresponding to the test statistic $t = 8.62$ must be less than .005. Because this test is a two-tailed test, we double this value to conclude that the p-value associated with $t = 8.62$ must be less than $2(.005) = .01$. Excel or Minitab show the p-value $= .000$. Because the p-value is less than $\alpha = .01$, we reject H_0 and conclude that β_1 is not equal to zero. This evidence is sufficient to conclude that a significant relationship exists between student population and quarterly sales. A summary of the t test for significance in simple linear regression follows.

---

t TEST FOR SIGNIFICANCE IN SIMPLE LINEAR REGRESSION

$$H_0: \beta_1 = 0$$
$$H_a: \beta_1 \neq 0$$

TEST STATISTIC

$$t = \frac{b_1}{s_{b_1}} \tag{14.19}$$

REJECTION RULE

p-value approach: Reject H_0 if p-value $\leq \alpha$

Critical value approach: Reject H_0 if $t \leq -t_{\alpha/2}$ or if $t \geq t_{\alpha/2}$

where $t_{\alpha/2}$ is based on a t distribution with $n - 2$ degrees of freedom.

Confidence Interval for β_1

The form of a confidence interval for β_1 is as follows:

$$b_1 \pm t_{\alpha/2} s_{b_1}$$

The point estimator is b_1 and the margin of error is $t_{\alpha/2} s_{b_1}$. The confidence coefficient associated with this interval is $1 - \alpha$, and $t_{\alpha/2}$ is the t value providing an area of $\alpha/2$ in the upper tail of a t distribution with $n - 2$ degrees of freedom. For example, suppose that we wanted to develop a 99% confidence interval estimate of β_1 for Armand's Pizza Parlors. From Table 2 of Appendix B we find that the t value corresponding to $\alpha = .01$ and $n - 2 = 10 - 2 = 8$ degrees of freedom is $t_{.005} = 3.355$. Thus, the 99% confidence interval estimate of β_1 is

$$b_1 \pm t_{\alpha/2} s_{b_1} = 5 \pm 3.355(.5803) = 5 \pm 1.95$$

or 3.05 to 6.95.

In using the t test for significance, the hypotheses tested were

$$H_0: \beta_1 = 0$$
$$H_a: \beta_1 \neq 0$$

At the $\alpha = .01$ level of significance, we can use the 99% confidence interval as an alternative for drawing the hypothesis testing conclusion for the Armand's data. Because 0, the hypothesized value of β_1, is not included in the confidence interval (3.05 to 6.95), we can reject

H_0 and conclude that a significant statistical relationship exists between the size of the student population and quarterly sales. In general, a confidence interval can be used to test any two-sided hypothesis about β_1. If the hypothesized value of β_1 is contained in the confidence interval, do not reject H_0. Otherwise, reject H_0.

F **Test**

An *F* test, based on the *F* probability distribution, can also be used to test for significance in regression. With only one independent variable, the *F* test will provide the same conclusion as the *t* test; that is, if the *t* test indicates $\beta_1 \neq 0$ and hence a significant relationship, the *F* test will also indicate a significant relationship. But with more than one independent variable, only the *F* test can be used to test for an overall significant relationship.

The logic behind the use of the *F* test for determining whether the regression relationship is statistically significant is based on the development of two independent estimates of σ^2. We explained how MSE provides an estimate of σ^2. If the null hypothesis $H_0: \beta_1 = 0$ is true, the sum of squares due to regression, SSR, divided by its degrees of freedom provides another independent estimate of σ^2. This estimate is called the *mean square due to regression,* or simply the *mean square regression,* and is denoted MSR. In general,

$$MSR = \frac{SSR}{\text{Regression degrees of freedom}}$$

For the models we consider in this text, the regression degrees of freedom is always equal to the number of independent variables in the model:

$$MSR = \frac{SSR}{\text{Number of independent variables}} \tag{14.20}$$

Because we consider only regression models with one independent variable in this chapter, we have MSR = SSR/1 = SSR. Hence, for Armand's Pizza Parlors, MSR = SSR = 14,200.

If the null hypothesis ($H_0: \beta_1 = 0$) is true, MSR and MSE are two independent estimates of σ^2 and the sampling distribution of MSR/MSE follows an *F* distribution with numerator degrees of freedom equal to one and denominator degrees of freedom equal to $n - 2$. Therefore, when $\beta_1 = 0$, the value of MSR/MSE should be close to one. However, if the null hypothesis is false ($\beta_1 \neq 0$), MSR will overestimate σ^2 and the value of MSR/MSE will be inflated; thus, large values of MSR/MSE lead to the rejection of H_0 and the conclusion that the relationship between *x* and *y* is statistically significant.

Let us conduct the *F* test for the Armand's Pizza Parlors example. The test statistic is

$$F = \frac{MSR}{MSE} = \frac{14,200}{191.25} = 74.25$$

The F test and the t test provide identical results for simple linear regression.

The *F* distribution table (Table 4 of Appendix B) shows that with one degree of freedom in the numerator and $n - 2 = 10 - 2 = 8$ degrees of freedom in the denominator, $F = 11.26$ provides an area of .01 in the upper tail. Thus, the area in the upper tail of the *F* distribution corresponding to the test statistic $F = 74.25$ must be less than .01. Thus, we conclude that the *p*-value must be less than .01. Excel or Minitab show the *p*-value = .000. Because the *p*-value is less than $\alpha = .01$, we reject H_0 and conclude that a significant relationship exists between the size of the student population and quarterly sales. A summary of the *F* test for significance in simple linear regression follows.

If H_0 is false, MSE still provides an unbiased estimate of σ^2 and MSR overestimates σ^2. If H_0 is true, both MSE and MSR provide unbiased estimates of σ^2; in this case the value of MSR/MSE should be close to 1.

F TEST FOR SIGNIFICANCE IN SIMPLE LINEAR REGRESSION

$$H_0: \beta_1 = 0$$
$$H_a: \beta_1 \neq 0$$

TEST STATISTIC

$$F = \frac{MSR}{MSE} \tag{14.21}$$

REJECTION RULE

p-value approach: Reject H_0 if p-value $\leq \alpha$

Critical value approach: Reject H_0 if $F \geq F_\alpha$

where F_α is based on an F distribution with 1 degree of freedom in the numerator and $n - 2$ degrees of freedom in the denominator.

In Chapter 13 we covered analysis of variance (ANOVA) and showed how an **ANOVA table** could be used to provide a convenient summary of the computational aspects of analysis of variance. A similar ANOVA table can be used to summarize the results of the F test for significance in regression. Table 14.5 is the general form of the ANOVA table for simple linear regression. Table 14.6 is the ANOVA table with the F test computations performed for Armand's Pizza Parlors. Regression, Error, and Total are the labels for the three sources of variation, with SSR, SSE, and SST appearing as the corresponding sum of squares in

TABLE 14.5 GENERAL FORM OF THE ANOVA TABLE FOR SIMPLE LINEAR REGRESSION

In every analysis of variance table the total sum of squares is the sum of the regression sum of squares and the error sum of squares; in addition, the total degrees of freedom is the sum of the regression degrees of freedom and the error degrees of freedom.

Source of Variation	Sum of Squares	Degrees of Freedom	Mean Square	F	p-value
Regression	SSR	1	$MSR = \frac{SSR}{1}$	$F = \frac{MSR}{MSE}$	
Error	SSE	$n-2$	$MSE = \frac{SSE}{n-2}$		
Total	SST	$n-1$			

TABLE 14.6 ANOVA TABLE FOR THE ARMAND'S PIZZA PARLORS PROBLEM

Source of Variation	Sum of Squares	Degrees of Freedom	Mean Square	F	p-value
Regression	14,200	1	$\frac{14,200}{1} = 14,200$	$\frac{14,200}{191.25} = 74.25$	.000
Error	1,530	8	$\frac{1530}{8} = 191.25$		
Total	15,730	9			

column 2. The degrees of freedom, 1 for SSR, $n - 2$ for SSE, and $n - 1$ for SST, are shown in column 3. Column 4 contains the values of MSR and MSE, column 5 contains the value of $F = $ MSR/MSE, and column 6 contains the p-value corresponding to the F value in column 5. Almost all computer printouts of regression analysis include an ANOVA table summary of the F test for significance.

Some Cautions About the Interpretation of Significance Tests

Regression analysis, which can be used to identify how variables are associated with one another, cannot be used as evidence of a cause-and-effect relationship.

Rejecting the null hypothesis $H_0: \beta_1 = 0$ and concluding that the relationship between x and y is significant does not enable us to conclude that a cause-and-effect relationship is present between x and y. Concluding a cause-and-effect relationship is warranted only if the analyst can provide some type of theoretical justification that the relationship is in fact causal. In the Armand's Pizza Parlors example, we can conclude that there is a significant relationship between the size of the student population x and quarterly sales y; moreover, the estimated regression equation $\hat{y} = 60 + 5x$ provides the least squares estimate of the relationship. We cannot, however, conclude that changes in student population x *cause* changes in quarterly sales y just because we identified a statistically significant relationship. The appropriateness of such a cause-and-effect conclusion is left to supporting theoretical justification and to good judgment on the part of the analyst. Armand's managers felt that increases in the student population were a likely cause of increased quarterly sales. Thus, the result of the significance test enabled them to conclude that a cause-and-effect relationship was present.

In addition, just because we are able to reject $H_0: \beta_1 = 0$ and demonstrate statistical significance does not enable us to conclude that the relationship between x and y is linear. We can state only that x and y are related and that a linear relationship explains a significant portion of the variability in y over the range of values for x observed in the sample. Figure 14.7 illustrates this situation. The test for significance calls for the rejection of the null hypothesis $H_0: \beta_1 = 0$ and leads to the conclusion that x and y are significantly related, but the figure shows that the actual relationship between x and y is not linear. Although the

FIGURE 14.7   EXAMPLE OF A LINEAR APPROXIMATION OF A NONLINEAR RELATIONSHIP

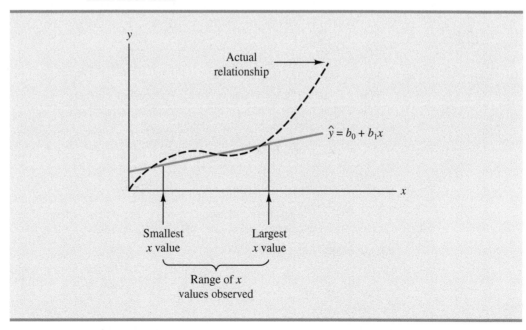

linear approximation provided by $\hat{y} = b_0 + b_1x$ is good over the range of x values observed in the sample, it becomes poor for x values outside that range.

Given a significant relationship, we should feel confident in using the estimated regression equation for predictions corresponding to x values within the range of the x values observed in the sample. For Armand's Pizza Parlors, this range corresponds to values of x between 2 and 26. Unless other reasons indicate that the model is valid beyond this range, predictions outside the range of the independent variable should be made with caution. For Armand's Pizza Parlors, because the regression relationship has been found significant at the .01 level, we should feel confident using it to predict sales for restaurants where the associated student population is between 2000 and 26,000.

NOTES AND COMMENTS

1. The assumptions made about the error term (Section 14.4) are what allow the tests of statistical significance in this section. The properties of the sampling distribution of b_1 and the subsequent t and F tests follow directly from these assumptions.

2. Do not confuse statistical significance with practical significance. With very large sample sizes, statistically significant results can be obtained for small values of b_1; in such cases, one must exercise care in concluding that the relationship has practical significance.

3. A test of significance for a linear relationship between x and y can also be performed by using the sample correlation coefficient r_{xy}. With ρ_{xy} denoting the population correlation coefficient, the hypotheses are as follows.

$$H_0: \rho_{xy} = 0$$
$$H_a: \rho_{xy} \neq 0$$

A significant relationship can be concluded if H_0 is rejected. The details of this test are provided in Appendix 14.2. However, the t and F tests presented previously in this section give the same result as the test for significance using the correlation coefficient. Conducting a test for significance using the correlation coefficient therefore is not necessary if a t or F test has already been conducted.

Exercises

Methods

23. The data from exercise 1 follow.

x_i	1	2	3	4	5
y_i	3	7	5	11	14

a. Compute the mean square error using equation (14.15).
b. Compute the standard error of the estimate using equation (14.16).
c. Compute the estimated standard deviation of b_1 using equation (14.18).
d. Use the t test to test the following hypotheses ($\alpha = .05$):

$$H_0: \beta_1 = 0$$
$$H_a: \beta_1 \neq 0$$

e. Use the F test to test the hypotheses in part (d) at a .05 level of significance. Present the results in the analysis of variance table format.

24. The data from exercise 2 follow.

x_i	3	12	6	20	14
y_i	55	40	55	10	15

a. Compute the mean square error using equation (14.15).
b. Compute the standard error of the estimate using equation (14.16).
c. Compute the estimated standard deviation of b_1 using equation (14.18).
d. Use the t test to test the following hypotheses ($\alpha = .05$):

$$H_0: \beta_1 = 0$$
$$H_a: \beta_1 \neq 0$$

e. Use the F test to test the hypotheses in part (d) at a .05 level of significance. Present the results in the analysis of variance table format.

25. The data from exercise 3 follow.

x_i	2	6	9	13	20
y_i	7	18	9	26	23

a. What is the value of the standard error of the estimate?
b. Test for a significant relationship by using the t test. Use $\alpha = .05$.
c. Use the F test to test for a significant relationship. Use $\alpha = .05$. What is your conclusion?

Applications

26. In exercise 18 the data on price ($) and the overall score for six stereo headphones tested by *Consumer Reports* were as follows (*Consumer Reports* website, March 5, 2012).

Brand	Price ($)	Score
Bose	180	76
Skullcandy	150	71
Koss	95	61
Phillips/O'Neill	70	56
Denon	70	40
JVC	35	26

a. Does the t test indicate a significant relationship between price and the overall score? What is your conclusion? Use $\alpha = .05$.
b. Test for a significant relationship using the F test. What is your conclusion? Use $\alpha = .05$.
c. Show the ANOVA table for these data.

27. The number of megapixels in a digital camera is one of the most important factors in determining picture quality. But, do digital cameras with more megapixels cost more? The following data show the number of megapixels and the price ($) for 10 digital cameras (*Consumer Reports*, March 2009).

DigitalCameras

Brand and Model	Megapixels	Price ($)
Canon PowerShot SD1100 IS	8	180
Casio Exilim Card EX-510	10	200
Sony Cyber-shot DSC-T70	7	230
Pentax Optio M50	8	120
Canon PowerShot G10	15	470
Canon PowerShot A590 IS	8	140
Canon PowerShot E1	10	180
Fujifilm FinePix F00FD	12	310
Sony Cyber-shot DSC-W170	10	250
Canon PowerShot A470	7	110

a. Use these data to develop an estimated regression equation that can be used to predict the price of a digital camera given the number of megapixels.
b. At the .05 level of significance, are the number of megapixels and the price related? Explain.
c. Would you feel comfortable using the estimated regression equation developed in part (a) to predict the price of a digital camera given the number of megapixels? Explain.
d. The Canon Power Shot S95 digital camera has 10 megapixels. Predict the price of this camera using the estimated regression equation developed in part (a).

WEB file

BrokerRatings

28. In exercise 8 ratings data on x = the quality of the speed of execution and y = overall satisfaction with electronic trades provided the estimated regression equation $\hat{y} = .2046 + .9077x$. At the .05 level of significance, test whether speed of execution and overall satisfaction are related. Show the ANOVA table. What is your conclusion?

29. Refer to exercise 21, where data on production volume and cost were used to develop an estimated regression equation relating production volume and cost for a particular manufacturing operation. Use $\alpha = .05$ to test whether the production volume is significantly related to the total cost. Show the ANOVA table. What is your conclusion?

30. Refer to excercise 5 where the following data were used to investigate whether higher prices are generally associated with higher ratings for elliptical trainers (*Consumer Reports,* February 2008).

WEB file

Ellipticals

Brand and Model	Price ($)	Rating
Precor 5.31	3700	87
Keys Fitness CG2	2500	84
Octane Fitness Q37e	2800	82
LifeFitness X1 Basic	1900	74
NordicTrack AudioStrider 990	1000	73
Schwinn 430	800	69
Vision Fitness X6100	1700	68
ProForm XP 520 Razor	600	55

With x = price ($) and y = rating, the estimated regression equation is $\hat{y} = 58.158 + .008449x$. For these data, SSE = 173.88 and SST = 756. Does the evidence indicate a significant relationship between price and rating?

WEB file

RacingBicycles

31. In exercise 20, data on x = weight (pounds) and y = price ($) for 10 road-racing bikes provided the estimated regression equation $\hat{y} = 28,574 - 1439x$. (*Bicycling* website, March 8, 2012). For these data SSE = 7,102,922.54 and SST = 52,120,800. Use the F test to determine whether the weight for a bike and the price are related at the .05 level of significance.

14.6 Using the Estimated Regression Equation for Estimation and Prediction

When using the simple linear regression model, we are making an assumption about the relationship between x and y. We then use the least squares method to obtain the estimated simple linear regression equation. If a significant relationship exists between x and y and the coefficient of determination shows that the fit is good, the estimated regression equation should be useful for estimation and prediction.

For the Armand's Pizza Parlors example, the estimated regression equation is $\hat{y} = 60 + 5x$. At the end of Section 14.1 we stated that $\hat{y}$ can be used as a *point estimator* of $E(y)$, the mean or expected value of y for a given value of x, and as a predictor of an individual value of y. For example, suppose Armand's managers want to estimate the mean quarterly sales for *all* restaurants located near college campuses with 10,000 students. Using the estimated regression equation $\hat{y} = 60 + 5x$, we see that for $x = 10$ (10,000 students), $\hat{y} = 60 + 5(10) = 110$. Thus, a *point estimate* of the mean quarterly sales for all restaurant locations near campuses with 10,000 students is $110,000. In this case we are using $\hat{y}$ as the point estimator of the mean value of y when $x = 10$.

We can also use the estimated regression equation to *predict* an individual value of y for a given value of x. For example, to predict quarterly sales for a new restaurant Armand's is considering building near Talbot College, a campus with 10,000 students, we would compute $\hat{y} = 60 + 5(10) = 110$. Hence, we would predict quarterly sales of $110,000 for such a new restaurant. In this case, we are using $\hat{y}$ as the *predictor* of y for a new observation when $x = 10$.

When we are using the estimated regression equation to estimate the mean value of y or to predict an individual value of y, it is clear that the estimate or prediction depends on the given value of x. For this reason, as we discuss in more depth the issues concerning estimation and prediction, the following notation will help clarify matters.

$$x^* = \text{the given value of the independent variable } x$$

$y^* = $ the random variable denoting the possible values of the dependent variable y when $x = x^*$

$E(y^*) = $ the mean or expected value of the dependent variable y when $x = x^*$

$\hat{y}^* = b_0 + b_1 x^* = $ the point estimator of $E(y^*)$ and the predictor of an individual value of y^* when $x = x^*$

To illustrate the use of this notation, suppose we want to estimate the mean value of quarterly sales for *all* Armand's restaurants located near a campus with 10,000 students. For this case, $x^* = 10$ and $E(y^*)$ denotes the unknown mean value of quarterly sales for all restaurants where $x^* = 10$. Thus, the point estimate of $E(y^*)$ is provided by $\hat{y}^* = 60 + 5(10) = 110$, or $110,000. But, using this notation, $\hat{y}^* = 110$ is also the predictor of quarterly sales for the new restaurant located near Talbot College, a school with 10,000 students.

Interval Estimation

Confidence intervals and prediction intervals show the precision of the regression results. Narrower intervals provide a higher degree of precision.

Point estimators and predictors do not provide any information about the precision associated with the estimate and/or prediction. For that we must develop confidence intervals and prediction intervals. A **confidence interval** is an interval estimate of the *mean value of* y for a given value of x. A **prediction interval** is used whenever we want to *predict an individual value of* y for a new observation corresponding to a given value of x. Although the predictor of y for a given value of x is the same as the point estimator of the mean value of y for a given value of x, the interval estimates we obtain for the two cases are different. As we will show, the margin of error is larger for a prediction interval. We begin by showing how to develop an interval estimate of the mean value of y.

Confidence Interval for the Mean Value of y

In general, we cannot expect $\hat{y}^*$ to equal $E(y^*)$ exactly. If we want to make an inference about how close $\hat{y}^*$ is to the true mean value $E(y^*)$, we will have to estimate the variance of $\hat{y}^*$. The formula for estimating the variance of $\hat{y}^*$, denoted by $s_{\hat{y}^*}^2$, is

$$s_{\hat{y}^*}^2 = s^2\left[\frac{1}{n} + \frac{(x^* - \bar{x})^2}{\Sigma(x_i - \bar{x})^2}\right] \tag{14.22}$$

The estimate of the standard deviation of $\hat{y}^*$ is given by the square root of equation (14.22).

$$s_{\hat{y}^*} = s\sqrt{\frac{1}{n} + \frac{(x^* - \bar{x})^2}{\Sigma(x_i - \bar{x})^2}} \tag{14.23}$$

The computational results for Armand's Pizza Parlors in Section 14.5 provided $s = 13.829$. With $x^* = 10$, $\bar{x} = 14$, and $\Sigma(x_i - \bar{x})^2 = 568$, we can use equation (14.23) to obtain

$$s_{\hat{y}^*} = 13.829\sqrt{\frac{1}{10} + \frac{(10 - 14)^2}{568}}$$

$$= 13.829\sqrt{.1282} = 4.95$$

The general expression for a confidence interval follows.

CONFIDENCE INTERVAL FOR $E(y^*)$

The margin of error associated with this confidence interval is $t_{\alpha/2}s_{\hat{y}^*}$.

$$\hat{y}^* \pm t_{\alpha/2}s_{\hat{y}^*} \tag{14.24}$$

where the confidence coefficient is $1 - \alpha$ and $t_{\alpha/2}$ is based on the t distribution with $n - 2$ degrees of freedom.

Using expression (14.24) to develop a 95% confidence interval of the mean quarterly sales for all Armand's restaurants located near campuses with 10,000 students, we need the value of t for $\alpha/2 = .025$ and $n - 2 = 10 - 2 = 8$ degrees of freedom. Using Table 2 of Appendix B, we have $t_{.025} = 2.306$. Thus, with $\hat{y}^* = 110$ and a margin of error of $t_{\alpha/2}s_{\hat{y}^*} = 2.306(4.95) = 11.415$, the 95% confidence interval estimate is

$$110 \pm 11.415$$

In dollars, the 95% confidence interval for the mean quarterly sales of all restaurants near campuses with 10,000 students is $110,000 \pm $11,415. Therefore, the 95% confidence interval for the mean quarterly sales when the student population is 10,000 is $98,585 to $121,415.

Note that the estimated standard deviation of $\hat{y}^*$ given by equation (14.23) is smallest when $x^* - \bar{x} = 0$. In this case the estimated standard deviation of $\hat{y}^*$ becomes

$$s_{\hat{y}^*} = s\sqrt{\frac{1}{n} + \frac{(\bar{x} - \bar{x})^2}{\Sigma(x_i - \bar{x})^2}} = s\sqrt{\frac{1}{n}}$$

This result implies that we can make the best or most precise estimate of the mean value of y whenever $x^* = \bar{x}$. In fact, the further x^* is from $\bar{x}$, the larger $x^* - \bar{x}$ becomes. As a result, the confidence interval for the mean value of y will become wider as x^* deviates more from $\bar{x}$. This pattern is shown graphically in Figure 14.8.

FIGURE 14.8   CONFIDENCE INTERVALS FOR THE MEAN SALES y AT GIVEN VALUES OF STUDENT POPULATION x

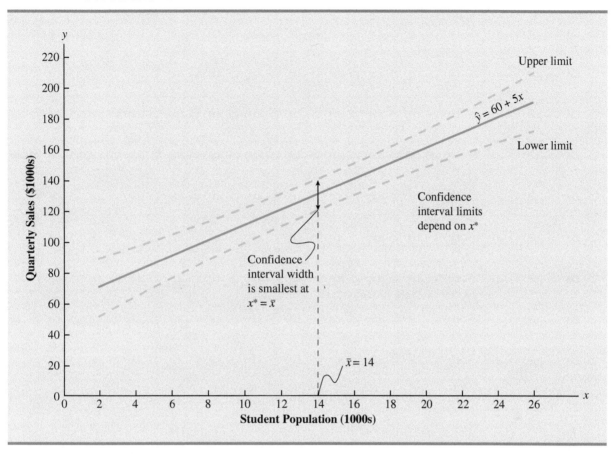

Prediction Interval for an Individual Value of y

Instead of estimating the mean value of quarterly sales for all Armand's restaurants located near campuses with 10,000 students, suppose we want to predict quarterly sales for a new restaurant Armand's is considering building near Talbot College, a campus with 10,000 students. As noted previously, the predictor of y^*, the value of y corresponding to the given x^*, is $\hat{y}^* = b_0 + b_1 x^*$. For the new restaurant located near Talbot College, $x^* = 10$ and the prediction of quarterly sales is $\hat{y}^* = 60 + 5(10) = 110$, or \$110,000. Note that the prediction of quarterly sales for the new Armand's restaurant near Talbot College is the same as the point estimate of the mean sales for all Armand's restaurants located near campuses with 10,000 students.

To develop a prediction interval, let us first determine the variance associated with using $\hat{y}^*$ as a predictor of y when $x = x^*$. This variance is made up of the sum of the following two components.

1. The variance of the y^* values about the mean $E(y^*)$, an estimate of which is given by s^2
2. The variance associated with using $\hat{y}^*$ to estimate $E(y^*)$, an estimate of which is given by $s_{\hat{y}^*}^2$

The formula for estimating the variance corresponding to the prediction of the value of y when $x = x^*$, denoted s_{pred}^2, is

$$s_{pred}^2 = s^2 + s_{\hat{y}^*}^2$$

$$= s^2 + s^2\left[\frac{1}{n} + \frac{(x^* - \bar{x})^2}{\Sigma(x_i - \bar{x})^2}\right]$$

$$= s^2\left[1 + \frac{1}{n} + \frac{(x^* - \bar{x})^2}{\Sigma(x_i - \bar{x})^2}\right] \tag{14.25}$$

Hence, an estimate of the standard deviation corresponding to the prediction of the value of y^* is

$$s_{pred} = s\sqrt{1 + \frac{1}{n} + \frac{(x^* - \bar{x})^2}{\Sigma(x_i - \bar{x})^2}} \tag{14.26}$$

For Armand's Pizza Parlors, the estimated standard deviation corresponding to the prediction of quarterly sales for a new restaurant located near Talbot College, a campus with 10,000 students, is computed as follows.

$$s_{pred} = 13.829\sqrt{1 + \frac{1}{10} + \frac{(10 - 14)^2}{568}}$$

$$= 13.829\sqrt{1.282}$$

$$= 14.69$$

The general expression for a prediction interval follows.

PREDICTION INTERVAL FOR y^*

$$\hat{y}^* \pm t_{\alpha/2}s_{pred} \tag{14.27}$$

where the confidence coefficient is $1 - \alpha$ and $t_{\alpha/2}$ is based on a t distribution with $n - 2$ degrees of freedom.

The margin of error associated with this prediction interval is $t_{\alpha/2}s_{pred}$.

The 95% prediction interval for quarterly sales for the new Armand's restaurant located near Talbot College can be found using $t_{\alpha/2} = t_{.025} = 2.306$ and $s_{pred} = 14.69$. Thus, with $\hat{y}^* = 110$ and a margin of error of $t_{.025}s_{pred} = 2.306(14.69) = 33.875$, the 95% prediction interval is

$$110 \pm 33.875$$

In dollars, this prediction interval is \$110,000 $\pm$ \$33,875 or \$76,125 to \$143,875. Note that the prediction interval for the new restaurant located near Talbot College, a campus with 10,000 students, is wider than the confidence interval for the mean quarterly sales of all restaurants located near campuses with 10,000 students. The difference reflects the fact that we are able to estimate the mean value of y more precisely than we can predict an individual value of y.

FIGURE 14.9   CONFIDENCE AND PREDICTION INTERVALS FOR SALES y AT GIVEN VALUES OF STUDENT POPULATION x

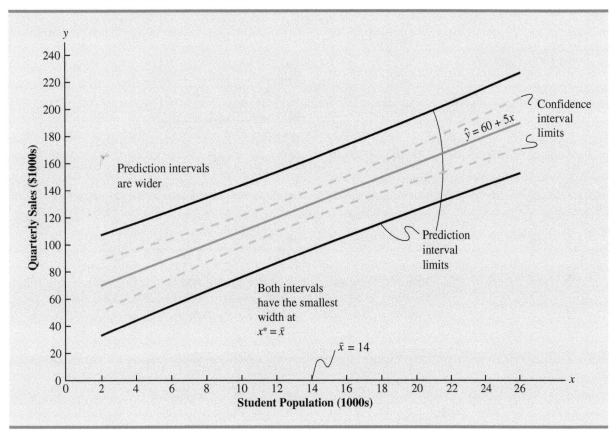

In general, the lines for the confidence interval limits and the prediction interval limits both have curvature.

Confidence intervals and prediction intervals are both more precise when the value of the independent variable x^* is closer to $\bar{x}$. The general shapes of confidence intervals and the wider prediction intervals are shown together in Figure 14.9.

NOTES AND COMMENTS

A prediction interval is used to predict the value of the dependent variable y for a *new observation*. As an illustration, we showed how to develop a prediction interval of quarterly sales for a new restaurant that Armand's is considering building near Talbot College, a campus with 10,000 students. The fact that the value of $x = 10$ is not one of the values of student population for the Armand's sample data in Table 14.1 is not meant to imply that prediction intervals cannot be developed for values of x in the sample data. But, for the ten restaurants that make up the data in Table 14.1, developing a prediction interval for quarterly sales for *one of these restaurants* does not make any sense because we already know the value of quarterly sales for each of these restaurants. In other words, a prediction interval only has meaning for something new, in this case a new observation corresponding to a particular value of x that may or may not equal one of the values of x in the sample.

Exercises

Methods

SELF test

32. The data from exercise 1 follow.

x_i	1	2	3	4	5
y_i	3	7	5	11	14

a. Use equation (14.23) to estimate the standard deviation of $\hat{y}^*$ when $x = 4$.
b. Use expression (14.24) to develop a 95% confidence interval for the expected value of y when $x = 4$.
c. Use equation (14.26) to estimate the standard deviation of an individual value of y when $x = 4$.
d. Use expression (14.27) to develop a 95% prediction interval for y when $x = 4$.

33. The data from exercise 2 follow.

x_i	3	12	6	20	14
y_i	55	40	55	10	15

a. Estimate the standard deviation of $\hat{y}^*$ when $x = 8$.
b. Develop a 95% confidence interval for the expected value of y when $x = 8$.
c. Estimate the standard deviation of an individual value of y when $x = 8$.
d. Develop a 95% prediction interval for y when $x = 8$.

34. The data from exercise 3 follow.

x_i	2	6	9	13	20
y_i	7	18	9	26	23

Develop the 95% confidence and prediction intervals when $x = 12$. Explain why these two intervals are different.

Applications

SELF test

35. The following data are the monthly salaries y and the grade point averages x for students who obtained a bachelor's degree in business administration.

GPA	Monthly Salary ($)
2.6	3600
3.4	3900
3.6	4300
3.2	3800
3.5	4200
2.9	3900

The estimated regression equation for these data is $\hat{y} = 2090.5 + 581.1x$ and MSE = 21,284.
a. Develop a point estimate of the starting salary for a student with a GPA of 3.0.
b. Develop a 95% confidence interval for the mean starting salary for all students with a 3.0 GPA.
c. Develop a 95% prediction interval for Ryan Dailey, a student with a GPA of 3.0.
d. Discuss the differences in your answers to parts (b) and (c).

Sales

36. In exercise 7, the data on y = annual sales ($1000s) for new customer accounts and x = number of years of experience for a sample of 10 salespersons provided the estimated regression equation $\hat{y} = 80 + 4x$. For these data $\bar{x} = 7$, $\sum(x_i - \bar{x})^2 = 142$, and $s = 4.6098$.
    a. Develop a 95% confidence interval for the mean annual sales for all salespersons with nine years of experience.
    b. The company is considering hiring Tom Smart, a salesperson with nine years of experience. Develop a 95% prediction interval of annual sales for Tom Smart.
    c. Discuss the differences in your answers to parts (a) and (b).

37. In exercise 13, data were given on the adjusted gross income x and the amount of itemized deductions taken by taxpayers. Data were reported in thousands of dollars. With the estimated regression equation $\hat{y} = 4.68 + .16x$, the point estimate of a reasonable level of total itemized deductions for a taxpayer with an adjusted gross income of $52,500 is $13,080.
    a. Develop a 95% confidence interval for the mean amount of total itemized deductions for all taxpayers with an adjusted gross income of $52,500.
    b. Develop a 95% prediction interval estimate for the amount of total itemized deductions for a particular taxpayer with an adjusted gross income of $52,500.
    c. If the particular taxpayer referred to in part (b) claimed total itemized deductions of $20,400, would the IRS agent's request for an audit appear to be justified?
    d. Use your answer to part (b) to give the IRS agent a guideline as to the amount of total itemized deductions a taxpayer with an adjusted gross income of $52,500 should claim before an audit is recommended.

38. Refer to Exercise 21, where data on the production volume x and total cost y for a particular manufacturing operation were used to develop the estimated regression equation $\hat{y} = 1246.67 + 7.6x$.
    a. The company's production schedule shows that 500 units must be produced next month. What is the point estimate of the total cost for next month?
    b. Develop a 99% prediction interval for the total cost for next month.
    c. If an accounting cost report at the end of next month shows that the actual production cost during the month was $6000, should managers be concerned about incurring such a high total cost for the month? Discuss.

39. Almost all U.S. light-rail systems use electric cars that run on tracks built at street level. The Federal Transit Administration claims light-rail is one of the safest modes of travel, with an accident rate of .99 accidents per million passenger miles as compared to 2.29 for buses. The following data show the miles of track and the weekday ridership in thousands of passengers for six light-rail systems (*USA Today*, January 7, 2003).

City	Miles of Track	Ridership (1000s)
Cleveland	15	15
Denver	17	35
Portland	38	81
Sacramento	21	31
San Diego	47	75
San Jose	31	30
St. Louis	34	42

    a. Use these data to develop an estimated regression equation that could be used to predict the ridership given the miles of track.
    b. Did the estimated regression equation provide a good fit? Explain.
    c. Develop a 95% confidence interval for the mean weekday ridership for all light-rail systems with 30 miles of track.

d.   Suppose that Charlotte is considering construction of a light-rail system with 30 miles of track. Develop a 95% prediction interval for the weekday ridership for the Charlotte system. Do you think that the prediction interval you developed would be of value to Charlotte planners in anticipating the number of weekday riders for their new light-rail system? Explain.

 # Computer Solution

Performing the regression analysis computations without the help of a computer can be quite time consuming. In this section we discuss how the computational burden can be minimized by using a computer software package such as Minitab.

We entered Armand's student population and sales data into a Minitab worksheet. The independent variable was named Pop and the dependent variable was named Sales to assist with interpretation of the computer output. Using Minitab, we obtained the printout for Armand's Pizza Parlors shown in Figure 14.10.[2] The interpretation of this printout follows.

1.   Minitab prints the estimated regression equation as Sales = 60.0 + 5.00 Pop.
2.   A table is printed that shows the values of the coefficients b_0 and b_1, the standard deviation of each coefficient, the t value obtained by dividing each coefficient value by its standard deviation, and the p-value associated with the t test. Because the p-value is zero (to three decimal places), the sample results indicate that the null hypothesis (H_0: $\beta_1 = 0$) should be rejected. Alternatively, we could compare 8.62 (located in the t-ratio column) to the appropriate critical value. This procedure for the t test was described in Section 14.5.

FIGURE 14.10   MINITAB OUTPUT FOR THE ARMAND'S PIZZA PARLORS PROBLEM

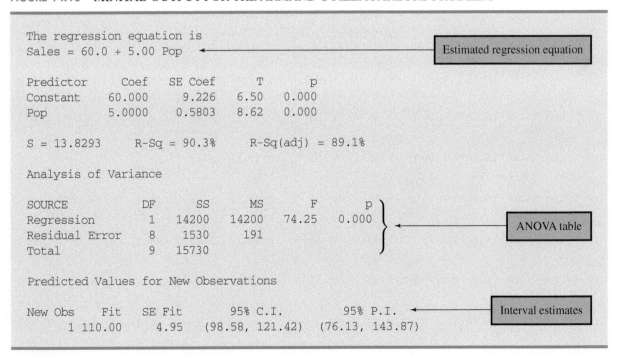

---

[2]The Minitab steps necessary to generate the output are given in Appendix 14.3.

3. Minitab prints the standard error of the estimate, $s = 13.8293$, as well as information about the goodness of fit. Note that "R-sq = 90.3%" is the coefficient of determination expressed as a percentage. The value "R-Sq(adj) = 89.1%" is discussed in Chapter 15.
4. The ANOVA table is printed below the heading Analysis of Variance. Minitab uses the label Residual Error for the error source of variation. Note that DF is an abbreviation for degrees of freedom and that MSR is given as 14,200 and MSE as 191. The ratio of these two values provides the F value of 74.25 and the corresponding p-value of 0.000. Because the p-value is zero (to three decimal places), the relationship between Sales and Pop is judged statistically significant.
5. The 95% confidence interval estimate of the expected sales and the 95% prediction interval estimate of sales for an individual restaurant located near a campus with 10,000 students are printed below the ANOVA table. The confidence interval is (98.58, 121.42) and the prediction interval is (76.13, 143.87) as we showed in Section 14.6.

Exercises

Applications

40. The commercial division of a real estate firm is conducting a regression analysis of the relationship between x, annual gross rents (in thousands of dollars), and y, selling price (in thousands of dollars) for apartment buildings. Data were collected on several properties recently sold and the following computer output was obtained.

```
The regression equation is
Y = 20.0 + 7.21 X

Predictor        Coef      SE Coef        T
Constant       20.000       3.2213     6.21
X               7.210       1.3626     5.29

Analysis of Variance

SOURCE               DF           SS
Regression            1      41587.3
Residual Error        7
Total                 8      51984.1
```

a. How many apartment buildings were in the sample?
b. Write the estimated regression equation.
c. What is the value of s_{b_1}?
d. Use the F statistic to test the significance of the relationship at a .05 level of significance.
e. Predict the selling price of an apartment building with gross annual rents of $50,000.

41. Following is a portion of the computer output for a regression analysis relating y = maintenance expense (dollars per month) to x = usage (hours per week) of a particular brand of computer terminal.

```
The regression equation is
Y = 6.1092 + .8951 X

Predictor        Coef      SE Coef
Constant       6.1092       0.9361
X              0.8951       0.1490


Analysis of Variance

SOURCE               DF          SS          MS
Regression            1     1575.76     1575.76
Residual Error        8      349.14       43.64
Total                 9     1924.90
```

a. Write the estimated regression equation.
b. Use a *t* test to determine whether monthly maintenance expense is related to usage at the .05 level of significance.
c. Use the estimated regression equation to predict monthly maintenance expense for any terminal that is used 25 hours per week.

42. A regression model relating x, number of salespersons at a branch office, to y, annual sales at the office (in thousands of dollars) provided the following computer output from a regression analysis of the data.

```
The regression equation is
Y = 80.0 + 50.00 X

Predictor        Coef      SE Coef          T
Constant         80.0       11.333       7.06
X                50.0        5.482       9.12


Analysis of Variance

SOURCE               DF          SS          MS
Regression            1      6828.6      6828.6
Residual Error       28      2298.8        82.1
Total                29      9127.4
```

a. Write the estimated regression equation.
b. How many branch offices were involved in the study?
c. Compute the *F* statistic and test the significance of the relationship at a .05 level of significance.
d. Predict the annual sales at the Memphis branch office. This branch employs 12 salespersons.

43. Out-of-state tuition and fees at the top graduate schools of business can be very expensive, but the starting salary and bonus paid to graduates from many of these schools can be substantial. The following data show the out-of-state tuition and fees (rounded to the nearest $1000) and the average starting salary and bonus paid to recent graduates (rounded to the nearest $1000) for a sample of 20 graduate schools of business (*U.S. News & World Report 2009 Edition America's Best Graduate Schools*).

School	Tuition & Fees ($1000s)	Salary & Bonus ($1000s)
Arizona State University	28	98
Babson College	35	94
Cornell University	44	119
Georgetown University	40	109
Georgia Institute of Technology	30	88
Indiana University—Bloomington	35	105
Michigan State University	26	99
Northwestern University	44	123
Ohio State University	35	97
Purdue University—West Lafayette	33	96
Rice University	36	102
Stanford University	46	135
University of California—Davis	35	89
University of Florida	23	71
University of Iowa	25	78
University of Minnesota—Twin Cities	37	100
University of Notre Dame	36	95
University of Rochester	38	99
University of Washington	30	94
University of Wisconsin—Madison	27	93

BusinessSchools

a.   Develop a scatter diagram with salary and bonus as the dependent variable.
b.   Does there appear to be any relationship between these variables? Explain.
c.   Develop an estimated regression equation that can be used to predict the starting salary and bonus paid to graduates given the cost of out-of-state tuition and fees at the school.
d.   Test for a significant relationship at the .05 level of significance. What is your conclusion?
e.   Did the estimated regression equation provide a good fit? Explain.
f.   Suppose that we randomly select a recent graduate of the University of Virginia graduate school of business. The school has an out-of-state tuition and fees of $43,000. Predict the starting salary and bonus for this graduate.

44. Automobile racing, high-performance driving schools, and driver education programs run by automobile clubs continue to grow in popularity. All these activities require the participant to wear a helmet that is certified by the Snell Memorial Foundation, a not-for-profit organization dedicated to research, education, testing, and development of helmet safety standards. Snell "SA" (Sports Application) rated professional helmets are designed for auto racing and provide extreme impact resistance and high fire protection. One of the key factors in selecting a helmet is weight, since lower weight helmets tend to place less stress on the neck. The following data show the weight and price for 18 SA helmets (SoloRacer website, April 20, 2008).

RaceHelmets

Helmet	Weight (oz)	Price ($)
Pyrotect Pro Airflow	64	248
Pyrotect Pro Airflow Graphics	64	278
RCi Full Face	64	200
RaceQuip RidgeLine	64	200
HJC AR-10	58	300
HJC Si-12	47	700

(*continued*)

Helmet	Weight (oz)	Price ($)
HJC HX-10	49	900
Impact Racing Super Sport	59	340
Zamp FSA-1	66	199
Zamp RZ-2	58	299
Zamp RZ-2 Ferrari	58	299
Zamp RZ-3 Sport	52	479
Zamp RZ-3 Sport Painted	52	479
Bell M2	63	369
Bell M4	62	369
Bell M4 Pro	54	559
G Force Pro Force 1	63	250
G Force Pro Force 1 Grafx	63	280

a. Develop a scatter diagram with weight as the independent variable.
b. Does there appear to be any relationship between these two variables?
c. Develop the estimated regression equation that could be used to predict the price given the weight.
d. Test for the significance of the relationship at the .05 level of significance.
e. Did the estimated regression equation provide a good fit? Explain.

14.8 Residual Analysis: Validating Model Assumptions

Residual analysis is the primary tool for determining whether the assumed regression model is appropriate.

As we noted previously, the *residual* for observation i is the difference between the observed value of the dependent variable (y_i) and the predicted value of the dependent variable ($\hat{y}_i$).

RESIDUAL FOR OBSERVATION i

$$y_i - \hat{y}_i \qquad\qquad (14.28)$$

where

y_i is the observed value of the dependent variable

$\hat{y}_i$ is the predicted value of the dependent variable

In other words, the ith residual is the error resulting from using the estimated regression equation to predict the value of the dependent variable. The residuals for the Armand's Pizza Parlors example are computed in Table 14.7. The observed values of the dependent variable are in the second column and the predicted values of the dependent variable, obtained using the estimated regression equation $\hat{y} = 60 + 5x$, are in the third column. An analysis of the corresponding residuals in the fourth column will help determine whether the assumptions made about the regression model are appropriate.

Let us now review the regression assumptions for the Armand's Pizza Parlors example. A simple linear regression model was assumed.

$$y = \beta_0 + \beta_1 x + \epsilon \qquad\qquad (14.29)$$

TABLE 14.7   RESIDUALS FOR ARMAND'S PIZZA PARLORS

Student Population x_i	Sales y_i	Predicted Sales $\hat{y}_i = 60 + 5x_i$	Residuals $y_i - \hat{y}_i$
2	58	70	−12
6	105	90	15
8	88	100	−12
8	118	100	18
12	117	120	−3
16	137	140	−3
20	157	160	−3
20	169	160	9
22	149	170	−21
26	202	190	12

This model indicates that we assumed quarterly sales (y) to be a linear function of the size of the student population (x) plus an error term ϵ. In Section 14.4 we made the following assumptions about the error term ϵ.

1. $E(\epsilon) = 0$.
2. The variance of ϵ, denoted by σ^2, is the same for all values of x.
3. The values of ϵ are independent.
4. The error term ϵ has a normal distribution.

These assumptions provide the theoretical basis for the t test and the F test used to determine whether the relationship between x and y is significant, and for the confidence and prediction interval estimates presented in Section 14.6. If the assumptions about the error term ϵ appear questionable, the hypothesis tests about the significance of the regression relationship and the interval estimation results may not be valid.

The residuals provide the best information about ϵ; hence an analysis of the residuals is an important step in determining whether the assumptions for ϵ are appropriate. Much of residual analysis is based on an examination of graphical plots. In this section, we discuss the following residual plots.

1. A plot of the residuals against values of the independent variable x
2. A plot of residuals against the predicted values of the dependent variable y
3. A standardized residual plot
4. A normal probability plot

Residual Plot Against x

A residual plot against the independent variable x is a graph in which the values of the independent variable are represented by the horizontal axis and the corresponding residual values are represented by the vertical axis. A point is plotted for each residual. The first coordinate for each point is given by the value of x_i and the second coordinate is given by the corresponding value of the residual $y_i - \hat{y}_i$. For a residual plot against x with the Armand's Pizza Parlors data from Table 14.7, the coordinates of the first point are (2, −12), corresponding to $x_1 = 2$ and $y_1 - \hat{y}_1 = -12$; the coordinates of the second point are (6, 15), corresponding to $x_2 = 6$ and $y_2 - \hat{y}_2 = 15$; and so on. Figure 14.11 shows the resulting residual plot.

Before interpreting the results for this residual plot, let us consider some general patterns that might be observed in any residual plot. Three examples appear in Figure 14.12. If the assumption that the variance of ϵ is the same for all values of x and the assumed regression model is an adequate representation of the relationship between the variables, the

FIGURE 14.11   PLOT OF THE RESIDUALS AGAINST THE INDEPENDENT VARIABLE x FOR ARMAND'S PIZZA PARLORS

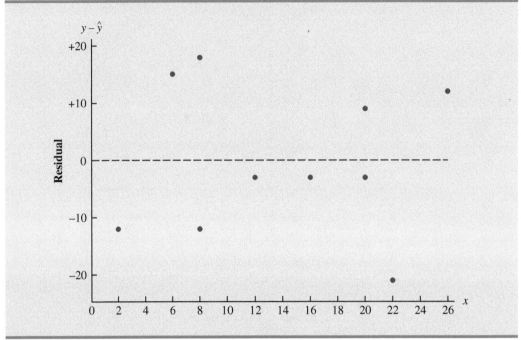

residual plot should give an overall impression of a horizontal band of points such as the one in Panel A of Figure 14.12. However, if the variance of ϵ is not the same for all values of x—for example, if variability about the regression line is greater for larger values of x—a pattern such as the one in Panel B of Figure 14.12 could be observed. In this case, the assumption of a constant variance of ϵ is violated. Another possible residual plot is shown in Panel C. In this case, we would conclude that the assumed regression model is not an adequate representation of the relationship between the variables. A curvilinear regression model or multiple regression model should be considered.

Now let us return to the residual plot for Armand's Pizza Parlors shown in Figure 14.11. The residuals appear to approximate the horizontal pattern in Panel A of Figure 14.12. Hence, we conclude that the residual plot does not provide evidence that the assumptions made for Armand's regression model should be challenged. At this point, we are confident in the conclusion that Armand's simple linear regression model is valid.

Experience and good judgment are always factors in the effective interpretation of residual plots. Seldom does a residual plot conform precisely to one of the patterns in Figure 14.12. Yet analysts who frequently conduct regression studies and frequently review residual plots become adept at understanding the differences between patterns that are reasonable and patterns that indicate the assumptions of the model should be questioned. A residual plot provides one technique to assess the validity of the assumptions for a regression model.

Residual Plot Against $\hat{y}$

Another residual plot represents the predicted value of the dependent variable $\hat{y}$ on the horizontal axis and the residual values on the vertical axis. A point is plotted for each residual. The first coordinate for each point is given by $\hat{y}_i$ and the second coordinate is given by the

FIGURE 14.12   RESIDUAL PLOTS FROM THREE REGRESSION STUDIES

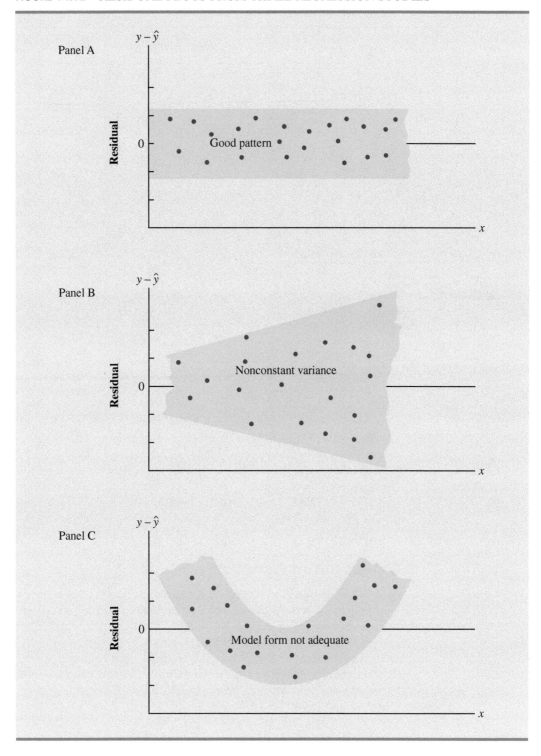

FIGURE 14.13   PLOT OF THE RESIDUALS AGAINST THE PREDICTED VALUES y FOR ARMAND'S PIZZA PARLORS

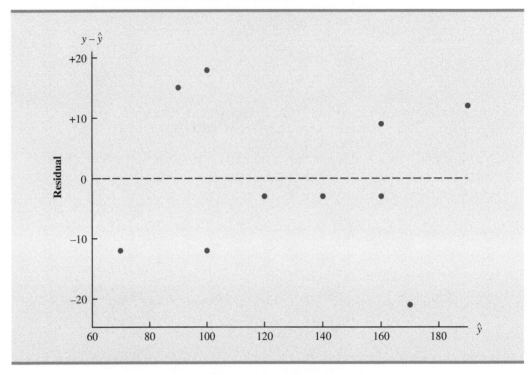

corresponding value of the ith residual $y_i - \hat{y}_i$. With the Armand's data from Table 14.7, the coordinates of the first point are $(70, -12)$, corresponding to $\hat{y}_1 = 70$ and $y_1 - \hat{y}_1 = -12$; the coordinates of the second point are $(90, 15)$; and so on. Figure 14.13 provides the residual plot. Note that the pattern of this residual plot is the same as the pattern of the residual plot against the independent variable x. It is not a pattern that would lead us to question the model assumptions. For simple linear regression, both the residual plot against x and the residual plot against $\hat{y}$ provide the same pattern. For multiple regression analysis, the residual plot against $\hat{y}$ is more widely used because of the presence of more than one independent variable.

Standardized Residuals

Many of the residual plots provided by computer software packages use a standardized version of the residuals. As demonstrated in preceding chapters, a random variable is standardized by subtracting its mean and dividing the result by its standard deviation. With the least squares method, the mean of the residuals is zero. Thus, simply dividing each residual by its standard deviation provides the **standardized residual**.

It can be shown that the standard deviation of residual i depends on the standard error of the estimate s and the corresponding value of the independent variable x_i.

STANDARD DEVIATION OF THE ith RESIDUAL[3]

$$s_{y_i - \hat{y}_i} = s\sqrt{1 - h_i} \tag{14.30}$$

---

[3]This equation actually provides an estimate of the standard deviation of the ith residual, because s is used instead of σ.

where

$$s_{y_i - \hat{y}_i} = \text{the standard deviation of residual } i$$
$$s = \text{the standard error of the estimate}$$
$$h_i = \frac{1}{n} + \frac{(x_i - \bar{x})^2}{\Sigma(x_i - \bar{x})^2}$$

(14.31)

Note that equation (14.30) shows that the standard deviation of the ith residual depends on x_i because of the presence of h_i in the formula.[4] Once the standard deviation of each residual is calculated, we can compute the standardized residual by dividing each residual by its corresponding standard deviation.

STANDARDIZED RESIDUAL FOR OBSERVATION i

$$\frac{y_i - \hat{y}_i}{s_{y_i - \hat{y}_i}}$$

(14.32)

Table 14.8 shows the calculation of the standardized residuals for Armand's Pizza Parlors. Recall that previous calculations showed $s = 13.829$. Figure 14.14 is the plot of the standardized residuals against the independent variable x.

Small departures from normality do not have a great effect on the statistical tests used in regression analysis.

The standardized residual plot can provide insight about the assumption that the error term ϵ has a normal distribution. If this assumption is satisfied, the distribution of the standardized residuals should appear to come from a standard normal probability distribution.[5] Thus, when looking at a standardized residual plot, we should expect to see approximately 95% of the standardized residuals between -2 and $+2$. We see in Figure 14.14 that for the

TABLE 14.8   COMPUTATION OF STANDARDIZED RESIDUALS FOR ARMAND'S PIZZA PARLORS

Restaurant i	x_i	$x_i - \bar{x}$	$(x_i - \bar{x})^2$	$\dfrac{(x_i - \bar{x})^2}{\Sigma(x_i - \bar{x})^2}$	h_i	$s_{y_i - \hat{y}_i}$	$y_i - \hat{y}_i$	Standardized Residual
1	2	−12	144	.2535	.3535	11.1193	−12	−1.0792
2	6	−8	64	.1127	.2127	12.2709	15	1.2224
3	8	−6	36	.0634	.1634	12.6493	−12	−.9487
4	8	−6	36	.0634	.1634	12.6493	18	1.4230
5	12	−2	4	.0070	.1070	13.0682	−3	−.2296
6	16	2	4	.0070	.1070	13.0682	−3	−.2296
7	20	6	36	.0634	.1634	12.6493	−3	−.2372
8	20	6	36	.0634	.1634	12.6493	9	.7115
9	22	8	64	.1127	.2127	12.2709	−21	−1.7114
10	26	12	144	.2535	.3535	11.1193	12	1.0792
		Total	568					

Note: The values of the residuals were computed in Table 14.7.

[4]h_i is referred to as the *leverage* of observation i. Leverage will be discussed further when we consider influential observations in Section 14.9.

[5]Because s is used instead of σ in equation (14.30), the probability distribution of the standardized residuals is not technically normal. However, in most regression studies, the sample size is large enough that a normal approximation is very good.

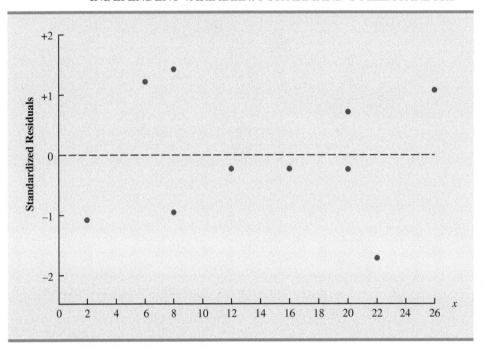

FIGURE 14.14   PLOT OF THE STANDARDIZED RESIDUALS AGAINST THE INDEPENDENT VARIABLE x FOR ARMAND'S PIZZA PARLORS

TABLE 14.9

NORMAL SCORES
FOR $n = 10$

Order Statistic	Normal Score
1	−1.55
2	−1.00
3	−.65
4	−.37
5	−.12
6	.12
7	.37
8	.65
9	1.00
10	1.55

TABLE 14.10

NORMAL SCORES
AND ORDERED
STANDARDIZED
RESIDUALS FOR
ARMAND'S PIZZA
PARLORS

Normal Scores	Ordered Standardized Residuals
−1.55	−1.7114
−1.00	−1.0792
−.65	−.9487
−.37	−.2372
−.12	−.2296
.12	−.2296
.37	.7115
.65	1.0792
1.00	1.2224
1.55	1.4230

Armand's example all standardized residuals are between −2 and +2. Therefore, on the basis of the standardized residuals, this plot gives us no reason to question the assumption that ϵ has a normal distribution.

Because of the effort required to compute the estimated values of $\hat{y}$, the residuals, and the standardized residuals, most statistical packages provide these values as optional regression output. Hence, residual plots can be easily obtained. For large problems computer packages are the only practical means for developing the residual plots discussed in this section.

Normal Probability Plot

Another approach for determining the validity of the assumption that the error term has a normal distribution is the **normal probability plot**. To show how a normal probability plot is developed, we introduce the concept of *normal scores*.

Suppose 10 values are selected randomly from a normal probability distribution with a mean of zero and a standard deviation of one, and that the sampling process is repeated over and over with the values in each sample of 10 ordered from smallest to largest. For now, let us consider only the smallest value in each sample. The random variable representing the smallest value obtained in repeated sampling is called the first-order statistic.

Statisticians show that for samples of size 10 from a standard normal probability distribution, the expected value of the first-order statistic is −1.55. This expected value is called a normal score. For the case with a sample of size $n = 10$, there are 10 order statistics and 10 normal scores (see Table 14.9). In general, a data set consisting of n observations will have n order statistics and hence n normal scores.

Let us now show how the 10 normal scores can be used to determine whether the standardized residuals for Armand's Pizza Parlors appear to come from a standard normal probability distribution. We begin by ordering the 10 standardized residuals from Table 14.8. The 10 normal scores and the ordered standardized residuals are shown together in Table 14.10. If the normality assumption is satisfied, the smallest standardized residual should be close to the smallest normal score, the next smallest standardized residual should be close to the next smallest normal

FIGURE 14.15   NORMAL PROBABILITY PLOT FOR ARMAND'S PIZZA PARLORS

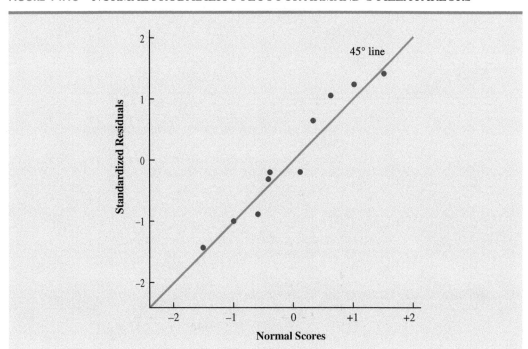

score, and so on. If we were to develop a plot with the normal scores on the horizontal axis and the corresponding standardized residuals on the vertical axis, the plotted points should cluster closely around a 45-degree line passing through the origin if the standardized residuals are approximately normally distributed. Such a plot is referred to as a *normal probability plot.*

Figure 14.15 is the normal probability plot for the Armand's Pizza Parlors example. Judgment is used to determine whether the pattern observed deviates from the line enough to conclude that the standardized residuals are not from a standard normal probability distribution. In Figure 14.15, we see that the points are grouped closely about the line. We therefore conclude that the assumption of the error term having a normal probability distribution is reasonable. In general, the more closely the points are clustered about the 45-degree line, the stronger the evidence supporting the normality assumption. Any substantial curvature in the normal probability plot is evidence that the residuals have not come from a normal distribution. Normal scores and the associated normal probability plot can be obtained easily from statistical packages such as Minitab.

NOTES AND COMMENTS

1. We use residual and normal probability plots to validate the assumptions of a regression model. If our review indicates that one or more assumptions are questionable, a different regression model or a transformation of the data should be considered. The appropriate corrective action when the assumptions are violated must be based on good judgment; recommendations from an experienced statistician can be valuable.

2. Analysis of residuals is the primary method statisticians use to verify that the assumptions associated with a regression model are valid. Even if no violations are found, it does not necessarily follow that the model will yield good predictions. However, if additional statistical tests support the conclusion of significance and the coefficient of determination is large, we should be able to develop good estimates and predictions using the estimated regression equation.

Exercises

Methods

45. Given are data for two variables, x and y.

x_i	6	11	15	18	20
y_i	6	8	12	20	30

   a. Develop an estimated regression equation for these data.
   b. Compute the residuals.
   c. Develop a plot of the residuals against the independent variable x. Do the assumptions about the error terms seem to be satisfied?
   d. Compute the standardized residuals.
   e. Develop a plot of the standardized residuals against $\hat{y}$. What conclusions can you draw from this plot?

46. The following data were used in a regression study.

Observation	x_i	y_i	Observation	x_i	y_i
1	2	4	6	7	6
2	3	5	7	7	9
3	4	4	8	8	5
4	5	6	9	9	11
5	7	4			

   a. Develop an estimated regression equation for these data.
   b. Construct a plot of the residuals. Do the assumptions about the error term seem to be satisfied?

Applications

47. Data on advertising expenditures and revenue (in thousands of dollars) for the Four Seasons Restaurant follow.

Advertising Expenditures	Revenue
1	19
2	32
4	44
6	40
10	52
14	53
20	54

   a. Let x equal advertising expenditures and y equal revenue. Use the method of least squares to develop a straight line approximation of the relationship between the two variables.
   b. Test whether revenue and advertising expenditures are related at a .05 level of significance.
   c. Prepare a residual plot of $y - \hat{y}$ versus $\hat{y}$. Use the result from part (a) to obtain the values of $\hat{y}$.
   d. What conclusions can you draw from residual analysis? Should this model be used, or should we look for a better one?

48. Refer to exercise 7, where an estimated regression equation relating years of experience and annual sales was developed.
    a. Compute the residuals and construct a residual plot for this problem.
    b. Do the assumptions about the error terms seem reasonable in light of the residual plot?

49. Recent family home sales in San Antonio provided the following data (San Antonio Realty Watch website, November 2008).

HomePrices

Square Footage	Price ($)
1580	142,500
1572	145,000
1352	115,000
2224	155,900
1556	95,000
1435	128,000
1438	100,000
1089	55,000
1941	142,000
1698	115,000
1539	115,000
1364	105,000
1979	155,000
2183	132,000
2096	140,000
1400	85,000
2372	145,000
1752	155,000
1386	80,000
1163	100,000

a. Develop the estimated regression equation that can be used to predict the sales prices given the square footage.
b. Construct a residual plot of the standardized residuals against the independent variable.
c. Do the assumptions about the error term and model form seem reasonable in light of the residual plot?

14.9 Residual Analysis: Outliers and Influential Observations

In Section 14.8 we showed how residual analysis could be used to determine when violations of assumptions about the regression model occur. In this section, we discuss how residual analysis can be used to identify observations that can be classified as outliers or as being especially influential in determining the estimated regression equation. Some steps that should be taken when such observations occur are discussed.

Detecting Outliers

Figure 14.16 is a scatter diagram for a data set that contains an **outlier**, a data point (observation) that does not fit the trend shown by the remaining data. Outliers represent observations that are suspect and warrant careful examination. They may represent erroneous data; if so, the data should be corrected. They may signal a violation of model assumptions; if so, another model should be considered. Finally, they may simply be unusual values that occurred by chance. In this case, they should be retained.

FIGURE 14.16   DATA SET WITH AN OUTLIER

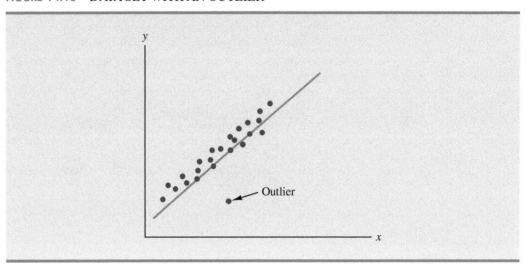

TABLE 14.11

DATA SET
ILLUSTRATING
THE EFFECT
OF AN OUTLIER

x_i	y_i
1	45
1	55
2	50
3	75
3	40
3	45
4	30
4	35
5	25
6	15

To illustrate the process of detecting outliers, consider the data set in Table 14.11; Figure 14.17 is a scatter diagram. Except for observation 4 ($x_4 = 3$, $y_4 = 75$), a pattern suggesting a negative linear relationship is apparent. Indeed, given the pattern of the rest of the data, we would expect y_4 to be much smaller and hence would identify the corresponding observation as an outlier. For the case of simple linear regression, one can often detect outliers by simply examining the scatter diagram.

The standardized residuals can also be used to identify outliers. If an observation deviates greatly from the pattern of the rest of the data (e.g., the outlier in Figure 14.16), the corresponding standardized residual will be large in absolute value. Many computer packages automatically identify observations with standardized residuals that are large in absolute value. In Figure 14.18 we show the Minitab output from a regression analysis of the data in Table 14.11. The next to last line of the output shows that the standardized residual for observation 4 is 2.67. Minitab provides a list of each observation with a standardized residual

FIGURE 14.17   SCATTER DIAGRAM FOR OUTLIER DATA SET

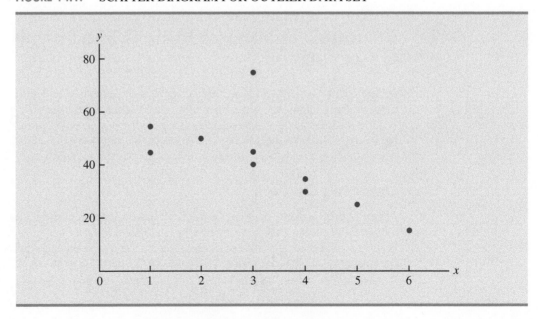

FIGURE 14.18   MINITAB OUTPUT FOR REGRESSION ANALYSIS OF THE OUTLIER
DATA SET

```
The regression equation is
y = 65.0 - 7.33 x

Predictor    Coef   SE Coef      T      p
Constant   64.958     9.258   7.02  0.000
X          -7.331     2.608  -2.81  0.023

S = 12.6704   R-Sq = 49.7%   R-Sq(adj) = 43.4%

Analysis of Variance

SOURCE          DF       SS      MS      F      p
Regression       1   1268.2  1268.2   7.90  0.023
Residual Error   8   1284.3   160.5
Total            9   2552.5

Unusual Observations
Obs    x       y     Fit   SE Fit   Residual   St Resid
  4  3.00   75.00   42.97    4.04      32.03       2.67R

R denotes an observation with a large standardized residual.
```

of less than -2 or greater than $+2$ in the Unusual Observation section of the output; in such cases, the observation is printed on a separate line with an R next to the standardized residual, as shown in Figure 14.18. With normally distributed errors, standardized residuals should be outside these limits approximately 5% of the time.

In deciding how to handle an outlier, we should first check to see whether it is a valid observation. Perhaps an error was made in initially recording the data or in entering the data into the computer file. For example, suppose that in checking the data for the outlier in Table 14.17, we find an error; the correct value for observation 4 is $x_4 = 3$, $y_4 = 30$. Figure 14.19 is the Minitab output obtained after correction of the value of y_4. We see that

FIGURE 14.19   MINITAB OUTPUT FOR THE REVISED OUTLIER DATA SET

```
The regression equation is
Y = 59.2 - 6.95 X

Predictor    Coef   SE Coef      T      p
Constant   59.237     3.835  15.45  0.000
X          -6.949     1.080  -6.43  0.000

S = 5.24808   R-Sq = 83.8%   R-Sq(adj) = 81.8%

Analysis of Variance

SOURCE          DF       SS      MS      F      p
Regression       1   1139.7  1139.7  41.38  0.000
Residual Error   8    220.3    27.5
Total            9   1360.0
```

using the incorrect data value substantially affected the goodness of fit. With the correct data, the value of R-sq increased from 49.7% to 83.8% and the value of b_0 decreased from 64.958 to 59.237. The slope of the line changed from -7.331 to -6.949. The identification of the outlier enabled us to correct the data error and improve the regression results.

Detecting Influential Observations

Sometimes one or more observations exert a strong influence on the results obtained. Figure 14.20 shows an example of an **influential observation** in simple linear regression. The estimated regression line has a negative slope. However, if the influential observation were dropped from the data set, the slope of the estimated regression line would change from negative to positive and the y-intercept would be smaller. Clearly, this one observation is much more influential in determining the estimated regression line than any of the others; dropping one of the other observations from the data set would have little effect on the estimated regression equation.

Influential observations can be identified from a scatter diagram when only one independent variable is present. An influential observation may be an outlier (an observation with a y value that deviates substantially from the trend), it may correspond to an x value far away from its mean (e.g., see Figure 14.20), or it may be caused by a combination of the two (a somewhat off-trend y value and a somewhat extreme x value).

Because influential observations may have such a dramatic effect on the estimated regression equation, they must be examined carefully. We should first check to make sure that no error was made in collecting or recording the data. If an error occurred, it can be corrected and a new estimated regression equation can be developed. If the observation is valid, we might consider ourselves fortunate to have it. Such a point, if valid, can contribute to a better understanding of the appropriate model and can lead to a better estimated regression equation. The presence of the influential observation in Figure 14.20, if valid, would suggest trying to obtain data on intermediate values of x to understand better the relationship between x and y.

Observations with extreme values for the independent variables are called **high leverage points**. The influential observation in Figure 14.20 is a point with high leverage. The leverage of an observation is determined by how far the values of the independent variables are from their mean values. For the single-independent-variable case, the leverage of the ith observation, denoted h_i, can be computed by using equation (14.33).

FIGURE 14.20 DATA SET WITH AN INFLUENTIAL OBSERVATION

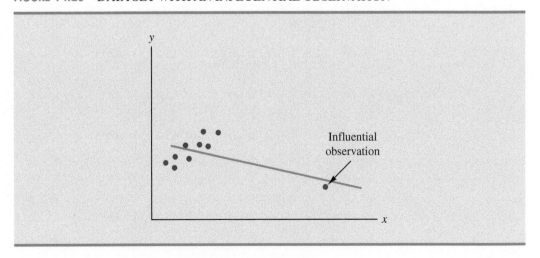

TABLE 14.12

DATA SET WITH A HIGH LEVERAGE OBSERVATION

x_i	y_i
10	125
10	130
15	120
20	115
20	120
25	110
70	100

LEVERAGE OF OBSERVATION i

$$h_i = \frac{1}{n} + \frac{(x_i - \bar{x})^2}{\Sigma(x_i - \bar{x})^2} \tag{14.33}$$

From the formula, it is clear that the farther x_i is from its mean $\bar{x}$, the higher the leverage of observation i.

Many statistical packages automatically identify observations with high leverage as part of the standard regression output. As an illustration of how the Minitab statistical package identifies points with high leverage, let us consider the data set in Table 14.12.

From Figure 14.21, a scatter diagram for the data set in Table 14.12, it is clear that observation 7 ($x = 70$, $y = 100$) is an observation with an extreme value of x. Hence, we would expect it to be identified as a point with high leverage. For this observation, the leverage is computed by using equation (14.33) as follows.

$$h_7 = \frac{1}{n} + \frac{(x_7 - \bar{x})^2}{\Sigma(x_i - \bar{x})^2} = \frac{1}{7} + \frac{(70 - 24.286)^2}{2621.43} = .94$$

Computer software packages are essential for performing the computations to identify influential observations. Minitab's selection rule is discussed here.

For the case of simple linear regression, Minitab identifies observations as having high leverage if $h_i > 6/n$ or .99, whichever is smaller. For the data set in Table 14.12, $6/n = 6/7 = .86$. Because $h_7 = .94 > .86$, Minitab will identify observation 7 as an observation whose x value gives it large influence. Figure 14.22 shows the Minitab output for a regression analysis of this data set. Observation 7 ($x = 70$, $y = 100$) is identified as having large influence; it is printed on a separate line at the bottom, with an X in the right margin.

Influential observations that are caused by an interaction of large residuals and high leverage can be difficult to detect. Diagnostic procedures are available that take both into account in determining when an observation is influential. One such measure, called Cook's D statistic, will be discussed in Chapter 15.

FIGURE 14.21   SCATTER DIAGRAM FOR THE DATA SET WITH A HIGH LEVERAGE OBSERVATION

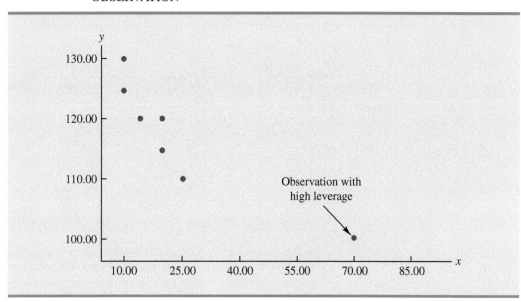

FIGURE 14.22 MINITAB OUTPUT FOR THE DATA SET WITH A HIGH LEVERAGE OBSERVATION

```
The regression equation is
y = 127 - 0.425 x

Predictor       Coef   SE Coef       T       p
Constant     127.466     2.961   43.04   0.000
X            -0.42507   0.09537   -4.46   0.007

S = 4.88282   R-sq = 79.9%   R-sq(adj) = 75.9%

Analysis of Variance

SOURCE            DF       SS       MS       F       p
Regression         1   473.65   473.65   19.87   0.007
Residual Error     5   119.21    23.84
Total              6   592.86

Unusual Observations
Obs     x       y      Fit   SE Fit   Residual   St Resid
  7  70.0  100.00   97.71     4.73       2.29      1.91 X

X denotes an observation whose X value gives it large influence.
```

NOTES AND COMMENTS

Once an observation is identified as potentially influential because of a large residual or high leverage, its impact on the estimated regression equation should be evaluated. More advanced texts discuss diagnostics for doing so. However, if one is not familiar with the more advanced material, a simple procedure is to run the regression analysis with and without the observation. This approach will reveal the influence of the observation on the results.

Exercises

Methods

50. Consider the following data for two variables, x and y.

x_i	135	110	130	145	175	160	120
y_i	145	100	120	120	130	130	110

a. Compute the standardized residuals for these data. Do the data include any outliers? Explain.
b. Plot the standardized residuals against $\hat{y}$. Does this plot reveal any outliers?
c. Develop a scatter diagram for these data. Does the scatter diagram indicate any outliers in the data? In general, what implications does this finding have for simple linear regression?

51. Consider the following data for two variables, x and y.

x_i	4	5	7	8	10	12	12	22
y_i	12	14	16	15	18	20	24	19

a. Compute the standardized residuals for these data. Do the data include any outliers? Explain.
b. Compute the leverage values for these data. Do there appear to be any influential observations in these data? Explain.
c. Develop a scatter diagram for these data. Does the scatter diagram indicate any influential observations? Explain.

Applications

52. Charity Navigator is America's leading independent charity evaluator. The following data show the total expenses ($), the percentage of the total budget spent on administrative expenses, the percentage spent on fundraising, and the percentage spent on program expenses for 10 supersized charities (Charity Navigator website, April 12, 2012). Administrative expenses include overhead, administrative staff and associated costs, and organizational meetings. Fundraising expenses are what a charity spends to raise money, and program expenses are what the charity spends on the programs and services it exists to deliver. The sum of the three percentages does not add to 100% because of rounding.

Charity	Total Expenses ($)	Administrative Expenses (%)	Fundraising Expenses (%)	Program Expenses (%)
American Red Cross	3,354,177,445	3.9	3.8	92.1
World Vision	1,205,887,020	4.0	7.5	88.3
Smithsonian Institution	1,080,995,083	23.5	2.6	73.7
Food For The Poor	1,050,829,851	.7	2.4	96.8
American Cancer Society	1,003,781,897	6.1	22.2	71.6
Volunteers of America	929,158,968	8.6	1.9	89.4
Dana-Farber Cancer Institute	877,321,613	13.1	1.6	85.2
AmeriCares	854,604,824	.4	.7	98.8
ALSAC—St. Jude Children's Research Hospital	829,662,076	9.6	16.9	73.4
City of Hope	736,176,619	13.7	3.0	83.1

a. Develop a scatter diagram with fundraising expenses (%) on the horizontal axis and program expenses (%) on the vertical axis. Looking at the data, do there appear to be any outliers and/or influential observations?
b. Develop an estimated regression equation that could be used to predict program expenses (%) given fundraising expenses (%).
c. Does the value for the slope of the estimated regression equation make sense in the context of this problem situation?
d. Use residual analysis to determine whether any outliers and/or influential observations are present. Briefly summarize your findings and conclusions.

53. Many countries, especially those in Europe, have significant gold holdings. But, many of these countries also have massive debts. The following data show the total value of gold holdings in billions of U.S. dollars and the debt as a percentage of the gross domestic product for nine countries (WordPress and Trading Economics websites, February 24, 2012).

WEB file

GoldHoldings

Country	Gold Value ($ billions)	Debt (% of GDP)
China	63	17.7
France	146	81.7
Germany	203	83.2
Indonesia	33	69.2
Italy	147	119.0
Netherlands	36	63.7
Russia	50	9.9
Switzerland	62	55.0
United States	487	93.2

a. Develop a scatter diagram for the total value of a country's gold holdings ($ billions) as the independent variable.

b. What does the scatter diagram developed in part (a) indicate about the relationship between the two variables? Do there appear to be any outliers and/or influential observations? Explain.

c. Using the entire data set, develop the estimated regression equation that can be used to predict the debt of a country given the total value of its gold holdings.

d. Use residual analysis to determine whether any outliers or influential observations are present.

e. Suppose that after looking at the scatter diagram in part (a) that you were able to visually identify what appears to be an influential observation. Drop this observation from the data set and fit an estimated regression equation to the remaining data. Compare the estimated slope for the new estimated regression equation to the estimated slope obtained in part (c). Does this approach confirm the conclusion you reached in part (d)? Explain.

54. The following data show the annual revenue ($ millions) and the estimated team value ($ millions) for the 32 teams in the National Football League (*Forbes* website, February 2009).

Team	Revenue ($ millions)	Value ($ millions)
Arizona Cardinals	203	914
Atlanta Falcons	203	872
Baltimore Ravens	226	1062
Buffalo Bills	206	885
Carolina Panthers	221	1040
Chicago Bears	226	1064
Cincinnati Bengals	205	941
Cleveland Browns	220	1035
Dallas Cowboys	269	1612
Denver Broncos	226	1061
Detroit Lions	204	917
Green Bay Packers	218	1023
Houston Texans	239	1125
Indianapolis Colts	203	1076
Jacksonville Jaguars	204	876
Kansas City Chiefs	214	1016
Miami Dolphins	232	1044
Minnesota Vikings	195	839
New England Patriots	282	1324
New Orleans Saints	213	937

WEB file

NFLValues

Team	Revenue ($ millions)	Value ($ millions)
New York Giants	214	1178
New York Jets	213	1170
Oakland Raiders	205	861
Philadelphia Eagles	237	1116
Pittsburgh Steelers	216	1015
San Diego Chargers	207	888
San Francisco 49ers	201	865
Seattle Seahawks	215	1010
St. Louis Rams	206	929
Tampa Bay Buccaneers	224	1053
Tennessee Titans	216	994
Washington Redskins	327	1538

a. Develop a scatter diagram with Revenue on the horizontal axis and Value on the vertical axis. Looking at the scatter diagram, does it appear that there are any outliers and/or influential observations in the data?

b. Develop the estimated regression equation that can be used to predict team value given the value of annual revenue.

c. Use residual analysis to determine whether any outliers and/or influential observations are present. Briefly summarize your findings and conclusions.

Summary

In this chapter we showed how regression analysis can be used to determine how a dependent variable y is related to an independent variable x. In simple linear regression, the regression model is $y = \beta_0 + \beta_1 x + \epsilon$. The simple linear regression equation $E(y) = \beta_0 + \beta_1 x$ describes how the mean or expected value of y is related to x. We used sample data and the least squares method to develop the estimated regression equation $\hat{y} = b_0 + b_1 x$. In effect, b_0 and b_1 are the sample statistics used to estimate the unknown model parameters β_0 and β_1.

The coefficient of determination was presented as a measure of the goodness of fit for the estimated regression equation; it can be interpreted as the proportion of the variation in the dependent variable y that can be explained by the estimated regression equation. We reviewed correlation as a descriptive measure of the strength of a linear relationship between two variables.

The assumptions about the regression model and its associated error term ϵ were discussed, and t and F tests, based on those assumptions, were presented as a means for determining whether the relationship between two variables is statistically significant. We showed how to use the estimated regression equation to develop confidence interval estimates of the mean value of y and prediction interval estimates of individual values of y.

The chapter concluded with a section on the computer solution of regression problems and two sections on the use of residual analysis to validate the model assumptions and to identify outliers and influential observations.

Glossary

Dependent variable The variable that is being predicted or explained. It is denoted by y.
Independent variable The variable that is doing the predicting or explaining. It is denoted by x.
Simple linear regression Regression analysis involving one independent variable and one dependent variable in which the relationship between the variables is approximated by a straight line.

Regression model The equation that describes how y is related to x and an error term; in simple linear regression, the regression model is $y = \beta_0 + \beta_1 x + \epsilon$.

Regression equation The equation that describes how the mean or expected value of the dependent variable is related to the independent variable; in simple linear regression, $E(y) = \beta_0 + \beta_1 x$.

Estimated regression equation The estimate of the regression equation developed from sample data by using the least squares method. For simple linear regression, the estimated regression equation is $\hat{y} = b_0 + b_1 x$.

Least squares method A procedure used to develop the estimated regression equation. The objective is to minimize $\Sigma(y_i - \hat{y}_i)^2$.

Scatter diagram A graph of bivariate data in which the independent variable is on the horizontal axis and the dependent variable is on the vertical axis.

Coefficient of determination A measure of the goodness of fit of the estimated regression equation. It can be interpreted as the proportion of the variability in the dependent variable y that is explained by the estimated regression equation.

***i*th residual** The difference between the observed value of the dependent variable and the value predicted using the estimated regression equation; for the ith observation the ith residual is $y_i - \hat{y}_i$.

Correlation coefficient A measure of the strength of the linear relationship between two variables (previously discussed in Chapter 3).

Mean square error The unbiased estimate of the variance of the error term σ^2. It is denoted by MSE or s^2.

Standard error of the estimate The square root of the mean square error, denoted by s. It is the estimate of σ, the standard deviation of the error term ϵ.

ANOVA table The analysis of variance table used to summarize the computations associated with the F test for significance.

Confidence interval The interval estimate of the mean value of y for a given value of x.

Prediction interval The interval estimate of an individual value of y for a given value of x.

Residual analysis The analysis of the residuals used to determine whether the assumptions made about the regression model appear to be valid. Residual analysis is also used to identify outliers and influential observations.

Residual plot Graphical representation of the residuals that can be used to determine whether the assumptions made about the regression model appear to be valid.

Standardized residual The value obtained by dividing a residual by its standard deviation.

Normal probability plot A graph of the standardized residuals plotted against values of the normal scores. This plot helps determine whether the assumption that the error term has a normal probability distribution appears to be valid.

Outlier A data point or observation that does not fit the trend shown by the remaining data.

Influential observation An observation that has a strong influence or effect on the regression results.

High leverage points Observations with extreme values for the independent variables.

Key Formulas

Simple Linear Regression Model

$$y = \beta_0 + \beta_1 x + \epsilon \tag{14.1}$$

Simple Linear Regression Equation

$$E(y) = \beta_0 + \beta_1 x \tag{14.2}$$

Estimated Simple Linear Regression Equation

$$\hat{y} = b_0 + b_1 x \tag{14.3}$$

Least Squares Criterion

$$\min \Sigma(y_i - \hat{y}_i)^2 \tag{14.5}$$

Slope and y-Intercept for the Estimated Regression Equation

$$b_1 = \frac{\Sigma(x_i - \bar{x})(y_i - \bar{y})}{\Sigma(x_i - \bar{x})^2} \tag{14.6}$$

$$b_0 = \bar{y} - b_1\bar{x} \tag{14.7}$$

Sum of Squares Due to Error

$$SSE = \Sigma(y_i - \hat{y}_i)^2 \tag{14.8}$$

Total Sum of Squares

$$SST = \Sigma(y_i - \bar{y})^2 \tag{14.9}$$

Sum of Squares Due to Regression

$$SSR = \Sigma(\hat{y}_i - \bar{y})^2 \tag{14.10}$$

Relationship Among SST, SSR, and SSE

$$SST = SSR + SSE \tag{14.11}$$

Coefficient of Determination

$$r^2 = \frac{SSR}{SST} \tag{14.12}$$

Sample Correlation Coefficient

$$\begin{aligned} r_{xy} &= (\text{sign of } b_1)\sqrt{\text{Coefficient of determination}} \\ &= (\text{sign of } b_1)\sqrt{r^2} \end{aligned} \tag{14.13}$$

Mean Square Error (Estimate of σ^2)

$$s^2 = MSE = \frac{SSE}{n - 2} \tag{14.15}$$

Standard Error of the Estimate

$$s = \sqrt{MSE} = \sqrt{\frac{SSE}{n - 2}} \tag{14.16}$$

Standard Deviation of b_1

$$\sigma_{b_1} = \frac{\sigma}{\sqrt{\Sigma(x_i - \bar{x})^2}} \tag{14.17}$$

Estimated Standard Deviation of b_1

$$s_{b_1} = \frac{s}{\sqrt{\Sigma(x_i - \bar{x})^2}} \tag{14.18}$$

t **Test Statistic**

$$t = \frac{b_1}{s_{b_1}}$$ (14.19)

Mean Square Regression

$$\text{MSR} = \frac{\text{SSR}}{\text{Number of independent variables}}$$ (14.20)

F **Test Statistic**

$$F = \frac{\text{MSR}}{\text{MSE}}$$ (14.21)

Estimated Standard Deviation of $\hat{y}^*$

$$s_{\hat{y}*} = s\sqrt{\frac{1}{n} + \frac{(x^* - \bar{x})^2}{\Sigma(x_i - \bar{x})^2}}$$ (14.23)

Confidence Interval for $E(y^*)$

$$\hat{y}^* \pm t_{\alpha/2}s_{\hat{y}*}$$ (14.24)

Estimated Standard Deviation of an Individual Value

$$s_{\text{pred}} = s\sqrt{1 + \frac{1}{n} + \frac{(x^* - \bar{x})^2}{\Sigma(x_i - \bar{x})^2}}$$ (14.26)

Prediction Interval for y^*

$$\hat{y}^* \pm t_{\alpha/2}s_{\text{pred}}$$ (14.27)

Residual for Observation *i*

$$y_i - \hat{y}_i$$ (14.28)

Standard Deviation of the *i*th **Residual**

$$s_{y_i - \hat{y}_i} = s\sqrt{1 - h_i}$$ (14.30)

Standardized Residual for Observation *i*

$$\frac{y_i - \hat{y}_i}{s_{y_i - \hat{y}_i}}$$ (14.32)

Leverage of Observation *i*

$$h_i = \frac{1}{n} + \frac{(x_i - \bar{x})^2}{\Sigma(x_i - \bar{x})^2}$$ (14.33)

Supplementary Exercises

55. Does a high value of r^2 imply that two variables are causally related? Explain.

56. In your own words, explain the difference between an interval estimate of the mean value of *y* for a given *x* and an interval estimate for an individual value of *y* for a given *x*.

57. What is the purpose of testing whether $\beta_1 = 0$? If we reject $\beta_1 = 0$, does it imply a good fit?

58. The Dow Jones Industrial Average (DJIA) and the Standard & Poor's 500 (S&P 500) indexes are used as measures of overall movement in the stock market. The DJIA is based on the price movements of 30 large companies; the S&P 500 is an index composed of 500 stocks. Some say the S&P 500 is a better measure of stock market performance because it is broader based. The closing price for the DJIA and the S&P 500 for 15 weeks, beginning with January 6, 2012, follow (*Barron*'s website, April 17, 2012).

DJIAS&P500

Date	DJIA	S&P
January 6	12,360	1278
January 13	12,422	1289
January 20	12,720	1315
January 27	12,660	1316
February 3	12,862	1345
February 10	12,801	1343
February 17	12,950	1362
February 24	12,983	1366
March 2	12,978	1370
March 9	12,922	1371
March 16	13,233	1404
March 23	13,081	1397
March 30	13,212	1408
April 5	13,060	1398
April 13	12,850	1370

a. Develop a scatter diagram with DJIA as the independent variable.
b. Develop the estimated regression equation.
c. Test for a significant relationship. Use $\alpha = .05$.
d. Did the estimated regression equation provide a good fit? Explain.
e. Suppose that the closing price for the DJIA is 13,500. Predict the closing price for the S&P 500.
f. Should we be concerned that the DJIA value of 13,500 used to predict the S&P 500 value in part (e) is beyond the range of the data used to develop the estimated regression equation?

59. The following data show Morningstar's Fair Value estimate and the Share Price for 28 companies. Fair Value is an estimate of a company's value per share that takes into account estimates of the company's growth, profitability, riskiness, and other factors over the next five years (*Morningstar Stocks 500,* 2008 edition).

Stocks500

Company	Fair Value ($)	Share Price ($)
Air Products and Chemicals	80	98.63
Allied Waste Industries	17	11.02
America Mobile	83	61.39
AT&T	35	41.56
Bank of America	70	41.26
Barclays PLC	68	40.37
Citigroup	53	29.44
Costco Wholesale Corp.	75	69.76
Covidien, Ltd.	58	44.29
Darden Restaurants	52	27.71
Dun & Bradstreet	87	88.63

(*continued*)

Company	Fair Value ($)	Share Price ($)
Equifax	42	36.36
Gannett Co.	38	39.00
Genuine Parts	48	46.30
GlaxoSmithKline PLC	57	50.39
Iron Mountain	33	37.02
ITT Corporation	83	66.04
Johnson & Johnson	80	66.70
Las Vegas Sands	98	103.05
Macrovision	23	18.33
Marriott International	39	34.18
Nalco Holding Company	29	24.18
National Interstate	25	33.10
Portugal Telecom	15	13.02
Qualcomm	48	39.35
Royal Dutch Shell Ltd.	87	84.20
SanDisk	60	33.17
Time Warner	42	27.60

a. Develop the estimated regression equation that could be used to estimate the share price given the fair value.
b. At the .05 level of significance, is there a significant relationship between the two variables?
c. Use the estimated regression equation to predict the share price for a company that has a fair value of $50.
d. Do you believe the estimated regression equation would provide a good prediction of the share price? Use r^2 to support your answer.

60. One of the biggest changes in higher education in recent years has been the growth of online universities. The Online Education Database is an independent organization whose mission is to build a comprehensive list of the top accredited online colleges. The following table shows the retention rate (%) and the graduation rate (%) for 29 online colleges (Online Education Database website, January 2009).

WEB file

OnlineEdu

College	Retention Rate (%)	Graduation Rate (%)
Western International University	7	25
South University	51	25
University of Phoenix	4	28
American InterContinental University	29	32
Franklin University	33	33
Devry University	47	33
Tiffin University	63	34
Post University	45	36
Peirce College	60	36
Everest University	62	36
Upper Iowa University	67	36
Dickinson State University	65	37
Western Governors University	78	37
Kaplan University	75	38
Salem International University	54	39
Ashford University	45	41

College	Retention Rate (%)	Graduation Rate (%)
ITT Technical Institute	38	44
Berkeley College	51	45
Grand Canyon University	69	46
Nova Southeastern University	60	47
Westwood College	37	48
Everglades University	63	50
Liberty University	73	51
LeTourneau University	78	52
Rasmussen College	48	53
Keiser University	95	55
Herzing College	68	56
National University	100	57
Florida National College	100	61

a. Develop a scatter diagram with retention rate as the independent variable. What does the scatter diagram indicate about the relationship between the two variables?
b. Develop the estimated regression equation.
c. Test for a significant relationship. Use $\alpha = .05$.
d. Did the estimated regression equation provide a good fit?
e. Suppose you were the president of South University. After reviewing the results, would you have any concerns about the performance of your university as compared to other online universities?
f. Suppose you were the president of the University of Phoenix. After reviewing the results, would you have any concerns about the performance of your university as compared to other online universities?

61. Jensen Tire & Auto is in the process of deciding whether to purchase a maintenance contract for its new computer wheel alignment and balancing machine. Managers feel that maintenance expense should be related to usage, and they collected the following information on weekly usage (hours) and annual maintenance expense (in hundreds of dollars).

WEB file

Jensen

Weekly Usage (hours)	Annual Maintenance Expense
13	17.0
10	22.0
20	30.0
28	37.0
32	47.0
17	30.5
24	32.5
31	39.0
40	51.5
38	40.0

a. Develop the estimated regression equation that relates annual maintenance expense to weekly usage.
b. Test the significance of the relationship in part (a) at a .05 level of significance.
c. Jensen expects to use the new machine 30 hours per week. Develop a 95% prediction interval for the company's annual maintenance expense.
d. If the maintenance contract costs $3000 per year, would you recommend purchasing it? Why or why not?

62. In a manufacturing process the assembly line speed (feet per minute) was thought to affect the number of defective parts found during the inspection process. To test this theory, managers devised a situation in which the same batch of parts was inspected visually at a variety of line speeds. They collected the following data.

Line Speed	Number of Defective Parts Found
20	21
20	19
40	15
30	16
60	14
40	17

a. Develop the estimated regression equation that relates line speed to the number of defective parts found.
b. At a .05 level of significance, determine whether line speed and number of defective parts found are related.
c. Did the estimated regression equation provide a good fit to the data?
d. Develop a 95% confidence interval to predict the mean number of defective parts for a line speed of 50 feet per minute.

63. A sociologist was hired by a large city hospital to investigate the relationship between the number of unauthorized days that employees are absent per year and the distance (miles) between home and work for the employees. A sample of 10 employees was chosen, and the following data were collected.

WEB file

Absent

Distance to Work (miles)	Number of Days Absent
1	8
3	5
4	8
6	7
8	6
10	3
12	5
14	2
14	4
18	2

a. Develop a scatter diagram for these data. Does a linear relationship appear reasonable? Explain.
b. Develop the least squares estimated regression equation.
c. Is there a significant relationship between the two variables? Use $\alpha = .05$.
d. Did the estimated regression equation provide a good fit? Explain.
e. Use the estimated regression equation developed in part (b) to develop a 95% confidence interval for the expected number of days absent for employees living 5 miles from the company.

64. The regional transit authority for a major metropolitan area wants to determine whether there is any relationship between the age of a bus and the annual maintenance cost. A sample of 10 buses resulted in the following data.

Age of Bus (years)	Maintenance Cost ($)
1	350
2	370
2	480
2	520
2	590
3	550
4	750
4	800
5	790
5	950

WEB file

AgeCost

a. Develop the least squares estimated regression equation.
b. Test to see whether the two variables are significantly related with $\alpha = .05$.
c. Did the least squares line provide a good fit to the observed data? Explain.
d. Develop a 95% prediction interval for the maintenance cost for a specific bus that is 4 years old.

65. A marketing professor at Givens College is interested in the relationship between hours spent studying and total points earned in a course. Data collected on 10 students who took the course last quarter follow.

Hours Spent Studying	Total Points Earned
45	40
30	35
90	75
60	65
105	90
65	50
90	90
80	80
55	45
75	65

WEB file

HoursPts

a. Develop an estimated regression equation showing how total points earned is related to hours spent studying.
b. Test the significance of the model with $\alpha = .05$.
c. Predict the total points earned by Mark Sweeney. He spent 95 hours studying.
d. Develop a 95% prediction interval for the total points earned by Mark Sweeney.

66. Reuters reported the market beta for Xerox was 1.22 (Reuters website, January 30, 2009). Market betas for individual stocks are determined by simple linear regression. For each stock, the dependent variable is its quarterly percentage return (capital appreciation plus dividends) minus the percentage return that could be obtained from a risk-free investment (the Treasury Bill rate is used as the risk-free rate). The independent variable is the quarterly percentage return (capital appreciation plus dividends) for the stock market (S&P 500) minus the percentage return from a risk-free investment. An estimated regression equation is developed with quarterly data; the market beta for the stock is the slope of the estimated regression equation (b_1). The value of the market beta is often interpreted as a measure of the risk associated with the stock. Market betas greater than 1 indicate that the stock is more volatile than the market average; market betas less than 1 indicate that the

stock is less volatile than the market average. Suppose that the following figures are the differences between the percentage return and the risk-free return for 10 quarters for the S&P 500 and Horizon Technology.

WEB file

MktBeta

S&P 500	Horizon
1.2	−.7
−2.5	−2.0
−3.0	−5.5
2.0	4.7
5.0	1.8
1.2	4.1
3.0	2.6
−1.0	2.0
.5	−1.3
2.5	5.5

a. Develop an estimated regression equation that can be used to predict the market beta for Horizon Technology. What is Horizon Technology's market beta?
b. Test for a significant relationship at the .05 level of significance.
c. Did the estimated regression equation provide a good fit? Explain.
d. Use the market betas of Xerox and Horizon Technology to compare the risk associated with the two stocks.

67. The Transactional Records Access Clearinghouse at Syracuse University reported data showing the odds of an Internal Revenue Service audit. The following table shows the average adjusted gross income reported and the percent of the returns that were audited for 20 selected IRS districts.

WEB file

IRSAudit

District	Adjusted Gross Income ($)	Percent Audited
Los Angeles	36,664	1.3
Sacramento	38,845	1.1
Atlanta	34,886	1.1
Boise	32,512	1.1
Dallas	34,531	1.0
Providence	35,995	1.0
San Jose	37,799	0.9
Cheyenne	33,876	0.9
Fargo	30,513	0.9
New Orleans	30,174	0.9
Oklahoma City	30,060	0.8
Houston	37,153	0.8
Portland	34,918	0.7
Phoenix	33,291	0.7
Augusta	31,504	0.7
Albuquerque	29,199	0.6
Greensboro	33,072	0.6
Columbia	30,859	0.5
Nashville	32,566	0.5
Buffalo	34,296	0.5

a. Develop the estimated regression equation that could be used to predict the percent audited given the average adjusted gross income reported.
b. At the .05 level of significance, determine whether the adjusted gross income and the percent audited are related.

c.   Did the estimated regression equation provide a good fit? Explain.
d.   Use the estimated regression equation developed in part (a) to calculate a 95% confidence interval for the expected percent audited for districts with an average adjusted gross income of $35,000.

68. The Toyota Camry is one of the best-selling cars in North America. The cost of a previously owned Camry depends upon many factors, including the model year, mileage, and condition. To investigate the relationship between the car's mileage and the sales price for a 2007 model year Camry, the following data show the mileage and sale price for 19 sales (PriceHub website, February 24, 2012).

WEB file

Camry

Miles (1000s)	Price ($1000s)
22	16.2
29	16.0
36	13.8
47	11.5
63	12.5
77	12.9
73	11.2
87	13.0
92	11.8
101	10.8
110	8.3
28	12.5
59	11.1
68	15.0
68	12.2
91	13.0
42	15.6
65	12.7
110	8.3

a.   Develop a scatter diagram with the car mileage on the horizontal axis and the price on the vertical axis.
b.   What does the scatter diagram developed in part (a) indicate about the relationship between the two variables?
c.   Develop the estimated regression equation that could be used to predict the price ($1000s) given the miles (1000s).
d.   Test for a significant relationship at the .05 level of significance.
e.   Did the estimated regression equation provide a good fit? Explain.
f.   Provide an interpretation for the slope of the estimated regression equation.
g.   Suppose that you are considering purchasing a previously owned 2007 Camry that has been driven 60,000 miles. Using the estimated regression equation developed in part (c), predict the price for this car. Is this the price you would offer the seller?

Case Problem 1   Measuring Stock Market Risk

One measure of the risk or volatility of an individual stock is the standard deviation of the total return (capital appreciation plus dividends) over several periods of time. Although the standard deviation is easy to compute, it does not take into account the extent to which the price of a given stock varies as a function of a standard market index, such as the S&P 500. As a result, many financial analysts prefer to use another measure of risk referred to as *beta*.

Betas for individual stocks are determined by simple linear regression. The dependent variable is the total return for the stock and the independent variable is the total return for

Beta

the stock market.* For this case problem we will use the S&P 500 index as the measure of the total return for the stock market, and an estimated regression equation will be developed using monthly data. The beta for the stock is the slope of the estimated regression equation (b_1). The data contained in the file named Beta provides the total return (capital appreciation plus dividends) over 36 months for eight widely traded common stocks and the S&P 500.

The value of beta for the stock market will always be 1; thus, stocks that tend to rise and fall with the stock market will also have a beta close to 1. Betas greater than 1 indicate that the stock is more volatile than the market, and betas less than 1 indicate that the stock is less volatile than the market. For instance, if a stock has a beta of 1.4, it is 40% *more* volatile than the market, and if a stock has a beta of .4, it is 60% *less* volatile than the market.

Managerial Report

You have been assigned to analyze the risk characteristics of these stocks. Prepare a report that includes but is not limited to the following items.

a. Compute descriptive statistics for each stock and the S&P 500. Comment on your results. Which stocks are the most volatile?

b. Compute the value of beta for each stock. Which of these stocks would you expect to perform best in an up market? Which would you expect to hold their value best in a down market?

c. Comment on how much of the return for the individual stocks is explained by the market.

Case Problem 2 U.S. Department of Transportation

As part of a study on transportation safety, the U.S. Department of Transportation collected data on the number of fatal accidents per 1000 licenses and the percentage of licensed drivers under the age of 21 in a sample of 42 cities. Data collected over a one-year period follow. These data are contained in the file named Safety.

Safety

Percent Under 21	Fatal Accidents per 1000 Licenses	Percent Under 21	Fatal Accidents per 1000 Licenses
13	2.962	17	4.100
12	0.708	8	2.190
8	0.885	16	3.623
12	1.652	15	2.623
11	2.091	9	0.835
17	2.627	8	0.820
18	3.830	14	2.890
8	0.368	8	1.267
13	1.142	15	3.224
8	0.645	10	1.014
9	1.028	10	0.493

---

*Various sources use different approaches for computing betas. For instance, some sources subtract the return that could be obtained from a risk-free investment (e.g., T-bills) from the dependent variable and the independent variable before computing the estimated regression equation. Some also use different indexes for the total return of the stock market; for instance, Value Line computes betas using the New York Stock Exchange composite index.

Percent Under 21	Fatal Accidents per 1000 Licenses	Percent Under 21	Fatal Accidents per 1000 Licenses
16	2.801	14	1.443
12	1.405	18	3.614
9	1.433	10	1.926
10	0.039	14	1.643
9	0.338	16	2.943
11	1.849	12	1.913
12	2.246	15	2.814
14	2.855	13	2.634
14	2.352	9	0.926
11	1.294	17	3.256

Managerial Report

1. Develop numerical and graphical summaries of the data.
2. Use regression analysis to investigate the relationship between the number of fatal accidents and the percentage of drivers under the age of 21. Discuss your findings.
3. What conclusion and recommendations can you derive from your analysis?

Case Problem 3 Selecting a Point-and-Shoot Digital Camera

Consumer Reports tested 166 different point-and-shoot digital cameras. Based upon factors such as the number of megapixels, weight (oz.), image quality, and ease of use, they developed an overall score for each camera tested. The overall score ranges from 0 to 100, with higher scores indicating better overall test results. Selecting a camera with many options can be a difficult process, and price is certainly a key issue for most consumers. By spending more, will a consumer really get a superior camera? And, do cameras that have more megapixels, a factor often considered to be a good measure of picture quality, cost more than cameras with fewer megapixels? Table 14.13 shows the brand, average retail price ($), number of megapixels, weight (oz.), and the overall score for 13 Canon and 15 Nikon subcompact cameras tested by *Consumer Reports* (*Consumer Reports* website, February 7, 2012).

Managerial Report

1. Develop numerical summaries of the data.
2. Using overall score as the dependent variable, develop three scatter diagrams, one using price as the independent variable, one using the number of megapixels as the independent variable, and one using weight as the independent variable. Which of the three independent variables appears to be the best predictor of overall score?
3. Using simple linear regression, develop an estimated regression equation that could be used to predict the overall score given the price of the camera. For this estimated regression equation, perform an analysis of the residuals and discuss your findings and conclusions.
4. Analyze the data using only the observations for the Canon cameras. Discuss the appropriateness of using simple linear regression and make any recommendations regarding the prediction of overall score using just the price of the camera.

TABLE 14.13   DATA FOR 28 POINT-AND-SHOOT DIGITAL CAMERAS

Cameras

Observation	Brand	Price ($)	Megapixels	Weight (oz.)	Score
1	Canon	330	10	7	66
2	Canon	200	12	5	66
3	Canon	300	12	7	65
4	Canon	200	10	6	62
5	Canon	180	12	5	62
6	Canon	200	12	7	61
7	Canon	200	14	5	60
8	Canon	130	10	7	60
9	Canon	130	12	5	59
10	Canon	110	16	5	55
11	Canon	90	14	5	52
12	Canon	100	10	6	51
13	Canon	90	12	7	46
14	Nikon	270	16	5	65
15	Nikon	300	16	7	63
16	Nikon	200	14	6	61
17	Nikon	400	14	7	59
18	Nikon	120	14	5	57
19	Nikon	170	16	6	56
20	Nikon	150	12	5	56
21	Nikon	230	14	6	55
22	Nikon	180	12	6	53
23	Nikon	130	12	6	53
24	Nikon	80	12	7	52
25	Nikon	80	14	7	50
26	Nikon	100	12	4	46
27	Nikon	110	12	5	45
28	Nikon	130	14	4	42

Case Problem 4   Finding the Best Car Value

When trying to decide what car to buy, real value is not necessarily determined by how much you spend on the initial purchase. Instead, cars that are reliable and don't cost much to own often represent the best values. But, no matter how reliable or inexpensive a car may cost to own, it must also perform well.

To measure value, *Consumer Reports* developed a statistic referred to as a value score. The value score is based upon five-year owner costs, overall road-test scores, and predicted reliability ratings. Five-year owner costs are based on the expenses incurred in the first five years of ownership, including depreciation, fuel, maintenance and repairs, and so on. Using a national average of 12,000 miles per year, an average cost per mile driven is used as the measure of five-year owner costs. Road-test scores are the results of more than 50 tests and evaluations and are based upon a 100-point scale, with higher scores indicating better performance, comfort, convenience, and fuel economy. The highest road-test score obtained in the tests conducted by *Consumer Reports* was a 99 for a Lexus LS 460L. Predicted-reliability ratings (1 = Poor, 2 = Fair, 3 = Good, 4 = Very Good, and 5 = Excellent) are based on data from *Consumer Reports'* Annual Auto Survey.

A car with a value score of 1.0 is considered to be "average-value." A car with a value score of 2.0 is considered to be twice as good a value as a car with a value score of 1.0; a car with a value score of 0.5 is considered half as good as average; and so on. The data for 20 family sedans, including the price ($) of each car tested, follow.

Car	Price ($)	Cost/Mile	Road-Test Score	Predicted Reliability	Value Score
Nissan Altima 2.5 S (4-cyl.)	23,970	0.59	91	4	1.75
Kia Optima LX (2.4)	21,885	0.58	81	4	1.73
Subaru Legacy 2.5i Premium	23,830	0.59	83	4	1.73
Ford Fusion Hybrid	32,360	0.63	84	5	1.70
Honda Accord LX-P (4-cyl.)	23,730	0.56	80	4	1.62
Mazda6 i Sport (4-cyl.)	22,035	0.58	73	4	1.60
Hyundai Sonata GLS (2.4)	21,800	0.56	89	3	1.58
Ford Fusion SE (4-cyl.)	23,625	0.57	76	4	1.55
Chevrolet Malibu LT (4-cyl.)	24,115	0.57	74	3	1.48
Kia Optima SX (2.0T)	29,050	0.72	84	4	1.43
Ford Fusion SEL (V6)	28,400	0.67	80	4	1.42
Nissan Altima 3.5 SR (V6)	30,335	0.69	93	4	1.42
Hyundai Sonata Limited (2.0T)	28,090	0.66	89	3	1.39
Honda Accord EX-L (V6)	28,695	0.67	90	3	1.36
Mazda6 s Grand Touring (V6)	30,790	0.74	81	4	1.34
Ford Fusion SEL (V6, AWD)	30,055	0.71	75	4	1.32
Subaru Legacy 3.6R Limited	30,094	0.71	88	3	1.29
Chevrolet Malibu LTZ (V6)	28,045	0.67	83	3	1.20
Chrysler 200 Limited (V6)	27,825	0.70	52	5	1.20
Chevrolet Impala LT (3.6)	28,995	0.67	63	3	1.05

WEB file

FamilySedans

Managerial Report

1. Develop numerical summaries of the data.
2. Use regression analysis to develop an estimated regression equation that could be used to predict the value score given the price of the car.
3. Use regression analysis to develop an estimated regression equation that could be used to predict the value score given the five-year owner costs (cost/mile).
4. Use regression analysis to develop an estimated regression equation that could be used to predict the value score given the road-test score.
5. Use regression analysis to develop an estimated regression equation that could be used to predict the value score given the predicted-reliability.
6. What conclusions can you derive from your analysis?

Appendix 14.1 Calculus-Based Derivation of Least Squares Formulas

As mentioned in the chapter, the least squares method is a procedure for determining the values of b_0 and b_1 that minimize the sum of squared residuals. The sum of squared residuals is given by

$$\Sigma(y_i - \hat{y}_i)^2$$

Substituting $\hat{y}_i = b_0 + b_1 x_i$, we get

$$\Sigma(y_i - b_0 - b_1 x_i)^2 \tag{14.34}$$

as the expression that must be minimized.

To minimize expression (14.34), we must take the partial derivatives with respect to b_0 and b_1, set them equal to zero, and solve. Doing so, we get

$$\frac{\partial \Sigma(y_i - b_0 - b_1 x_i)^2}{\partial b_0} = -2\Sigma(y_i - b_0 - b_1 x_i) = 0 \tag{14.35}$$

$$\frac{\partial \Sigma(y_i - b_0 - b_1 x_i)^2}{\partial b_1} = -2\Sigma x_i(y_i - b_0 - b_1 x_i) = 0 \tag{14.36}$$

Dividing equation (14.35) by two and summing each term individually yields

$$-\Sigma y_i + \Sigma b_0 + \Sigma b_1 x_i = 0$$

Bringing Σy_i to the other side of the equal sign and noting that $\Sigma b_0 = n b_0$, we obtain

$$n b_0 + (\Sigma x_i) b_1 = \Sigma y_i \tag{14.37}$$

Similar algebraic simplification applied to equation (14.36) yields

$$(\Sigma x_i) b_0 + (\Sigma x_i^2) b_1 = \Sigma x_i y_i \tag{14.38}$$

Equations (14.37) and (14.38) are known as the *normal equations*. Solving equation (14.37) for b_0 yields

$$b_0 = \frac{\Sigma y_i}{n} - b_1 \frac{\Sigma x_i}{n} \tag{14.39}$$

Using equation (14.39) to substitute for b_0 in equation (14.38) provides

$$\frac{\Sigma x_i \Sigma y_i}{n} - \frac{(\Sigma x_i)^2}{n} b_1 + (\Sigma x_i^2) b_1 = \Sigma x_i y_i \tag{14.40}$$

By rearranging the terms in equation (14.40), we obtain

$$b_1 = \frac{\Sigma x_i y_i - (\Sigma x_i \Sigma y_i)/n}{\Sigma x_i^2 - (\Sigma x_i)^2/n} = \frac{\Sigma(x_i - \bar{x})(y_i - \bar{y})}{\Sigma(x_i - \bar{x})^2} \tag{14.41}$$

Because $\bar{y} = \Sigma y_i/n$ and $\bar{x} = \Sigma x_i/n$, we can rewrite equation (14.39) as

$$b_0 = \bar{y} - b_1 \bar{x} \tag{14.42}$$

Equations (14.41) and (14.42) are the formulas (14.6) and (14.7) we used in the chapter to compute the coefficients in the estimated regression equation.

Appendix 14.2   A Test for Significance Using Correlation

Using the sample correlation coefficient r_{xy}, we can determine whether the linear relationship between x and y is significant by testing the following hypotheses about the population correlation coefficient ρ_{xy}.

$$H_0: \rho_{xy} = 0$$
$$H_a: \rho_{xy} \neq 0$$

If H_0 is rejected, we can conclude that the population correlation coefficient is not equal to zero and that the linear relationship between the two variables is significant. This test for significance follows.

A TEST FOR SIGNIFICANCE USING CORRELATION

$$H_0: \rho_{xy} = 0$$
$$H_a: \rho_{xy} \neq 0$$

TEST STATISTIC

$$t = r_{xy} \sqrt{\frac{n-2}{1 - r_{xy}^2}} \qquad (14.43)$$

REJECTION RULE

p-value approach: Reject H_0 if p-value $\leq \alpha$

Critical value approach: Reject H_0 if $t \leq -t_{\alpha/2}$ or if $t \geq t_{\alpha/2}$

where $t_{\alpha/2}$ is based on a t distribution with $n - 2$ degrees of freedom.

In Section 14.3, we found that the sample with $n = 10$ provided the sample correlation coefficient for student population and quarterly sales of $r_{xy} = .9501$. The test statistic is

$$t = r_{xy} \sqrt{\frac{n-2}{1 - r_{xy}^2}} = .9501 \sqrt{\frac{10-2}{1 - (.9501)^2}} = 8.61$$

The t distribution table shows that with $n - 2 = 10 - 2 = 8$ degrees of freedom, $t = 3.355$ provides an area of .005 in the upper tail. Thus, the area in the upper tail of the t distribution corresponding to the test statistic $t = 8.61$ must be less than .005. Because this test is a two-tailed test, we double this value to conclude that the p-value associated with $t = 8.61$ must be less than $2(.005) = .01$. Excel or Minitab show the p-value $= .000$. Because the p-value is less than $\alpha = .01$, we reject H_0 and conclude that ρ_{xy} is not equal to zero. This evidence is sufficient to conclude that a significant linear relationship exists between student population and quarterly sales.

Note that except for rounding, the test statistic t and the conclusion of a significant relationship are identical to the results obtained in Section 14.5 for the t test conducted using Armand's estimated regression equation $\hat{y} = 60 + 5x$. Performing regression analysis provides the conclusion of a significant relationship between x and y and in addition provides the equation showing how the variables are related. Most analysts therefore use modern computer packages to perform regression analysis and find that using correlation as a test of significance is unnecessary.

Appendix 14.3   Regression Analysis with Minitab

WEB file

Armand's

In Section 14.7 we discussed the computer solution of regression problems by showing Minitab's output for the Armand's Pizza Parlors problem. In this appendix, we describe the steps required to generate the Minitab computer solution. First, the data must be entered in a Minitab worksheet. Student population data are entered in column C1 and quarterly sales data are entered in column C2. The variable names Pop and Sales are entered as the column headings on the worksheet. In subsequent steps, we refer to the data by using the variable names Pop and Sales or the column indicators C1 and C2. The following steps describe how to use Minitab to produce the regression results shown in Figure 14.10.

Step 1. Select the **Stat** menu
Step 2. Select the **Regression** menu
Step 3. Choose **Regression**
Step 4. When the Regression dialog box appears:
Enter Sales in the **Response** box
Enter Pop in the **Predictors** box
Click the **Options** button
When the Regression-Options dialog box appears:
Enter 10 in the **Prediction intervals for new observations** box
Click **OK**
When the Regression dialog box reappears:
Click **OK**

The Minitab regression dialog box provides additional capabilities that can be obtained by selecting the desired options. For instance, to obtain a residual plot that shows the predicted value of the dependent variable $\hat{y}$ on the horizontal axis and the standardized residual values on the vertical axis, step 4 would be as follows:

Step 4. When the Regression dialog box appears:
Enter Sales in the **Response** box
Enter Pop in the **Predictors** box
Click the **Graphs** button
When the Regression-Graphs dialog box appears:
Select **Standardized** under Residuals for Plots
Select **Residuals versus fits** under Residual Plots
Click **OK**
When the Regression dialog box reappears:
Click **OK**

Appendix 14.4   Regression Analysis with Excel

WEB file

Armand's

In this appendix we will illustrate how Excel's Regression tool can be used to perform the regression analysis computations for the Armand's Pizza Parlors problem. Refer to Figure 14.23 as we describe the steps involved. The labels Restaurant, Population, and Sales are entered into cells A1:C1 of the worksheet. To identify each of the 10 observations, we entered the numbers 1 through 10 into cells A2:A11. The sample data are entered into cells B2:C11. The following steps describe how to use Excel to produce the regression results.

Step 1. Click the **Data** tab on the Ribbon
Step 2. In the **Analysis** group, click **Data Analysis**
Step 3. Choose **Regression** from the list of Analysis Tools
Step 4. Click **OK**

FIGURE 14.23   EXCEL SOLUTION TO THE ARMAND'S PIZZA PARLORS PROBLEM

| | A1 | | f_x | Restaurant | | | | | | |

	A	B	C	D	E	F	G	H	I	J
1	**Restaurant**	**Population**	**Sales**							
2	1	2	58							
3	2	6	105							
4	3	8	88							
5	4	8	118							
6	5	12	117							
7	6	16	137							
8	7	20	157							
9	8	20	169							
10	9	22	149							
11	10	26	202							
12										
13	SUMMARY OUTPUT									
14										
15	*Regression Statistics*									
16	Multiple R	0.9501								
17	R Square	0.9027								
18	Adjusted R Square	0.8906								
19	Standard Error	13.8293								
20	Observations	10								
21										
22	ANOVA									
23		*df*	*SS*	*MS*	*F*	*Significance F*				
24	Regression	1	14200	14200	74.2484	2.55E-05				
25	Residual	8	1530	191.25						
26	Total	9	15730							
27										
28		*Coefficients*	*Standard Error*	*t Stat*	*P-value*	*Lower 95%*	*Upper 95%*	*Lower 99.0%*	*Upper 99.0%*	
29	Intercept	60	9.2260	6.5033	0.0002	38.7247	81.2753	29.0431	90.9569	
30	Population	5	0.5803	8.6167	2.55E-05	3.6619	6.3381	3.0530	6.9470	
31										

Step 5. When the Regression dialog box appears:
> Enter C1:C11 in the **Input Y Range** box
> Enter B1:B11 in the **Input X Range** box
> Select **Labels**
> Select **Confidence Level**
> Enter 99 in the **Confidence Level** box
> Select **Output Range**
> Enter A13 in the **Output Range** box
>> (Any upper left-hand corner cell indicating where the output is to begin may be entered here.)
> Click **OK**

The first section of the output, entitled *Regression Statistics,* contains summary statistics such as the coefficient of determination (R Square). The second section of the output, titled ANOVA, contains the analysis of variance table. The last section of the output, which is not titled, contains the estimated regression coefficients and related information. We will begin our discussion of the interpretation of the regression output with the information contained in cells A28:I30.

Interpretation of Estimated Regression Equation Output

The y intercept of the estimated regression line, $b_0 = 60$, is shown in cell B29, and the slope of the estimated regression line, $b_1 = 5$, is shown in cell B30. The label Intercept in cell A29 and the label Population in cell A30 are used to identify these two values.

In Section 14.5 we showed that the estimated standard deviation of b_1 is $s_{b_1} = .5803$. Note that the value in cell C30 is .5803. The label Standard Error in cell C28 is Excel's way of indicating that the value in cell C30 is the standard error, or standard deviation, of b_1. Recall that the t test for a significant relationship required the computation of the t statistic, $t = b_1/s_{b_1}$. For the Armand's data, the value of t that we computed was $t = 5/.5803 = 8.62$. The label in cell D28, t *Stat,* reminds us that cell D30 contains the value of the t test statistic.

The value in cell E30 is the p-value associated with the t test for significance. Excel has displayed the p-value in cell E30 using scientific notation. To obtain the decimal value, we move the decimal point 5 places to the left, obtaining a value of .0000255. Because the p-value $= .0000255 < \alpha = .01$, we can reject H_0 and conclude that we have a significant relationship between student population and quarterly sales.

The information in cells F28:I30 can be used to develop confidence interval estimates of the y intercept and slope of the estimated regression equation. Excel always provides the lower and upper limits for a 95% confidence interval. Recall that in step 4 we selected Confidence Level and entered 99 in the Confidence Level box. As a result, Excel's Regression tool also provides the lower and upper limits for a 99% confidence interval. The value in cell H30 is the lower limit for the 99% confidence interval estimate of β_1 and the value in cell I30 is the upper limit. Thus, after rounding, the 99% confidence interval estimate of β_1 is 3.05 to 6.95. The values in cells F30 and G30 provide the lower and upper limits for the 95% confidence interval. Thus, the 95% confidence interval is 3.66 to 6.34.

Interpretation of ANOVA Output

The information in cells A22:F26 is a summary of the analysis of variance computations. The three sources of variation are labeled Regression, Residual, and Total. The label *df* in cell B23 stands for degrees of freedom, the label *SS* in cell C23 stands for sum of squares, and the label *MS* in cell D23 stands for mean square.

In Section 14.5 we stated that the mean square error, obtained by dividing the error or residual sum of squares by its degrees of freedom, provides an estimate of σ^2. The value in cell D25, 191.25, is the mean square error for the Armand's regression output. In Section 14.5 we showed that an F test could also be used to test for significance in regression. The value in cell F24, .0000255, is the p-value associated with the F test for significance. Because the p-value $= .0000255 < \alpha = .01$, we can reject H_0 and conclude that we have a significant relationship between student population and quarterly sales. The label Excel uses to identify the p-value for the F test for significance, shown in cell F23, is *Significance F.*

The label Significance F may be more meaningful if you think of the value in cell F24 as the observed level of significance for the F test.

Interpretation of Regression Statistics Output

The coefficient of determination, .9027, appears in cell B17; the corresponding label, R Square, is shown in cell A17. The square root of the coefficient of determination provides the sample correlation coefficient of .9501 shown in cell B16. Note that Excel uses the label Multiple R (cell A16) to identify this value. In cell A19, the label Standard Error is used to identify the value of the standard error of the estimate shown in cell B19. Thus, the standard error of the estimate is 13.8293. We caution the reader to keep in mind that in the Excel output, the label Standard Error appears in two different places. In the Regression Statistics section of the output, the label Standard Error refers to the estimate of σ. In the Estimated Regression Equation section of the output, the label *Standard Error* refers to s_{b_1}, the standard deviation of the sampling distribution of b_1.

Appendix 14.5   Regression Analysis Using StatTools

Armand's

In this appendix we show how StatTools can be used to perform the regression analysis computations for the Armand's Pizza Parlors problem. Begin by using the Data Set Manager to create a StatTools data set for these data using the procedure described in the appendix in Chapter 1. The following steps describe how StatTools can be used to provide the regression results.

Step 1. Click the **StatTools** tab on the Ribbon
Step 2. In the **Analyses** group, click **Regression and Classification**
Step 3. Choose the **Regression** option
Step 4. When the StatTools-Regression dialog box appears:
  Select **Multiple** in the **Regression Type** box
  In the **Variables** section,
    Click the **Format button** and select **Unstacked**
    In the column labeled **I** select **Population**
    In the column labeled **D** select **Sales**
  Click **OK**

The regression analysis output will appear.

Note that in step 4 we selected Multiple in the Regression Type box. In StatTools, the Multiple option is used for both simple linear regression and multiple regression. The StatTools-Regression dialog box contains a number of more advanced options for developing prediction interval estimates and producing residual plots. The StatTools Help facility provides information on using all of these options.

CHAPTER 15

Multiple Regression

CONTENTS

STATISTICS IN PRACTICE:
dunnhumby

15.1 MULTIPLE REGRESSION MODEL
Regression Model and
Regression Equation
Estimated Multiple Regression
Equation

15.2 LEAST SQUARES METHOD
An Example: Butler Trucking
Company
Note on Interpretation of
Coefficients

15.3 MULTIPLE COEFFICIENT OF DETERMINATION

15.4 MODEL ASSUMPTIONS

15.5 TESTING FOR SIGNIFICANCE
F Test
t Test
Multicollinearity

15.6 USING THE ESTIMATED REGRESSION EQUATION FOR ESTIMATION AND PREDICTION

15.7 CATEGORICAL INDEPENDENT VARIABLES
An Example: Johnson
Filtration, Inc.
Interpreting the Parameters
More Complex Categorical
Variables

15.8 RESIDUAL ANALYSIS
Detecting Outliers
Studentized Deleted Residuals
and Outliers
Influential Observations
Using Cook's Distance Measure
to Identify Influential
Observations

15.9 LOGISTIC REGRESSION
Logistic Regression Equation
Estimating the Logistic
Regression Equation
Testing for Significance
Managerial Use
Interpreting the Logistic
Regression Equation
Logit Transformation

STATISTICS *in* PRACTICE

dunnhumby*
LONDON, ENGLAND

Founded in 1989 by the husband-and-wife team of Clive Humby (a mathematician) and Edwina Dunn (a marketer), dunnhumby combines proven natural abilities with big ideas to find clues and patterns as to what customers are buying and why. The company turns these insights into actionable strategies that create dramatic growth and sustainable loyalty, ultimately improving brand value and the customer experience.

Employing more than 950 people in Europe, Asia, and the Americas, dunnhumby serves a prestigious list of companies, including Kroger, Tesco, Coca-Cola, General Mills, Kimberly-Clark, PepsiCo, Procter & Gamble, and Home Depot. dunnhumbyUSA is a joint venture between the Kroger Company and dunnhumby and has offices in New York, Chicago, Atlanta, Minneapolis, Cincinnati, and Portland.

The company's research begins with data collected about a client's customers. Data come from customer reward or discount card purchase records, electronic point-of-sale transactions, and traditional market research. Analysis of the data often translates billions of data points into detailed insights about the behavior, preferences, and lifestyles of the customers. Such insights allow for more effective merchandising programs to be activated, including strategy recommendations on pricing, promotion, advertising, and product assortment decisions.

Researchers have used a multiple regression technique referred to as logistic regression to help in their analysis of customer-based data. Using logistic regression, an estimated multiple regression equation of the following form is developed.

$$\hat{y} = b_0 + b_1 x_1 + b_2 x_2 + b_3 x_3 + \cdots + b_p x_p$$

The dependent variable $\hat{y}$ is a prediction of the probability that a customer belongs to a particular customer group. The independent variables $x_1, x_2, x_3, \ldots, x_p$ are measures of the customer's actual shopping behavior and may include the specific items purchased, number of items purchased, amount purchased, day of the week, hour of the day, and so on. The analysis helps identify the independent variables that are most relevant in predict-

dunnhumby uses logistic regression to predict customer shopping behavior. © Micro 10x/ Shutterstock.com.

ing the customer's group and provides a better understanding of the customer population, enabling further analysis with far greater confidence. The focus of the analysis is on understanding the customer to the point of developing merchandising, marketing, and direct marketing programs that will maximize the relevancy and service to the customer group.

In this chapter, we will introduce multiple regression and show how the concepts of simple linear regression introduced in Chapter 14 can be extended to the multiple regression case. In addition, we will show how computer software packages are used for multiple regression. In the final section of the chapter we introduce logistic regression using an example that illustrates how the technique is used in a marketing research application.

---

*The authors are indebted to Paul Hunter, Senior Vice President of Solutions for dunnhumby for providing this Statistics in Practice.

In Chapter 14 we presented simple linear regression and demonstrated its use in developing an estimated regression equation that describes the relationship between two variables. Recall that the variable being predicted or explained is called the dependent variable and the variable being used to predict or explain the dependent variable is called the independent variable. In this chapter we continue our study of regression analysis by considering situations involving two or more independent variables. This subject area, called **multiple regression analysis**, enables us to consider more factors and thus obtain better predictions than are possible with simple linear regression.

15.1 Multiple Regression Model

Multiple regression analysis is the study of how a dependent variable y is related to two or more independent variables. In the general case, we will use p to denote the number of independent variables.

Regression Model and Regression Equation

The concepts of a regression model and a regression equation introduced in the preceding chapter are applicable in the multiple regression case. The equation that describes how the dependent variable y is related to the independent variables $x_1, x_2, \ldots, x_p$ and an error term is called the **multiple regression model**. We begin with the assumption that the multiple regression model takes the following form.

MULTIPLE REGRESSION MODEL

$$y = \beta_0 + \beta_1 x_1 + \beta_2 x_2 + \cdots + \beta_p x_p + \epsilon \qquad (15.1)$$

In the multiple regression model, $\beta_0, \beta_1, \beta_2, \ldots, \beta_p$ are the parameters and the error term ϵ (the Greek letter epsilon) is a random variable. A close examination of this model reveals that y is a linear function of $x_1, x_2, \ldots, x_p$ (the $\beta_0 + \beta_1 x_1 + \beta_2 x_2 + \cdots + \beta_p x_p$ part) plus the error term ϵ. The error term accounts for the variability in y that cannot be explained by the linear effect of the p independent variables.

In Section 15.4 we will discuss the assumptions for the multiple regression model and ϵ. One of the assumptions is that the mean or expected value of ϵ is zero. A consequence of this assumption is that the mean or expected value of y, denoted $E(y)$, is equal to $\beta_0 + \beta_1 x_1 + \beta_2 x_2 + \cdots + \beta_p x_p$. The equation that describes how the mean value of y is related to $x_1, x_2, \ldots, x_p$ is called the **multiple regression equation**.

MULTIPLE REGRESSION EQUATION

$$E(y) = \beta_0 + \beta_1 x_1 + \beta_2 x_2 + \cdots + \beta_p x_p \qquad (15.2)$$

Estimated Multiple Regression Equation

If the values of $\beta_0, \beta_1, \beta_2, \ldots, \beta_p$ were known, equation (15.2) could be used to compute the mean value of y at given values of $x_1, x_2, \ldots, x_p$. Unfortunately, these parameter values will not, in general, be known and must be estimated from sample data. A simple random sample is used to compute sample statistics $b_0, b_1, b_2, \ldots, b_p$ that are used as the point

FIGURE 15.1   THE ESTIMATION PROCESS FOR MULTIPLE REGRESSION

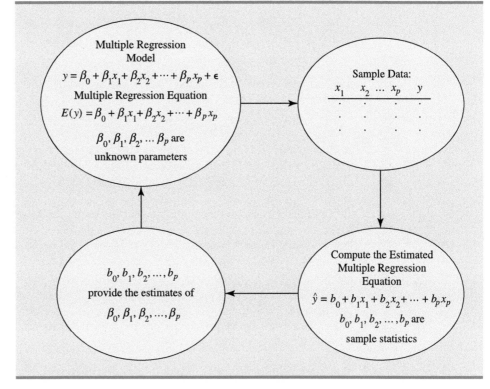

In simple linear regression, b_0 and b_1 were the sample statistics used to estimate the parameters β_0 and β_1. Multiple regression parallels this statistical inference process, with b_0, $b_1, b_2, \ldots, b_p$ denoting the sample statistics used to estimate the parameters $\beta_0, \beta_1, \beta_2, \ldots, \beta_p$.

estimators of the parameters $\beta_0, \beta_1, \beta_2, \ldots, \beta_p$. These sample statistics provide the following **estimated multiple regression equation**.

ESTIMATED MULTIPLE REGRESSION EQUATION

$$\hat{y} = b_0 + b_1x_1 + b_2x_2 + \cdots + b_px_p \qquad \textbf{(15.3)}$$

where

$b_0, b_1, b_2, \ldots, b_p$ are the estimates of $\beta_0, \beta_1, \beta_2, \ldots, \beta_p$
$\hat{y}$ = predicted value of the dependent variable

The estimation process for multiple regression is shown in Figure 15.1.

Least Squares Method

In Chapter 14, we used the **least squares method** to develop the estimated regression equation that best approximated the straight-line relationship between the dependent and independent variables. This same approach is used to develop the estimated multiple regression equation. The least squares criterion is restated as follows.

LEAST SQUARES CRITERION

$$\min \Sigma(y_i - \hat{y}_i)^2 \qquad \textbf{(15.4)}$$

where

y_i = observed value of the dependent variable for the ith observation

$\hat{y}_i$ = predicted value of the dependent variable for the ith observation

The predicted values of the dependent variable are computed by using the estimated multiple regression equation,

$$\hat{y} = b_0 + b_1 x_1 + b_2 x_2 + \cdots + b_p x_p$$

As expression (15.4) shows, the least squares method uses sample data to provide the values of $b_0, b_1, b_2, \ldots, b_p$ that make the sum of squared residuals [the deviations between the observed values of the dependent variable (y_i) and the predicted values of the dependent variable ($\hat{y}_i$)] a minimum.

In Chapter 14 we presented formulas for computing the least squares estimators b_0 and b_1 for the estimated simple linear regression equation $\hat{y} = b_0 + b_1 x$. With relatively small data sets, we were able to use those formulas to compute b_0 and b_1 by manual calculations. In multiple regression, however, the presentation of the formulas for the regression coefficients $b_0, b_1, b_2, \ldots, b_p$ involves the use of matrix algebra and is beyond the scope of this text. Therefore, in presenting multiple regression, we focus on how computer software packages can be used to obtain the estimated regression equation and other information. The emphasis will be on how to interpret the computer output rather than on how to make the multiple regression computations.

An Example: Butler Trucking Company

As an illustration of multiple regression analysis, we will consider a problem faced by the Butler Trucking Company, an independent trucking company in southern California. A major portion of Butler's business involves deliveries throughout its local area. To develop better work schedules, the managers want to predict the total daily travel time for their drivers.

Initially the managers believed that the total daily travel time would be closely related to the number of miles traveled in making the daily deliveries. A simple random sample of 10 driving assignments provided the data shown in Table 15.1 and the scatter diagram shown in Figure 15.2. After reviewing this scatter diagram, the managers hypothesized that the simple linear regression model $y = \beta_0 + \beta_1 x_1 + \epsilon$ could be used to describe the relationship between the total travel time (y) and the number of miles traveled (x_1). To estimate

TABLE 15.1   PRELIMINARY DATA FOR BUTLER TRUCKING

Driving Assignment	x_1 = Miles Traveled	y = Travel Time (hours)
1	100	9.3
2	50	4.8
3	100	8.9
4	100	6.5
5	50	4.2
6	80	6.2
7	75	7.4
8	65	6.0
9	90	7.6
10	90	6.1

FIGURE 15.2   SCATTER DIAGRAM OF PRELIMINARY DATA FOR BUTLER TRUCKING

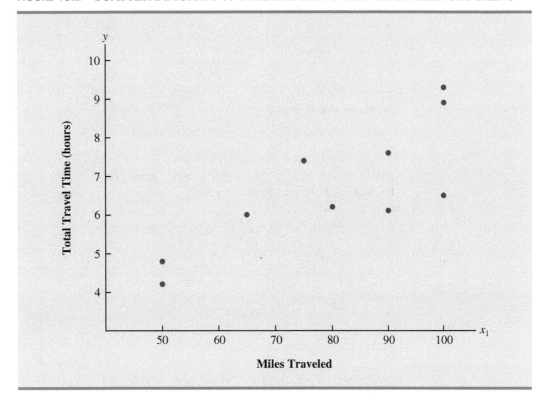

the parameters β_0 and β_1, the least squares method was used to develop the estimated regression equation.

$$\hat{y} = b_0 + b_1 x_1 \tag{15.5}$$

In Figure 15.3, we show the Minitab computer output from applying simple linear regression to the data in Table 15.1. The estimated regression equation is

$$\hat{y} = 1.27 + .0678 x_1$$

At the .05 level of significance, the F value of 15.81 and its corresponding p-value of .004 indicate that the relationship is significant; that is, we can reject H_0: $\beta_1 = 0$ because the p-value is less than $\alpha = .05$. Note that the same conclusion is obtained from the t value of 3.98 and its associated p-value of .004. Thus, we can conclude that the relationship between the total travel time and the number of miles traveled is significant; longer travel times are associated with more miles traveled. With a coefficient of determination (expressed as a percentage) of R-Sq = 66.4%, we see that 66.4% of the variability in travel time can be explained by the linear effect of the number of miles traveled. This finding is fairly good, but the managers might want to consider adding a second independent variable to explain some of the remaining variability in the dependent variable.

In attempting to identify another independent variable, the managers felt that the number of deliveries could also contribute to the total travel time. The Butler Trucking data, with the number of deliveries added, are shown in Table 15.2. The Minitab computer solution with both miles traveled (x_1) and number of deliveries (x_2) as independent variables is shown in Figure 15.4. The estimated regression equation is

The Minitab steps necessary to generate the output shown in Figure 15.4 are given in Appendix 15.1.

$$\hat{y} = -.869 + .0611 x_1 + .923 x_2 \tag{15.6}$$

**FIGURE 15.3   MINITAB OUTPUT FOR BUTLER TRUCKING WITH ONE
INDEPENDENT VARIABLE**

*In the Minitab output the
variable names* Miles *and*
Time *were entered as the
column headings on the
worksheet; thus,* $x_1 =$ Miles
and $y =$ Time.

```
The regression equation is
Time = 1.27 + 0.0678 Miles

Predictor       Coef   SE Coef      T       p
Constant       1.274     1.401   0.91   0.390
Miles        0.06783   0.01706   3.98   0.004

S = 1.00179   R-Sq = 66.4%   R-Sq(adj) = 62.2%

Analysis of Variance

SOURCE           DF       SS      MS      F       p
Regression        1   15.871  15.871  15.81   0.004
Residual Error    8    8.029   1.004
Total             9   23.900
```

In the next section we will discuss the use of the coefficient of multiple determination in measuring how good a fit is provided by this estimated regression equation. Before doing so, let us examine more carefully the values of $b_1 = .0611$ and $b_2 = .923$ in equation (15.6).

Note on Interpretation of Coefficients

One observation can be made at this point about the relationship between the estimated regression equation with only the miles traveled as an independent variable and the equation that includes the number of deliveries as a second independent variable. The value of b_1 is not the same in both cases. In simple linear regression, we interpret b_1 as an estimate of the change in y for a one-unit change in the independent variable. In multiple regression analysis, this interpretation must be modified somewhat. That is, in multiple regression analysis, we interpret each regression coefficient as follows: b_i represents an estimate of the change in y corresponding to a one-unit change in x_i when all other independent variables are held constant. In the Butler Trucking example involving two independent variables, $b_1 = .0611$. Thus,

**TABLE 15.2   DATA FOR BUTLER TRUCKING WITH MILES TRAVELED (x_1) AND NUMBER
OF DELIVERIES (x_2) AS THE INDEPENDENT VARIABLES**

WEB file

Butler

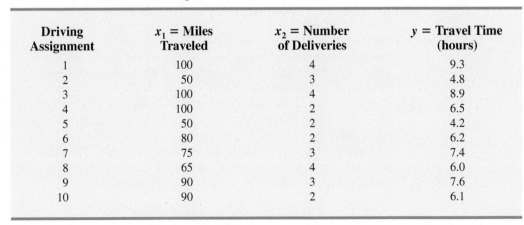

Driving Assignment	$x_1 =$ Miles Traveled	$x_2 =$ Number of Deliveries	$y =$ Travel Time (hours)
1	100	4	9.3
2	50	3	4.8
3	100	4	8.9
4	100	2	6.5
5	50	2	4.2
6	80	2	6.2
7	75	3	7.4
8	65	4	6.0
9	90	3	7.6
10	90	2	6.1

**FIGURE 15.4   MINITAB OUTPUT FOR BUTLER TRUCKING WITH TWO
INDEPENDENT VARIABLES**

*In the Minitab output the
variable names* Miles,
Deliveries, *and* Time *were
entered as the column
headings on the worksheet;
thus,* x_1 = Miles, x_2 =
Deliveries, *and* y = Time.

```
The regression equation is
Time = - 0.869 + 0.0611 Miles + 0.923 Deliveries

Predictor       Coef    SE Coef       T       p
Constant     -0.8687     0.9515   -0.91   0.392
Miles       0.061135   0.009888    6.18   0.000
Deliveries    0.9234     0.2211    4.18   0.004

S = 0.573142    R-Sq = 90.4%    R-Sq(adj) = 87.6%

Analysis of Variance

SOURCE           DF      SS       MS       F       p
Regression        2   21.601   10.800   32.88   0.000
Residual Error    7    2.299    0.328
Total             9   23.900
```

.0611 hours is an estimate of the expected increase in travel time corresponding to an increase
of one mile in the distance traveled when the number of deliveries is held constant. Similarly,
because b_2 = .923, an estimate of the expected increase in travel time corresponding to an increase of one delivery when the number of miles traveled is held constant is .923 hours.

Exercises

Note to student: The exercises involving data in this and subsequent sections were designed
to be solved using a computer software package.

Methods

1. The estimated regression equation for a model involving two independent variables and
   10 observations follows.

   $$\hat{y} = 29.1270 + .5906x_1 + .4980x_2$$

   a.   Interpret b_1 and b_2 in this estimated regression equation.
   b.   Predict y when x_1 = 180 and x_2 = 310.

2. Consider the following data for a dependent variable y and two independent variables, x_1
   and x_2.

Exer2

x_1	x_2	y
30	12	94
47	10	108
25	17	112
51	16	178
40	5	94
51	19	175
74	7	170
36	12	117
59	13	142
76	16	211

a. Develop an estimated regression equation relating y to x_1. Predict y if $x_1 = 45$.
b. Develop an estimated regression equation relating y to x_2. Predict y if $x_2 = 15$.
c. Develop an estimated regression equation relating y to x_1 and x_2. Predict y if $x_1 = 45$ and $x_2 = 15$.

3. In a regression analysis involving 30 observations, the following estimated regression equation was obtained.

$$\hat{y} = 17.6 + 3.8x_1 - 2.3x_2 + 7.6x_3 + 2.7x_4$$

a. Interpret b_1, b_2, b_3, and b_4 in this estimated regression equation.
b. Predict y when $x_1 = 10$, $x_2 = 5$, $x_3 = 1$, and $x_4 = 2$.

Applications

4. A shoe store developed the following estimated regression equation relating sales to inventory investment and advertising expenditures.

$$\hat{y} = 25 + 10x_1 + 8x_2$$

where

$$x_1 = \text{inventory investment (\$1000s)}$$
$$x_2 = \text{advertising expenditures (\$1000s)}$$
$$y = \text{sales (\$1000s)}$$

a. Predict the sales resulting from a $15,000 investment in inventory and an advertising budget of $10,000.
b. Interpret b_1 and b_2 in this estimated regression equation.

5. The owner of Showtime Movie Theaters, Inc., would like to predict weekly gross revenue as a function of advertising expenditures. Historical data for a sample of eight weeks follow.

Showtime

Weekly Gross Revenue ($1000s)	Television Advertising ($1000s)	Newspaper Advertising ($1000s)
96	5.0	1.5
90	2.0	2.0
95	4.0	1.5
92	2.5	2.5
95	3.0	3.3
94	3.5	2.3
94	2.5	4.2
94	3.0	2.5

a. Develop an estimated regression equation with the amount of television advertising as the independent variable.
b. Develop an estimated regression equation with both television advertising and newspaper advertising as the independent variables.
c. Is the estimated regression equation coefficient for television advertising expenditures the same in part (a) and in part (b)? Interpret the coefficient in each case.
d. Predict weekly gross revenue for a week when $3500 is spent on television advertising and $1800 is spent on newspaper advertising?

6. The National Football League (NFL) records a variety of performance data for individuals and teams. To investigate the importance of passing on the percentage of games won by a team, the following data show the conference (Conf), average number of passing yards per

attempt (Yds/Att), the number of interceptions thrown per attempt (Int/Att), and the percentage of games won (Win%) for a random sample of 16 NFL teams for the 2011 season (NFL website, February 12, 2012).

NFLPassing

Team	Conf	Yds/Att	Int/Att	Win%
Arizona Cardinals	NFC	6.5	.042	50.0
Atlanta Falcons	NFC	7.1	.022	62.5
Carolina Panthers	NFC	7.4	.033	37.5
Cincinnati Bengals	AFC	6.2	.026	56.3
Detroit Lions	NFC	7.2	.024	62.5
Green Bay Packers	NFC	8.9	.014	93.8
Houstan Texans	AFC	7.5	.019	62.5
Indianapolis Colts	AFC	5.6	.026	12.5
Jacksonville Jaguars	AFC	4.6	.032	31.3
Minnesota Vikings	NFC	5.8	.033	18.8
New England Patriots	AFC	8.3	.020	81.3
New Orleans Saints	NFC	8.1	.021	81.3
Oakland Raiders	AFC	7.6	.044	50.0
San Francisco 49ers	NFC	6.5	.011	81.3
Tennessee Titans	AFC	6.7	.024	56.3
Washington Redskins	NFC	6.4	.041	31.3

a. Develop the estimated regression equation that could be used to predict the percentage of games won given the average number of passing yards per attempt.

b. Develop the estimated regression equation that could be used to predict the percentage of games won given the number of interceptions thrown per attempt.

c. Develop the estimated regression equation that could be used to predict the percentage of games won given the average number of passing yards per attempt and the number of interceptions thrown per attempt.

d. The average number of passing yards per attempt for the Kansas City Chiefs was 6.2 and the number of interceptions thrown per attempt was .036. Use the estimated regression equation developed in part (c) to predict the percentage of games won by the Kansas City Chiefs. (*Note:* For the 2011 season the Kansas City Chiefs' record was 7 wins and 9 losses.) Compare your prediction to the actual percentage of games won by the Kansas City Chiefs.

7. *PC World* rated four component characteristics for 10 ultraportable laptop computers: features; performance; design; and price. Each characteristic was rated using a 0–100 point scale. An overall rating, referred to as the *PCW World* Rating, was then developed for each laptop. The following table shows the performance rating, features rating, and the *PCW World* Rating for the 10 laptop computers (*PC World* website, February 5, 2009).

Laptop

Model	Performance	Features	PCW Rating
Thinkpad X200	77	87	83
VGN-Z598U	97	85	82
U6V	83	80	81
Elitebook 2530P	77	75	78
X360	64	80	78
Thinkpad X300	56	76	78
Ideapad U110	55	81	77
Micro Express JFT2500	76	73	75
Toughbook W7	46	79	73
HP Voodoo Envy133	54	68	72

a. Determine the estimated regression equation that can be used to predict the *PCW World* Rating using the performance rating as the independent variable.

b. Determine the estimated regression equation that can be used to predict the *PCW World* Rating using both the performance rating and the features rating.

c. Predict the *PCW World* Rating for a laptop computer that has a performance rating of 80 and a features rating of 70.

8. The *Condé Nast Traveler* Gold List for 2012 provided ratings for the top 20 small cruise ships (*Condé Nast Traveler* website, March 1, 2012). The data shown below are the scores each ship received based upon the results from *Condé Nast Traveler*'s annual Readers' Choice Survey. Each score represents the percentage of respondents who rated a ship as excellent or very good on several criteria, including Shore Excursions and Food/Dining. An overall score was also reported and used to rank the ships. The highest ranked ship, the *Seabourn Odyssey,* has an overall score of 94.4, the highest component of which is 97.8 for Food/Dining.

Ships

Ship	Overall	Shore Excursions	Food/Dining
Seabourn Odyssey	94.4	90.9	97.8
Seabourn Pride	93.0	84.2	96.7
National Geographic Endeavor	92.9	100.0	88.5
Seabourn Sojourn	91.3	94.8	97.1
Paul Gauguin	90.5	87.9	91.2
Seabourn Legend	90.3	82.1	98.8
Seabourn Spirit	90.2	86.3	92.0
Silver Explorer	89.9	92.6	88.9
Silver Spirit	89.4	85.9	90.8
Seven Seas Navigator	89.2	83.3	90.5
Silver Whisperer	89.2	82.0	88.6
National Geographic Explorer	89.1	93.1	89.7
Silver Cloud	88.7	78.3	91.3
Celebrity Xpedition	87.2	91.7	73.6
Silver Shadow	87.2	75.0	89.7
Silver Wind	86.6	78.1	91.6
SeaDream II	86.2	77.4	90.9
Wind Star	86.1	76.5	91.5
Wind Surf	86.1	72.3	89.3
Wind Spirit	85.2	77.4	91.9

a. Determine an estimated regression equation that can be used to predict the overall score given the score for Shore Excursions.

b. Consider the addition of the independent variable Food/Dining. Develop the estimated regression equation that can be used to predict the overall score given the scores for Shore Excursions and Food/Dining.

c. Predict the overall score for a cruise ship with a Shore Excursions score of 80 and a Food/Dining Score of 90.

9. Waterskiing and wakeboarding are two popular water-sports. Finding a model that best suits your intended needs, whether it is waterskiing, wakeboading, or general boating, can be a difficult task. *WaterSki* magazine did extensive testing for 88 boats and provided a wide variety of information to help consumers select the best boat. A portion of the data they reported for 20 boats with a length of between 20 and 22 feet follows (*WaterSki,* January/February 2006). Beam is the maximum width of the boat in inches, HP is the horsepower of the boat's engine, and TopSpeed is the top speed in miles per hour (mph).

Make and Model	Beam	HP	TopSpeed
Calabria Cal Air Pro V-2	100.0	330	45.3
Correct Craft Air Nautique 210	91.0	330	47.3
Correct Craft Air Nautique SV-211	93.0	375	46.9
Correct Craft Ski Nautique 206 Limited	91.0	330	46.7
Gekko GTR 22	96.0	375	50.1
Gekko GTS 20	83.0	375	52.2
Malibu Response LXi	93.5	340	47.2
Malibu Sunsettter LXi	98.0	400	46.0
Malibu Sunsetter 21 XTi	98.0	340	44.0
Malibu Sunscape 21 LSV	98.0	400	47.5
Malibu Wakesetter 21 XTi	98.0	340	44.9
Malibu Wakesetter VLX	98.0	400	47.3
Malibu vRide	93.5	340	44.5
Malibu Ride XTi	93.5	320	44.5
Mastercraft ProStar 209	96.0	350	42.5
Mastercraft X-1	90.0	310	45.8
Mastercraft X-2	94.0	310	42.8
Mastercraft X-9	96.0	350	43.2
MB Sports 190 Plus	92.0	330	45.3
Svfara SVONE	91.0	330	47.7

Boats

a. Using these data, develop an estimated regression equation relating the top speed with the boat's beam and horsepower rating.

b. The Svfara SV609 has a beam of 85 inches and an engine with a 330 horsepower rating. Use the estimated regression equation developed in part (a) to predict the top speed for the Svfara SV609.

10. Major League Baseball (MLB) consists of teams that play in the American League and the National League. MLB collects a wide variety of team and player statistics. Some of the statistics often used to evaluate pitching performance are as follows:

ERA: The average number of earned runs given up by the pitcher per nine innings. An earned run is any run that the opponent scores off a particular pitcher except for runs scored as a result of errors.

SO/IP: The average number of strikeouts per inning pitched.

HR/IP: The average number of home runs per inning pitched.

R/IP: The number of runs given up per inning pitched.

The following data show values for these statistics for a random sample of 20 pitchers from the American League for the 2011 season (MLB website, March 1, 2012).

MLBPitching

Player	Team	W	L	ERA	SO/IP	HR/IP	R/IP
Verlander, J	DET	24	5	2.40	1.00	.10	.29
Beckett, J	BOS	13	7	2.89	.91	.11	.34
Wilson, C	TEX	16	7	2.94	.92	.07	.40
Sabathia, C	NYY	19	8	3.00	.97	.07	.37
Haren, D	LAA	16	10	3.17	.81	.08	.38
McCarthy, B	OAK	9	9	3.32	.72	.06	.43
Santana, E	LAA	11	12	3.38	.78	.11	.42

(*continued*)

Player	Team	W	L	ERA	SO/IP	HR/IP	R/IP
Lester, J	BOS	15	9	3.47	.95	.10	.40
Hernandez, F	SEA	14	14	3.47	.95	.08	.42
Buehrle, M	CWS	13	9	3.59	.53	.10	.45
Pineda, M	SEA	9	10	3.74	1.01	.11	.44
Colon, B	NYY	8	10	4.00	.82	.13	.52
Tomlin, J	CLE	12	7	4.25	.54	.15	.48
Pavano, C	MIN	9	13	4.30	.46	.10	.55
Danks, J	CWS	8	12	4.33	.79	.11	.52
Guthrie, J	BAL	9	17	4.33	.63	.13	.54
Lewis, C	TEX	14	10	4.40	.84	.17	.51
Scherzer, M	DET	15	9	4.43	.89	.15	.52
Davis, W	TB	11	10	4.45	.57	.13	.52
Porcello, R	DET	14	9	4.75	.57	.10	.57

a. Develop an estimated regression equation that can be used to predict the average number of runs given up per inning given the average number of strikeouts per inning pitched.

b. Develop an estimated regression equation that can be used to predict the average number of runs given up per inning given the average number of home runs per inning pitched.

c. Develop an estimated regression equation that can be used to predict the average number of runs given up per inning given the average number of strikeouts per inning pitched and the average number of home runs per inning pitched.

d. A. J. Burnett, a pitcher for the New York Yankees, had an average number of strikeouts per inning pitched of .91 and an average number of home runs per inning of .16. Use the estimated regression equation developed in part (c) to predict the average number of runs given up per inning for A. J. Burnett. (*Note:* The actual value for R/IP was .6.)

e. Suppose a suggestion was made to also use the earned run average as another independent variable in part (c). What do you think of this suggestion?

15.3 Multiple Coefficient of Determination

In simple linear regression we showed that the total sum of squares can be partitioned into two components: the sum of squares due to regression and the sum of squares due to error. The same procedure applies to the sum of squares in multiple regression.

RELATIONSHIP AMONG SST, SSR, AND SSE

$$SST = SSR + SSE \qquad (15.7)$$

where

$$SST = \text{total sum of squares} = \Sigma(y_i - \bar{y})^2$$
$$SSR = \text{sum of squares due to regression} = \Sigma(\hat{y}_i - \bar{y})^2$$
$$SSE = \text{sum of squares due to error} = \Sigma(y_i - \hat{y}_i)^2$$

Because of the computational difficulty in computing the three sums of squares, we rely on computer packages to determine those values. The analysis of variance part of the Minitab output in Figure 15.4 shows the three values for the Butler Trucking problem with two independent variables: SST = 23.900, SSR = 21.601, and SSE = 2.299. With only one independent variable (number of miles traveled), the Minitab output in Figure 15.3 shows that SST = 23.900, SSR = 15.871, and SSE = 8.029. The value of SST is the same in both cases because it does not depend on $\hat{y}$, but SSR increases and SSE decreases when a second independent variable (number of deliveries) is added. The implication is that the estimated multiple regression equation provides a better fit for the observed data.

In Chapter 14, we used the coefficient of determination, $r^2 = $ SSR/SST, to measure the goodness of fit for the estimated regression equation. The same concept applies to multiple regression. The term **multiple coefficient of determination** indicates that we are measuring the goodness of fit for the estimated multiple regression equation. The multiple coefficient of determination, denoted R^2, is computed as follows.

MULTIPLE COEFFICIENT OF DETERMINATION

$$R^2 = \frac{\text{SSR}}{\text{SST}} \tag{15.8}$$

The multiple coefficient of determination can be interpreted as the proportion of the variability in the dependent variable that can be explained by the estimated multiple regression equation. Hence, when multiplied by 100, it can be interpreted as the percentage of the variability in y that can be explained by the estimated regression equation.

In the two-independent-variable Butler Trucking example, with SSR = 21.601 and SST = 23.900, we have

$$R^2 = \frac{21.601}{23.900} = .904$$

Therefore, 90.4% of the variability in travel time y is explained by the estimated multiple regression equation with miles traveled and number of deliveries as the independent variables. In Figure 15.4, we see that the multiple coefficient of determination (expressed as a percentage) is also provided by the Minitab output; it is denoted by R-Sq = 90.4%.

Adding independent variables causes the prediction errors to become smaller, thus reducing the sum of squares due to error, SSE. Because SSR = SST − SSE, when SSE becomes smaller, SSR becomes larger, causing $R^2 = $ SSR/SST to increase.

Figure 15.3 shows that the R-Sq value for the estimated regression equation with only one independent variable, number of miles traveled (x_1), is 66.4%. Thus, the percentage of the variability in travel times that is explained by the estimated regression equation increases from 66.4% to 90.4% when number of deliveries is added as a second independent variable. In general, R^2 always increases as independent variables are added to the model.

Many analysts prefer adjusting R^2 for the number of independent variables to avoid overestimating the impact of adding an independent variable on the amount of variability explained by the estimated regression equation. With n denoting the number of observations and p denoting the number of independent variables, the **adjusted multiple coefficient of determination** is computed as follows.

If a variable is added to the model, R^2 becomes larger even if the variable added is not statistically significant. The adjusted multiple coefficient of determination compensates for the number of independent variables in the model.

ADJUSTED MULTIPLE COEFFICIENT OF DETERMINATION

$$R_a^2 = 1 - (1 - R^2)\frac{n - 1}{n - p - 1} \tag{15.9}$$

For the Butler Trucking example with $n = 10$ and $p = 2$, we have

$$R_a^2 = 1 - (1 - .904)\frac{10 - 1}{10 - 2 - 1} = .88$$

Thus, after adjusting for the two independent variables, we have an adjusted multiple coefficient of determination of .88. This value (expressed as a percentage) is provided by the Minitab output in Figure 15.4 as R-Sq(adj) = 87.6%; the value we calculated differs because we used a rounded value of R^2 in the calculation.

NOTES AND COMMENTS

If the value of R^2 is small and the model contains a large number of independent variables, the adjusted coefficient of determination can take a negative value; in such cases, Minitab sets the adjusted coefficient of determination to zero.

Exercises

Methods

11. In exercise 1, the following estimated regression equation based on 10 observations was presented.

$$\hat{y} = 29.1270 + .5906x_1 + .4980x_2$$

The values of SST and SSR are 6724.125 and 6216.375, respectively.
    a. Find SSE.
    b. Compute R^2.
    c. Compute R_a^2.
    d. Comment on the goodness of fit.

12. In exercise 2, 10 observations were provided for a dependent variable y and two independent variables x_1 and x_2; for these data SST = 15,182.9, and SSR = 14,052.2.
    a. Compute R^2.
    b. Compute R_a^2.
    c. Does the estimated regression equation explain a large amount of the variability in the data? Explain.

13. In exercise 3, the following estimated regression equation based on 30 observations was presented.

$$\hat{y} = 17.6 + 3.8x_1 - 2.3x_2 + 7.6x_3 + 2.7x_4$$

The values of SST and SSR are 1805 and 1760, respectively.

a. Compute R^2.
b. Compute R^2_a.
c. Comment on the goodness of fit.

Applications

14. In exercise 4, the following estimated regression equation relating sales to inventory investment and advertising expenditures was given.

$$\hat{y} = 25 + 10x_1 + 8x_2$$

The data used to develop the model came from a survey of 10 stores; for those data, SST = 16,000 and SSR = 12,000.
   a. For the estimated regression equation given, compute R^2.
   b. Compute R^2_a.
   c. Does the model appear to explain a large amount of variability in the data? Explain.

15. In exercise 5, the owner of Showtime Movie Theaters, Inc., used multiple regression analysis to predict gross revenue (y) as a function of television advertising (x_1) and newspaper advertising (x_2). The estimated regression equation was

$$\hat{y} = 83.2 + 2.29x_1 + 1.30x_2$$

Showtime

The computer solution provided SST = 25.5 and SSR = 23.435.
   a. Compute and interpret R^2 and R^2_a.
   b. When television advertising was the only independent variable, $R^2 = .653$ and $R^2_a = .595$. Do you prefer the multiple regression results? Explain.

NFLPassing

16. In exercise 6, data were given on the average number of passing yards per attempt (Yds/Att), the number of interceptions thrown per attempt (Int/Att), and the percentage of games won (Win%) for a random sample of 16 National Football League (NFL) teams for the 2011 season (NFL website, February 12, 2012).
   a. Did the estimated regression equation that uses only the average number of passing yards per attempt as the independent variable to predict the percentage of games won provide a good fit?
   b. Discuss the benefit of using both the average number of passing yards per attempt and the number of interceptions thrown per attempt to predict the percentage of games won.

Boats

17. In exercise 9, an estimated regression equation was developed relating the top speed for a boat to the boat's beam and horsepower rating.
   a. Compute and interpret and R^2 and R^2_a.
   b. Does the estimated regression equation provide a good fit to the data? Explain.

MLBPitching

18. Refer to exercise 10, where Major League Baseball (MLB) pitching statistics were reported for a random sample of 20 pitchers from the American League for the 2011 season (MLB website, March 1, 2012).
   a. In part (c) of exercise 10, an estimated regression equation was developed relating the average number of runs given up per inning pitched given the average number of strikeouts per inning pitched and the average number of home runs per inning pitched. What are the values of R^2 and R^2_a?
   b. Does the estimated regression equation provide a good fit to the data? Explain.
   c. Suppose the earned run average (ERA) is used as the dependent variable in part (c) instead of the average number of runs given up per inning pitched. Does the estimated regression equation that uses the ERA provide a good fit to the data? Explain.

Model Assumptions

In Section 15.1 we introduced the following multiple regression model.

MULTIPLE REGRESSION MODEL

$$y = \beta_0 + \beta_1 x_1 + \beta_2 x_2 + \cdots + \beta_p x_p + \epsilon \tag{15.10}$$

The assumptions about the error term ϵ in the multiple regression model parallel those for the simple linear regression model.

ASSUMPTIONS ABOUT THE ERROR TERM ϵ IN THE MULTIPLE REGRESSION MODEL $y = \beta_0 + \beta_1 x_1 + \cdots + \beta_p x_p + \epsilon$

1. The error term ϵ is a random variable with mean or expected value of zero; that is, $E(\epsilon) = 0$.
   Implication: For given values of $x_1, x_2, \ldots, x_p$, the expected, or average, value of y is given by

$$E(y) = \beta_0 + \beta_1 x_1 + \beta_2 x_2 + \cdots + \beta_p x_p \tag{15.11}$$

   Equation (15.11) is the multiple regression equation we introduced in Section 15.1. In this equation, $E(y)$ represents the average of all possible values of y that might occur for the given values of $x_1, x_2, \ldots, x_p$.
2. The variance of ϵ is denoted by σ^2 and is the same for all values of the independent variables $x_1, x_2, \ldots, x_p$.
   Implication: The variance of y about the regression line equals σ^2 and is the same for all values of $x_1, x_2, \ldots, x_p$.
3. The values of ϵ are independent.
   Implication: The value of ϵ for a particular set of values for the independent variables is not related to the value of ϵ for any other set of values.
4. The error term ϵ is a normally distributed random variable reflecting the deviation between the y value and the expected value of y given by $\beta_0 + \beta_1 x_1 + \beta_2 x_2 + \cdots + \beta_p x_p$.
   Implication: Because $\beta_0, \beta_1, \ldots, \beta_p$ are constants for the given values of $x_1, x_2, \ldots, x_p$, the dependent variable y is also a normally distributed random variable.

To obtain more insight about the form of the relationship given by equation (15.11), consider the following two-independent-variable multiple regression equation.

$$E(y) = \beta_0 + \beta_1 x_1 + \beta_2 x_2$$

The graph of this equation is a plane in three-dimensional space. Figure 15.5 provides an example of such a graph. Note that the value of ϵ shown is the difference between the actual y value and the expected value of y, $E(y)$, when $x_1 = x_1^*$ and $x_2 = x_2^*$.

FIGURE 15.5 GRAPH OF THE REGRESSION EQUATION FOR MULTIPLE REGRESSION ANALYSIS WITH TWO INDEPENDENT VARIABLES

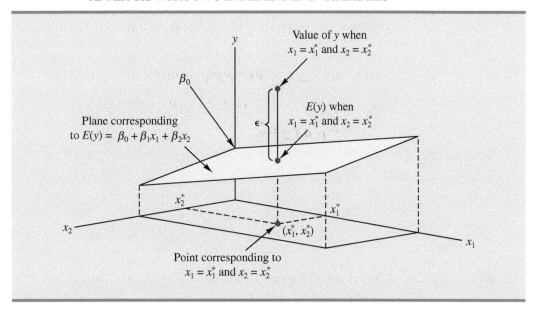

In regression analysis, the term *response variable* is often used in place of the term *dependent variable*. Furthermore, since the multiple regression equation generates a plane or surface, its graph is called a *response surface*.

15.5 Testing for Significance

In this section we show how to conduct significance tests for a multiple regression relationship. The significance tests we used in simple linear regression were a t test and an F test. In simple linear regression, both tests provide the same conclusion; that is, if the null hypothesis is rejected, we conclude that $\beta_1 \neq 0$. In multiple regression, the t test and the F test have different purposes.

1. The F test is used to determine whether a significant relationship exists between the dependent variable and the set of all the independent variables; we will refer to the F test as the test for *overall significance*.
2. If the F test shows an overall significance, the t test is used to determine whether each of the individual independent variables is significant. A separate t test is conducted for each of the independent variables in the model; we refer to each of these t tests as a test for *individual significance*.

In the material that follows, we will explain the F test and the t test and apply each to the Butler Trucking Company example.

F Test

The multiple regression model as defined in Section 15.4 is

$$y = \beta_0 + \beta_1 x_1 + \beta_2 x_2 + \cdots + \beta_p x_p + \epsilon$$

The hypotheses for the F test involve the parameters of the multiple regression model.

$$H_0: \beta_1 = \beta_2 = \cdots = \beta_p = 0$$
$$H_a: \text{One or more of the parameters is not equal to zero}$$

If H_0 is rejected, the test gives us sufficient statistical evidence to conclude that one or more of the parameters is not equal to zero and that the overall relationship between y and the set of independent variables $x_1, x_2, \ldots, x_p$ is significant. However, if H_0 cannot be rejected, we do not have sufficient evidence to conclude that a significant relationship is present.

Before describing the steps of the F test, we need to review the concept of *mean square*. A mean square is a sum of squares divided by its corresponding degrees of freedom. In the multiple regression case, the total sum of squares has $n - 1$ degrees of freedom, the sum of squares due to regression (SSR) has p degrees of freedom, and the sum of squares due to error has $n - p - 1$ degrees of freedom. Hence, the mean square due to regression (MSR) is SSR/p and the mean square due to error (MSE) is SSE/$(n - p - 1)$.

$$MSR = \frac{SSR}{p} \qquad (15.12)$$

and

$$MSE = \frac{SSE}{n - p - 1} \qquad (15.13)$$

As discussed in Chapter 14, MSE provides an unbiased estimate of σ^2, the variance of the error term ϵ. If $H_0: \beta_1 = \beta_2 = \cdots = \beta_p = 0$ is true, MSR also provides an unbiased estimate of σ^2, and the value of MSR/MSE should be close to 1. However, if H_0 is false, MSR overestimates σ^2 and the value of MSR/MSE becomes larger. To determine how large the value of MSR/MSE must be to reject H_0, we make use of the fact that if H_0 is true and the assumptions about the multiple regression model are valid, the sampling distribution of MSR/MSE is an F distribution with p degrees of freedom in the numerator and $n - p - 1$ in the denominator. A summary of the F test for significance in multiple regression follows.

F TEST FOR OVERALL SIGNIFICANCE

$H_0: \beta_1 = \beta_2 = \cdots = \beta_p = 0$
H_a: One or more of the parameters is not equal to zero

TEST STATISTIC

$$F = \frac{MSR}{MSE} \qquad (15.14)$$

REJECTION RULE

p-value approach: Reject H_0 if p-value $\leq \alpha$
Critical value approach: Reject H_0 if $F \geq F_\alpha$

where F_α is based on an F distribution with p degrees of freedom in the numerator and $n - p - 1$ degrees of freedom in the denominator.

Let us apply the F test to the Butler Trucking Company multiple regression problem. With two independent variables, the hypotheses are written as follows.

$$H_0: \beta_1 = \beta_2 = 0$$
$$H_a: \beta_1 \text{ and/or } \beta_2 \text{ is not equal to zero}$$

FIGURE 15.6 MINITAB OUTPUT FOR BUTLER TRUCKING WITH TWO INDEPENDENT
VARIABLES, MILES TRAVELED (x_1) AND NUMBER OF DELIVERIES (x_2)

```
The regression equation is
Time = - 0.869 + 0.0611 Miles + 0.923 Deliveries

Predictor        Coef    SE Coef      T      p
Constant       -0.8687    0.9515   -0.91   0.392
Miles         0.061135  0.009888    6.18   0.000
Deliveries      0.9234    0.2211    4.18   0.004

S = 0.573142   R-Sq = 90.4%   R-Sq(adj) = 87.6%

Analysis of Variance

SOURCE           DF       SS       MS       F      p
Regression        2   21.601   10.800   32.88   0.000
Residual Error    7    2.299    0.328
Total             9   23.900
```

Figure 15.6 is the Minitab output for the multiple regression model with miles traveled (x_1) and number of deliveries (x_2) as the two independent variables. In the analysis of variance part of the output, we see that MSR = 10.8 and MSE = .328. Using equation (15.14), we obtain the test statistic.

$$F = \frac{10.8}{.328} = 32.9$$

Note that the F value on the Minitab output is $F = 32.88$; the value we calculated differs because we used rounded values for MSR and MSE in the calculation. Using $\alpha = .01$, the p-value = 0.000 in the last column of the analysis of variance table (Figure 15.6) indicates that we can reject H_0: $\beta_1 = \beta_2 = 0$ because the p-value is less than $\alpha = .01$. Alternatively, Table 4 of Appendix B shows that with two degrees of freedom in the numerator and seven degrees of freedom in the denominator, $F_{.01} = 9.55$. With $32.9 > 9.55$, we reject H_0: $\beta_1 = \beta_2 = 0$ and conclude that a significant relationship is present between travel time y and the two independent variables, miles traveled and number of deliveries.

As noted previously, the mean square error provides an unbiased estimate of σ^2, the variance of the error term ϵ. Referring to Figure 15.6, we see that the estimate of σ^2 is MSE = .328. The square root of MSE is the estimate of the standard deviation of the error term. As defined in Section 14.5, this standard deviation is called the standard error of the estimate and is denoted s. Hence, we have $s = \sqrt{MSE} = \sqrt{.328} = .573$. Note that the value of the standard error of the estimate appears in the Minitab output in Figure 15.6.

Table 15.3 is the general analysis of variance (ANOVA) table that provides the F test results for a multiple regression model. The value of the F test statistic appears in the last column and can be compared to F_α with p degrees of freedom in the numerator and $n - p - 1$ degrees of freedom in the denominator to make the hypothesis test conclusion. By reviewing the Minitab output for Butler Trucking Company in Figure 15.6, we see that Minitab's analysis of variance table contains this information. Moreover, Minitab also provides the p-value corresponding to the F test statistic.

TABLE 15.3   ANOVA TABLE FOR A MULTIPLE REGRESSION MODEL WITH p INDEPENDENT VARIABLES

Source	Sum of Squares	Degrees of Freedom	Mean Square	F
Regression	SSR	p	$\text{MSR} = \dfrac{\text{SSR}}{p}$	$F = \dfrac{\text{MSR}}{\text{MSE}}$
Error	SSE	$n - p - 1$	$\text{MSE} = \dfrac{\text{SSE}}{n - p - 1}$	
Total	SST	$n - 1$		

t Test

If the F test shows that the multiple regression relationship is significant, a t test can be conducted to determine the significance of each of the individual parameters. The t test for individual significance follows.

t TEST FOR INDIVIDUAL SIGNIFICANCE

For any parameter β_i

$$H_0: \beta_i = 0$$
$$H_a: \beta_i \neq 0$$

TEST STATISTIC

$$t = \frac{b_i}{s_{b_i}} \tag{15.15}$$

REJECTION RULE

p-value approach: Reject H_0 if p-value $\leq \alpha$

Critical value approach: Reject H_0 if $t \leq -t_{\alpha/2}$ or if $t \geq t_{\alpha/2}$

where $t_{\alpha/2}$ is based on a t distribution with $n - p - 1$ degrees of freedom.

In the test statistic, s_{b_i} is the estimate of the standard deviation of b_i. The value of s_{b_i} will be provided by the computer software package.

Let us conduct the t test for the Butler Trucking regression problem. Refer to the section of Figure 15.6 that shows the Minitab output for the t-ratio calculations. Values of b_1, b_2, s_{b_1}, and s_{b_2} are as follows.

$$b_1 = .061135 \quad s_{b_1} = .009888$$
$$b_2 = .9234 \quad\ \ \ s_{b_2} = .2211$$

Using equation (15.15), we obtain the test statistic for the hypotheses involving parameters β_1 and β_2.

$$t = .061135/.009888 = 6.18$$
$$t = .9234/.2211 = 4.18$$

Note that both of these t-ratio values and the corresponding p-values are provided by the Minitab output in Figure 15.6. Using $\alpha = .01$, the p-values of .000 and .004 on the Minitab output indicate that we can reject $H_0: \beta_1 = 0$ and $H_0: \beta_2 = 0$. Hence, both parameters are statistically significant. Alternatively, Table 2 of Appendix B shows that with $n - p - 1 = 10 - 2 - 1 = 7$ degrees of freedom, $t_{.005} = 3.499$. With $6.18 > 3.499$, we reject $H_0: \beta_1 = 0$. Similarly, with $4.18 > 3.499$, we reject $H_0: \beta_2 = 0$.

Multicollinearity

We use the term *independent variable* in regression analysis to refer to any variable being used to predict or explain the value of the dependent variable. The term does not mean, however, that the independent variables themselves are independent in any statistical sense. On the contrary, most independent variables in a multiple regression problem are correlated to some degree with one another. For example, in the Butler Trucking example involving the two independent variables x_1 (miles traveled) and x_2 (number of deliveries), we could treat the miles traveled as the dependent variable and the number of deliveries as the independent variable to determine whether those two variables are themselves related. We could then compute the sample correlation coefficient $r_{x_1 x_2}$ to determine the extent to which the variables are related. Doing so yields $r_{x_1 x_2} = .16$. Thus, we find some degree of linear association between the two independent variables. In multiple regression analysis, **multicollinearity** refers to the correlation among the independent variables.

To provide a better perspective of the potential problems of multicollinearity, let us consider a modification of the Butler Trucking example. Instead of x_2 being the number of deliveries, let x_2 denote the number of gallons of gasoline consumed. Clearly, x_1 (the miles traveled) and x_2 are related; that is, we know that the number of gallons of gasoline used depends on the number of miles traveled. Hence, we would conclude logically that x_1 and x_2 are highly correlated independent variables.

Assume that we obtain the equation $\hat{y} = b_0 + b_1 x_1 + b_2 x_2$ and find that the F test shows the relationship to be significant. Then suppose we conduct a t test on β_1 to determine whether $\beta_1 \neq 0$, and we cannot reject $H_0: \beta_1 = 0$. Does this result mean that travel time is not related to miles traveled? Not necessarily. What it probably means is that with x_2 already in the model, x_1 does not make a significant contribution to determining the value of y. This interpretation makes sense in our example; if we know the amount of gasoline consumed, we do not gain much additional information useful in predicting y by knowing the miles traveled. Similarly, a t test might lead us to conclude $\beta_2 = 0$ on the grounds that, with x_1 in the model, knowledge of the amount of gasoline consumed does not add much.

A sample correlation coefficient greater than $+.7$ or less than $-.7$ for two independent variables is a rule of thumb warning of potential problems with multicollinearity.

To summarize, in t tests for the significance of individual parameters, the difficulty caused by multicollinearity is that it is possible to conclude that none of the individual parameters are significantly different from zero when an F test on the overall multiple regression equation indicates a significant relationship. This problem is avoided when there is little correlation among the independent variables.

Statisticians have developed several tests for determining whether multicollinearity is high enough to cause problems. According to the rule of thumb test, multicollinearity is a potential problem if the absolute value of the sample correlation coefficient exceeds .7 for any two of the independent variables. The other types of tests are more advanced and beyond the scope of this text.

When the independent variables are highly correlated, it is not possible to determine the separate effect of any particular independent variable on the dependent variable.

If possible, every attempt should be made to avoid including independent variables that are highly correlated. In practice, however, strict adherence to this policy is rarely possible. When decision makers have reason to believe substantial multicollinearity is present, they must realize that separating the effects of the individual independent variables on the dependent variable is difficult.

NOTES AND COMMENTS

Ordinarily, multicollinearity does not affect the way in which we perform our regression analysis or interpret the output from a study. However, when multicollinearity is severe—that is, when two or more of the independent variables are highly correlated with one another—we can have difficulty interpreting the results of t tests on the individual parameters. In addition to the type of problem illustrated in this section, severe cases of multicollinearity have been shown to result in least squares estimates that have the wrong sign. That is,

in simulated studies where researchers created the underlying regression model and then applied the least squares technique to develop estimates of β_0, β_1, β_2, and so on, it has been shown that under conditions of high multicollinearity the least squares estimates can have a sign opposite that of the parameter being estimated. For example, β_2 might actually be $+10$ and b_2, its estimate, might turn out to be -2. Thus, little faith can be placed in the individual coefficients if multicollinearity is present to a high degree.

Exercises

Methods

19. In exercise 1, the following estimated regression equation based on 10 observations was presented.

$$\hat{y} = 29.1270 + .5906x_1 + .4980x_2$$

Here SST = 6724.125, SSR = 6216.375, $s_{b_1} = .0813$, and $s_{b_2} = .0567$.
   a. Compute MSR and MSE.
   b. Compute F and perform the appropriate F test. Use $\alpha = .05$.
   c. Perform a t test for the significance of β_1. Use $\alpha = .05$.
   d. Perform a t test for the significance of β_2. Use $\alpha = .05$.

20. Refer to the data presented in exercise 2. The estimated regression equation for these data is

$$\hat{y} = -18.37 + 2.01x_1 + 4.74x_2$$

Here SST = 15,182.9, SSR = 14,052.2, $s_{b_1} = .2471$, and $s_{b_2} = .9484$.
   a. Test for a significant relationship among x_1, x_2, and y. Use $\alpha = .05$.
   b. Is β_1 significant? Use $\alpha = .05$.
   c. Is β_2 significant? Use $\alpha = .05$.

21. The following estimated regression equation was developed for a model involving two independent variables.

$$\hat{y} = 40.7 + 8.63x_1 + 2.71x_2$$

After x_2 was dropped from the model, the least squares method was used to obtain an estimated regression equation involving only x_1 as an independent variable.

$$\hat{y} = 42.0 + 9.01x_1$$

   a. Give an interpretation of the coefficient of x_1 in both models.
   b. Could multicollinearity explain why the coefficient of x_1 differs in the two models? If so, how?

Applications

22. In exercise 4, the following estimated regression equation relating sales to inventory investment and advertising expenditures was given.

$$\hat{y} = 25 + 10x_1 + 8x_2$$

The data used to develop the model came from a survey of 10 stores; for these data SST = 16,000 and SSR = 12,000.

a. Compute SSE, MSE, and MSR.
b. Use an F test and a .05 level of significance to determine whether there is a relationship among the variables.

23. Refer to exercise 5.

   a. Use $\alpha = .01$ to test the hypotheses

$$H_0: \beta_1 = \beta_2 = 0$$
$$H_a: \beta_1 \text{ and/or } \beta_2 \text{ is not equal to zero}$$

   for the model $y = \beta_0 + \beta_1 x_1 + \beta_2 x_2 + \epsilon$, where

$$x_1 = \text{television advertising (\$1000s)}$$
$$x_2 = \text{newspaper advertising (\$1000s)}$$

   b. Use $\alpha = .05$ to test the significance of β_1. Should x_1 be dropped from the model?
   c. Use $\alpha = .05$ to test the significance of β_2. Should x_2 be dropped from the model?

24. *The Wall Street Journal* conducted a study of basketball spending at top colleges. A portion of the data showing the revenue ($ millions), percentage of wins, and the coach's salary ($ millions) for 39 of the country's top basketball programs follows (*The Wall Street Journal,* March 11–12, 2006).

School	Revenue	% Wins	Salary
Alabama	6.5	61	1.00
Arizona	16.6	63	.70
Arkansas	11.1	72	.80
Boston College	3.4	80	.53
.	.	.	.
.	.	.	.
.	.	.	.
Washington	5.0	83	.89
West Virginia	4.9	67	.70
Wichita State	3.1	75	.41
Wisconsin	12.0	66	.70

   a. Develop the estimated regression equation that can be used to predict the coach's salary given the revenue generated by the program and the percentage of wins.
   b. Use the F test to determine the overall significance of the relationship. What is your conclusion at the .05 level of significance?
   c. Use the t test to determine the significance of each independent variable. What is your conclusion at the .05 level of significance?

25. The *Condé Nast Traveler* Gold List for 2012 provided ratings for the top 20 small cruise ships (*Condé Nast Traveler* website, March 1, 2012). The data shown below are the scores each ship received based upon the results from *Condé Nast Traveler's* annual Readers' Choice Survey. Each score represents the percentage of respondents who rated a ship as excellent or very good on several criteria, including Itineraries/Schedule, Shore Excursions, and Food/Dining. An overall score was also reported and used to rank the ships. The highest ranked ship, the *Seabourn Odyssey,* has an overall score of 94.4, the highest component of which is 97.8 for Food/Dining.

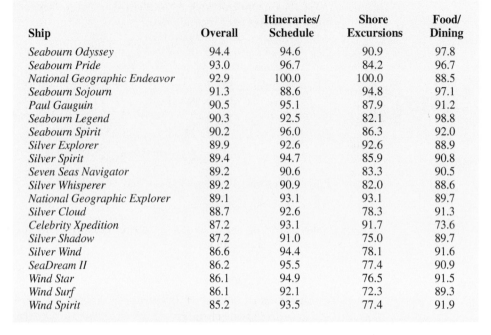

Ship	Overall	Itineraries/ Schedule	Shore Excursions	Food/ Dining
Seabourn Odyssey	94.4	94.6	90.9	97.8
Seabourn Pride	93.0	96.7	84.2	96.7
National Geographic Endeavor	92.9	100.0	100.0	88.5
Seabourn Sojourn	91.3	88.6	94.8	97.1
Paul Gauguin	90.5	95.1	87.9	91.2
Seabourn Legend	90.3	92.5	82.1	98.8
Seabourn Spirit	90.2	96.0	86.3	92.0
Silver Explorer	89.9	92.6	92.6	88.9
Silver Spirit	89.4	94.7	85.9	90.8
Seven Seas Navigator	89.2	90.6	83.3	90.5
Silver Whisperer	89.2	90.9	82.0	88.6
National Geographic Explorer	89.1	93.1	93.1	89.7
Silver Cloud	88.7	92.6	78.3	91.3
Celebrity Xpedition	87.2	93.1	91.7	73.6
Silver Shadow	87.2	91.0	75.0	89.7
Silver Wind	86.6	94.4	78.1	91.6
SeaDream II	86.2	95.5	77.4	90.9
Wind Star	86.1	94.9	76.5	91.5
Wind Surf	86.1	92.1	72.3	89.3
Wind Spirit	85.2	93.5	77.4	91.9

a. Determine the estimated regression equation that can be used to predict the overall score given the scores for Itineraries/Schedule, Shore Excursions, and Food/Dining.

b. Use the F test to determine the overall significance of the relationship. What is your conclusion at the .05 level of significance?

c. Use the t test to determine the significance of each independent variable. What is your conclusion at the .05 level of significance?

d. Remove any independent variable that is not significant from the estimated regression equation. What is your recommended estimated regression equation?

26. In exercise 10, data showing the values of several pitching statistics for a random sample of 20 pitchers from the American League of Major League Baseball were provided. In part (c) of this exercise an estimated regression equation was developed to predict the average number of runs given up per inning pitched (R/IP) given the average number of strikeouts per inning pitched (SO/IP) and the average number of home runs per inning pitched (HR/IP).

a. Use the F test to determine the overall significance of the relationship. What is your conclusion at the .05 level of significance?

b. Use the t test to determine the significance of each independent variable. What is your conclusion at the .05 level of significance?

15.6 Using the Estimated Regression Equation for Estimation and Prediction

The procedures for estimating the mean value of y and predicting an individual value of y in multiple regression are similar to those in regression analysis involving one independent variable. First, recall that in Chapter 14 we showed that the point estimate of the expected value of y for a given value of x was the same as the point estimate of an individual value of y. In both cases, we used $\hat{y} = b_0 + b_1x$ as the point estimate.

In multiple regression we use the same procedure. That is, we substitute the given values of $x_1, x_2, \ldots, x_p$ into the estimated regression equation and use the corresponding value of $\hat{y}$ as the point estimate. Suppose that for the Butler Trucking example we want to use the

TABLE 15.4   THE 95% CONFIDENCE AND PREDICTION INTERVALS FOR BUTLER TRUCKING

Value of x_1	Value of x_2	Confidence Interval		Prediction Interval	
		Lower Limit	Upper Limit	Lower Limit	Upper Limit
50	2	3.146	4.924	2.414	5.656
50	3	4.127	5.789	3.368	6.548
50	4	4.815	6.948	4.157	7.607
100	2	6.258	7.926	5.500	8.683
100	3	7.385	8.645	6.520	9.510
100	4	8.135	9.742	7.362	10.515

estimated regression equation involving x_1 (miles traveled) and x_2 (number of deliveries) to develop two interval estimates:

1. A *confidence interval* of the mean travel time for all trucks that travel 100 miles and make two deliveries
2. A *prediction interval* of the travel time for *one specific* truck that travels 100 miles and makes two deliveries

Using the estimated regression equation $\hat{y} = -.869 + .0611x_1 + .923x_2$ with $x_1 = 100$ and $x_2 = 2$, we obtain the following value of $\hat{y}$.

$$\hat{y} = -.869 + .0611(100) + .923(2) = 7.09$$

Hence, the point estimate of travel time in both cases is approximately seven hours.

To develop interval estimates for the mean value of y and for an individual value of y, we use a procedure similar to that for regression analysis involving one independent variable. The formulas required are beyond the scope of the text, but computer packages for multiple regression analysis will often provide confidence intervals once the values of x_1, $x_2, \ldots, x_p$ are specified by the user. In Table 15.4 we show the 95% confidence and prediction intervals for the Butler Trucking example for selected values of x_1 and x_2; these values were obtained using Minitab. Note that the interval estimate for an individual value of y is wider than the interval estimate for the expected value of y. This difference simply reflects the fact that for given values of x_1 and x_2 we can estimate the mean travel time for all trucks with more precision than we can predict the travel time for one specific truck.

Exercises

Methods

27. In exercise 1, the following estimated regression equation based on 10 observations was presented.

$$\hat{y} = 29.1270 + .5906x_1 + .4980x_2$$

   a.   Develop a point estimate of the mean value of y when $x_1 = 180$ and $x_2 = 310$.
   b.   Develop a point estimate for an individual value of y when $x_1 = 180$ and $x_2 = 310$.

28. Refer to the data in exercise 2. The estimated regression equation for those data is

$$\hat{y} = -18.4 + 2.01x_1 + 4.74x_2$$

   a.   Develop a 95% confidence interval for the mean value of y when $x_1 = 45$ and $x_2 = 15$.
   b.   Develop a 95% prediction interval for y when $x_1 = 45$ and $x_2 = 15$.

Applications

29. In exercise 5, the owner of Showtime Movie Theaters, Inc., used multiple regression analysis to predict gross revenue (y) as a function of television advertising (x_1) and newspaper advertising (x_2). The estimated regression equation was

$$\hat{y} = 83.2 + 2.29x_1 + 1.30x_2$$

a. What is the gross revenue expected for a week when $3500 is spent on television advertising ($x_1 = 3.5$) and $1800 is spent on newspaper advertising ($x_2 = 1.8$)?
b. Provide a 95% confidence interval for the mean revenue of all weeks with the expenditures listed in part (a).
c. Provide a 95% prediction interval for next week's revenue, assuming that the advertising expenditures will be allocated as in part (a).

Boats

30. In exercise 9 an estimated regression equation was developed relating the top speed for a boat to the boat's beam and horsepower rating.
a. Develop a 95% confidence interval for the mean top speed of a boat with a beam of 85 inches and an engine with a 330 horsepower rating.
b. The Svfara SV609 has a beam of 85 inches and an engine with a 330 horsepower rating. Develop a 95% prediction interval for the mean top speed for the Svfara SV609.

31. The American Association of Individual Investors (AAII) On-Line Discount Broker Survey polls members on their experiences with electronic trades handled by discount brokers. As part of the survey, members were asked to rate their satisfaction with the trade price and the speed of execution, as well as provide an overall satisfaction rating. Possible responses (scores) were no opinion (0), unsatisfied (1), somewhat satisfied (2), satisfied (3), and very satisfied (4). For each broker, summary scores were computed by computing a weighted average of the scores provided by each respondent. A portion of the survey results follows (AAII website, February 7, 2012).

Broker

Brokerage	Trade Price	Speed of Execution	Satisfaction Electronic Trades
Scottrade, Inc.	3.4	3.4	3.5
Charles Schwab	3.2	3.3	3.4
Fidelity Brokerage Services	3.1	3.4	3.9
TD Ameritrade	2.9	3.6	3.7
E*Trade Financial	2.9	3.2	2.9
(Not listed)	2.5	3.2	2.7
Vanguard Brokerage Services	2.6	3.8	2.8
USAA Brokerage Services	2.4	3.8	3.6
Thinkorswim	2.6	2.6	2.6
Wells Fargo Investments	2.3	2.7	2.3
Interactive Brokers	3.7	4.0	4.0
Zecco.com	2.5	2.5	2.5
Firstrade Securities	3.0	3.0	4.0
Banc of America Investment Services	4.0	1.0	2.0

a. Develop an estimated regression equation using trade price and speed of execution to predict overall satisfaction with the broker.
b. Finger Lakes Investments has developed a new electronic trading system and would like to predict overall customer satisfaction assuming they can provide satisfactory levels of service levels (3) for both trade price and speed of execution. Use the estimated repression equation developed in part (a) to predict overall satisfaction level for Finger Lakes Investments if they can achieve these performance levels.

c. Develop a 95% confidence interval estimate of the overall satisfaction of electronic trades for all brokers that provide satisfactory levels of service for both trade price and speed of execution.

d. Develop a 95% prediction interval of overall satisfaction for Finger Lakes Investments assuming they achieve service levels of 3 for both trade price and speed of execution.

15.7 Categorical Independent Variables

The independent variables may be categorical or quantitative.

Thus far, the examples we have considered involved quantitative independent variables such as student population, distance traveled, and number of deliveries. In many situations, however, we must work with **categorical independent variables** such as gender (male, female), method of payment (cash, credit card, check), and so on. The purpose of this section is to show how categorical variables are handled in regression analysis. To illustrate the use and interpretation of a categorical independent variable, we will consider a problem facing the managers of Johnson Filtration, Inc.

An Example: Johnson Filtration, Inc.

Johnson Filtration, Inc., provides maintenance service for water-filtration systems throughout southern Florida. Customers contact Johnson with requests for maintenance service on their water-filtration systems. To estimate the service time and the service cost, Johnson's managers want to predict the repair time necessary for each maintenance request. Hence, repair time in hours is the dependent variable. Repair time is believed to be related to two factors, the number of months since the last maintenance service and the type of repair problem (mechanical or electrical). Data for a sample of 10 service calls are reported in Table 15.5.

Let y denote the repair time in hours and x_1 denote the number of months since the last maintenance service. The regression model that uses only x_1 to predict y is

$$y = \beta_0 + \beta_1 x_1 + \epsilon$$

Using Minitab to develop the estimated regression equation, we obtained the output shown in Figure 15.7. The estimated regression equation is

$$\hat{y} = 2.15 + .304x_1 \tag{15.16}$$

At the .05 level of significance, the p-value of .016 for the t (or F) test indicates that the number of months since the last service is significantly related to repair time. R-sq = 53.4% indicates that x_1 alone explains 53.4% of the variability in repair time.

TABLE 15.5   DATA FOR THE JOHNSON FILTRATION EXAMPLE

Service Call	Months Since Last Service	Type of Repair	Repair Time in Hours
1	2	electrical	2.9
2	6	mechanical	3.0
3	8	electrical	4.8
4	3	mechanical	1.8
5	2	electrical	2.9
6	7	electrical	4.9
7	9	mechanical	4.2
8	8	mechanical	4.8
9	4	electrical	4.4
10	6	electrical	4.5

In the Minitab output the variable names Months *and* Time *were entered as the column headings on the worksheet; thus,* x_1 = Months *and* y = Time.

```
The regression equation is
Time = 2.15 + 0.304 Months


Predictor      Coef    SE Coef       T       p
Constant     2.1473     0.6050    3.55   0.008
Months       0.3041     0.1004    3.03   0.016


S = 0.781022    R-Sq = 53.4%    R-Sq(adj) = 47.6%


Analysis of Variance


SOURCE             DF        SS       MS       F       p
Regression          1    5.5960   5.5960    9.17   0.016
Residual Error      8    4.8800   0.6100
Total               9   10.4760
```

To incorporate the type of repair into the regression model, we define the following variable.

$$x_2 = \begin{cases} 0 \text{ if the type of repair is mechanical} \\ 1 \text{ if the type of repair is electrical} \end{cases}$$

In regression analysis x_2 is called a **dummy** or *indicator* **variable**. Using this dummy variable, we can write the multiple regression model as

$$y = \beta_0 + \beta_1 x_1 + \beta_2 x_2 + \epsilon$$

Table 15.6 is the revised data set that includes the values of the dummy variable. Using Minitab and the data in Table 15.6, we can develop estimates of the model parameters. The Minitab output in Figure 15.8 shows that the estimated multiple regression equation is

$$\hat{y} = .93 + .388x_1 + 1.26x_2 \qquad (15.17)$$

TABLE 15.6   DATA FOR THE JOHNSON FILTRATION EXAMPLE WITH TYPE OF REPAIR
INDICATED BY A DUMMY VARIABLE (x_2 = 0 FOR MECHANICAL; x_2 = 1
FOR ELECTRICAL)

WEB file

Johnson

Customer	Months Since Last Service (x_1)	Type of Repair (x_2)	Repair Time in Hours (y)
1	2	1	2.9
2	6	0	3.0
3	8	1	4.8
4	3	0	1.8
5	2	1	2.9
6	7	1	4.9
7	9	0	4.2
8	8	0	4.8
9	4	1	4.4
10	6	1	4.5

FIGURE 15.8   MINITAB OUTPUT FOR JOHNSON FILTRATION WITH MONTHS SINCE LAST SERVICE (x_1) AND TYPE OF REPAIR (x_2) AS THE INDEPENDENT VARIABLES

In the Minitab output the variable names Months, Type, *and* Time *were entered as the column headings on the worksheet; thus,* x_1 = Months, x_2 = Type, *and* y = Time.

```
The regression equation is
Time = 0.930 + 0.388 Months + 1.26 Type

Predictor      Coef    SE Coef      T       p
Constant     0.9305     0.4670    1.99   0.087
Months      0.38762    0.06257    6.20   0.000
Type         1.2627     0.3141    4.02   0.005

S = 0.459048    R-Sq = 85.9%    R-Sq(adj) = 81.9%

Analysis of Variance

SOURCE          DF        SS       MS       F       p
Regression       2    9.0009   4.5005   21.36   0.001
Residual Error   7    1.4751   0.2107
Total            9   10.4760
```

At the .05 level of significance, the p-value of .001 associated with the F test ($F = 21.36$) indicates that the regression relationship is significant. The t test part of the printout in Figure 15.8 shows that both months since last service (p-value = .000) and type of repair (p-value = .005) are statistically significant. In addition, R-Sq = 85.9% and R-Sq (adj) = 81.9% indicate that the estimated regression equation does a good job of explaining the variability in repair times. Thus, equation (15.17) should prove helpful in predicting the repair time necessary for the various service calls.

Interpreting the Parameters

The multiple regression equation for the Johnson Filtration example is

$$E(y) = \beta_0 + \beta_1 x_1 + \beta_2 x_2 \tag{15.18}$$

To understand how to interpret the parameters β_0, β_1, and β_2 when a categorical variable is present, consider the case when $x_2 = 0$ (mechanical repair). Using $E(y \mid \text{mechanical})$ to denote the mean or expected value of repair time *given* a mechanical repair, we have

$$E(y \mid \text{mechanical}) = \beta_0 + \beta_1 x_1 + \beta_2(0) = \beta_0 + \beta_1 x_1 \tag{15.19}$$

Similarly, for an electrical repair ($x_2 = 1$), we have

$$\begin{aligned} E(y \mid \text{electrical}) &= \beta_0 + \beta_1 x_1 + \beta_2(1) = \beta_0 + \beta_1 x_1 + \beta_2 \\ &= (\beta_0 + \beta_2) + \beta_1 x_1 \end{aligned} \tag{15.20}$$

Comparing equations (15.19) and (15.20), we see that the mean repair time is a linear function of x_1 for both mechanical and electrical repairs. The slope of both equations is β_1, but the y-intercept differs. The y-intercept is β_0 in equation (15.19) for mechanical repairs and ($\beta_0 + \beta_2$) in equation (15.20) for electrical repairs. The interpretation of β_2 is that it indicates the difference between the mean repair time for an electrical repair and the mean repair time for a mechanical repair.

If β_2 is positive, the mean repair time for an electrical repair will be greater than that for a mechanical repair; if β_2 is negative, the mean repair time for an electrical repair will be less than that for a mechanical repair. Finally, if $\beta_2 = 0$, there is no difference in the mean repair time between electrical and mechanical repairs and the type of repair is not related to the repair time.

Using the estimated multiple regression equation $\hat{y} = .93 + .388x_1 + 1.26x_2$, we see that .93 is the estimate of β_0 and 1.26 is the estimate of β_2. Thus, when $x_2 = 0$ (mechanical repair)

$$\hat{y} = .93 + .388x_1 \qquad\qquad\text{(15.21)}$$

and when $x_2 = 1$ (electrical repair)

$$\begin{aligned} \hat{y} &= .93 + .388x_1 + 1.26(1) \qquad\qquad\text{(15.22)} \\ &= 2.19 + .388x_1 \end{aligned}$$

In effect, the use of a dummy variable for type of repair provides two estimated regression equations that can be used to predict the repair time, one corresponding to mechanical repairs and one corresponding to electrical repairs. In addition, with $b_2 = 1.26$, we learn that, on average, electrical repairs require 1.26 hours longer than mechanical repairs.

Figure 15.9 is the plot of the Johnson data from Table 15.6. Repair time in hours (y) is represented by the vertical axis and months since last service (x_1) is represented by the horizontal axis. A data point for a mechanical repair is indicated by an M and a data point for an electrical repair is indicated by an E. Equations (15.21) and (15.22) are plotted on the graph to show graphically the two equations that can be used to predict the repair time, one corresponding to mechanical repairs and one corresponding to electrical repairs.

FIGURE 15.9   SCATTER DIAGRAM FOR THE JOHNSON FILTRATION REPAIR DATA FROM TABLE 15.6

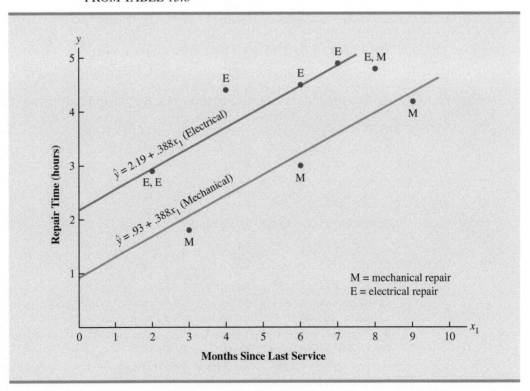

More Complex Categorical Variables

Because the categorical variable for the Johnson Filtration example had two levels (mechanical and electrical), defining a dummy variable with zero indicating a mechanical repair and one indicating an electrical repair was easy. However, when a categorical variable has more than two levels, care must be taken in both defining and interpreting the dummy variables. As we will show, if a categorical variable has k levels, $k - 1$ dummy variables are required, with each dummy variable being coded as 0 or 1.

A categorical variable with k levels must be modeled using k − 1 dummy variables. Care must be taken in defining and interpreting the dummy variables.

For example, suppose a manufacturer of copy machines organized the sales territories for a particular state into three regions: A, B, and C. The managers want to use regression analysis to help predict the number of copiers sold per week. With the number of units sold as the dependent variable, they are considering several independent variables (the number of sales personnel, advertising expenditures, and so on). Suppose the managers believe sales region is also an important factor in predicting the number of copiers sold. Because sales region is a categorical variable with three levels, A, B and C, we will need $3 - 1 = 2$ dummy variables to represent the sales region. Each variable can be coded 0 or 1 as follows.

$$x_1 = \begin{cases} 1 \text{ if sales region B} \\ 0 \text{ otherwise} \end{cases}$$

$$x_2 = \begin{cases} 1 \text{ if sales region C} \\ 0 \text{ otherwise} \end{cases}$$

With this definition, we have the following values of x_1 and x_2.

Region	x_1	x_2
A	0	0
B	1	0
C	0	1

Observations corresponding to region A would be coded $x_1 = 0$, $x_2 = 0$; observations corresponding to region B would be coded $x_1 = 1$, $x_2 = 0$; and observations corresponding to region C would be coded $x_1 = 0$, $x_2 = 1$.

The regression equation relating the expected value of the number of units sold, $E(y)$, to the dummy variables would be written as

$$E(y) = \beta_0 + \beta_1 x_1 + \beta_2 x_2$$

To help us interpret the parameters β_0, β_1, and β_2, consider the following three variations of the regression equation.

$$E(y \mid \text{region A}) = \beta_0 + \beta_1(0) + \beta_2(0) = \beta_0$$
$$E(y \mid \text{region B}) = \beta_0 + \beta_1(1) + \beta_2(0) = \beta_0 + \beta_1$$
$$E(y \mid \text{region C}) = \beta_0 + \beta_1(0) + \beta_2(1) = \beta_0 + \beta_2$$

Thus, β_0 is the mean or expected value of sales for region A; β_1 is the difference between the mean number of units sold in region B and the mean number of units sold in region A; and β_2 is the difference between the mean number of units sold in region C and the mean number of units sold in region A.

Two dummy variables were required because sales region is a categorical variable with three levels. But the assignment of $x_1 = 0$, $x_2 = 0$ to indicate region A, $x_1 = 1$, $x_2 = 0$ to indicate region B, and $x_1 = 0$, $x_2 = 1$ to indicate region C was arbitrary. For example, we could have chosen $x_1 = 1$, $x_2 = 0$ to indicate region A, $x_1 = 0$, $x_2 = 0$ to indicate region B, and $x_1 = 0$, $x_2 = 1$ to indicate region C. In that case, β_1 would have been interpreted as the mean difference between regions A and B and β_2 as the mean difference between regions C and B.

The important point to remember is that when a categorical variable has k levels, $k - 1$ dummy variables are required in the multiple regression analysis. Thus, if the sales region example had a fourth region, labeled D, three dummy variables would be necessary. For example, the three dummy variables can be coded as follows.

$$x_1 = \begin{cases} 1 \text{ if sales region B} \\ 0 \text{ otherwise} \end{cases} \qquad x_2 = \begin{cases} 1 \text{ if sales region C} \\ 0 \text{ otherwise} \end{cases} \qquad x_3 = \begin{cases} 1 \text{ if sales region D} \\ 0 \text{ otherwise} \end{cases}$$

Exercises

Methods

32. Consider a regression study involving a dependent variable y, a quantitative independent variable x_1, and a categorical independent variable with two levels (level 1 and level 2).
    a. Write a multiple regression equation relating x_1 and the categorical variable to y.
    b. What is the expected value of y corresponding to level 1 of the categorical variable?
    c. What is the expected value of y corresponding to level 2 of the categorical variable?
    d. Interpret the parameters in your regression equation.

33. Consider a regression study involving a dependent variable y, a quantitative independent variable x_1, and a categorical independent variable with three possible levels (level 1, level 2, and level 3).
    a. How many dummy variables are required to represent the categorical variable?
    b. Write a multiple regression equation relating x_1 and the categorical variable to y.
    c. Interpret the parameters in your regression equation.

Applications

34. Management proposed the following regression model to predict sales at a fast-food outlet.

$$y = \beta_0 + \beta_1 x_1 + \beta_2 x_2 + \beta_3 x_3 + \epsilon$$

where

$$x_1 = \text{number of competitors within one mile}$$
$$x_2 = \text{population within one mile (1000s)}$$
$$x_3 = \begin{cases} 1 \text{ if drive-up window present} \\ 0 \text{ otherwise} \end{cases}$$
$$y = \text{sales (\$1000s)}$$

The following estimated regression equation was developed after 20 outlets were surveyed.

$$\hat{y} = 10.1 - 4.2x_1 + 6.8x_2 + 15.3x_3$$

a. What is the expected amount of sales attributable to the drive-up window?
b. Predict sales for a store with two competitors, a population of 8000 within one mile, and no drive-up window.
c. Predict sales for a store with one competitor, a population of 3000 within one mile, and a drive-up window.

35. Refer to the Johnson Filtration problem introduced in this section. Suppose that in addition to information on the number of months since the machine was serviced and whether a mechanical or an electrical repair was necessary, the managers obtained a list showing which repairperson performed the service. The revised data follow.

WEB file

Repair

Repair Time in Hours	Months Since Last Service	Type of Repair	Repairperson
2.9	2	Electrical	Dave Newton
3.0	6	Mechanical	Dave Newton
4.8	8	Electrical	Bob Jones
1.8	3	Mechanical	Dave Newton
2.9	2	Electrical	Dave Newton
4.9	7	Electrical	Bob Jones
4.2	9	Mechanical	Bob Jones
4.8	8	Mechanical	Bob Jones
4.4	4	Electrical	Bob Jones
4.5	6	Electrical	Dave Newton

a. Ignore for now the months since the last maintenance service (x_1) and the repairperson who performed the service. Develop the estimated simple linear regression equation to predict the repair time (y) given the type of repair (x_2). Recall that $x_2 = 0$ if the type of repair is mechanical and 1 if the type of repair is electrical.

b. Does the equation that you developed in part (a) provide a good fit for the observed data? Explain.

c. Ignore for now the months since the last maintenance service and the type of repair associated with the machine. Develop the estimated simple linear regression equation to predict the repair time given the repairperson who performed the service. Let $x_3 = 0$ if Bob Jones performed the service and $x_3 = 1$ if Dave Newton performed the service.

d. Does the equation that you developed in part (c) provide a good fit for the observed data? Explain.

36. This problem is an extension of the situation described in exercise 35.

a. Develop the estimated regression equation to predict the repair time given the number of months since the last maintenance service, the type of repair, and the repairperson who performed the service.

b. At the .05 level of significance, test whether the estimated regression equation developed in part (a) represents a significant relationship between the independent variables and the dependent variable.

c. Is the addition of the independent variable x_3, the repairperson who performed the service, statistically significant? Use $\alpha = .05$. What explanation can you give for the results observed?

37. The *Consumer Reports* Restaurant Customer Satisfaction Survey is based upon 148,599 visits to full-service restaurant chains (*Consumer Reports* website, February 11, 2009). Assume the following data are representative of the results reported. The variable type indicates whether the restaurant is an Italian restaurant or a seafood/steakhouse. Price indicates the average amount paid per person for dinner and drinks, minus the tip. Score reflects diners' overall satisfaction, with higher values indicating greater overall satisfaction. A score of 80 can be interpreted as very satisfied.

WEB file

RestaurantRatings

Restaurant	Type	Price ($)	Score
Bertucci's	Italian	16	77
Black Angus Steakhouse	Seafood/Steakhouse	24	79
Bonefish Grill	Seafood/Steakhouse	26	85

(*continued*)

Restaurant	Type	Price ($)	Score
Bravo! Cucina Italiana	Italian	18	84
Buca di Beppo	Italian	17	81
Bugaboo Creek Steak House	Seafood/Steakhouse	18	77
Carrabba's Italian Grill	Italian	23	86
Charlie Brown's Steakhouse	Seafood/Steakhouse	17	75
Il Fornaio	Italian	28	83
Joe's Crab Shack	Seafood/Steakhouse	15	71
Johnny Carino's Italian	Italian	17	81
Lone Star Steakhouse & Saloon	Seafood/Steakhouse	17	76
LongHorn Steakhouse	Seafood/Steakhouse	19	81
Maggiano's Little Italy	Italian	22	83
McGrath's Fish House	Seafood/Steakhouse	16	81
Olive Garden	Italian	19	81
Outback Steakhouse	Seafood/Steakhouse	20	80
Red Lobster	Seafood/Steakhouse	18	78
Romano's Macaroni Grill	Italian	18	82
The Old Spaghetti Factory	Italian	12	79
Uno Chicago Grill	Italian	16	76

a. Develop the estimated regression equation to show how overall customer satisfaction is related to the independent variable average meal price.

b. At the .05 level of significance, test whether the estimated regression equation developed in part (a) indicates a significant relationship between overall customer satisfaction and average meal price.

c. Develop a dummy variable that will account for the type of restaurant (Italian or seafood/steakhouse).

d. Develop the estimated regression equation to show how overall customer satisfaction is related to the average meal price and the type of restaurant.

e. Is type of restaurant a significant factor in overall customer satisfaction?

f. Predict the *Consumer Reports* customer satisfaction score for a seafood/steakhouse that has an average meal price of $20. How much would the predicted score have changed for an Italian restaurant?

38. A 10-year study conducted by the American Heart Association provided data on how age, blood pressure, and smoking relate to the risk of strokes. Assume that the following data are from a portion of this study. Risk is interpreted as the probability (times 100) that the patient will have a stroke over the next 10-year period. For the smoking variable, define a dummy variable with 1 indicating a smoker and 0 indicating a nonsmoker.

WEB file

Stroke

Risk	Age	Pressure	Smoker
12	57	152	No
24	67	163	No
13	58	155	No
56	86	177	Yes
28	59	196	No
51	76	189	Yes
18	56	155	Yes
31	78	120	No
37	80	135	Yes
15	78	98	No
22	71	152	No
36	70	173	Yes

Risk	Age	Pressure	Smoker
15	67	135	Yes
48	77	209	Yes
15	60	199	No
36	82	119	Yes
8	66	166	No
34	80	125	Yes
3	62	117	No
37	59	207	Yes

a. Develop an estimated regression equation that relates risk of a stroke to the person's age, blood pressure, and whether the person is a smoker.
b. Is smoking a significant factor in the risk of a stroke? Explain. Use $\alpha = .05$.
c. What is the probability of a stroke over the next 10 years for Art Speen, a 68-year-old smoker who has blood pressure of 175? What action might the physician recommend for this patient?

Residual Analysis

In Chapter 14 we pointed out that standardized residuals are frequently used in residual plots and in the identification of outliers. The general formula for the standardized residual for observation i follows.

STANDARDIZED RESIDUAL FOR OBSERVATION i

$$\frac{y_i - \hat{y}_i}{s_{y_i - \hat{y}_i}} \qquad (15.23)$$

where

$$s_{y_i - \hat{y}_i} = \text{the standard deviation of residual } i$$

The general formula for the standard deviation of residual i is defined as follows.

STANDARD DEVIATION OF RESIDUAL i

$$s_{y_i - \hat{y}_i} = s\sqrt{1 - h_i} \qquad (15.24)$$

where

$$s = \text{standard error of the estimate}$$
$$h_i = \text{leverage of observation } i$$

As we stated in Chapter 14, the **leverage** of an observation is determined by how far the values of the independent variables are from their means. The computation of h_i, $s_{y_i - \hat{y}_i}$, and hence the standardized residual for observation i in multiple regression analysis is too complex to be

TABLE 15.7   RESIDUALS AND STANDARDIZED RESIDUALS FOR THE BUTLER TRUCKING REGRESSION ANALYSIS

Miles Traveled (x_1)	Deliveries (x_2)	Travel Time (y)	Predicted Value ($\hat{y}$)	Residual ($y - \hat{y}$)	Standardized Residual
100	4	9.3	8.93846	.361541	.78344
50	3	4.8	4.95830	−.158304	−.34962
100	4	8.9	8.93846	−.038460	−.08334
100	2	6.5	7.09161	−.591609	−1.30929
50	2	4.2	4.03488	.165121	.38167
80	2	6.2	5.86892	.331083	.65431
75	3	7.4	6.48667	.913331	1.68917
65	4	6.0	6.79875	−.798749	−1.77372
90	3	7.6	7.40369	.196311	.36703
90	2	6.1	6.48026	−.380263	−.77639

done by hand. However, the standardized residuals can be easily obtained as part of the output from statistical software packages. Table 15.7 lists the predicted values, the residuals, and the standardized residuals for the Butler Trucking example presented previously in this chapter; we obtained these values by using the Minitab statistical software package. The predicted values in the table are based on the estimated regression equation $\hat{y} = -.869 + .0611x_1 + .923x_2$.

The standardized residuals and the predicted values of y from Table 15.7 are used in Figure 15.10, the standardized residual plot for the Butler Trucking multiple regression example. This standardized residual plot does not indicate any unusual abnormalities. Also, all the standardized residuals are between -2 and $+2$; hence, we have no reason to question the assumption that the error term ϵ is normally distributed. We conclude that the model assumptions are reasonable.

FIGURE 15.10   STANDARDIZED RESIDUAL PLOT FOR BUTLER TRUCKING

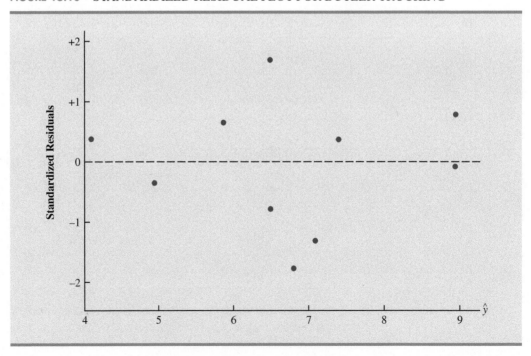

A normal probability plot also can be used to determine whether the distribution of ϵ appears to be normal. The procedure and interpretation for a normal probability plot were discussed in Section 14.8. The same procedure is appropriate for multiple regression. Again, we would use a statistical software package to perform the computations and provide the normal probability plot.

Detecting Outliers

An **outlier** is an observation that is unusual in comparison with the other data; in other words, an outlier does not fit the pattern of the other data. In Chapter 14 we showed an example of an outlier and discussed how standardized residuals can be used to detect outliers. Minitab classifies an observation as an outlier if the value of its standardized residual is less than -2 or greater than $+2$. Applying this rule to the standardized residuals for the Butler Trucking example (see Table 15.7), we do not detect any outliers in the data set.

In general, the presence of one or more outliers in a data set tends to increase s, the standard error of the estimate, and hence increase $s_{y-\hat{y}_i}$, the standard deviation of residual i. Because $s_{y_i-\hat{y}_i}$ appears in the denominator of the formula for the standardized residual (15.23), the size of the standardized residual will decrease as s increases. As a result, even though a residual may be unusually large, the large denominator in expression (15.23) may cause the standardized residual rule to fail to identify the observation as being an outlier. We can circumvent this difficulty by using a form of the standardized residuals called **studentized deleted residuals**.

Studentized Deleted Residuals and Outliers

Suppose the ith observation is deleted from the data set and a new estimated regression equation is developed with the remaining $n - 1$ observations. Let $s_{(i)}$ denote the standard error of the estimate based on the data set with the ith observation deleted. If we compute the standard deviation of residual i using $s_{(i)}$ instead of s, and then compute the standardized residual for observation i using the revised $s_{y_i-\hat{y}_i}$ value, the resulting standardized residual is called a studentized deleted residual. If the ith observation is an outlier, $s_{(i)}$ will be less than s. The absolute value of the ith studentized deleted residual therefore will be larger than the absolute value of the standardized residual. In this sense, studentized deleted residuals may detect outliers that standardized residuals do not detect.

Many statistical software packages provide an option for obtaining studentized deleted residuals. Using Minitab, we obtained the studentized deleted residuals for the Butler Trucking example; the results are reported in Table 15.8. The t distribution can be used to

TABLE 15.8 STUDENTIZED DELETED RESIDUALS FOR BUTLER TRUCKING

Miles Traveled (x_1)	Deliveries (x_2)	Travel Time (y)	Standardized Residual	Studentized Deleted Residual
100	4	9.3	.78344	.75939
50	3	4.8	−.34962	−.32654
100	4	8.9	−.08334	−.07720
100	2	6.5	−1.30929	−1.39494
50	2	4.2	.38167	.35709
80	2	6.2	.65431	.62519
75	3	7.4	1.68917	2.03187
65	4	6.0	−1.77372	−2.21314
90	3	7.6	.36703	.34312
90	2	6.1	−.77639	−.75190

TABLE 15.9   LEVERAGE AND COOK'S DISTANCE MEASURES FOR BUTLER TRUCKING

Miles Traveled (x_1)	Deliveries (x_2)	Travel Time (y)	Leverage (h_i)	Cook's D (D_i)
100	4	9.3	.351704	.110994
50	3	4.8	.375863	.024536
100	4	8.9	.351704	.001256
100	2	6.5	.378451	.347923
50	2	4.2	.430220	.036663
80	2	6.2	.220557	.040381
75	3	7.4	.110009	.117562
65	4	6.0	.382657	.650029
90	3	7.6	.129098	.006656
90	2	6.1	.269737	.074217

determine whether the studentized deleted residuals indicate the presence of outliers. Recall that p denotes the number of independent variables and n denotes the number of observations. Hence, if we delete the ith observation, the number of observations in the reduced data set is $n - 1$; in this case the error sum of squares has $(n - 1) - p - 1$ degrees of freedom. For the Butler Trucking example with $n = 10$ and $p = 2$, the degrees of freedom for the error sum of squares with the ith observation deleted is $9 - 2 - 1 = 6$. At a .05 level of significance, the t distribution (Table 2 of Appendix B) shows that with six degrees of freedom, $t_{.025} = 2.447$. If the value of the ith studentized deleted residual is less than -2.447 or greater than $+2.447$, we can conclude that the ith observation is an outlier. The studentized deleted residuals in Table 15.8 do not exceed those limits; therefore, we conclude that outliers are not present in the data set.

Influential Observations

In Section 14.9 we discussed how the leverage of an observation can be used to identify observations for which the value of the independent variable may have a strong influence on the regression results. As we indicated in the discussion of standardized residuals, the leverage of an observation, denoted h_i, measures how far the values of the independent variables are from their mean values. The leverage values are easily obtained as part of the output from statistical software packages. Minitab computes the leverage values and uses the rule of thumb $h_i > 3(p + 1)/n$ to identify **influential observations**. For the Butler Trucking example with $p = 2$ independent variables and $n = 10$ observations, the critical value for leverage is $3(2 + 1)/10 = .9$. The leverage values for the Butler Trucking example obtained by using Minitab are reported in Table 15.9. Because h_i does not exceed .9, we do not detect influential observations in the data set.

Using Cook's Distance Measure to Identify Influential Observations

A problem that can arise in using leverage to identify influential observations is that an observation can be identified as having high leverage and not necessarily be influential in terms of the resulting estimated regression equation. For example, Table 15.10 is a data set consisting of eight observations and their corresponding leverage values (obtained by using Minitab). Because the leverage for the eighth observation is $.91 > .75$ (the critical leverage value), this observation is identified as influential. Before reaching any final conclusions, however, let us consider the situation from a different perspective.

TABLE 15.10

DATA SET ILLUSTRATING POTENTIAL PROBLEM USING THE LEVERAGE CRITERION

x_i	y_i	Leverage h_i
1	18	.204170
1	21	.204170
2	22	.164205
3	21	.138141
4	23	.125977
4	24	.125977
5	26	.127715
15	39	.909644

FIGURE 15.11   SCATTER DIAGRAM FOR THE DATA SET IN TABLE 15.10

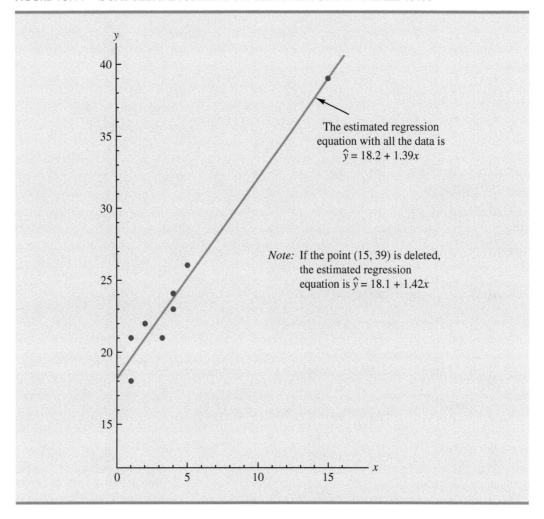

Figure 15.11 shows the scatter diagram corresponding to the data set in Table 15.10. We used Minitab to develop the following estimated regression equation for these data.

$$\hat{y} = 18.2 + 1.39x$$

The straight line in Figure 15.11 is the graph of this equation. Now, let us delete the observation $x = 15$, $y = 39$ from the data set and fit a new estimated regression equation to the remaining seven observations; the new estimated regression equation is

$$\hat{y} = 18.1 + 1.42x$$

We note that the y-intercept and slope of the new estimated regression equation are very close to the values obtained using all the data. Although the leverage criterion identified the eighth observation as influential, this observation clearly had little influence on the results obtained. Thus, in some situations using only leverage to identify influential observations can lead to wrong conclusions.

   Cook's distance measure uses both the leverage of observation i, h_i, and the residual for observation i, $(y_i - \hat{y}_i)$, to determine whether the observation is influential.

COOK'S DISTANCE MEASURE

$$D_i = \frac{(y_i - \hat{y}_i)^2}{(p + 1)s^2}\left[\frac{h_i}{(1 - h_i)^2}\right]$$

(15.25)

where

$$D_i = \text{Cook's distance measure for observation } i$$
$$y_i - \hat{y}_i = \text{the residual for observation } i$$
$$h_i = \text{the leverage for observation } i$$
$$p = \text{the number of independent variables}$$
$$s = \text{the standard error of the estimate}$$

The value of Cook's distance measure will be large and indicate an influential observation if the residual or the leverage is large. As a rule of thumb, values of $D_i > 1$ indicate that the ith observation is influential and should be studied further. The last column of Table 15.9 provides Cook's distance measure for the Butler Trucking problem as given by Minitab. Observation 8 with $D_i = .650029$ has the most influence. However, applying the rule $D_i > 1$, we should not be concerned about the presence of influential observations in the Butler Trucking data set.

NOTES AND COMMENTS

1. The procedures for identifying outliers and influential observations provide warnings about the potential effects some observations may have on the regression results. Each outlier and influential observation warrants careful examination. If data errors are found, the errors can be corrected and the regression analysis repeated. In general, outliers and influential observations should not be removed from the data set unless clear evidence shows that they are not based on elements of the population being studied and should not have been included in the original data set.

2. To determine whether the value of Cook's distance measure D_i is large enough to conclude that the ith observation is influential, we can also compare the value of D_i to the 50th percentile of an F distribution (denoted $F_{.50}$) with $p + 1$ numerator degrees of freedom and $n - p - 1$ denominator degrees of freedom. F tables corresponding to a .50 level of significance must be available to carry out the test. The rule of thumb we provided ($D_i > 1$) is based on the fact that the table value is close to one for a wide variety of cases.

Exercises

Methods

39. Data for two variables, x and y, follow.

x_i	1	2	3	4	5
y_i	3	7	5	11	14

a. Develop the estimated regression equation for these data.
b. Plot the standardized residuals versus $\hat{y}$. Do there appear to be any outliers in these data? Explain.
c. Compute the studentized deleted residuals for these data. At the .05 level of significance, can any of these observations be classified as an outlier? Explain.

40. Data for two variables, x and y, follow.

x_i	22	24	26	28	40
y_i	12	21	31	35	70

   a. Develop the estimated regression equation for these data.
   b. Compute the studentized deleted residuals for these data. At the .05 level of significance, can any of these observations be classified as an outlier? Explain.
   c. Compute the leverage values for these data. Do there appear to be any influential observations in these data? Explain.
   d. Compute Cook's distance measure for these data. Are any observations influential? Explain.

Applications

41. Exercise 5 gave the following data on weekly gross revenue, television advertising, and newspaper advertising for Showtime Movie Theaters.

Showtime

Weekly Gross Revenue ($1000s)	Television Advertising ($1000s)	Newspaper Advertising ($1000s)
96	5.0	1.5
90	2.0	2.0
95	4.0	1.5
92	2.5	2.5
95	3.0	3.3
94	3.5	2.3
94	2.5	4.2
94	3.0	2.5

   a. Find an estimated regression equation relating weekly gross revenue to television and newspaper advertising.
   b. Plot the standardized residuals against $\hat{y}$. Does the residual plot support the assumptions about ϵ? Explain.
   c. Check for any outliers in these data. What are your conclusions?
   d. Are there any influential observations? Explain.

42. The following data show the curb weight, horsepower, and ¼-mile speed for 16 popular sports and GT cars. Suppose that the price of each sports and GT car is also available. The complete data set is as follows:

Auto2

Sports & GT Car	Price ($1000s)	Curb Weight (lb.)	Horsepower	Speed at ¼ Mile (mph)
Acura Integra Type R	25.035	2577	195	90.7
Acura NSX-T	93.758	3066	290	108.0
BMW Z3 2.8	40.900	2844	189	93.2
Chevrolet Camaro Z28	24.865	3439	305	103.2
Chevrolet Corvette Convertible	50.144	3246	345	102.1
Dodge Viper RT/10	69.742	3319	450	116.2
Ford Mustang GT	23.200	3227	225	91.7
Honda Prelude Type SH	26.382	3042	195	89.7
Mercedes-Benz CLK320	44.988	3240	215	93.0
Mercedes-Benz SLK230	42.762	3025	185	92.3
Mitsubishi 3000GT VR-4	47.518	3737	320	99.0

(continued)

Sports & GT Car	Price ($1000s)	Curb Weight (lb.)	Horsepower	Speed at ¼ Mile (mph)
Nissan 240SX SE	25.066	2862	155	84.6
Pontiac Firebird Trans Am	27.770	3455	305	103.2
Porsche Boxster	45.560	2822	201	93.2
Toyota Supra Turbo	40.989	3505	320	105.0
Volvo C70	41.120	3285	236	97.0

    a.   Find the estimated regression equation that uses price and horsepower to predict ¼-mile speed.

    b.   Plot the standardized residuals against $\hat{y}$. Does the residual plot support the assumption about ϵ? Explain.

    c.   Check for any outliers. What are your conclusions?

    d.   Are there any influential observations? Explain.

LPGA

43. The Ladies Professional Golfers Association (LPGA) maintains statistics on performance and earnings for members of the LPGA Tour. Year-end performance statistics for the 30 players who had the highest total earnings in LPGA Tour events for 2005 appear in the file named LPGA (LPGA website, 2006). Earnings ($1000s) is the total earnings in thousands of dollars; Scoring Avg. is the average score for all events; Greens in Reg. is the percentage of time a player is able to hit the green in regulation; and Putting Avg. is the average number of putts taken on greens hit in regulation. A green is considered hit in regulation if any part of the ball is touching the putting surface and the difference between the value of par for the hole and the number of strokes taken to hit the green is at least 2.

    a.   Develop an estimated regression equation that can be used to predict the average score for all events given the percentage of time a player is able to hit the green in regulation and the average number of putts taken on greens hit in regulation.

    b.   Plot the standardized residuals against $\hat{y}$. Does the residual plot support the assumption about ϵ? Explain.

    c.   Check for any outliers. What are your conclusions?

    d.   Are there any influential observations? Explain.

15.9   Logistic Regression

In many regression applications the dependent variable may only assume two discrete values. For instance, a bank might like to develop an estimated regression equation for predicting whether a person will be approved for a credit card. The dependent variable can be coded as $y = 1$ if the bank approves the request for a credit card and $y = 0$ if the bank rejects the request for a credit card. Using logistic regression we can estimate the probability that the bank will approve the request for a credit card given a particular set of values for the chosen independent variables.

Let us consider an application of logistic regression involving a direct mail promotion being used by Simmons Stores. Simmons owns and operates a national chain of women's apparel stores. Five thousand copies of an expensive four-color sales catalog have been printed, and each catalog includes a coupon that provides a $50 discount on purchases of $200 or more. The catalogs are expensive and Simmons would like to send them to only those customers who have the highest probability of using the coupon.

Management thinks that annual spending at Simmons Stores and whether a customer has a Simmons credit card are two variables that might be helpful in predicting whether a customer who receives the catalog will use the coupon. Simmons conducted a pilot study using a random sample of 50 Simmons credit card customers and 50 other customers who do not have a Simmons credit card. Simmons sent the catalog to each of the 100 customers selected. At the end of a test period, Simmons noted whether the customer used the coupon. The sample data for the first 10 catalog recipients are shown in Table 15.11. The amount each customer spent last year at Simmons is shown in thousands of dollars and the credit card information has been coded as 1 if the customer has a Simmons credit card and 0 if not. In the Coupon column, a 1 is recorded if the sampled customer used the coupon and 0 if not.

We might think of building a multiple regression model using the data in Table 15.11 to help Simmons estimate whether a catalog recipient will use the coupon. We would use Annual Spending ($1000) and Simmons Card as independent variables and Coupon as the dependent variable. Because the dependent variable may only assume the values of 0 or 1, however, the ordinary multiple regression model is not applicable. This example shows the type of situation for which logistic regression was developed. Let us see how logistic regression can be used to help Simmons estimate which type of customer is most likely to take advantage of their promotion.

Logistic Regression Equation

In many ways logistic regression is like ordinary regression. It requires a dependent variable, y, and one or more independent variables. In multiple regression analysis, the mean or expected value of y is referred to as the multiple regression equation.

$$E(y) = \beta_0 + \beta_1 x_1 + \beta_2 x_2 + \cdots + \beta_p x_p \tag{15.26}$$

In logistic regression, statistical theory as well as practice has shown that the relationship between $E(y)$ and $x_1, x_2, \ldots, x_p$ is better described by the following nonlinear equation.

LOGISTIC REGRESSION EQUATION

$$E(y) = \frac{e^{\beta_0 + \beta_1 x_1 + \beta_2 x_2 + \cdots + \beta_p x_p}}{1 + e^{\beta_0 + \beta_1 x_1 + \beta_2 x_2 + \cdots + \beta_p x_p}} \tag{15.27}$$

If the two values of the dependent variable y are coded as 0 or 1, the value of $E(y)$ in equation (15.27) provides the *probability* that $y = 1$ given a particular set of values for the

TABLE 15.11   PARTIAL SAMPLE DATA FOR THE SIMMONS STORES EXAMPLE

Customer	Annual Spending ($1000)	Simmons Card	Coupon
1	2.291	1	0
2	3.215	1	0
3	2.135	1	0
4	3.924	0	0
5	2.528	1	0
6	2.473	0	1
7	2.384	0	0
8	7.076	0	0
9	1.182	1	1
10	3.345	0	0

WEB file

Simmons

independent variables $x_1, x_2, \ldots, x_p$. Because of the interpretation of $E(y)$ as a probability, the **logistic regression equation** is often written as follows.

INTERPRETATION OF $E(y)$ AS A PROBABILITY IN LOGISTIC REGRESSION

$$E(y) = P(y = 1 | x_1, x_2, \ldots, x_p) \tag{15.28}$$

To provide a better understanding of the characteristics of the logistic regression equation, suppose the model involves only one independent variable x and the values of the model parameters are $\beta_0 = -7$ and $\beta_1 = 3$. The logistic regression equation corresponding to these parameter values is

$$E(y) = P(y = 1 | x) = \frac{e^{\beta_0 + \beta_1 x}}{1 + e^{\beta_0 + \beta_1 x}} = \frac{e^{-7+3x}}{1 + e^{-7+3x}} \tag{15.29}$$

Figure 15.12 shows a graph of equation (15.29). Note that the graph is S-shaped. The value of $E(y)$ ranges from 0 to 1, with the value of $E(y)$ gradually approaching 1 as the value of x becomes larger and the value of $E(y)$ approaching 0 as the value of x becomes smaller. Note also that the values of $E(y)$, representing probability, increase fairly rapidly as x increases from 2 to 3. The fact that the values of $E(y)$ range from 0 to 1 and that the curve is S-shaped makes equation (15.29) ideally suited to model the probability the dependent variable is equal to 1.

Estimating the Logistic Regression Equation

In simple linear and multiple regression the least squares method is used to compute b_0, $b_1, \ldots, b_p$ as estimates of the model parameters $(\beta_0, \beta_1, \ldots, \beta_p)$. The nonlinear form of the logistic regression equation makes the method of computing estimates more complex and beyond the scope of this text. We will use computer software to provide the estimates. The **estimated logistic regression equation** is

FIGURE 15.12   LOGISTIC REGRESSION EQUATION FOR $\beta_0 = -7$ AND $\beta_1 = 3$

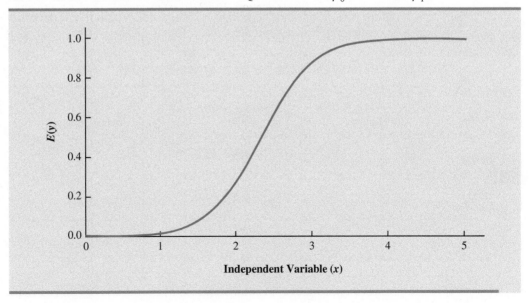

ESTIMATED LOGISTIC REGRESSION EQUATION

$$\hat{y} = \text{estimate of } P(y = 1 | x_1, x_2, \ldots, x_p) = \frac{e^{b_0 + b_1 x_1 + b_2 x_2 + \cdots + b_p x_p}}{1 + e^{b_0 + b_1 x_1 + b_2 x_2 + \cdots + b_p x_p}} \quad (15.30)$$

Here, $\hat{y}$ provides an estimate of the probability that $y = 1$ given a particular set of values for the independent variables.

Let us now return to the Simmons Stores example. The variables in the study are defined as follows:

$$y = \begin{cases} 0 \text{ if the customer did not use the coupon} \\ 1 \text{ if the customer used the coupon} \end{cases}$$

$$x_1 = \text{annual spending at Simmons Stores (\$1000s)}$$

$$x_2 = \begin{cases} 0 \text{ if the customer does not have a Simmons credit card} \\ 1 \text{ if the customer has a Simmons credit card} \end{cases}$$

Thus, we choose a logistic regression equation with two independent variables.

$$E(y) = \frac{e^{\beta_0 + \beta_1 x_1 + \beta_2 x_2}}{1 + e^{\beta_0 + \beta_1 x_1 + \beta_2 x_2}} \quad (15.31)$$

In Appendix 15.3 we show how Minitab is used to generate the output in Figure 15.13.

Using the sample data (see Table 15.11), Minitab's binary logistic regression procedure was used to compute estimates of the model parameters β_0, β_1, and β_2. A portion of the output obtained is shown in Figure 15.13. We see that $b_0 = -2.14637$, $b_1 = .341643$, and $b_2 = 1.09873$. Thus, the estimated logistic regression equation is

$$\hat{y} = \frac{e^{b_0 + b_1 x_1 + b_2 x_2}}{1 + e^{b_0 + b_1 x_1 + b_2 x_2}} = \frac{e^{-2.14637 + .341643 x_1 + 1.09873 x_2}}{1 + e^{-2.14637 + .341643 x_1 + 1.09873 x_2}} \quad (15.32)$$

We can now use equation (15.32) to estimate the probability of using the coupon for a particular type of customer. For example, to estimate the probability of using the coupon for customers who spend \$2000 annually and do not have a Simmons credit card, we substitute $x_1 = 2$ and $x_2 = 0$ into equation (15.32).

FIGURE 15.13 PARTIAL LOGISTIC REGRESSION OUTPUT FOR THE SIMMONS STORES EXAMPLE

In the Minitab output, x_1 = Spending and x_2 = Card.

```
Logistic Regression Table
                                             Odds    95%   CI
Predictor      Coef    SE Coef     Z      p  Ratio  Lower Upper
Constant   -2.14637   0.577245  -3.72  0.000
Spending    0.341643  0.128672   2.66  0.008  1.41   1.09  1.81
Card        1.09873   0.444696   2.47  0.013  3.00   1.25  7.17


Log-Likelihood = -60.487
Test that all slopes are zero: G = 13.628, DF = 2, P-Value = 0.001
```

$$\hat{y} = \frac{e^{-2.14637 + .341643(2) + 1.09873(0)}}{1 + e^{-2.14637 + .341643(2) + 1.09873(0)}} = \frac{e^{-1.4631}}{1 + e^{-1.4631}} = \frac{.2315}{1.2315} = .1880$$

Thus, an estimate of the probability of using the coupon for this particular group of customers is approximately 0.19. Similarly, to estimate the probability of using the coupon for customers who spent $2000 last year and have a Simmons credit card, we substitute $x_1 = 2$ and $x_2 = 1$ into equation (15.32).

$$\hat{y} = \frac{e^{-2.14637 + .341643(2) + 1.09873(1)}}{1 + e^{-2.14637 + .341643(2) + 1.09873(1)}} = \frac{e^{-.3644}}{1 + e^{-.3644}} = \frac{.6946}{1.6946} = .4099$$

Thus, for this group of customers, the probability of using the coupon is approximately 0.41. It appears that the probability of using the coupon is much higher for customers with a Simmons credit card. Before reaching any conclusions, however, we need to assess the statistical significance of our model.

Testing for Significance

Testing for significance in logistic regression is similar to testing for significance in multiple regression. First we conduct a test for overall significance. For the Simmons Stores example, the hypotheses for the test of overall significance follow:

$$H_0: \beta_1 = \beta_2 = 0$$
$$H_a: \text{One or both of the parameters is not equal to zero}$$

The test for overall significance is based upon the value of a G test statistic. If the null hypothesis is true, the sampling distribution of G follows a chi-square distribution with degrees of freedom equal to the number of independent variables in the model. Although the computation of G is beyond the scope of the book, the value of G and its corresponding p-value are provided as part of Minitab's binary logistic regression output. Referring to the last line in Figure 15.13, we see that the value of G is 13.628, its degrees of freedom are 2, and its p-value is .001. Thus, at any level of significance $\alpha \geq .001$, we would reject the null hypothesis and conclude that the overall model is significant.

If the G test shows an overall significance, a z test can be used to determine whether each of the individual independent variables is making a significant contribution to the overall model. For the independent variables x_i, the hypotheses are

$$H_0: \beta_i = 0$$
$$H_a: \beta_i \neq 0$$

If the null hypothesis is true, the value of the estimated coefficient divided by its standard error follows a standard normal probability distribution. The column labeled Z in the Minitab output contains the values of $z_i = b_i/s_{b_i}$ for each of the estimated coefficients and the column labeled p contains the corresponding p-values. Suppose we use $\alpha = .05$ to test for the significance of the independent variables in the Simmons model. For the independent variable x_1 the z value is 2.66 and the corresponding p-value is .008. Thus, at the .05 level of significance we can reject $H_0: \beta_1 = 0$. In a similar fashion we can also reject $H_0: \beta_2 = 0$ because the p-value corresponding to $z = 2.47$ is .013. Hence, at the .05 level of significance, both independent variables are statistically significant.

Managerial Use

We described how to develop the estimated logistic regression equation and how to test it for significance. Let us now use it to make a decision recommendation concerning the Simmons Stores catalog promotion. For Simmons Stores, we already computed $P(y = 1|x_1 = 2, x_2 = 1) = .4099$ and $P(y = 1|x_1 = 2, x_2 = 0) = .1880$. These probabilities indicate that for customers with annual spending of $2000 the presence of a Simmons credit card increases the probability of using the coupon. In Table 15.12 we show estimated probabilities for values of annual spending ranging from $1000 to $7000 for both customers who have a Simmons credit card and customers who do not have a Simmons credit card. How can Simmons use this information to better target customers for the new promotion? Suppose Simmons wants to send the promotional catalog only to customers who have a 0.40 or higher probability of using the coupon. Using the estimated probabilities in Table 15.12, Simmons promotion strategy would be:

Customers who have a Simmons credit card: Send the catalog to every customer who spent $2000 or more last year.

Customers who do not have a Simmons credit card: Send the catalog to every customer who spent $6000 or more last year.

Looking at the estimated probabilities further, we see that the probability of using the coupon for customers who do not have a Simmons credit card but spend $5000 annually is .3922. Thus, Simmons may want to consider revising this strategy by including those customers who do not have a credit card, as long as they spent $5000 or more last year.

Interpreting the Logistic Regression Equation

Interpreting a regression equation involves relating the independent variables to the business question that the equation was developed to answer. With logistic regression, it is difficult to interpret the relation between the independent variables and the probability that $y = 1$ directly because the logistic regression equation is nonlinear. However, statisticians have shown that the relationship can be interpreted indirectly using a concept called the odds ratio.

The **odds in favor of an event occurring** is defined as the probability the event will occur divided by the probability the event will not occur. In logistic regression the event of interest is always $y = 1$. Given a particular set of values for the independent variables, the odds in favor of $y = 1$ can be calculated as follows:

$$\text{odds} = \frac{P(y = 1|x_1, x_2, \ldots, x_p)}{P(y = 0|x_1, x_2, \ldots, x_p)} = \frac{P(y = 1|x_1, x_2, \ldots, x_p)}{1 - P(y = 1|x_1, x_2, \ldots, x_p)} \qquad (15.33)$$

The **odds ratio** measures the impact on the odds of a one-unit increase in only one of the independent variables. The odds ratio is the odds that $y = 1$ given that one of the

TABLE 15.12   ESTIMATED PROBABILITIES FOR SIMMONS STORES

| | | Annual Spending | | | | | | |
		$1000	$2000	$3000	$4000	$5000	$6000	$7000
Credit Card	Yes	.3305	.4099	.4943	.5791	.6594	.7315	.7931
	No	.1413	.1880	.2457	.3144	.3922	.4759	.5610

independent variables has been increased by one unit (odds_1) divided by the odds that $y = 1$ given no change in the values for the independent variables (odds_0).

ODDS RATIO

$$\text{Odds Ratio} = \frac{\text{odds}_1}{\text{odds}_0} \qquad (15.34)$$

For example, suppose we want to compare the odds of using the coupon for customers who spend \$2000 annually and have a Simmons credit card ($x_1 = 2$ and $x_2 = 1$) to the odds of using the coupon for customers who spend \$2000 annually and do not have a Simmons credit card ($x_1 = 2$ and $x_2 = 0$). We are interested in interpreting the effect of a one-unit increase in the independent variable x_2. In this case

$$\text{odds}_1 = \frac{P(y = 1 | x_1 = 2, x_2 = 1)}{1 - P(y = 1 | x_1 = 2, x_2 = 1)}$$

and

$$\text{odds}_0 = \frac{P(y = 1 | x_1 = 2, x_2 = 0)}{1 - P(y = 1 | x_1 = 2, x_2 = 0)}$$

Previously we showed that an estimate of the probability that $y = 1$ given $x_1 = 2$ and $x_2 = 1$ is .4099, and an estimate of the probability that $y = 1$ given $x_1 = 2$ and $x_2 = 0$ is .1880. Thus,

$$\text{estimate of odds}_1 = \frac{.4099}{1 - .4099} = .6946$$

and

$$\text{estimate of odds}_0 = \frac{.1880}{1 - .1880} = .2315$$

The estimated odds ratio is

$$\text{Estimated odds ratio} = \frac{.6946}{.2315} = 3.00$$

Thus, we can conclude that the estimated odds in favor of using the coupon for customers who spent \$2000 last year and have a Simmons credit card are 3 times greater than the estimated odds in favor of using the coupon for customers who spent \$2000 last year and do not have a Simmons credit card.

The odds ratio for each independent variable is computed while holding all the other independent variables constant. But it does not matter what constant values are used for the other independent variables. For instance, if we computed the odds ratio for the Simmons credit card variable (x_2) using \$3000, instead of \$2000, as the value for the annual spending variable (x_1), we would still obtain the same value for the estimated odds ratio (3.00). Thus, we can conclude that the estimated odds of using the coupon for customers who have a Simmons credit card are 3 times greater than the estimated odds of using the coupon for customers who do not have a Simmons credit card.

The odds ratio is standard output for logistic regression software packages. Refer to the Minitab output in Figure 15.13. The column with the heading Odds Ratio contains the estimated odds ratios for each of the independent variables. The estimated odds ratio for x_1 is 1.41 and the estimated odds ratio for x_2 is 3.00. We already showed how to interpret the estimated odds ratio for the binary independent variable x_2. Let us now consider the interpretation of the estimated odds ratio for the continuous independent variable x_1.

The value of 1.41 in the Odds Ratio column of the Minitab output tells us that the estimated odds in favor of using the coupon for customers who spent \$3000 last year is 1.41 times greater than the estimated odds in favor of using the coupon for customers who spent \$2000 last year. Moreover, this interpretation is true for any one-unit change in x_1. For instance, the estimated odds in favor of using the coupon for someone who spent \$5000 last year is 1.41 times greater than the odds in favor of using the coupon for a customer who spent \$4000 last year. But suppose we are interested in the change in the odds for an increase of more than one unit for an independent variable. Note that x_1 can range from 1 to 7. The odds ratio given by the Minitab output does not answer this question. To answer this question we must explore the relationship between the odds ratio and the regression coefficients.

A unique relationship exists between the odds ratio for a variable and its corresponding regression coefficient. For each independent variable in a logistic regression equation it can be shown that

$$\text{Odds ratio} = e^{\beta_i}$$

To illustrate this relationship, consider the independent variable x_1 in the Simmons example. The estimated odds ratio for x_1 is

$$\text{Estimated odds ratio} = e^{b_1} = e^{.341643} = 1.41$$

Similarly, the estimated odds ratio for x_2 is

$$\text{Estimated odds ratio} = e^{b_2} = e^{1.09873} = 3.00$$

This relationship between the odds ratio and the coefficients of the independent variables makes it easy to compute estimated odds ratios once we develop estimates of the model parameters. Moreover, it also provides us with the ability to investigate changes in the odds ratio of more than or less than one unit for a continuous independent variable.

The odds ratio for an independent variable represents the change in the odds for a one-unit change in the independent variable holding all the other independent variables constant. Suppose that we want to consider the effect of a change of more than one unit, say c units. For instance, suppose in the Simmons example that we want to compare the odds of using the coupon for customers who spend \$5000 annually ($x_1 = 5$) to the odds of using the coupon for customers who spend \$2000 annually ($x_1 = 2$). In this case $c = 5 - 2 = 3$ and the corresponding estimated odds ratio is

$$e^{cb_1} = e^{3(.341643)} = e^{1.0249} = 2.79$$

This result indicates that the estimated odds of using the coupon for customers who spend \$5000 annually is 2.79 times greater than the estimated odds of using the coupon for customers who spend \$2000 annually. In other words, the estimated odds ratio for an increase of \$3000 in annual spending is 2.79.

In general, the odds ratio enables us to compare the odds for two different events. If the value of the odds ratio is 1, the odds for both events are the same. Thus, if the independent variable we are considering (such as Simmons credit card status) has a positive impact on the probability of the event occurring, the corresponding odds ratio will be greater than 1. Most logistic regression software packages provide a confidence interval for the odds ratio. The Minitab output in Figure 15.13 provides a 95% confidence interval for each of the odds ratios. For example, the point estimate of the odds ratio for x_1 is 1.41 and the 95% confidence interval is 1.09 to 1.81. Because the confidence interval does not contain the value of 1, we can conclude that x_1, has a significant effect on the estimated odds ratio. Similarly, the 95% confidence interval for the odds ratio for x_2 is 1.25 to 7.17. Because this interval does not contain the value of 1, we can also conclude that x_2 has a significant effect on the odds ratio.

Logit Transformation

An interesting relationship can be observed between the odds in favor of $y = 1$ and the exponent for e in the logistic regression equation. It can be shown that

$$\ln(\text{odds}) = \beta_0 + \beta_1 x_1 + \beta_2 x_2 + \cdots + \beta_p x_p$$

This equation shows that the natural logarithm of the odds in favor of $y = 1$ is a linear function of the independent variables. This linear function is called the **logit**. We will use the notation $g(x_1, x_2, \ldots, x_p)$ to denote the logit.

LOGIT

$$g(x_1, x_2, \ldots, x_p) = \beta_0 + \beta_1 x_1 + \beta_2 x_2 + \cdots + \beta_p x_p \qquad \textbf{(15.35)}$$

Substituting $g(x_1, x_2, \ldots, x_p)$ for $\beta_1 + \beta_1 x_1 + \beta_2 x_2 + \cdots + \beta_p x_p$ in equation (15.27), we can write the logistic regression equation as

$$E(y) = \frac{e^{g(x_1, x_2, \ldots, x_p)}}{1 + e^{g(x_1, x_2, \ldots, x_p)}} \qquad \textbf{(15.36)}$$

Once we estimate the parameters in the logistic regression equation, we can compute an estimate of the logit. Using $\hat{g}(x_1, x_2, \ldots, x_p)$ to denote the **estimated logit**, we obtain

ESTIMATED LOGIT

$$\hat{g}(x_1, x_2, \ldots, x_p) = b_0 + b_1 x_1 + b_2 x_2 + \cdots + b_p x_p \qquad \textbf{(15.37)}$$

Thus, in terms of the estimated logit, the estimated regression equation is

$$\hat{y} = \frac{e^{b_0 + b_1 x_1 + b_2 x_2 + \cdots + b_p x_p}}{1 + e^{b_0 + b_1 x_1 + b_2 x_2 + \cdots + b_p x_p}} = \frac{e^{\hat{g}(x_1, x_2, \ldots, x_p)}}{1 + e^{\hat{g}(x_1, x_2, \ldots, x_p)}} \qquad \textbf{(15.38)}$$

For the Simmons Stores example, the estimated logit is

$$\hat{g}(x_1, x_2) = -2.14637 + .341643x_1 + 1.09873x_2$$

and the estimated regression equation is

$$\hat{y} = \frac{e^{\hat{g}(x_1, x_2)}}{1 + e^{\hat{g}(x_1, x_2)}} = \frac{e^{-2.14637 + .341643x_1 + 1.09873x_2}}{1 + e^{-2.14637 + .341643x_1 + 1.09873x_2}}$$

Thus, because of the unique relationship between the estimated logit and the estimated logistic regression equation, we can compute the estimated probabilities for Simmons Stores by dividing $e^{\hat{g}(x_1, x_2)}$ by $1 + e^{\hat{g}(x_1, x_2)}$.

NOTES AND COMMENTS

1. Because of the unique relationship between the estimated coefficients in the model and the corresponding odds ratios, the overall test for significance based upon the G statistic is also a test of overall significance for the odds ratios. In addition, the z test for the individual significance of a model parameter also provides a statistical test of significance for the corresponding odds ratio.

2. In simple and multiple regression, the coefficient of determination is used to measure the goodness of fit. In logistic regression, no single measure provides a similar interpretation. A discussion of goodness of fit is beyond the scope of our introductory treatment of logistic regression.

Exercises

Applications

Simmons

44. Refer to the Simmons Stores example introduced in this section. The dependent variable is coded as $y = 1$ if the customer used the coupon and 0 if not. Suppose that the only information available to help predict whether the customer will use the coupon is the customer's credit card status, coded as $x = 1$ if the customer has a Simmons credit card and $x = 0$ if not.
    a. Write the logistic regression equation relating x to y.
    b. What is the interpretation of $E(y)$ when $x = 0$?
    c. For the Simmons data in Table 15.11, use Minitab to compute the estimated logit.
    d. Use the estimated logit computed in part (c) to estimate the probability of using the coupon for customers who do not have a Simmons credit card and to estimate the probability of using the coupon for customers who have a Simmons credit card.
    e. What is the estimated odds ratio? What is its interpretation?

45. In Table 15.12 we provided estimates of the probability of using the coupon in the Simmons Stores catalog promotion. A different value is obtained for each combination of values for the independent variables.
    a. Compute the odds in favor of using the coupon for a customer with annual spending of $4000 who does not have a Simmons credit card ($x_1 = 4$, $x_2 = 0$).
    b. Use the information in Table 15.12 and part (a) to compute the odds ratio for the Simmons credit card variable $x_2 = 0$, holding annual spending constant at $x_1 = 4$.
    c. In the text, the odds ratio for the credit card variable was computed using the information in the $2000 column of Table 15.12. Did you get the same value for the odds ratio in part (b)?

46. Community Bank would like to increase the number of customers who use payroll direct deposit. Management is considering a new sales campaign that will require each branch manager to call each customer who does not currently use payroll direct deposit. As an incentive to sign up for payroll direct deposit, each customer contacted will be offered free checking for two years. Because of the time and cost associated with the new campaign, management would like to focus their efforts on customers who have the highest probability of signing up for payroll direct deposit. Management believes that the average monthly balance in a customer's checking account may be a useful predictor of whether the customer will sign up for direct payroll deposit. To investigate the relationship between these two variables, Community Bank tried the new campaign using a sample of 50 checking account customers who do not currently use payroll direct deposit. The sample data show the average monthly checking account balance (in hundreds of dollars) and whether the customer contacted signed up for payroll direct deposit (coded 1 if the customer signed up for payroll direct deposit and 0 if not). The data are contained in the data set named Bank; a portion of the data follows.

Bank

Customer	x = Monthly Balance	y = Direct Deposit
1	1.22	0
2	1.56	0
3	2.10	0
4	2.25	0
5	2.89	0
6	3.55	0
7	3.56	0
8	3.65	1
.	.	.
.	.	.
.	.	.
48	18.45	1
49	24.98	0
50	26.05	1

a. Write the logistic regression equation relating x to y.
b. For the Community Bank data, use Minitab to compute the estimated logistic regression equation.
c. Conduct a test of significance using the G test statistic. Use $\alpha = .05$.
d. Estimate the probability that customers with an average monthly balance of $1000 will sign up for direct payroll deposit.
e. Suppose Community Bank only wants to contact customers who have a .50 or higher probability of signing up for direct payroll deposit. What is the average monthly balance required to achieve this level of probability?
f. What is the estimated odds ratio? What is its interpretation?

47. Over the past few years the percentage of students who leave Lakeland College at the end of the first year has increased. Last year Lakeland started a voluntary one-week orientation program to help first-year students adjust to campus life. If Lakeland is able to show that the orientation program has a positive effect on retention, they will consider making the program a requirement for all first-year students. Lakeland's administration also suspects that students with lower GPAs have a higher probability of leaving Lakeland at the end of the first year. In order to investigate the relation of these variables to retention, Lakeland selected a random sample of 100 students from last year's entering class. The data are contained in the data set named Lakeland; a portion of the data follows.

Lakeland

Student	GPA	Program	Return
1	3.78	1	1
2	2.38	0	1
3	1.30	0	0
4	2.19	1	0
5	3.22	1	1
6	2.68	1	1
.	.	.	.
.	.	.	.
.	.	.	.
98	2.57	1	1
99	1.70	1	1
100	3.85	1	1

The dependent variable was coded as $y = 1$ if the student returned to Lakeland for the sophomore year and $y = 0$ if not. The two independent variables are:

$$x_1 = \text{GPA at the end of the first semester}$$

$$x_2 = \begin{cases} 0 \text{ if the student did not attend the orientation program} \\ 1 \text{ if the student attended the orientation program} \end{cases}$$

a. Write the logistic regression equation relating x_1 and x_2 to y.
b. What is the interpretation of $E(y)$ when $x_2 = 0$?
c. Use both independent variables and Minitab to compute the estimated logit.
d. Conduct a test for overall significance using $\alpha = .05$.
e. Use $\alpha = .05$ to determine whether each of the independent variables is significant.
f. Use the estimated logit computed in part (c) to estimate the probability that students with a 2.5 grade point average who did not attend the orientation program will return to Lakeland for their sophomore year. What is the estimated probability for students with a 2.5 grade point average who attended the orientation program?
g. What is the estimated odds ratio for the orientation program? Interpret it.
h. Would you recommend making the orientation program a required activity? Why or why not?

48. The Tire Rack maintains an independent consumer survey to help drivers help each other by sharing their long-term tire experiences. The data contained in the file named TireRatings show survey results for 68 all-season tires (Tire Rack website, March 21, 2012). Performance traits are rated using the following 10-point scale.

TireRatings

Superior		Excellent		Good		Fair		Unacceptable	
10	9	8	7	6	5	4	3	2	1

The values for the variable labeled Wet are the average of the ratings for each tire's wet traction performance and the values for the variable labeled Noise are the average of the ratings for the noise level generated by each tire. Respondents were also asked whether they would buy the tire again using the following 10-point scale:

Definitely		Probably		Possibly		Probably Not		Definitely Not	
10	9	8	7	6	5	4	3	2	1

The values for the variable labeled Buy Again are the average of the buy-again responses. For the purposes of this exercise, we created the following binary dependent variable:

$$\text{Purchase} = \begin{cases} 1 \text{ if the value of the Buy-Again variable is 7 or greater} \\ 0 \text{ if the value of the Buy-Again variable is less than 7} \end{cases}$$

Thus, if Purchase $= 1$, the respondent would probably or definitely buy the tire again.

a. Write the logistic regression equation relating $x_1 = $ Wet performance rating and $x_2 = $ Noise performance rating to $y = $ Purchase.
b. Use Minitab to compute the estimated logit.
c. Use the estimated logit to compute an estimate of the probability that a customer will probably or definitely purchase a particular tire again with a Wet performance rating of 8 and a Noise performance rating of 8.
d. Suppose that the Wet and Noise performance ratings were 7. How does that affect the probability that a customer will probably or definitely purchase a particular tire again with these performance ratings?
e. If you were the CEO of a tire company, what do the results for parts (c) and (d) tell you?

Summary

In this chapter, we introduced multiple regression analysis as an extension of simple linear regression analysis presented in Chapter 14. Multiple regression analysis enables us to understand how a dependent variable is related to two or more independent variables. The mulitple regression equation $E(y) = \beta_0 + \beta_1 x_1 + \beta_2 x_2 + \cdots + \beta_p x_p$ shows that the mean or expected value of the dependent variable y, denoted $E(y)$, is related to the values of the independent variables $x_1, x_2, \ldots, x_p$. Sample data and the least squares method are used to develop the estimated multiple regression equation $\hat{y} = b_0 + b_1 x_1 + b_2 x_2 + \cdots + b_p x_p$. In effect $b_0, b_1, b_2, \ldots, b_p$ are sample statistics used to estimate the unknown model parameters $\beta_0, \beta_1, \beta_2, \ldots, \beta_p$. Computer printouts were used throughout the chapter to emphasize the fact that statistical software packages are the only realistic means of performing the numerous computations required in multiple regression analysis.

The multiple coefficient of determination was presented as a measure of the goodness of fit of the estimated regression equation. It determines the proportion of the variation of y that can be explained by the estimated regression equation. The adjusted multiple coefficient of determination is a similar measure of goodness of fit that adjusts for the number of independent variables and thus avoids overestimating the impact of adding more independent variables.

An F test and a t test were presented as ways to determine statistically whether the relationship among the variables is significant. The F test is used to determine whether there is a significant overall relationship between the dependent variable and the set of all independent variables. The t test is used to determine whether there is a significant relationship between the dependent variable and an individual independent variable given the other independent variables in the regression model. Correlation among the independent variables, known as multicollinearity, was discussed.

The section on categorical independent variables showed how dummy variables can be used to incorporate categorical data into multiple regression analysis. The section on residual analysis showed how residual analysis can be used to validate the model assumptions, detect outliers, and identify influential observations. Standardized residuals, leverage, studentized deleted residuals, and Cook's distance measure were discussed. The chapter concluded with a section on how logistic regression can be used to model situations in which the dependent variable may only assume two values.

Glossary

Multiple regression analysis Regression analysis involving two or more independent variables.

Multiple regression model The mathematical equation that describes how the dependent variable y is related to the independent variables $x_1, x_2, \ldots, x_p$ and an error term ϵ.

Multiple regression equation The mathematical equation relating the expected value or mean value of the dependent variable to the values of the independent variables; that is, $E(y) = \beta_0 + \beta_1 x_1 + \beta_2 x_2 + \cdots + \beta_p x_p$.

Estimated multiple regression equation The estimate of the multiple regression equation based on sample data and the least squares method; it is $\hat{y} = b_0 + b_1 x_1 + b_2 x_2 + \cdots + b_p x_p$.

Least squares method The method used to develop the estimated regression equation. It minimizes the sum of squared residuals (the deviations between the observed values of the dependent variable, y_i, and the predicted values of the dependent variable, $\hat{y}_i$).

Multiple coefficient of determination A measure of the goodness of fit of the estimated multiple regression equation. It can be interpreted as the proportion of the variability in the dependent variable that is explained by the estimated regression equation.

Adjusted multiple coefficient of determination A measure of the goodness of fit of the estimated multiple regression equation that adjusts for the number of independent variables in the model and thus avoids overestimating the impact of adding more independent variables.

Multicollinearity The term used to describe the correlation among the independent variables.

Categorical independent variable An independent variable with categorical data.

Dummy variable A variable used to model the effect of categorical independent variables. A dummy variable may take only the value zero or one.

Leverage A measure of how far the values of the independent variables are from their mean values.

Outlier An observation that does not fit the pattern of the other data.

Studentized deleted residuals Standardized residuals that are based on a revised standard error of the estimate obtained by deleting observation i from the data set and then performing the regression analysis and computations.

Influential observation An observation that has a strong influence on the regression results.

Cook's distance measure A measure of the influence of an observation based on both the leverage of observation i and the residual for observation i.

Logistic regression equation The mathematical equation relating $E(y)$, the probability that $y = 1$, to the values of the independent variables; that is, $E(y) = P(y = 1|x_1, x_2, \ldots, x_p) = \dfrac{e^{\beta_0+\beta_1 x_1+\beta_2 x_2+\cdots+\beta_p x_p}}{1 + e^{\beta_0+\beta_1 x_1+\beta_2 x_2+\cdots+\beta_p x_p}}$.

Estimated logistic regression equation The estimate of the logistic regression equation based on sample data; that is, $\hat{y} = $ estimate of $P(y = 1|x_1, x_2, \ldots, x_p) = \dfrac{e^{b_0+b_1 x_1+b_2 x_2+\cdots+b_p x_p}}{1 + e^{b_0+b_1 x_1+b_2 x_2+\cdots+b_p x_p}}$.

Odds in favor of an event occurring The probability the event will occur divided by the probability the event will not occur.

Odds ratio The odds that $y = 1$ given that one of the independent variables increased by one unit (odds$_1$) divided by the odds that $y = 1$ given no change in the values for the independent variables (odds$_0$); that is, Odds ratio = odds$_1$/odds$_0$.

Logit The natural logarithm of the odds in favor of $y = 1$; that is, $g(x_1, x_2, \ldots, x_p) = \beta_0 + \beta_1 x_1 + \beta_2 x_2 + \cdots + \beta_p x_p$.

Estimated logit An estimate of the logit based on sample data; that is, $\hat{g}(x_1, x_2, \ldots, x_p) = b_0 + b_1 x_1 + b_2 x_2 + \cdots + b_p x_p$.

Key Formulas

Multiple Regression Model

$$y = \beta_0 + \beta_1 x_1 + \beta_2 x_2 + \cdots + \beta_p x_p + \epsilon \tag{15.1}$$

Multiple Regression Equation

$$E(y) = \beta_0 + \beta_1 x_1 + \beta_2 x_2 + \cdots + \beta_p x_p \tag{15.2}$$

Estimated Multiple Regression Equation

$$\hat{y} = b_0 + b_1 x_1 + b_2 x_2 + \cdots + b_p x_p \tag{15.3}$$

Least Squares Criterion

$$\min \Sigma(y_i - \hat{y}_i)^2 \tag{15.4}$$

Relationship Among SST, SSR, and SSE

$$SST = SSR + SSE \tag{15.7}$$

Multiple Coefficient of Determination

$$R^2 = \frac{SSR}{SST} \tag{15.8}$$

Adjusted Multiple Coefficient of Determination

$$R_a^2 = 1 - (1 - R^2)\frac{n-1}{n-p-1} \tag{15.9}$$

Mean Square Due to Regression

$$MSR = \frac{SSR}{p} \tag{15.12}$$

Mean Square Due to Error

$$MSE = \frac{SSE}{n-p-1} \tag{15.13}$$

F Test Statistic

$$F = \frac{MSR}{MSE} \tag{15.14}$$

t Test Statistic

$$t = \frac{b_i}{s_{b_i}} \tag{15.15}$$

Standardized Residual for Observation i

$$\frac{y_i - \hat{y}_i}{s_{y_i - \hat{y}_i}} \tag{15.23}$$

Standard Deviation of Residual i

$$s_{y_i - \hat{y}_i} = s\sqrt{1 - h_i} \tag{15.24}$$

Cook's Distance Measure

$$D_i = \frac{(y_i - \hat{y}_i)^2}{(p+1)s^2}\left[\frac{h_i}{(1 - h_i)^2}\right] \tag{15.25}$$

Logistic Regression Equation

$$E(y) = \frac{e^{\beta_0 + \beta_1 x_1 + \beta_2 x_2 + \cdots + \beta_p x_p}}{1 + e^{\beta_0 + \beta_1 x_1 + \beta_2 x_2 + \cdots + \beta_p x_p}} \tag{15.27}$$

Estimated Logistic Regression Equation

$$\hat{y} = \text{estimate of } P(y = 1 \mid x_1, x_2, \ldots, x_p) = \frac{e^{b_0 + b_1 x_1 + b_2 x_2 + \cdots + b_p x_p}}{1 + e^{b_0 + b_1 x_1 + b_2 x_2 + \cdots + b_p x_p}} \quad (15.30)$$

Odds Ratio

$$\text{Odds ratio} = \frac{\text{odds}_1}{\text{odds}_0} \quad (15.34)$$

Logit

$$g(x_1, x_2, \ldots, x_p) = \beta_0 + \beta_1 x_1 + \beta_2 x_2 + \cdots + \beta_p x_p \quad (15.35)$$

Estimated Logit

$$\hat{g}(x_1, x_2, \ldots, x_p) = b_0 + b_1 x_1 + b_2 x_2 + \cdots + b_p x_p \quad (15.37)$$

Supplementary Exercises

49. The admissions officer for Clearwater College developed the following estimated regression equation relating the final college GPA to the student's SAT mathematics score and high-school GPA.

$$\hat{y} = -1.41 + .0235x_1 + .00486x_2$$

where

$$x_1 = \text{high-school grade point average}$$
$$x_2 = \text{SAT mathematics score}$$
$$y = \text{final college grade point average}$$

a. Interpret the coefficients in this estimated regression equation.
b. Predict the final college GPA for a student who has a high-school average of 84 and a score of 540 on the SAT mathematics test.

50. The personnel director for Electronics Associates developed the following estimated regression equation relating an employee's score on a job satisfaction test to his or her length of service and wage rate.

$$\hat{y} = 14.4 - 8.69x_1 + 13.5x_2$$

where

$$x_1 = \text{length of service (years)}$$
$$x_2 = \text{wage rate (dollars)}$$
$$y = \text{job satisfaction test score (higher scores indicate greater job satisfaction)}$$

a. Interpret the coefficients in this estimated regression equation.
b. Predict the job satisfaction test score for an employee who has four years of service and makes $6.50 per hour.

51. A partial computer output from a regression analysis follows.

```
The regression equation is
Y = 8.103 + 7.602 X1 + 3.111 X2

Predictor              Coef          SE Coef              T
Constant             _____         2.667           _____
X1                   _____         2.105           _____
X2                   _____         0.613           _____

S = 3.335      R-Sq = 92.3%      R-Sq(adj) = _____%

Analysis of Variance

SOURCE                 DF             SS            MS            F
Regression          _____        1612        _____      _____
Residual Error         12         _____      _____
Total               _____      _____
```

a. Compute the missing entries in this output.
b. Use the F test and $\alpha = .05$ to see whether a significant relationship is present.
c. Use the t test and $\alpha = .05$ to test $H_0: \beta_1 = 0$ and $H_0: \beta_2 = 0$.
d. Compute R_a^2.

52. Recall that in exercise 49, the admissions officer for Clearwater College developed the following estimated regression equation relating final college GPA to the student's SAT mathematics score and high-school GPA.

$$\hat{y} = -1.41 + .0235x_1 + .00486x_2$$

where

$$x_1 = \text{high-school grade point average}$$
$$x_2 = \text{SAT mathematics score}$$
$$y = \text{final college grade point average}$$

A portion of the Minitab computer output follows.

```
The regression equation is
Y = -1.41 + .0235 X1 + .00486 X2

Predictor              Coef          SE Coef              T
Constant            -1.4053          0.4848          _____
X1                  0.023467         0.008666        _____
X2                  _____         0.001077        _____

S = 0.1298     R-Sq = _____      R-Sq(adj) = _____

Analysis of Variance

SOURCE                 DF             SS            MS            F
Regression          _____        1.76209        _____      _____
Residual Error      _____       _____       _____
Total                  9         1.88000
```

    a.   Complete the missing entries in this output.

    b.   Use the F test and a .05 level of significance to see whether a significant relationship is present.

    c.   Use the t test and $\alpha = .05$ to test $H_0: \beta_1 = 0$ and $H_0: \beta_2 = 0$.

    d.   Did the estimated regression equation provide a good fit to the data? Explain.

53.   Recall that in exercise 50 the personnel director for Electronics Associates developed the following estimated regression equation relating an employee's score on a job satisfaction test to length of service and wage rate.

$$\hat{y} = 14.4 - 8.69x_1 + 13.5x_2$$

where

$$x_1 = \text{length of service (years)}$$
$$x_2 = \text{wage rate (dollars)}$$
$$y = \text{job satisfaction test score (higher scores indicate greater job satisfaction)}$$

A portion of the Minitab computer output follows.

```
The regression equation is
Y = 14.4 - 8.69 X1 + 13.52 X2

Predictor            Coef          SE Coef              T
Constant            14.448           8.191           1.76
X1                                   1.555         _____
X2                  13.517           2.085         _____

S = 3.773        R-Sq = _____%   R-Sq(adj) = _____%

Analysis of Variance

SOURCE              DF             SS             MS            F
Regression           2         _____         _____       _____
Residual Error  _____          71.17         _____
Total                7          720.0
```

    a.   Complete the missing entries in this output.

    b.   Compute F and test using $\alpha = .05$ to see whether a significant relationship is present.

    c.   Did the estimated regression equation provide a good fit to the data? Explain.

    d.   Use the t test and $\alpha = .05$ to test $H_0: \beta_1 = 0$ and $H_0: \beta_2 = 0$.

54.   The Tire Rack, America's leading online distributor of tires and wheels, conducts extensive testing to provide customers with products that are right for their vehicle, driving style, and driving conditions. In addition, the Tire Rack maintains an independent consumer survey to help drivers help each other by sharing their long-term tire experiences. The following data show survey ratings (1 to 10 scale with 10 the highest rating) for 18 maximum performance summer tires (Tire Rack website, February 3, 2009). The variable Steering rates the tire's steering responsiveness, Tread Wear rates quickness of wear based on the driver's expectations, and Buy Again rates the driver's overall tire satisfaction and desire to purchase the same tire again.

Tire	Steering	Tread Wear	Buy Again
Goodyear Assurance TripleTred	8.9	8.5	8.1
Michelin HydroEdge	8.9	9.0	8.3
Michelin Harmony	8.3	8.8	8.2
Dunlop SP 60	8.2	8.5	7.9
Goodyear Assurance ComforTred	7.9	7.7	7.1
Yokohama Y372	8.4	8.2	8.9
Yokohama Aegis LS4	7.9	7.0	7.1
Kumho Power Star 758	7.9	7.9	8.3
Goodyear Assurance	7.6	5.8	4.5
Hankook H406	7.8	6.8	6.2
Michelin Energy LX4	7.4	5.7	4.8
Michelin MX4	7.0	6.5	5.3
Michelin Symmetry	6.9	5.7	4.2
Kumho 722	7.2	6.6	5.0
Dunlop SP 40 A/S	6.2	4.2	3.4
Bridgestone Insignia SE200	5.7	5.5	3.6
Goodyear Integrity	5.7	5.4	2.9
Dunlop SP20 FE	5.7	5.0	3.3

TireRack

a. Develop an estimated regression equation that can be used to predict the Buy Again rating given based on the Steering rating. At the .05 level of significance, test for a significant relationship.

b. Did the estimated regression equation developed in part (a) provide a good fit to the data? Explain.

c. Develop an estimated regression equation that can be used to predict the Buy Again rating given the Steering rating and the Tread Wear rating.

d. Is the addition of the Tread Wear independent variable significant? Use $\alpha = .05$.

2012FuelEcon

55. The Department of Energy and the U.S. Environmental Protection Agency's *2012 Fuel Economy Guide* provides fuel efficiency data for 2012 model year cars and trucks (Department of Energy website, April 16, 2012). The file named 2012FuelEcon provides a portion of the data for 309 cars. The column labeled Manufacturer shows the name of the company that manufactured the car; the column labeled Displacement shows the engine's displacement in liters; the column labeled Fuel shows the required or recommended type of fuel (regular or premium gasoline); the column labeled Drive identifies the type of drive (F for front wheel, R for rear wheel, and A for all wheel); and the column labeled Hwy MPG shows the fuel efficiency rating for highway driving in terms of miles per gallon.

a. Develop an estimated regression equation that can be used to predict the fuel efficiency for highway driving given the engine's displacement. Test for significance using $\alpha = .05$.

b. Consider the addition of the dummy variable FuelPremium, where the value of FuelPremium is 1 if the required or recommended type of fuel is premium gasoline and 0 if the type of fuel is regular gasoline. Develop the estimated regression equation that can be used to predict the fuel efficiency for highway driving given the engine's displacement and the dummy variable FuelPremium.

c. Use $\alpha = .05$ to determine whether the dummy variable added in part (b) is significant.

d. Consider the addition of the dummy variables FrontWheel and RearWheel. The value of FrontWheel is 1 if the car has front wheel drive and 0 otherwise; the value of RearWheel is 1 if the car has rear wheel drive and 0 otherwise. Thus, for a car that has all-wheel drive, the value of FrontWheel and the value of RearWheel is 0. Develop the estimated regression equation that can be used to predict the fuel efficiency for highway driving given the engine's displacement, the dummy variable FuelPremium, and the dummy variables FrontWheel and RearWheel.

e. For the estimated regression equation developed in part (d), test for overall significance and individual significance using $\alpha = .05$.

56. A portion of a data set containing information for 45 mutual funds that are part of the *Morningstar Funds 500* for 2008 follows. The complete data set is available in the file named MutualFunds. The data set includes the following five variables:

Fund Type: The type of fund, labeled DE (Domestic Equity), IE (International Equity), and FI (Fixed Income).

Net Asset Value ($): The closing price per share on December 31, 2007.

5-Year Average Return (%): The average annual return for the fund over the past five years.

Expense Ratio (%): The percentage of assets deducted each fiscal year for fund expenses.

Morningstar Rank: The risk adjusted star rating for each fund; Morningstar ranks go from a low of 1-Star to a high of 5-Stars.

MutualFunds

Fund Name	Fund Type	Net Asset Value ($)	5-Year Average Return (%)	Expense Ratio (%)	Morningstar Rank
Amer Cent Inc & Growth Inv	DE	28.88	12.39	.67	2-Star
American Century Intl. Disc	IE	14.37	30.53	1.41	3-Star
American Century Tax-Free Bond	FI	10.73	3.34	.49	4-Star
American Century Ultra	DE	24.94	10.88	.99	3-Star
Ariel	DE	46.39	11.32	1.03	2-Star
Artisan Intl Val	IE	25.52	24.95	1.23	3-Star
Artisan Small Cap	DE	16.92	15.67	1.18	3-Star
Baron Asset	DE	50.67	16.77	1.31	5-Star
Brandywine	DE	36.58	18.14	1.08	4-Star
⋮	⋮	⋮	⋮	⋮	⋮

a. Develop an estimated regression equation that can be used to predict the 5-year average return given the type of fund. At the .05 level of significance, test for a significant relationship.

b. Did the estimated regression equation developed in part (a) provide a good fit to the data? Explain.

c. Develop the estimated regression equation that can be used to predict the 5-year average return given the type of fund, the net asset value, and the expense ratio. At the .05 level of significance, test for a significant relationship. Do you think any variables should be deleted from the estimated regression equation? Explain.

d. Morningstar Rank is a categorical variable. Because the data set contains only funds with four ranks (2-Star through 5-Star), use the following dummy variables: 3Star-Rank = 1 for a 3-Star fund, 0 otherwise; 4StarRank = 1 for a 4-Star fund, 0 otherwise; and 5StarRank = 1 for a 5-Star fund, 0 otherwise. Develop an estimated regression equation that can be used to predict the 5-year average return given the type of fund, the expense ratio, and the Morningstar Rank. Using $\alpha = .05$, remove any independent variables that are not significant.

e. Use the estimated regression equation developed in part (d) to predict the 5-year average return for a domestic equity fund with an expense ratio of 1.05% and a 3-Star Morningstar Rank.

57. *Fortune* magazine publishes an annual list of the 100 best companies to work for. The data in the file named FortuneBest shows a portion of the data for a random sample of 30 of the companies that made the top 100 list for 2012 (*Fortune,* February 6, 2012). The column labeled Rank shows the rank of the company in the Fortune 100 list; the column labeled Size indicates whether the company is a small, midsize, or large company; the column labeled Salaried ($1000s) shows the average annual salary for salaried employees rounded to the nearest $1000; and the column labeled Hourly ($1000s) shows the average annual salary for hourly employees rounded to the nearest $1000. *Fortune* defines large companies as having more than 10,000 employees, midsize companies as having between 2500 and 10,000 employees, and small companies as having fewer than 2500 employees.

Rank	Company	Size	Salaried ($1000s)	Hourly ($1000s)
4	Wegmans Food Markets	Large	56	29
6	NetApp	Midsize	143	76
7	Camden Property Trust	Small	71	37
8	Recreational Equipment (REI)	Large	103	28
10	Quicken Loans	Midsize	78	54
11	Zappos.com	Midsize	48	25
12	Mercedes-Benz USA	Small	118	50
20	USAA	Large	96	47
22	The Container Store	Midsize	71	45
25	Ultimate Software	Small	166	56
37	Plante Moran	Small	73	45
42	Baptist Health South Florida	Large	126	80
50	World Wide Technology	Small	129	31
53	Methodist Hospital	Large	100	83
58	Perkins Coie	Small	189	63
60	American Express	Large	114	35
64	TDIndustries	Small	93	47
66	QuikTrip	Large	69	44
72	EOG Resources	Small	189	81
75	FactSet Research Systems	Small	103	51
80	Stryker	Large	71	43
81	SRC	Small	84	33
84	Booz Allen Hamilton	Large	105	77
91	CarMax	Large	57	34
93	GoDaddy.com	Midsize	105	71
94	KPMG	Large	79	59
95	Navy Federal Credit Union	Midsize	77	39
97	Schweitzer Engineering Labs	Small	99	28
99	Darden Restaurants	Large	57	24
100	Intercontinental Hotels Group	Large	63	26

WEB file

FortuneBest

a. Use these data to develop an estimated regression equation that could be used to predict the average annual salary for salaried employees given the average annual salary for hourly employees.
b. Use $\alpha = .05$ to test for overall significance.
c. To incorporate the effect of size, a categorical variable with three levels, we used two dummy variables: Size-Midsize and Size-Small. The value of Size-Midsize = 1 if the company is a midsize company and 0 otherwise. And, the value of Size-Small = 1 if the company is a small company and 0 otherwise. Develop an estimated regression equation that could be used to predict the average annual salary for salaried employees given the average annual salary for hourly employees and the size of the company.
d. For the estimated regression equation developed in part (c), use the *t* test to determine the significance of the independent variables. Use $\alpha = .05$.

e.   Based upon your findings in part (d), develop an estimated regression equation that can be used to predict the average annual salary for salaried employees given the average annual salary for hourly employees and the size of the company.

Case Problem 1 Consumer Research, Inc.

Consumer Research, Inc., is an independent agency that conducts research on consumer attitudes and behaviors for a variety of firms. In one study, a client asked for an investigation of consumer characteristics that can be used to predict the amount charged by credit card users. Data were collected on annual income, household size, and annual credit card charges for a sample of 50 consumers. The following data are contained in the file named Consumer.

WEB file

Consumer

Income ($1000s)	Household Size	Amount Charged ($)	Income ($1000s)	Household Size	Amount Charged ($)
54	3	4016	54	6	5573
30	2	3159	30	1	2583
32	4	5100	48	2	3866
50	5	4742	34	5	3586
31	2	1864	67	4	5037
55	2	4070	50	2	3605
37	1	2731	67	5	5345
40	2	3348	55	6	5370
66	4	4764	52	2	3890
51	3	4110	62	3	4705
25	3	4208	64	2	4157
48	4	4219	22	3	3579
27	1	2477	29	4	3890
33	2	2514	39	2	2972
65	3	4214	35	1	3121
63	4	4965	39	4	4183
42	6	4412	54	3	3730
21	2	2448	23	6	4127
44	1	2995	27	2	2921
37	5	4171	26	7	4603
62	6	5678	61	2	4273
21	3	3623	30	2	3067
55	7	5301	22	4	3074
42	2	3020	46	5	4820
41	7	4828	66	4	5149

Managerial Report

1. Use methods of descriptive statistics to summarize the data. Comment on the findings.
2. Develop estimated regression equations, first using annual income as the independent variable and then using household size as the independent variable. Which variable is the better predictor of annual credit card charges? Discuss your findings.
3. Develop an estimated regression equation with annual income and household size as the independent variables. Discuss your findings.
4. What is the predicted annual credit card charge for a three-person household with an annual income of $40,000?
5. Discuss the need for other independent variables that could be added to the model. What additional variables might be helpful?

Case Problem 2   Predicting Winnings for NASCAR Drivers

Matt Kenseth won the 2012 Daytona 500, the most important race of the NASCAR season. His win was no surprise because for the 2011 season he finished fourth in the point standings with 2330 points, behind Tony Stewart (2403 points), Carl Edwards (2403 points), and Kevin Harvick (2345 points). In 2011 he earned $6,183,580 by winning three Poles (fastest driver in qualifying), winning three races, finishing in the top five 12 times, and finishing in the top ten 20 times. NASCAR's point system in 2011 allocated 43 points to the driver who finished first, 42 points to the driver who finished second, and so on down to 1 point for the driver who finished in the 43rd position. In addition any driver who led a lap received 1 bonus point, the driver who led the most laps received an additional bonus point, and the race winner was awarded 3 bonus points. But, the maximum number of points a driver could earn in any race was 48. Table 15.13 shows data for the 2011 season for the top 35 drivers (NASCAR website, February 28, 2011).

TABLE 15.13   NASCAR RESULTS FOR THE 2011 SEASON

Driver	Points	Poles	Wins	Top 5	Top 10	Winnings ($)
Tony Stewart	2403	1	5	9	19	6,529,870
Carl Edwards	2403	3	1	19	26	8,485,990
Kevin Harvick	2345	0	4	9	19	6,197,140
Matt Kenseth	2330	3	3	12	20	6,183,580
Brad Keselowski	2319	1	3	10	14	5,087,740
Jimmie Johnson	2304	0	2	14	21	6,296,360
Dale Earnhardt Jr.	2290	1	0	4	12	4,163,690
Jeff Gordon	2287	1	3	13	18	5,912,830
Denny Hamlin	2284	0	1	5	14	5,401,190
Ryan Newman	2284	3	1	9	17	5,303,020
Kurt Busch	2262	3	2	8	16	5,936,470
Kyle Busch	2246	1	4	14	18	6,161,020
Clint Bowyer	1047	0	1	4	16	5,633,950
Kasey Kahne	1041	2	1	8	15	4,775,160
A. J. Allmendinger	1013	0	0	1	10	4,825,560
Greg Biffle	997	3	0	3	10	4,318,050
Paul Menard	947	0	1	4	8	3,853,690
Martin Truex Jr.	937	1	0	3	12	3,955,560
Marcos Ambrose	936	0	1	5	12	4,750,390
Jeff Burton	935	0	0	2	5	3,807,780
Juan Montoya	932	2	0	2	8	5,020,780
Mark Martin	930	2	0	2	10	3,830,910
David Ragan	906	2	1	4	8	4,203,660
Joey Logano	902	2	0	4	6	3,856,010
Brian Vickers	846	0	0	3	7	4,301,880
Regan Smith	820	0	1	2	5	4,579,860
Jamie McMurray	795	1	0	2	4	4,794,770
David Reutimann	757	1	0	1	3	4,374,770
Bobby Labonte	670	0	0	1	2	4,505,650
David Gilliland	572	0	0	1	2	3,878,390
Casey Mears	541	0	0	0	0	2,838,320
Dave Blaney	508	0	0	1	1	3,229,210
Andy Lally	398	0	0	0	0	2,868,220
Robby Gordon	268	0	0	0	0	2,271,890
J. J. Yeley	192	0	0	0	0	2,559,500

WEB file

NASCAR

Managerial Report

1. Suppose you wanted to predict Winnings ($) using only the number of poles won (Poles), the number of wins (Wins), the number of top five finishes (Top 5), or the number of top ten finishes (Top 10). Which of these four variables provides the best single predictor of winnings?

2. Develop an estimated regression equation that can be used to predict Winnings ($) given the number of poles won (Poles), the number of wins (Wins), the number of top five finishes (Top 5), and the number of top ten (Top 10) finishes. Test for individual significance and discuss your findings and conclusions.

3. Create two new independent variables: Top 2–5 and Top 6–10. Top 2–5 represents the number of times the driver finished between second and fifth place and Top 6–10 represents the number of times the driver finished between sixth and tenth place. Develop an estimated regression equation that can be used to predict Winnings ($) using Poles, Wins, Top 2–5, and Top 6–10. Test for individual significance and discuss your findings and conclusions.

4. Based upon the results of your analysis, what estimated regression equation would you recommend using to predict Winnings ($)? Provide an interpretation of the estimated regression coefficients for this equation.

Case Problem 3   Finding the Best Car Value

When trying to decide what car to buy, real value is not necessarily determined by how much you spend on the initial purchase. Instead, cars that are reliable and don't cost much to own often represent the best values. But no matter how reliable or inexpensive a car may cost to own, it must also perform well.

To measure value, *Consumer Reports* developed a statistic referred to as a value score. The value score is based upon five-year owner costs, overall road-test scores, and predicted-reliability ratings. Five-year owner costs are based upon the expenses incurred in the first five years of ownership, including depreciation, fuel, maintenance and repairs, and so on. Using a national average of 12,000 miles per year, an average cost per mile driven is used as the measure of five-year owner costs. Road-test scores are the results of more than 50 tests and evaluations and are based on a 100-point scale, with higher scores indicating better performance, comfort, convenience, and fuel economy. The highest road-test score obtained in the tests conducted by *Consumer Reports* was a 99 for a Lexus LS 460L. Predicted-reliability ratings (1 = Poor, 2 = Fair, 3 = Good, 4 = Very Good, and 5 = Excellent) are based upon data from *Consumer Reports'* Annual Auto Survey.

CarValues

A car with a value score of 1.0 is considered to be an "average-value" car. A car with a value score of 2.0 is considered to be twice as good a value as a car with a value score of 1.0; a car with a value score of 0.5 is considered half as good as average; and so on. The data for three sizes of cars (13 small sedans, 20 family sedans, and 21 upscale sedans), including the price ($) of each car tested, are contained in the file named CarValues (*Consumer Reports* website, April 18, 2012). To incorporate the effect of size of car, a categorical variable with three values (small sedan, family sedan, and upscale sedan), use the following dummy variables:

$$\text{Family-Sedan} = \begin{cases} 1 \text{ if the car is a Family Sedan} \\ 0 \text{ otherwise} \end{cases}$$

$$\text{Upscale-Sedan} = \begin{cases} 1 \text{ if the car is an Upscale Sedan} \\ 0 \text{ otherwise} \end{cases}$$

Managerial Report

1. Treating Cost/Mile as the dependent variable, develop an estimated regression with Family-Sedan and Upscale-Sedan as the independent variables. Discuss your findings.
2. Treating Value Score as the dependent variable, develop an estimated regression equation using Cost/Mile, Road-Test Score, Predicted Reliability, Family-Sedan, and Upscale-Sedan as the independent variables.
3. Delete any independent variables that are not significant from the estimated regression equation developed in part 2 using a .05 level of significance. After deleting any independent variables that are not significant, develop a new estimated regression equation.
4. Suppose someone claims that "smaller cars provide better values than larger cars." For the data in this case, the Small Sedans represent the smallest type of car and the Upscale Sedans represent the largest type of car. Does your analysis support this claim?
5. Use regression analysis to develop an estimated regression equation that could be used to predict the value score given the value of the Road-Test Score.
6. Use regression analysis to develop an estimated regression equation that could be used to predict the value score given the Predicted Reliability.
7. What conclusions can you derive from your analysis?

Appendix 15.1 Multiple Regression with Minitab

Butler

In Section 15.2 we discussed the computer solution of multiple regression problems by showing Minitab's output for the Butler Trucking Company problem. In this appendix we describe the steps required to generate the Minitab computer solution. First, the data must be entered in a Minitab worksheet. The miles traveled are entered in column C1, the number of deliveries are entered in column C2, and the travel times (hours) are entered in column C3. The variable names Miles, Deliveries, and Time were entered as the column headings on the worksheet. In subsequent steps, we refer to the data by using the variable names Miles, Deliveries, and Time or the column indicators C1, C2, and C3. The following steps describe how to use Minitab to produce the regression results shown in Figure 15.4.

Step 1. Select the **Stat** menu
Step 2. Select the **Regression** menu
Step 3. Choose **Regression**
Step 4. When the **Regression** dialog box appears:
        Enter Time in the **Response** box
        Enter Miles and Deliveries in the **Predictors** box
        Click **OK**

Appendix 15.2 Multiple Regression with Excel

Butler

In Section 15.2 we discussed the computer solution of multiple regression problems by showing Minitab's output for the Butler Trucking Company problem. In this appendix we describe how to use Excel's Regression tool to develop the estimated multiple regression equation for the Butler Trucking problem. Refer to Figure 15.14 as we describe the tasks involved. First, the labels Assignment, Miles, Deliveries, and Time are entered into cells A1:D1 of the worksheet, and the sample data into cells B2:D11. The numbers 1–10 in cells A2:A11 identify each observation.

FIGURE 15.14   EXCEL OUTPUT FOR BUTLER TRUCKING WITH TWO INDEPENDENT VARIABLES

	A	B	C	D	E	F	G	H	I	J
1	Assignment	Miles	Deliveries	Time						
2	1	100	4	9.3						
3	2	50	3	4.8						
4	3	100	4	8.9						
5	4	100	2	6.5						
6	5	50	2	4.2						
7	6	80	2	6.2						
8	7	75	3	7.4						
9	8	65	4	6						
10	9	90	3	7.6						
11	10	90	2	6.1						
12										
13	SUMMARY OUTPUT									
14										
15	*Regression Statistics*									
16	Multiple R	0.9507								
17	R Square	0.9038								
18	Adjusted R Square	0.8763								
19	Standard Error	0.5731								
20	Observations	10								
21										
22	ANOVA									
23		*df*	*SS*	*MS*	*F*	*Significance F*				
24	Regression	2	21.6006	10.8003	32.8784	0.0003				
25	Residual	7	2.2994	0.3285						
26	Total	9	23.9							
27										
28		*Coefficients*	*Standard Error*	*t Stat*	*P-value*	*Lower 95%*	*Upper 95%*	*Lower 99.0%*	*Upper 99.0%*	
29	Intercept	-0.8687	0.9515	-0.9129	0.3916	-3.1188	1.3813	-4.1986	2.4612	
30	Miles	0.0611	0.0099	6.1824	0.0005	0.0378	0.0845	0.0265	0.0957	
31	Deliveries	0.9234	0.2211	4.1763	0.0042	0.4006	1.4463	0.1496	1.6972	
32										

The following steps describe how to use the Regression tool for the multiple regression analysis.

Step 1. Click the **Data** tab on the Ribbon
Step 2. In the **Analysis** group, click **Data Analysis**
Step 3. Choose **Regression** from the list of Analysis Tools
Step 4. When the Regression dialog box appears:
  Enter D1:D11 in the **Input Y Range** box
  Enter B1:C11 in the **Input X Range** box
  Select **Labels**
  Select **Confidence Level**
  Enter 99 in the **Confidence Level** box
  Select **Output Range**
  Enter A13 in the **Output Range** box (to identify the upper left corner of the section of the worksheet where the output will appear)
  Click **OK**

In the Excel output shown in Figure 15.14 the label for the independent variable x_1 is Miles (see cell A30), and the label for the independent variable x_2 is Deliveries (see cell A31). The estimated regression equation is

$$\hat{y} = -.8687 + .0611x_1 + .9234x_2$$

Note that using Excel's Regression tool for multiple regression is almost the same as using it for simple linear regression. The major difference is that in the multiple regression case a larger range of cells is required in order to identify the independent variables.

Appendix 15.3 Logistic Regression with Minitab

Simmons

Minitab calls logistic regression with a dependent variable that can only assume the values 0 and 1 Binary Logistic Regression. In this appendix we describe the steps required to use Minitab's Binary Logistic Regression procedure to generate the computer output for the Simmons Stores problem shown in Figure 15.13. First, the data must be entered in a Minitab worksheet. The amounts customers spent last year at Simmons (in thousands of dollars) are entered into column C2, the credit card data (1 if a Simmons card; 0 otherwise) are entered into column C3, and the coupon use data (1 if the customer used the coupon; 0 otherwise) are entered in column C4. The variable names Spending, Card, and Coupon are entered as the column headings on the worksheet. In subsequent steps, we refer to the data by using the variable names Spending, Card, and Coupon or the column indicators C2, C3, and C4. The following steps will generate the logistic regression output.

Step 1. Select the **Stat** menu
Step 2. Select the **Regression** menu
Step 3. Choose **Binary Logistic Regression**
Step 4. When the **Binary Logistic Regression** dialog box appears:
　　　　 Enter Coupon in the **Response** box
　　　　 Enter Spending and Card in the **Model** box
　　　　 Click **OK**

The information in Figure 15.13 will now appear as a portion of the output.

Appendix 15.4 Multiple Regression Analysis Using StatTools

Butler

In this appendix we show how StatTools can be used to perform the regression analysis computations for the Butler Trucking problem. Begin by using the Data Set Manager to create a StatTools data set for these data using the procedure described in the appendix in Chapter 1. The following steps describe how StatTools can be used to provide the regression results.

Step 1. Click the **StatTools** tab on the Ribbon
Step 2. In the **Analyses** group, click **Regression and Classification**
Step 3. Choose the **Regression** option
Step 4. When the StatTools-Regression dialog box appears:
　　　　 Select **Multiple** in the **Regression Type** box
　　　　 In the **Variables** section:
　　　　　 Click the **Format** button and select **Unstacked**
　　　　　 In the column labeled **I** select **Miles**
　　　　　 In the column labeled **I** select **Deliveries**
　　　　　 In the column labeled **D** select **Time**
　　　　 Click **OK**

The regression analysis output will appear.

　　　 The StatTools-Regression dialog box contains a number of more advanced options for developing prediction interval estimates and producing residual plots. The StatTools Help facility provides information on using all of these options.

CHAPTER 16

Regression Analysis: Model Building

CONTENTS

STATISTICS IN PRACTICE:
MONSANTO COMPANY

16.1 GENERAL LINEAR MODEL
Modeling Curvilinear
Relationships
Interaction
Transformations Involving the
Dependent Variable
Nonlinear Models That Are
Intrinsically Linear

16.2 DETERMINING WHEN TO
ADD OR DELETE VARIABLES
General Case
Use of p-Values

16.3 ANALYSIS OF A LARGER
PROBLEM

16.4 VARIABLE SELECTION
PROCEDURES
Stepwise Regression
Forward Selection
Backward Elimination
Best-Subsets Regression
Making the Final Choice

16.5 MULTIPLE REGRESSION
APPROACH TO
EXPERIMENTAL DESIGN

16.6 AUTOCORRELATION AND
THE DURBIN-WATSON TEST

STATISTICS *in* PRACTICE

MONSANTO COMPANY*
ST. LOUIS, MISSOURI

Monsanto Company traces its roots to one entrepreneur's investment of $500 and a dusty warehouse on the Mississippi riverfront, where in 1901 John F. Queeney began manufacturing saccharin. Today, Monsanto is one of the nation's largest chemical companies, producing more than a thousand products ranging from industrial chemicals to synthetic playing surfaces used in modern sports stadiums. Monsanto is a worldwide corporation with manufacturing facilities, laboratories, technical centers, and marketing operations in 65 countries.

Monsanto's Nutrition Chemical Division manufactures and markets a methionine supplement used in poultry, swine, and cattle feed products. Because poultry growers work with high volumes and low profit margins, cost-effective poultry feed products with the best possible nutrition value are needed. Optimal feed composition will result in rapid growth and high final body weight for a given level of feed intake. The chemical industry works closely with poultry growers to optimize poultry feed products. Ultimately, success depends on keeping the cost of poultry low in comparison with the cost of beef and other meat products.

Monsanto used regression analysis to model the relationship between body weight y and the amount of methionine x added to the poultry feed. Initially, the following simple linear estimated regression equation was developed.

$$\hat{y} = .21 + .42x$$

This estimated regression equation proved statistically significant; however, the analysis of the residuals indicated that a curvilinear relationship would be a better model of the relationship between body weight and methionine.

Monsanto researchers used regression analysis to develop an optimal feed composition for poultry growers. © Krugloff/Shutterstock.com.

Further research conducted by Monsanto showed that although small amounts of methionine tended to increase body weight, at some point body weight leveled off and additional amounts of the methionine were of little or no benefit. In fact, when the amount of methionine increased beyond nutritional requirements, body weight tended to decline. The following estimated multiple regression equation was used to model the curvilinear relationship between body weight and methionine.

$$\hat{y} = -1.89 + 1.32x - .506x^2$$

Use of the regression results enabled Monsanto to determine the optimal level of methionine to be used in poultry feed products.

In this chapter we will extend the discussion of regression analysis by showing how curvilinear models such as the one used by Monsanto can be developed. In addition, we will describe a variety of tools that help determine which independent variables lead to the best estimated regression equation.

*The authors are indebted to James R. Ryland and Robert M. Schisla, Senior Research Specialists, Monsanto Nutrition Chemical Division, for providing this Statistics in Practice.

Model building is the process of developing an estimated regression equation that describes the relationship between a dependent variable and one or more independent variables. The major issues in model building are finding the proper functional form of the relationship and selecting the independent variables to be included in the model. In Section 16.1 we establish the framework for model building by introducing the concept of a general linear model. Section 16.2, which provides the foundation for the more sophisticated computer-based procedures, introduces a general approach for determining when to add or delete independent variables. In Section 16.3 we consider a larger regression problem involving eight independent variables and 25 observations; this problem is used to illustrate the variable selection procedures presented in Section 16.4, including stepwise regression, the forward selection procedure, the backward elimination procedure, and best-subsets regression. In Section 16.5 we show how multiple regression analysis can provide another approach to solving experimental design problems, and in Section 16.6 we show how the Durbin-Watson test can be used to detect serial or autocorrelation.

16.1   General Linear Model

Suppose we collected data for one dependent variable y and k independent variables x_1, $x_2, \ldots, x_k$. Our objective is to use these data to develop an estimated regression equation that provides the best relationship between the dependent and independent variables. As a general framework for developing more complex relationships among the independent variables, we introduce the concept of a **general linear model** involving p independent variables.

If you can write a regression model in the form of equation (16.1), the standard multiple regression procedures described in Chapter 15 are applicable.

> **GENERAL LINEAR MODEL**
> $$y = \beta_0 + \beta_1 z_1 + \beta_2 z_2 + \cdots + \beta_p z_p + \epsilon \qquad \text{(16.1)}$$

In equation (16.1), each of the independent variables z_j (where $j = 1, 2, \ldots, p$) is a function of $x_1, x_2, \ldots, x_k$ (the variables for which data are collected). In some cases, each z_j may be a function of only one x variable. The simplest case is when we collect data for just one variable x_1 and want to predict y by using a straight-line relationship. In this case $z_1 = x_1$ and equation (16.1) becomes

$$y = \beta_0 + \beta_1 x_1 + \epsilon \qquad \text{(16.2)}$$

Equation (16.2) is the simple linear regression model introduced in Chapter 14 with the exception that the independent variable is labeled x_1 instead of x. In the statistical modeling literature, this model is called a *simple first-order model with one predictor variable*.

Modeling Curvilinear Relationships

More complex types of relationships can be modeled with equation (16.1). To illustrate, let us consider the problem facing Reynolds, Inc., a manufacturer of industrial scales and laboratory equipment. Managers at Reynolds want to investigate the relationship between length of employment of their salespeople and the number of electronic laboratory scales sold. Table 16.1 gives the number of scales sold by 15 randomly selected salespeople for the most recent sales period and the number of months each salesperson has been employed by the firm. Figure 16.1 is the scatter diagram for these data. The scatter diagram indicates a possible curvilinear relationship between the length of time employed and the number of units sold. Before considering how to develop a curvilinear relationship for Reynolds, let us consider the Minitab output in Figure 16.2 corresponding to a simple first-order model; the estimated regression is

$$\text{Sales} = 111 + 2.38 \text{ Months}$$

where

$$\text{Sales} = \text{number of electronic laboratory scales sold}$$
$$\text{Months} = \text{the number of months the salesperson has been employed}$$

TABLE 16.1

DATA FOR THE REYNOLDS EXAMPLE

Months Employed	Scales Sold
41	275
106	296
76	317
104	376
22	162
12	150
85	367
111	308
40	189
51	235
9	83
12	112
6	67
56	325
19	189

WEB file

Reynolds

FIGURE 16.1 SCATTER DIAGRAM FOR THE REYNOLDS EXAMPLE

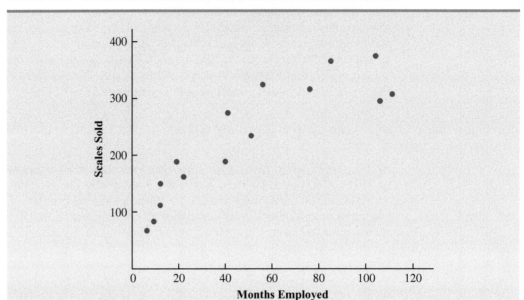

Figure 16.3 is the corresponding standardized residual plot. Although the computer output shows that the relationship is significant (p-value $= .000$) and that a linear relationship explains a high percentage of the variability in sales (R-Sq $= 78.1\%$), the standardized residual plot suggests that a curvilinear relationship is needed.

To account for the curvilinear relationship, we set $z_1 = x_1$ and $z_2 = x_1^2$ in equation (16.1) to obtain the model

$$y = \beta_0 + \beta_1 x_1 + \beta_2 x_1^2 + \epsilon \tag{16.3}$$

This model is called a *second-order model with one predictor variable.* To develop an estimated regression equation corresponding to this second-order model, the statistical

FIGURE 16.2 MINITAB OUTPUT FOR THE REYNOLDS EXAMPLE: FIRST-ORDER MODEL

```
The regression equation is
Sales = 111 + 2.38 Months

Predictor     Coef   SE Coef      T       p
Constant    111.23     21.63   5.14   0.000
Months      2.3768    0.3489   6.81   0.000

S = 49.5158   R-Sq = 78.1%   R-Sq(adj) = 76.4%

Analysis of Variance

SOURCE          DF       SS       MS       F       p
Regression       1   113783   113783   46.41   0.000
Residual Error  13    31874     2452
Total           14   145657
```

FIGURE 16.3   STANDARDIZED RESIDUAL PLOT FOR THE REYNOLDS EXAMPLE: FIRST-ORDER MODEL

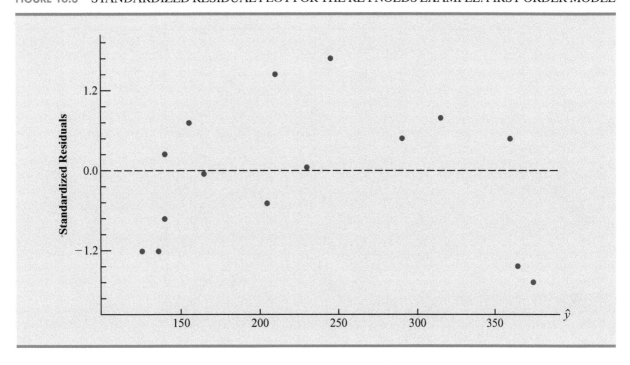

software package we are using needs the original data in Table 16.1, as well as that data corresponding to adding a second independent variable that is the square of the number of months the employee has been with the firm. In Figure 16.4 we show the Minitab output corresponding to the second-order model; the estimated regression equation is

$$\text{Sales} = 45.3 + 6.34 \text{ Months} - .0345 \text{ MonthsSq}$$

The data for the MonthsSq *independent variable is obtained by squaring the values of* Months.

where

$$\text{MonthsSq} = \text{the square of the number of months the}$$
$$\text{salesperson has been employed}$$

Figure 16.5 is the corresponding standardized residual plot. It shows that the previous curvilinear pattern has been removed. At the .05 level of significance, the computer output shows that the overall model is significant (*p*-value for the *F* test is .000); note also that the *p*-value corresponding to the *t*-ratio for MonthsSq (*p*-value = .002) is less than .05, and hence we can conclude that adding MonthsSq to the model involving Months is significant. With R-Sq(adj) = 88.6%, we should be pleased with the fit provided by this estimated regression equation. More important, however, is seeing how easy it is to handle curvilinear relationships in regression analysis.

Clearly, many types of relationships can be modeled by using equation (16.1). The regression techniques with which we have been working are definitely not limited to linear, or straight-line, relationships. In multiple regression analysis the word *linear* in the term "general linear model" refers only to the fact that $\beta_0, \beta_1, \ldots, \beta_p$ all have exponents of 1; it does not imply that the relationship between *y* and the x_i's is linear. Indeed, in this section we have seen one example of how equation (16.1) can be used to model a curvilinear relationship.

FIGURE 16.4 MINITAB OUTPUT FOR THE REYNOLDS EXAMPLE: SECOND-ORDER MODEL

```
The regression equation is
Sales = 45.3 + 6.34 Months - 0.0345 MonthsSq

Predictor         Coef    SE Coef      T       p
Constant         45.35      22.77    1.99   0.070
Months           6.345      1.058    6.00   0.000
MonthsSq     -0.034486   0.008948   -3.85   0.002

S = 34.4528    R-Sq = 90.2%    R-Sq(adj) = 88.6%

Analysis of Variance

SOURCE          DF       SS      MS       F       p
Regression       2   131413   65707   55.36   0.000
Residual Error  12    14244    1187
Total           14   145657
```

FIGURE 16.5 STANDARDIZED RESIDUAL PLOT FOR THE REYNOLDS EXAMPLE: SECOND-ORDER MODEL

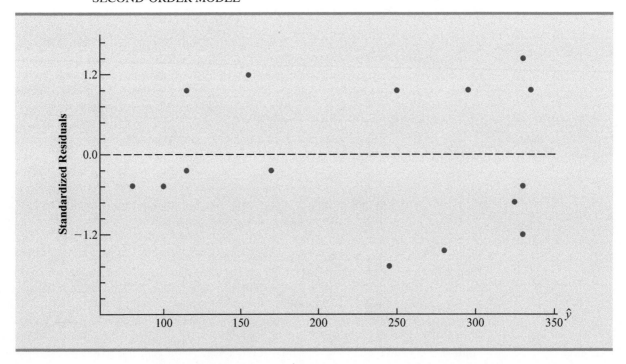

Interaction

If the original data set consists of observations for y and two independent variables x_1 and x_2, we can develop a second-order model with two predictor variables by setting $z_1 = x_1$, $z_2 = x_2$, $z_3 = x_1^2$, $z_4 = x_2^2$, and $z_5 = x_1 x_2$ in the general linear model of equation (16.1). The model obtained is

$$y = \beta_0 + \beta_1 x_1 + \beta_2 x_2 + \beta_3 x_1^2 + \beta_4 x_2^2 + \beta_5 x_1 x_2 + \epsilon \tag{16.4}$$

TABLE 16.2   DATA FOR THE TYLER PERSONAL CARE EXAMPLE

Price	Advertising Expenditure ($1000s)	Sales (1000s)	Price	Advertising Expenditure ($1000s)	Sales (1000s)
$2.00	50	478	$2.00	100	810
$2.50	50	373	$2.50	100	653
$3.00	50	335	$3.00	100	345
$2.00	50	473	$2.00	100	832
$2.50	50	358	$2.50	100	641
$3.00	50	329	$3.00	100	372
$2.00	50	456	$2.00	100	800
$2.50	50	360	$2.50	100	620
$3.00	50	322	$3.00	100	390
$2.00	50	437	$2.00	100	790
$2.50	50	365	$2.50	100	670
$3.00	50	342	$3.00	100	393

In this second-order model, the variable $z_5 = x_1 x_2$ is added to account for the potential effects of the two variables acting together. This type of effect is called **interaction**.

To provide an illustration of interaction and what it means, let us review the regression study conducted by Tyler Personal Care for one of its new shampoo products. Two factors believed to have the most influence on sales are unit selling price and advertising expenditure. To investigate the effects of these two variables on sales, prices of $2.00, $2.50, and $3.00 were paired with advertising expenditures of $50,000 and $100,000 in 24 test markets. The unit sales (in thousands) that were observed are reported in Table 16.2.

Table 16.3 is a summary of these data. Note that the sample mean sales corresponding to a price of $2.00 and an advertising expenditure of $50,000 is 461,000, and the sample mean sales corresponding to a price of $2.00 and an advertising expenditure of $100,000 is 808,000. Hence, with price held constant at $2.00, the difference in the sample mean sales between advertising expenditures of $50,000 and $100,000 is $808,000 - 461,000 = 347,000$ units. When the price of the product is $2.50, the difference in the sample mean sales is $646,000 - 364,000 = 282,000$ units. Finally, when the price is $3.00, the difference in the sample mean sales is $375,000 - 332,000 = 43,000$ units. Clearly, the difference in the sample mean sales between advertising expenditures of $50,000 and $100,000 depends on the price of the product. In other words, at higher selling prices, the effect of increased advertising expenditure diminishes. These observations provide evidence of interaction between the price and advertising expenditure variables.

TABLE 16.3   SAMPLE MEAN UNIT SALES (1000s) FOR THE TYLER PERSONAL CARE EXAMPLE

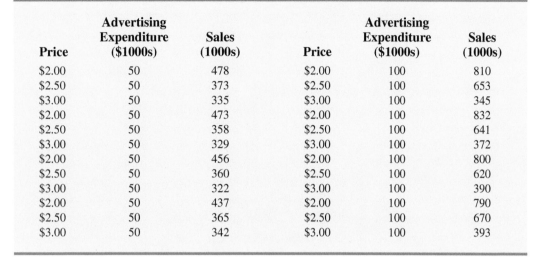

		Price		
		$2.00	**$2.50**	**$3.00**
Advertising Expenditure	**$50,000**	461	364	332
	$100,000	808	646	375

Mean sales of 808,000 units when price = $2.00 and advertising expenditure = $100,000

FIGURE 16.6 SAMPLE MEAN UNIT SALES (1000s) AS A FUNCTION OF SELLING PRICE AND ADVERTISING EXPENDITURE

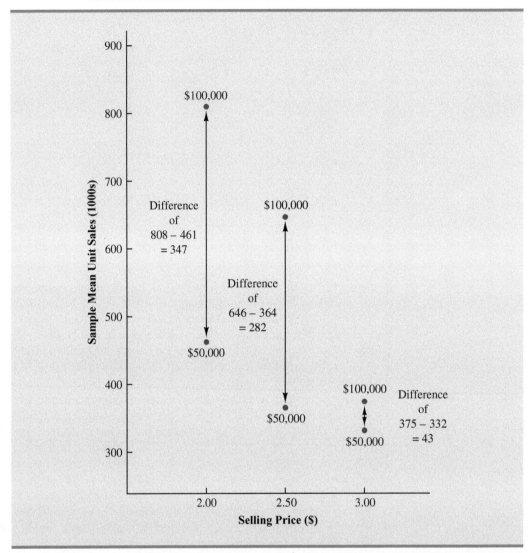

To provide another perspective of interaction, Figure 16.6 shows the sample mean sales for the six price-advertising expenditure combinations. This graph also shows that the effect of advertising expenditure on the sample mean sales depends on the price of the product; we again see the effect of interaction. When interaction between two variables is present, we cannot study the effect of one variable on the response y independently of the other variable. In other words, meaningful conclusions can be developed only if we consider the joint effect that both variables have on the response.

To account for the effect of interaction, we will use the following regression model.

$$y = \beta_0 + \beta_1 x_1 + \beta_2 x_2 + \beta_3 x_1 x_2 + \epsilon \qquad \textbf{(16.5)}$$

where

$$y = \text{unit sales (1000s)}$$
$$x_1 = \text{price (\$)}$$
$$x_2 = \text{advertising expenditure (\$1000s)}$$

Note that equation (16.5) reflects Tyler's belief that the number of units sold depends linearly on selling price and advertising expenditure (accounted for by the $\beta_1 x_1$ and $\beta_2 x_2$ terms), and that there is interaction between the two variables (accounted for by the $\beta_3 x_1 x_2$ term).

To develop an estimated regression equation, a general linear model involving three independent variables (z_1, z_2, and z_3) was used.

$$y = \beta_0 + \beta_1 z_1 + \beta_2 z_2 + \beta_3 z_3 + \epsilon \tag{16.6}$$

where

$$z_1 = x_1$$
$$z_2 = x_2$$
$$z_3 = x_1 x_2$$

Figure 16.7 is the Minitab output corresponding to the interaction model for the Tyler Personal Care example. The resulting estimated regression equation is

$$\text{Sales} = -276 + 175 \text{ Price} + 19.7 \text{ AdvExp} - 6.08 \text{ PriceAdv}$$

where

The data for the PriceAdv independent variable is obtained by multiplying each value of Price times the corresponding value of AdvExp.

$$\text{Sales} = \text{unit sales (1000s)}$$
$$\text{Price} = \text{price of the product (\$)}$$
$$\text{AdvExp} = \text{advertising expenditure (\$1000s)}$$
$$\text{PriceAdv} = \text{interaction term (Price times AdvExp)}$$

Because the model is significant (p-value for the F test is .000) and the p-value corresponding to the t test for PriceAdv is .000, we conclude that interaction is significant given the linear effect of the price of the product and the advertising expenditure. Thus, the regression results show that the effect of advertising expenditure on sales depends on the price.

FIGURE 16.7   MINITAB OUTPUT FOR THE TYLER PERSONAL CARE EXAMPLE

```
The regression equation is
Sales = - 276 + 175 Price + 19.7 AdvExpen - 6.08 PriceAdv

Predictor      Coef    SE Coef        T       p
Constant     -275.8      112.8    -2.44   0.024
Price        175.00      44.55     3.93   0.001
Adver        19.680      1.427    13.79   0.000
PriceAdv    -6.0800     0.5635   -10.79   0.000

S = 28.1739    R-Sq = 97.8%    R-Sq(adj) = 97.5%

Analysis of Variance

SOURCE            DF       SS       MS       F       p
Regression         3   709316   236439  297.87   0.000
Residual Error    20    15875      794
Total             23   725191
```

TABLE 16.4

MILES-PER-GALLON RATINGS AND WEIGHTS FOR 12 AUTOMOBILES

Weight	Miles per Gallon
2289	28.7
2113	29.2
2180	34.2
2448	27.9
2026	33.3
2702	26.4
2657	23.9
2106	30.5
3226	18.1
3213	19.5
3607	14.3
2888	20.9

Transformations Involving the Dependent Variable

In showing how the general linear model can be used to model a variety of possible relationships between the independent variables and the dependent variable, we have focused attention on transformations involving one or more of the independent variables. Often it is worthwhile to consider transformations involving the dependent variable y. As an illustration of when we might want to transform the dependent variable, consider the data in Table 16.4, which shows the miles-per-gallon ratings and weights for 12 automobiles. The scatter diagram in Figure 16.8 indicates a negative linear relationship between these two variables. Therefore, we use a simple first-order model to relate the two variables. The Minitab output is shown in Figure 16.9; the resulting estimated regression equation is

$$MPG = 56.1 - 0.0116 \text{ Weight}$$

where

$$MPG = \text{miles-per-gallon rating}$$
$$Weight = \text{weight of the car in pounds}$$

The model is significant (p-value for the F test is .000) and the fit is very good (R-sq = 93.5%). However, we note in Figure 16.9 that observation 3 is identified as having a large standardized residual.

Figure 16.10 is the standardized residual plot corresponding to the first-order model. The pattern we observe does not look like the horizontal band we should expect to find if the assumptions about the error term are valid. Instead, the variability in the residuals appears to increase as the value of $\hat{y}$ increases. In other words, we see the wedge-shaped pattern referred to in Chapters 14 and 15 as being indicative of a nonconstant variance. We are not justified in reaching any conclusions about the statistical significance of the resulting estimated regression equation when the underlying assumptions for the tests of significance do not appear to be satisfied.

WEB file

MPG

FIGURE 16.8   SCATTER DIAGRAM FOR THE MILES-PER-GALLON EXAMPLE

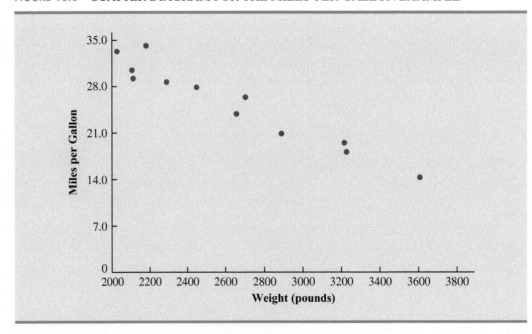

FIGURE 16.9 MINITAB OUTPUT FOR THE MILES-PER-GALLON EXAMPLE

```
The regression equation is
MPG = 56.1 - 0.0116 Weight

Predictor          Coef     SE Coef        T       p
Constant         56.096       2.582    21.72   0.000
Weight       -0.0116436   0.0009677   -12.03   0.000

S = 1.67053    R-Sq = 93.5%    R-Sq(adj) = 92.9%

Analysis of Variance

SOURCE           DF      SS       MS        F       p
Regression        1  403.98   403.98   144.76   0.000
Residual Error   10   27.91     2.79
Total            11  431.88

Unusual Observations
Obs  Weight    MPG     Fit   SE Fit   Residual   St Resid
  3    2180  34.200  30.713    0.644      3.487      2.26R

R denotes an observation with a large standardized residual.
```

FIGURE 16.10 STANDARDIZED RESIDUAL PLOT FOR THE MILES-PER-GALLON EXAMPLE

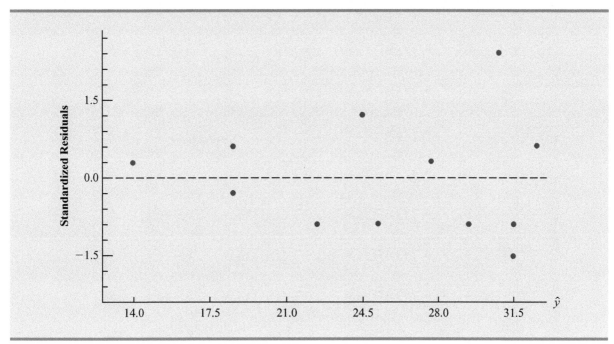

Often the problem of nonconstant variance can be corrected by transforming the dependent variable to a different scale. For instance, if we work with the logarithm of the dependent variable instead of the original dependent variable, the effect will be to compress the values of the dependent variable and thus diminish the effects of nonconstant variance.

Most statistical packages provide the ability to apply logarithmic transformations using either the base 10 (common logarithm) or the base $e = 2.71828 \ldots$ (natural logarithm). We applied a natural logarithmic transformation to the miles-per-gallon data and developed the estimated regression equation relating weight to the natural logarithm of miles-per-gallon. The regression results obtained by using the natural logarithm of miles-per-gallon as the dependent variable, labeled LogeMPG in the output, are shown in Figure 16.11; Figure 16.12 is the corresponding standardized residual plot.

FIGURE 16.11   MINITAB OUTPUT FOR THE MILES-PER-GALLON EXAMPLE: LOGARITHMIC TRANSFORMATION

```
The regression equation is
LogeMPG = 4.52 -0.000501 Weight

Predictor          Coef      SE Coef        T       p
Constant        4.52423      0.09932    45.55   0.000
Weight       -0.00050110  0.00003722   -13.46   0.000


S = 0.0642547    R-Sq = 94.8%   R-Sq(adj) = 94.2%

Analysis of Variance

SOURCE           DF        SS          MS        F       p
Regression        1   0.74822     0.74822   181.22   0.000
Residual Error   10   0.04129     0.00413
Total            11   0.78950
```

FIGURE 16.12   STANDARDIZED RESIDUAL PLOT FOR THE MILES-PER-GALLON EXAMPLE: LOGARITHMIC TRANSFORMATION

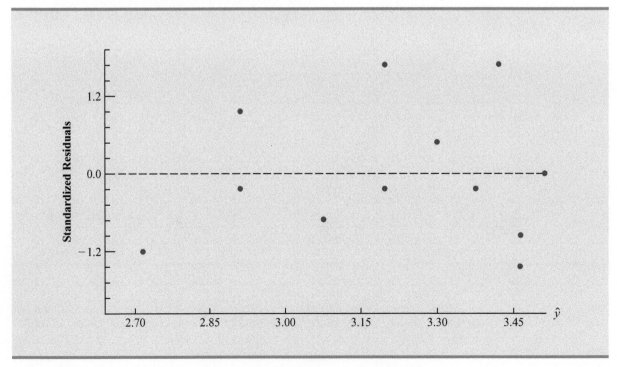

Looking at the residual plot in Figure 16.12, we see that the wedge-shaped pattern has now disappeared. Moreover, none of the observations are identified as having a large standardized residual. The model with the logarithm of miles per gallon as the dependent variable is statistically significant and provides an excellent fit to the observed data. Hence, we would recommend using the estimated regression equation

$$\text{LogeMPG} = 4.52 - .000501 \text{ Weight}$$

To predict the miles-per-gallon rating for an automobile that weighs 2500 pounds, we first develop an estimate of the logarithm of the miles-per-gallon rating.

$$\text{LogeMPG} = 4.52 - .000501(2500) = 3.2675$$

The miles-per-gallon estimate is obtained by finding the number whose natural logarithm is 3.2675. Using a calculator with an exponential function, or raising e to the power 3.2675, we obtain 26.2 miles per gallon.

Another approach to problems of nonconstant variance is to use $1/y$ as the dependent variable instead of y. This type of transformation is called a *reciprocal transformation*. For instance, if the dependent variable is measured in miles per gallon, the reciprocal transformation would result in a new dependent variable whose units would be 1/(miles per gallon) or gallons per mile. In general, there is no way to determine whether a logarithmic transformation or a reciprocal transformation will perform best without actually trying each of them.

Nonlinear Models That Are Intrinsically Linear

Models in which the parameters $(\beta_0, \beta_1, \ldots, \beta_p)$ have exponents other than 1 are called nonlinear models. However, for the case of the exponential model, we can perform a transformation of variables that will enable us to perform regression analysis with equation (16.1), the general linear model. The exponential model involves the following regression equation.

$$E(y) = \beta_0 \beta_1^x \tag{16.7}$$

This regression equation is appropriate when the dependent variable y increases or decreases by a constant percentage, instead of by a fixed amount, as x increases.

As an example, suppose sales for a product y are related to advertising expenditure x (in thousands of dollars) according to the following regression equation.

$$E(y) = 500(1.2)^x$$

Thus, for $x = 1$, $E(y) = 500(1.2)^1 = 600$; for $x = 2$, $E(y) = 500(1.2)^2 = 720$; and for $x = 3$, $E(y) = 500(1.2)^3 = 864$. Note that $E(y)$ is not increasing by a constant amount in this case, but by a constant percentage; the percentage increase is 20%.

We can transform this nonlinear regression equation to a linear regression equation by taking the logarithm of both sides of equation (16.7).

$$\log E(y) = \log \beta_0 + x \log \beta_1 \tag{16.8}$$

Now if we let $y' = \log E(y)$, $\beta_0' = \log \beta_0$, and $\beta_1' = \log \beta_1$, we can rewrite equation (16.8) as

$$y' = \beta_0' + \beta_1' x$$

It is clear that the formulas for simple linear regression can now be used to develop estimates of β_0' and β_1'. Denoting the estimates as b_0' and b_1' leads to the following estimated regression equation.

$$\hat{y}' = b_0' + b_1' x \tag{16.9}$$

To obtain predictions of the original dependent variable y given a value of x, we would first substitute the value of x into equation (16.9) and compute $\hat{y}'$. The antilog of $\hat{y}'$ would be the prediction of y, or the expected value of y.

Many nonlinear models cannot be transformed into an equivalent linear model. However, such models have had limited use in business and economic applications. Furthermore, the mathematical background needed for study of such models is beyond the scope of this text.

Exercises

Methods

1. Consider the following data for two variables, x and y.

x	22	24	26	30	35	40
y	12	21	33	35	40	36

   a. Develop an estimated regression equation for the data of the form $\hat{y} = b_0 + b_1x$.
   b. Use the results from part (a) to test for a significant relationship between x and y. Use $\alpha = .05$.
   c. Develop a scatter diagram for the data. Does the scatter diagram suggest an estimated regression equation of the form $\hat{y} = b_0 + b_1x + b_2x^2$? Explain.
   d. Develop an estimated regression equation for the data of the form $\hat{y} = b_0 + b_1x + b_2x^2$.
   e. Refer to part (d). Is the relationship between x, x^2, and y significant? Use $\alpha = .05$.
   f. Predict the value of y when $x = 25$.

2. Consider the following data for two variables, x and y.

x	9	32	18	15	26
y	10	20	21	16	22

   a. Develop an estimated regression equation for the data of the form $\hat{y} = b_0 + b_1x$. Comment on the adequacy of this equation for predicting y.
   b. Develop an estimated regression equation for the data of the form $\hat{y} = b_0 + b_1x + b_2x^2$. Comment on the adequacy of this equation for predicting y.
   c. Predict the value of y when $x = 20$.

3. Consider the following data for two variables, x and y.

x	2	3	4	5	7	7	7	8	9
y	4	5	4	6	4	6	9	5	11

   a. Does there appear to be a linear relationship between x and y? Explain.
   b. Develop the estimated regression equation relating x and y.
   c. Plot the standardized residuals versus $\hat{y}$ for the estimated regression equation developed in part (b). Do the model assumptions appear to be satisfied? Explain.
   d. Perform a logarithmic transformation on the dependent variable y. Develop an estimated regression equation using the transformed dependent variable. Do the model assumptions appear to be satisfied by using the transformed dependent variable? Does a reciprocal transformation work better in this case? Explain.

Applications

4. A highway department is studying the relationship between traffic flow and speed. The following model has been hypothesized.

$$y = \beta_0 + \beta_1 x + \epsilon$$

where

$$y = \text{traffic flow in vehicles per hour}$$
$$x = \text{vehicle speed in miles per hour}$$

The following data were collected during rush hour for six highways leading out of the city.

Traffic Flow (y)	Vehicle Speed (x)
1256	35
1329	40
1226	30
1335	45
1349	50
1124	25

a. Develop an estimated regression equation for the data.
b. Use $\alpha = .01$ to test for a significant relationship.

5. In working further with the problem of exercise 4, statisticians suggested the use of the following curvilinear estimated regression equation.

$$\hat{y} = b_0 + b_1 x + b_2 x^2$$

a. Use the data of exercise 4 to estimate the parameters of this estimated regression equation.
b. Use $\alpha = .01$ to test for a significant relationship.
c. Predict the traffic flow in vehicles per hour at a speed of 38 miles per hour.

6. A study of emergency service facilities investigated the relationship between the number of facilities and the average distance traveled to provide the emergency service. The following table gives the data collected.

Number of Facilities	Average Distance (miles)
9	1.66
11	1.12
16	.83
21	.62
27	.51
30	.47

a. Develop a scatter diagram for these data, treating average distance traveled as the dependent variable.
b. Does a simple linear regression model appear to be appropriate? Explain.
c. Develop an estimated regression equation for the data that you believe will best explain the relationship between these two variables.

7. In 2011, home prices and mortgage rates fell so far that in a number of cities the monthly cost of owning a home was less expensive than renting. The following data show the average asking rent and the monthly mortgage on the median-priced home

(including taxes and insurance) for 10 cities where the average monthly mortgage payment was less than the average asking rent (*The Wall Street Journal,* November 26–27, 2011).

RentMortgage

City	Rent ($)	Mortgage ($)
Atlanta	840	539
Chicago	1062	1002
Detroit	823	626
Jacksonville, Fla.	779	711
Las Vegas	796	655
Miami	1071	977
Minneapolis	953	776
Orlando, Fla.	851	695
Phoenix	762	651
St. Louis	723	654

a. Develop a scatter diagram for these data, treating the average asking rent as the independent variable. Does a simple linear regression model appear to be appropriate?

b. Use a simple linear regression model to develop an estimated regression equation to predict the monthly mortgage on the median-priced home given the average asking rent. Construct a standardized residual plot. Based upon the standardized residual plot, does a simple linear regression model appear to be appropriate?

c. Using a second-order model, develop an estimated regression equation to predict the monthly mortgage on the median-priced home given the average asking rent.

d. Do you prefer the estimated regression equation developed in part (a) or part (c)? Explain.

8. Corvette, Ferrari, and Jaguar produced a variety of classic cars that continue to increase in value. The following data, based upon the Martin Rating System for Collectible Cars, show the rarity rating (1–20) and the high price ($1000) for 15 classic cars (*BusinessWeek* website, February 2006).

ClassicCars

Year	Make	Model	Rating	Price ($1000)
1984	Chevrolet	Corvette	18	1600.0
1956	Chevrolet	Corvette 265/225-hp	19	4000.0
1963	Chevrolet	Corvette coupe (340-bhp 4-speed)	18	1000.0
1978	Chevrolet	Corvette coupe Silver Anniversary	19	1300.0
1960–1963	Ferrari	250 GTE 2+2	16	350.0
1962–1964	Ferrari	250 GTL Lusso	19	2650.0
1962	Ferrari	250 GTO	18	375.0
1967–1968	Ferrari	275 GTB/4 NART Spyder	17	450.0
1968–1973	Ferrari	365 GTB/4 Daytona	17	140.0
1962–1967	Jaguar	E-type OTS	15	77.5
1969–1971	Jaguar	E-type Series II OTS	14	62.0
1971–1974	Jaguar	E-type Series III OTS	16	125.0
1951–1954	Jaguar	XK 120 roadster (steel)	17	400.0
1950–1953	Jaguar	XK C-type	16	250.0
1956–1957	Jaguar	XKSS	13	70.0

a. Develop a scatter diagram of the data using the rarity rating as the independent variable and price as the independent variable. Does a simple linear regression model appear to be appropriate?

b. Develop an estimated multiple regression equation with x = rarity rating and x^2 as the two independent variables.

c. Consider the nonlinear relationship shown by equation (16.7). Use logarithms to develop an estimated regression equation for this model.

d. Do you prefer the estimated regression equation developed in part (b) or part (c)? Explain.

9. *Kiplinger's Personal Finance Magazine* rated 359 U.S. metropolitan areas to determine the best cities to live, work, and play. The data contained in the data set named MetroAreas show the data from the Kiplinger study for the 50 metropolitan areas with a population of 1,000,000 or more (Kiplinger's website, March 2, 2009). The data set includes the following variables: Population, Income, Cost of Living Index, and Creative (%). Population is the size of the population in 1000s; Income is the median household income in $1000s; Cost of Living Index is based on 100 being the national average; and Creative (%) is the percentage of the workforce in creative fields such as science, engineering, architecture, education, art, and entertainment. Workers in creative fields are generally considered an important factor in the vitality and livability of a city and a key to future economic prosperity.

MetroAreas

a. Develop a scatter diagram for these data with median household income as the independent variable and the percentage of the workforce in creative fields as the dependent variable. Does a simple linear regression model appear to be appropriate?

b. Develop a scatter diagram for these data with the cost of living index as the independent variable and the percentage of the workforce in creative fields as the dependent variable. Does a simple linear regression model appear to be appropriate?

c. Use the data provided to develop the best estimated multiple regression equation for estimating the percentage of the workforce in creative fields.

d. The Tucson, Arizona, metropolitan area has a population of 946,362, a median household income of $42,984, and cost of living index of 99. Develop a prediction of the percentage of the workforce in creative fields for Tucson. Are there any factors that should be considered before using this predicted value?

16.2 Determining When to Add or Delete Variables

In this section we will show how an F test can be used to determine whether it is advantageous to add one or more independent variables to a multiple regression model. This test is based on a determination of the amount of reduction in the error sum of squares resulting from adding one or more independent variables to the model. We will first illustrate how the test can be used in the context of the Butler Trucking example.

In Chapter 15, the Butler Trucking example was introduced to illustrate the use of multiple regression analysis. Recall that the managers wanted to develop an estimated regression equation to predict total daily travel time for trucks using two independent variables: miles traveled and number of deliveries. With miles traveled x_1 as the only independent variable, the least squares procedure provided the following estimated regression equation.

$$\hat{y} = 1.27 + .0678x_1$$

In Chapter 15 we showed that the error sum of squares for this model was SSE = 8.029. When x_2, the number of deliveries, was added as a second independent variable, we obtained the following estimated regression equation.

$$\hat{y} = -.869 + .0611x_1 + .923x_2$$

The error sum of squares for this model was SSE = 2.299. Clearly, adding x_2 resulted in a reduction of SSE. The question we want to answer is: Does adding the variable x_2 lead to a *significant* reduction in SSE?

We use the notation SSE(x_1) to denote the error sum of squares when x_1 is the only independent variable in the model, SSE(x_1, x_2) to denote the error sum of squares when x_1 and x_2 are both in the model, and so on. Hence, the reduction in SSE resulting from adding x_2 to the model involving just x_1 is

$$\text{SSE}(x_1) - \text{SSE}(x_1, x_2) = 8.029 - 2.299 = 5.730$$

An F test is conducted to determine whether this reduction is significant.

The numerator of the F statistic is the reduction in SSE divided by the number of independent variables added to the original model. Here only one variable, x_2, has been added; thus, the numerator of the F statistic is

$$\frac{SSE(x_1) - SSE(x_1, x_2)}{1} = 5.730$$

The result is a measure of the reduction in SSE per independent variable added to the model. The denominator of the F statistic is the mean square error for the model that includes all of the independent variables. For Butler Trucking this corresponds to the model containing both x_1 and x_2; thus, $p = 2$ and

$$MSE = \frac{SSE(x_1, x_2)}{n - p - 1} = \frac{2.299}{7} = .3284$$

The following F statistic provides the basis for testing whether the addition of x_2 is statistically significant.

$$F = \frac{\dfrac{SSE(x_1) - SSE(x_1, x_2)}{1}}{\dfrac{SSE(x_1, x_2)}{n - p - 1}} \qquad (16.10)$$

The numerator degrees of freedom for this F test is equal to the number of variables added to the model, and the denominator degrees of freedom is equal to $n - p - 1$.

For the Butler Trucking problem, we obtain

$$F = \frac{\dfrac{5.730}{1}}{\dfrac{2.299}{7}} = \frac{5.730}{.3284} = 17.45$$

Refer to Table 4 of Appendix B. We find that for a level of significance of $\alpha = .05$, $F_{.05} = 5.59$. Because $F = 17.45 > F_{.05} = 5.59$, we can reject the null hypothesis that x_2 is not statistically significant; in other words, adding x_2 to the model involving only x_1 results in a significant reduction in the error sum of squares.

When we want to test for the significance of adding only one more independent variable to a model, the result found with the F test just described could also be obtained by using the t test for the significance of an individual parameter (described in Section 15.4). Indeed, the F statistic we just computed is the square of the t statistic used to test the significance of an individual parameter.

Because the t test is equivalent to the F test when only one independent variable is being added to the model, we can now further clarify the proper use of the t test for testing the significance of an individual parameter. If an individual parameter is not significant, the corresponding variable can be dropped from the model. However, if the t test shows that two or more parameters are not significant, no more than one independent variable can ever be dropped from a model on the basis of a t test; if one variable is dropped, a second variable that was not significant initially might become significant.

We now turn to a consideration of whether the addition of more than one independent variable—as a set—results in a significant reduction in the error sum of squares.

General Case

Consider the following multiple regression model involving q independent variables, where $q < p$.

$$y = \beta_0 + \beta_1 x_1 + \beta_2 x_2 + \cdots + \beta_q x_q + \epsilon \tag{16.11}$$

If we add variables $x_{q+1}, x_{q+2}, \ldots, x_p$ to this model, we obtain a model involving p independent variables.

$$\begin{aligned} y = \beta_0 + \beta_1 x_1 + \beta_2 x_2 + \cdots + \beta_q x_q \\ + \beta_{q+1} x_{q+1} + \beta_{q+2} x_{q+2} + \cdots + \beta_p x_p + \epsilon \end{aligned} \tag{16.12}$$

To test whether the addition of $x_{q+1}, x_{q+2}, \ldots, x_p$ is statistically significant, the null and alternative hypotheses can be stated as follows.

$$H_0: \beta_{q+1} = \beta_{q+2} = \cdots = \beta_p = 0$$
$$H_a: \text{One or more of the parameters is not equal to zero}$$

The following F statistic provides the basis for testing whether the additional independent variables are statistically significant.

$$F = \frac{\dfrac{\text{SSE}(x_1, x_2, \ldots, x_q) - \text{SSE}(x_1, x_2, \ldots, x_q, x_{q+1}, \ldots, x_p)}{p - q}}{\dfrac{\text{SSE}(x_1, x_2, \ldots, x_q, x_{q+1}, \ldots, x_p)}{n - p - 1}} \tag{16.13}$$

This computed F value is then compared with F_α, the table value with $p - q$ numerator degrees of freedom and $n - p - 1$ denominator degrees of freedom. If $F > F_\alpha$, we reject H_0 and conclude that the set of additional independent variables is statistically significant. Note that for the special case where $q = 1$ and $p = 2$, equation (16.13) reduces to equation (16.10).

Many students find equation (16.13) somewhat complex. To provide a simpler description of this F ratio, we can refer to the model with the smaller number of independent variables as the reduced model and the model with the larger number of independent variables as the full model. If we let SSE(reduced) denote the error sum of squares for the reduced model and SSE(full) denote the error sum of squares for the full model, we can write the numerator of (16.13) as

$$\frac{\text{SSE(reduced)} - \text{SSE(full)}}{\text{number of extra terms}} \tag{16.14}$$

Many computer packages, such as Minitab, provide extra sums of squares corresponding to the order in which each independent variable enters the model; in such cases, the computation of the F test for determining whether to add or delete a set of variables is simplified.

Note that "number of extra terms" denotes the difference between the number of independent variables in the full model and the number of independent variables in the reduced model. The denominator of equation (16.13) is the error sum of squares for the full model divided by the corresponding degrees of freedom; in other words, the denominator is the mean square error for the full model. Denoting the mean square error for the full model as MSE(full) enables us to write it as

$$F = \frac{\dfrac{\text{SSE(reduced)} - \text{SSE(full)}}{\text{number of extra terms}}}{\text{MSE(full)}} \tag{16.15}$$

To illustrate the use of this F statistic, suppose we have a regression problem involving 30 observations. One model with the independent variables x_1, x_2, and x_3 has an error sum of squares of 150 and a second model with the independent variables x_1, x_2, x_3, x_4, and x_5 has an error sum of squares of 100. Did the addition of the two independent variables x_4 and x_5 result in a significant reduction in the error sum of squares?

First, note that the degrees of freedom for SST is $30 - 1 = 29$ and that the degrees of freedom for the regression sum of squares for the full model is five (the number of independent variables in the full model). Thus, the degrees of freedom for the error sum of squares for the full model is $29 - 5 = 24$, and hence MSE(full) $= 100/24 = 4.17$. Therefore the F statistic is

$$F = \frac{\dfrac{150 - 100}{2}}{4.17} = 6.00$$

This computed F value is compared with the table F value with two numerator and 24 denominator degrees of freedom. At the .05 level of significance, Table 4 of Appendix B shows $F_{.05} = 3.40$. Because $F = 6.00$ is greater than 3.40, we conclude that the addition of variables x_4 and x_5 is statistically significant.

Use of p-Values

The p-value criterion can also be used to determine whether it is advantageous to add one or more independent variables to a multiple regression model. In the preceding example, we showed how to perform an F test to determine if the addition of two independent variables, x_4 and x_5, to a model with three independent variables, x_1, x_2, and x_3, was statistically significant. For this example, the computed F statistic was 6.00 and we concluded (by comparing $F = 6.00$ to the critical value $F_{.05} = 3.40$) that the addition of variables x_4 and x_5 was significant. Using Minitab or Excel, the p-value associated with $F = 6.00$ (2 numerator and 24 denominator degrees of freedom) is .008. With a p-value $= .008 < \alpha = .05$, we also conclude that the addition of the two independent variables is statistically significant. It is difficult to determine the p-value directly from tables of the F distribution, but computer software packages, such as Minitab or Excel, make computing the p-value easy.

NOTES AND COMMENTS

Computation of the F statistic can also be based on the difference in the regression sums of squares. To show this form of the F statistic, we first note that

$$\text{SSE(reduced)} = \text{SST} - \text{SSR(reduced)}$$
$$\text{SSE(full)} = \text{SST} - \text{SSR(full)}$$

Hence

$$\text{SSE(reduced)} - \text{SSE(full)} = [\text{SST} - \text{SSR(reduced)}] - [\text{SST} - \text{SSR(full)}]$$
$$= \text{SSR(full)} - \text{SSR(reduced)}$$

Thus,

$$F = \frac{\dfrac{\text{SSR(full)} - \text{SSR(reduced)}}{\text{number of extra terms}}}{\text{MSE(full)}}$$

Exercises

Methods

10. In a regression analysis involving 27 observations, the following estimated regression equation was developed.

$$\hat{y} = 25.2 + 5.5x_1$$

For this estimated regression equation SST = 1550 and SSE = 520.

a. At $\alpha = .05$, test whether x_1 is significant.

Suppose that variables x_2 and x_3 are added to the model and the following regression equation is obtained.

$$\hat{y} = 16.3 + 2.3x_1 + 12.1x_2 - 5.8x_3$$

For this estimated regression equation SST = 1550 and SSE = 100.

b. Use an F test and a .05 level of significance to determine whether x_2 and x_3 contribute significantly to the model.

11. In a regression analysis involving 30 observations, the following estimated regression equation was obtained.

$$\hat{y} = 17.6 + 3.8x_1 - 2.3x_2 + 7.6x_3 + 2.7x_4$$

For this estimated regression equation SST = 1805 and SSR = 1760.

a. At $\alpha = .05$, test the significance of the relationship among the variables.

Suppose variables x_1 and x_4 are dropped from the model and the following estimated regression equation is obtained.

$$\hat{y} = 11.1 - 3.6x_2 + 8.1x_3$$

For this model SST = 1805 and SSR = 1705.

b. Compute SSE(x_1, x_2, x_3, x_4).
c. Compute SSE(x_2, x_3).
d. Use an F test and a .05 level of significance to determine whether x_1 and x_4 contribute significantly to the model.

Applications

12. The Ladies Professional Golfers Association (LPGA) maintains statistics on performance and earnings for members of the LPGA Tour. Year-end performance statistics for the 30 players who had the highest total earnings in LPGA Tour events for 2005 appear in the file named LPGATour (LPGA Tour website, 2006). Earnings ($1000) is the total earnings in thousands of dollars; Scoring Avg. is the average score for all events; Greens in Reg. is the percentage of time a player is able to hit the green in regulation; Putting Avg. is the average number of putts taken on greens hit in regulation; and Sand Saves is the percentage of time a player is able to get "up and down" once in a greenside sand bunker. A green is considered hit in regulation if any part of the ball is touching the putting surface and the difference between the value of par for the hole and the number of strokes taken to hit the green is at least 2.

a. Develop an estimated regression equation that can be used to predict the average score for all events given the average number of putts taken on greens hit in regulation.

b. Develop an estimated regression equation that can be used to predict the average score for all events given the percentage of time a player is able to hit the green in regulation, the average number of putts taken on greens hit in regulation, and the percentage of time a player is able to get "up and down" once in a greenside sand bunker.

c.   At the .05 level of significance, test whether the two independent variables added in part (b), the percentage of time a player is able to hit the green in regulation and the percentage of time a player is able to get "up and down" once in a greenside sand bunker, contribute significantly to the estimated regression equation developed in part (a). Explain.

13.   Refer to exercise 12.

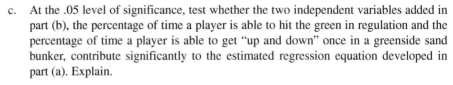

LPGATour

a.   Develop an estimated regression equation that can be used to predict the total earnings for all events given the average number of putts taken on greens hit in regulation.

b.   Develop an estimated regression equation that can be used to predict the total earnings for all events given the percentage of time a player is able to hit the green in regulation, the average number of putts taken on greens hit in regulation, and the percentage of time a player is able to get "up and down" once in a greenside sand bunker.

c.   At the .05 level of significance, test whether the two independent variables added in part (b), the percentage of time a player is able to hit the green in regulation and the percentage of time a player is able to get "up and down" once in a greenside sand bunker, contribute significantly to the estimated regression equation developed in part (a). Explain.

d.   In general, lower scores should lead to higher earnings. To investigate this option to predicting total earnings, develop an estimated regression equation that can be used to predict total earnings for all events given the average score for all events. Would you prefer to use this equation to predict total earnings or the estimated regression equation developed in part (b)? Explain.

14.   A 10-year study conducted by the American Heart Association provided data on how age, blood pressure, and smoking relate to the risk of strokes. Data from a portion of this study follow. Risk is interpreted as the probability (times 100) that a person will have a stroke over the next 10-year period. For the smoker variable, 1 indicates a smoker and 0 indicates a nonsmoker.

Stroke

Risk	Age	Blood Pressure	Smoker
12	57	152	0
24	67	163	0
13	58	155	0
56	86	177	1
28	59	196	0
51	76	189	1
18	56	155	1
31	78	120	0
37	80	135	1
15	78	98	0
22	71	152	0
36	70	173	1
15	67	135	1
48	77	209	1
15	60	199	0
36	82	119	1
8	66	166	0
34	80	125	1
3	62	117	0
37	59	207	1

a.   Develop an estimated regression equation that can be used to predict the risk of stroke given the age and blood-pressure level.

b.   Consider adding two independent variables to the model developed in part (a), one for the interaction between age and blood-pressure level and the other for whether the person is a smoker. Develop an estimated regression equation using these four independent variables.

c.   At a .05 level of significance, test to see whether the addition of the interaction term and the smoker variable contribute significantly to the estimated regression equation developed in part (a).

15. In baseball, an earned run is any run that the opposing team scores off the pitcher except for runs scored as a result of errors. The earned run average (ERA), the statistic most often used to compare the performance of pitchers, is computed as follows:

$$\text{ERA} = \left(\frac{\text{earned runs given up}}{\text{innings pitched}}\right)9$$

MLBPitching

Note that the average number of earned runs per inning pitched is multiplied by nine, the number of innings in a regulation game. Thus, ERA represents the average number of runs the pitcher gives up per nine innings. For instance, in 2008, Roy Halladay, a pitcher for the Toronto Blue Jays, pitched 246 innings and gave up 76 earned runs; his ERA was $(76/246)9 = 2.78$. To investigate the relationship between ERA and other measures of pitching performance, data for 50 Major League Baseball pitchers for the 2008 season appear in the data set named MLBPitching (MLB website, February 2009). Descriptions for variables which appear on the data set follow:

W	Number of games won
L	Number of games lost
WPCT	Percentage of games won
H/9	Average number of hits given up per nine innings
HR/9	Average number of home runs given up per nine innings
BB/9	Average number of bases on balls given up per nine innings

a.   Develop an estimated regression equation that can be used to predict the earned run average given the average number hits given up per nine innings.

b.   Develop an estimated regression equation that can be used to predict the earned run average given the average number hits given up per nine innings, the average number of home runs given up per nine innings, and the average number of bases on balls given up per nine innings.

c.   At the .05 level of significance, test whether the two independent variables added in part (b), the average number of home runs given up per nine innings and the average number of bases on ball given up per nine innings, contribute significantly to the estimated regression equation developed in part (a).

16.3 Analysis of a Larger Problem

In introducing multiple regression analysis, we used the Butler Trucking example extensively. The small size of this problem was an advantage in exploring introductory concepts but would make it difficult to illustrate some of the variable selection issues involved in model building. To provide an illustration of the variable selection procedures discussed in the next section, we introduce a data set consisting of 25 observations on eight independent variables. Permission to use these data was provided by Dr. David W. Cravens of the Department of Marketing at Texas Christian University. Consequently, we refer to the data set as the Cravens data.[1]

The Cravens data are for a company that sells products in several sales territories, each of which is assigned to a single sales representative. A regression analysis was conducted

---

[1]For details see David W. Cravens, Robert B. Woodruff, and Joe C. Stamper, "An Analytical Approach for Evaluating Sales Territory Performance," *Journal of Marketing,* 36 (January 1972): 31–37. Copyright © 1972 American Marketing Association.

TABLE 16.5   CRAVENS DATA

Cravens

Sales	Time	Poten	AdvExp	Share	Change	Accounts	Work	Rating
3,669.88	43.10	74,065.1	4,582.9	2.51	.34	74.86	15.05	4.9
3,473.95	108.13	58,117.3	5,539.8	5.51	.15	107.32	19.97	5.1
2,295.10	13.82	21,118.5	2,950.4	10.91	−.72	96.75	17.34	2.9
4,675.56	186.18	68,521.3	2,243.1	8.27	.17	195.12	13.40	3.4
6,125.96	161.79	57,805.1	7,747.1	9.15	.50	180.44	17.64	4.6
2,134.94	8.94	37,806.9	402.4	5.51	.15	104.88	16.22	4.5
5,031.66	365.04	50,935.3	3,140.6	8.54	.55	256.10	18.80	4.6
3,367.45	220.32	35,602.1	2,086.2	7.07	−.49	126.83	19.86	2.3
6,519.45	127.64	46,176.8	8,846.2	12.54	1.24	203.25	17.42	4.9
4,876.37	105.69	42,053.2	5,673.1	8.85	.31	119.51	21.41	2.8
2,468.27	57.72	36,829.7	2,761.8	5.38	.37	116.26	16.32	3.1
2,533.31	23.58	33,612.7	1,991.8	5.43	−.65	142.28	14.51	4.2
2,408.11	13.82	21,412.8	1,971.5	8.48	.64	89.43	19.35	4.3
2,337.38	13.82	20,416.9	1,737.4	7.80	1.01	84.55	20.02	4.2
4,586.95	86.99	36,272.0	10,694.2	10.34	.11	119.51	15.26	5.5
2,729.24	165.85	23,093.3	8,618.6	5.15	.04	80.49	15.87	3.6
3,289.40	116.26	26,878.6	7,747.9	6.64	.68	136.58	7.81	3.4
2,800.78	42.28	39,572.0	4,565.8	5.45	.66	78.86	16.00	4.2
3,264.20	52.84	51,866.1	6,022.7	6.31	−.10	136.58	17.44	3.6
3,453.62	165.04	58,749.8	3,721.1	6.35	−.03	138.21	17.98	3.1
1,741.45	10.57	23,990.8	861.0	7.37	−1.63	75.61	20.99	1.6
2,035.75	13.82	25,694.9	3,571.5	8.39	−.43	102.44	21.66	3.4
1,578.00	8.13	23,736.3	2,845.5	5.15	.04	76.42	21.46	2.7
4,167.44	58.44	34,314.3	5,060.1	12.88	.22	136.58	24.78	2.8
2,799.97	21.14	22,809.5	3,552.0	9.14	−.74	88.62	24.96	3.9

to determine whether a variety of predictor (independent) variables could explain sales in each territory. A random sample of 25 sales territories resulted in the data in Table 16.5; the variable definitions are given in Table 16.6.

As a preliminary step, let us consider the sample correlation coefficients between each pair of variables. Figure 16.13 is the correlation matrix obtained using Minitab. Note that the sample correlation coefficient between Sales and Time is .623, between Sales and Poten is .598, and so on.

TABLE 16.6   VARIABLE DEFINITIONS FOR THE CRAVENS DATA

Variable	Definition
Sales	Total sales credited to the sales representative
Time	Length of time employed in months
Poten	Market potential; total industry sales in units for the sales territory*
AdvExp	Advertising expenditure in the sales territory
Share	Market share; weighted average for the past four years
Change	Change in the market share over the previous four years
Accounts	Number of accounts assigned to the sales representative*
Work	Workload; a weighted index based on annual purchases and concentrations of accounts
Rating	Sales representative overall rating on eight performance dimensions; an aggregate rating on a 1–7 scale

*These data were coded to preserve confidentiality.

FIGURE 16.13 SAMPLE CORRELATION COEFFICIENTS FOR THE CRAVENS DATA

	Sales	Time	Poten	AdvExp	Share	Change	Accounts	Work
Time	0.623							
Poten	0.598	0.454						
AdvExp	0.596	0.249	0.174					
Share	0.484	0.106	-0.21	0.264				
Change	0.489	0.251	0.268	0.377	0.085			
Accounts	0.754	0.758	0.479	0.200	0.403	0.327		
Work	-0.117	-0.179	-0.259	-0.272	0.349	-0.288	-0.199	
Rating	0.402	0.101	0.359	0.411	-0.024	0.549	0.229	-0.277

Looking at the sample correlation coefficients between the independent variables, we see that the correlation between Time and Accounts is .758; hence, if Accounts were used as an independent variable, Time would not add much more explanatory power to the model. Recall the rule-of-thumb test from the discussion of multicollinearity in Section 15.4: Multicollinearity can cause problems if the absolute value of the sample correlation coefficient exceeds .7 for any two of the independent variables. If possible, then, we should avoid including both Time and Accounts in the same regression model. The sample correlation coefficient of .549 between Change and Rating is also high and may warrant further consideration.

Looking at the sample correlation coefficients between Sales and each of the independent variables can give us a quick indication of which independent variables are, by themselves, good predictors. We see that the single best predictor of Sales is Accounts, because it has the highest sample correlation coefficient (.754). Recall that for the case of one independent variable, the square of the sample correlation coefficient is the coefficient of determination. Thus, Accounts can explain $(.754)^2(100)$, or 56.85%, of the variability in Sales. The next most important independent variables are Time, Poten, and AdvExp, each with a sample correlation coefficient of approximately .6.

Although there are potential multicollinearity problems, let us consider developing an estimated regression equation using all eight independent variables. The Minitab computer package provided the results in Figure 16.14. The eight-variable multiple regression model has an R-Sq (adj) value of 88.3%. Note, however, that the p-values for the t tests of individual parameters show that only Poten, AdvExp, and Share are significant at the $\alpha = .05$ level, given the effect of all the other variables. Hence, we might be inclined to investigate the results that would be obtained if we used just those three variables. Figure 16.15 shows the Minitab results obtained for the estimated regression equation with those three variables. We see that the estimated regression equation has an R-Sq (adj) value of 82.7%, which, although not quite as good as that for the eight-independent-variable estimated regression equation, is high.

How can we find an estimated regression equation that will do the best job given the data available? One approach is to compute all possible regressions. That is, we could develop 8 one-variable estimated regression equations (each of which corresponds to one of the independent variables), 28 two-variable estimated regression equations (the number of combinations of eight variables taken two at a time), and so on. In all, for the Cravens data, 255 different estimated regression equations involving one or more independent variables would have to be fitted to the data.

With the excellent computer packages available today, it is possible to compute all possible regressions. But doing so involves a great amount of computation and requires the model builder to review a large volume of computer output, much of which is associated with obviously poor models. Statisticians prefer a more systematic approach to selecting the subset of independent variables that provide the best estimated regression equation. In the next section, we introduce some of the more popular approaches.

FIGURE 16.14   MINITAB OUTPUT FOR THE MODEL INVOLVING ALL EIGHT INDEPENDENT VARIABLES

```
The regression equation is
Sales = - 1508 + 2.01 Time + 0.0372 Poten + 0.151 AdvExp + 199 Share
        + 291 Change + 5.55 Accounts + 19.8 Work + 8 Rating

Predictor      Coef    SE Coef       T       p
Constant    -1507.8      778.6   -1.94   0.071
Time          2.010      1.931    1.04   0.313
Poten      0.037206   0.008202    4.54   0.000
AdvExp      0.15094    0.04711    3.21   0.006
Share        199.08      67.03    2.97   0.009
Change        290.9      186.8    1.56   0.139
Accounts      5.550      4.775    1.16   0.262
Work          19.79      33.68    0.59   0.565
Rating          8.2      128.5    0.06   0.950

S = 449.015   R-Sq = 92.2%   R-Sq(adj) = 88.3%

Analysis of Variance

SOURCE          DF         SS        MS       F       p
Regression       8   38153712   4769214   23.66   0.000
Residual Error  16    3225837    201615
Total           24   41379549
```

FIGURE 16.15   MINITAB OUTPUT FOR THE MODEL INVOLVING Poten, AdvExp, AND Share

```
The regression equation is
Sales = - 1604 + 0.0543 Poten + 0.167 AdvExp + 283 Share

Predictor      Coef    SE Coef       T       p
Constant    -1603.6      505.6   -3.17   0.005
Poten      0.054286   0.007474    7.26   0.000
AdvExp      0.16748    0.04427    3.78   0.001
Share        282.75      48.76    5.80   0.000

S = 545.515   R-Sq = 84.9%   R-Sq(adj) = 82.7%

Analysis of Variance

SOURCE          DF         SS         MS       F       p
Regression       3   35130228   11710076   39.35   0.000
Residual Error  21    6249321     297587
Total           24   41379549
```

Variable Selection Procedures

Variable selection procedures are particularly useful in the early stages of building a model, but they cannot substitute for experience and judgment on the part of the analyst.

In this section we discuss four **variable selection procedures**: stepwise regression, forward selection, backward elimination, and best-subsets regression. Given a data set with several possible independent variables, we can use these procedures to identify which independent variables provide the best model. The first three procedures are iterative; at each step of the procedure a single independent variable is added or deleted and the new model is evaluated. The process continues until a stopping criterion indicates that the procedure cannot find a better model. The last procedure (best subsets) is not a one-variable-at-a-time procedure; it evaluates regression models involving different subsets of the independent variables.

In the stepwise regression, forward selection, and backward elimination procedures, the criterion for selecting an independent variable to add or delete from the model at each step is based on the F statistic introduced in Section 16.2. Suppose, for instance, that we are considering adding x_2 to a model involving x_1 or deleting x_2 from a model involving x_1 and x_2. To test whether the addition or deletion of x_2 is statistically significant, the null and alternative hypotheses can be stated as follows:

$$H_0: \beta_2 = 0$$
$$H_a: \beta_2 \neq 0$$

In Section 16.2 (see equation (16.10)) we showed that

$$F = \frac{\dfrac{SSE(x_1) - SSE(x_1, x_2)}{1}}{\dfrac{SSE(x_1, x_2)}{n - p - 1}}$$

can be used as a criterion for determining whether the presence of x_2 in the model causes a significant reduction in the error sum of squares. The p-value corresponding to this F statistic is the criterion used to determine whether an independent variable should be added or deleted from the regression model. The usual rejection rule applies: Reject H_0 if p-value $\leq \alpha$.

Stepwise Regression

The stepwise regression procedure begins each step by determining whether any of the variables *already in the model* should be removed. It does so by first computing an F statistic and a corresponding p-value for each independent variable in the model. The level of significance α for determining whether an independent variable should be removed from the model is referred to in Minitab as *Alpha to remove.* If the p-value for any independent variable is greater than *Alpha to remove,* the independent variable with the largest p-value is removed from the model and the stepwise regression procedure begins a new step.

If no independent variable can be removed from the model, the procedure attempts to enter another independent variable into the model. It does so by first computing an F statistic and corresponding p-value for each independent variable that is not in the model. The level of significance α for determining whether an independent variable should be entered into the model is referred to in Minitab as *Alpha to enter.* The independent variable with the smallest p-value is entered into the model provided its p-value is less than or equal to *Alpha to enter.* The procedure continues in this manner until no independent variables can be deleted from or added to the model.

Figure 16.16 shows the results obtained by using the Minitab stepwise regression procedure for the Cravens data using values of .05 for *Alpha to remove* and .05 for *Alpha to enter.*

FIGURE 16.16 MINITAB STEPWISE REGRESSION OUTPUT FOR THE CRAVENS DATA

```
       Alpha-to-Enter: 0.05      Alpha-to-Remove: 0.05

       Response is Sales on 8 predictors, with N = 25

            Step         1        2         3          4
            Constant  709.32    50.29   -327.24   -1441.93

            Accounts    21.7     19.0      15.6        9.2
            T-Value     5.50     6.41      5.19       3.22
            P-Value    0.000    0.000     0.000      0.004

            AdvExp               0.227     0.216      0.175
            T-Value              4.50      4.77       4.74
            P-Value              0.000     0.000      0.000

            Poten                          0.0219     0.0382
            T-Value                        2.53       4.79
            P-Value                        0.019      0.000

            Share                                      190
            T-Value                                   3.82
            P-Value                                   0.001

            S            881      650       583        454
            R-Sq       56.85    77.51     82.77      90.04
            R-Sq(adj)  54.97    75.47     80.31      88.05
            Mallows Cp  67.6     27.2      18.4        5.4
```

The stepwise procedure terminated after four steps. The estimated regression equation identified by the Minitab stepwise regression procedure is

$$\hat{y} = -1441.93 + 9.2 \text{ Accounts} + .175 \text{ AdvExp} + .0382 \text{ Poten} + 190 \text{ Share}$$

Because the stepwise procedure does not consider every possible subset for a given number of independent variables, it will not necessarily select the estimated regression equation with the highest R-sq value.

Note also in Figure 16.16 that $s = \sqrt{\text{MSE}}$ has been reduced from 881 with the best one-variable model (using Accounts) to 454 after four steps. The value of R-sq has been increased from 56.85% to 90.04%, and the recommended estimated regression equation has an R-Sq(adj) value of 88.05%.

In summary, at each step of the stepwise regression procedure the first consideration is to see whether any independent variable can be removed from the current model. If none of the independent variables can be removed from the model, the procedure checks to see whether any of the independent variables that are not currently in the model can be entered. Because of the nature of the stepwise regression procedure, an independent variable can enter the model at one step, be removed at a subsequent step, and then enter the model at a later step. The procedure stops when no independent variables can be removed from or entered into the model.

Forward Selection

The forward selection procedure starts with no independent variables. It adds variables one at a time using the same procedure as stepwise regression for determining whether an independent variable should be entered into the model. However, the forward selection procedure does not permit a variable to be removed from the model once it has been entered. The procedure stops if the *p*-value for each of the independent variables not in the model is greater than *Alpha to enter.*

The estimated regression equation obtained using Minitab's forward selection procedure is

$$\hat{y} = -1441.93 + 9.2 \text{ Accounts} + .175 \text{ AdvExp} + .0382 \text{ Poten} + 190 \text{ Share}$$

Thus, for the Cravens data, the forward selection procedure (using .05 for *Alpha to enter*) leads to the same estimated regression equation as the stepwise procedure.

Backward Elimination

The backward elimination procedure begins with a model that includes all the independent variables. It then deletes one independent variable at a time using the same procedure as stepwise regression. However, the backward elimination procedure does not permit an independent variable to be reentered once it has been removed. The procedure stops when none of the independent variables in the model have a *p*-value greater than *Alpha to remove.*

The estimated regression equation obtained using Minitab's backward elimination procedure for the Cravens data (using .05 for *Alpha to remove*) is

$$\hat{y} = -1312 + 3.8 \text{ Time} + .0444 \text{ Poten} + .152 \text{ AdvExp} + 259 \text{ Share}$$

Comparing the estimated regression equation identified using the backward elimination procedure to the estimated regression equation identified using the forward selection procedure, we see that three independent variables—AdvExp, Poten, and Share—are common to both. However, the backward elimination procedure has included Time instead of Accounts.

Forward selection and backward elimination may lead to different models.

Forward selection and backward elimination are the two extremes of model building; the forward selection procedure starts with no independent variables in the model and adds independent variables one at a time, whereas the backward elimination procedure starts with all independent variables in the model and deletes variables one at a time. The two procedures may lead to the same estimated regression equation. It is possible, however, for them to lead to two different estimated regression equations, as we saw with the Cravens data. Deciding which estimated regression equation to use remains a topic for discussion. Ultimately, the analyst's judgment must be applied. The best-subsets model building procedure we discuss next provides additional model-building information to be considered before a final decision is made.

Best-Subsets Regression

Stepwise regression, forward selection, and backward elimination are approaches to choosing the regression model by adding or deleting independent variables one at a time. None of them guarantees that the best model for a given number of variables will be found. Hence, these one-variable-at-a-time methods are properly viewed as heuristics for selecting a good regression model.

The complete best-subsets output also includes values for the Mallows Cp statistic. More advanced texts discuss the use of this statistic.

Some software packages use a procedure called best-subsets regression that enables the user to find, given a specified number of independent variables, the best regression model. Minitab has such a procedure. Figure 16.17 is a portion of the computer output obtained by using the best-subsets procedure for the Cravens data set.

This output identifies the two best one-variable estimated regression equations, the two best two-variable equations, the two best three-variable equations, and so on. The criterion used in determining which estimated regression equations are best for any number of

FIGURE 16.17   PORTION OF MINITAB BEST-SUBSETS REGRESSION OUTPUT

```
                                                          A
                                                          c
                                                    A   C c     R
                                                  P d S h o     a
                                                T o v h a u W   t
                                                i t E a n n o   I
                                                m e x r g t r   n
       Vars   R-Sq   R-Sq(adj)       S          e n p e e s K   g

        1     56.8     55.0       881.09                    X
        1     38.8     36.1       1049.3        X
        2     77.5     75.5       650.39            X       X
        2     74.6     72.3       691.11          X   X
        3     84.9     82.7       545.52          X X X
        3     82.8     80.3       582.64          X X       X
        4     90.0     88.1       453.84          X X X     X
        4     89.6     87.5       463.93        X X X X
        5     91.5     89.3       430.21        X X X X X
        5     91.2     88.9       436.75          X X X X X
        6     92.0     89.4       427.99        X X X X X X
        6     91.6     88.9       438.20          X X X X X X
        7     92.2     89.0       435.66        X X X X X X X
        7     92.0     88.8       440.29        X X X X X X   X
        8     92.2     88.3       449.02        X X X X X X X X
```

predictors is the value of the coefficient of determination (R-Sq). For instance, Accounts, with an R-Sq = 56.8%, provides the best estimated regression equation using only one independent variable; AdvExp and Accounts, with an R-Sq = 77.5%, provides the best estimated regression equation using two independent variables; and Poten, AdvExp, and Share, with an R-Sq = 84.9%, provides the best estimated regression equation with three independent variables. For the Cravens data, the adjusted coefficient of determination (R-Sq (adj) = 89.4%) is largest for the model with six independent variables: Time, Poten, AdvExp, Share, Change, and Accounts. However, the best model with four independent variables (Poten, AdvExp, Share, Accounts) has an adjusted coefficient of determination almost as high (R-Sq (adj) = 88.1%). All other things being equal, a simpler model with fewer variables is usually preferred.

Making the Final Choice

The analysis performed on the Cravens data to this point is good preparation for choosing a final model, but more analysis should be conducted before the final choice. As we noted in Chapters 14 and 15, a careful analysis of the residuals should be done. We want the residual plot for the chosen model to resemble approximately a horizontal band. Let us assume the residuals are not a problem and that we want to use the results of the best-subsets procedure to help choose the model.

The best-subsets procedure shows us that the best four-variable model contains the independent variables Poten, AdvExp, Share, and Accounts. This result also happens to be the four-variable model identified with the stepwise regression procedure. Table 16.7 is helpful in making the final choice. It shows several possible models consisting of some or all of these four independent variables.

TABLE 16.7 SELECTED MODELS INVOLVING Accounts, AdvExp, Poten, AND Share

Model	Independent Variables	R-Sq (adj)
1	Accounts	55.0
2	AdvExp, Accounts	75.5
3	Poten, Share	72.3
4	Poten, AdvExp, Accounts	80.3
5	Poten, AdvExp, Share	82.7
6	Poten, AdvExp, Share, Accounts	88.1

From Table 16.7, we see that the model with just AdvExp and Accounts is good. The adjusted coefficient of determination is R-Sq (adj) = 75.5%, and the model with all four variables provides only a 12.6-percentage-point improvement. The simpler two-variable model might be preferred, for instance, if it is difficult to measure market potential (Poten). However, if the data are readily available and highly accurate predictions of sales are needed, the model builder would clearly prefer the model with all four variables.

NOTES AND COMMENTS

1. The stepwise procedure requires that *Alpha to remove* be greater than or equal to *Alpha to enter*. This requirement prevents the same variable from being removed and then reentered at the same step.
2. Functions of the independent variables can be used to create new independent variables for use with any of the procedures in this section. For instance, if we wanted $x_1 x_2$ in the model to account for interaction, we would use the data for x_1 and x_2 to create the data for $z = x_1 x_2$.
3. None of the procedures that add or delete variables one at a time can be guaranteed to identify the best regression model. But they are excellent approaches to finding good models—especially when little multicollinearity is present.

Exercises

Applications

16. A study provided data on variables that may be related to the number of weeks a manufacturing worker has been jobless. The dependent variable in the study (Weeks) was defined as the number of weeks a worker has been jobless due to a layoff. The following independent variables were used in the study.

WEB file

Layoffs

Age	The age of the worker
Educ	The number of years of education
Married	A dummy variable; 1 if married, 0 otherwise
Head	A dummy variable; 1 if the head of household, 0 otherwise
Tenure	The number of years on the previous job
Manager	A dummy variable; 1 if management occupation, 0 otherwise
Sales	A dummy variable; 1 if sales occupation, 0 otherwise

The data are available in the file named Layoffs.
a. Develop the best one-variable estimated regression equation.
b. Use the stepwise procedure to develop the best estimated regression equation. Use values of .05 for *Alpha to enter* and *Alpha to remove*.

c.   Use the forward selection procedure to develop the best estimated regression equation. Use a value of .05 for *Alpha to enter*.
d.   Use the backward elimination procedure to develop the best estimated regression equation. Use a value of .05 for *Alpha to remove*.
e.   Use the best-subsets regression procedure to develop the best estimated regression equation.

LPGATour2

17. The Ladies Professional Golfers Association (LPGA) maintains statistics on performance and earnings for members of the LPGA Tour. Year-end performance statistics for the 30 players who had the highest total earnings in LPGA Tour events for 2005 appear in the file named LPGATour2 (LPGA Tour website, 2006). Earnings ($1000) is the total earnings in thousands of dollars; Scoring Avg. is the average score for all events; Drive Average is the average length of a players drive in yards; Greens in Reg. is the percentage of time a player is able to hit the green in regulation; Putting Avg. is the average number of putts taken on greens hit in regulation; and Sand Saves is the percentage of time a player is able to get "up and down" once in a greenside sand bunker. A green is considered hit in regulation if any part of the ball is touching the putting surface and the difference between the value of par for the hole and the number of strokes taken to hit the green is at least 2. Let DriveGreens denote a new independent variable that represents the interaction between the average length of a player's drive and the percentage of time a player is able to hit the green in regulation. Use the methods in this section to develop the best estimated multiple regression equation for predicting a player's average score for all events.

18. Jeff Sagarin has been providing sports ratings for *USA Today* since 1985. In baseball his predicted RPG (runs/game) statistic takes into account the entire player's offensive statistics, and is claimed to be the best measure of a player's true offensive value. The following data show the RPG and a variety of offensive statistics for the 2005 Major League Baseball (MLB) season for 20 members of the New York Yankees (*USA Today* website, March 3, 2006). The labels on columns are defined as follows: RPG, predicted runs per game statistic; H, hits; 2B, doubles; 3B, triples; HR, home runs; RBI, runs batted in; BB, bases on balls (walks); SO, strikeouts; SB, stolen bases; CS, caught stealing; OBP, on-base percentage; SLG, slugging percentage; and AVG, batting average.

Yankees

Player	RPG	H	2B	3B	HR	RBI	BB	SO	SB	CS	OBP	SLG	AVG
D Jeter	6.51	202	25	5	19	70	77	117	14	5	.389	.450	.309
H Matsui	6.32	192	45	3	23	116	63	78	2	2	.367	.496	.305
A Rodriguez	9.06	194	29	1	48	130	91	139	21	6	.421	.610	.321
G Sheffield	6.93	170	27	0	34	123	78	76	10	2	.379	.512	.291
R Cano	5.01	155	34	4	14	62	16	68	1	3	.320	.458	.297
B Williams	4.14	121	19	1	12	64	53	75	1	2	.321	.367	.249
J Posada	5.36	124	23	0	19	71	66	94	1	0	.352	.430	.262
J Giambi	9.11	113	14	0	32	87	108	109	0	0	.440	.535	.271
T Womack	2.91	82	8	1	0	15	12	49	27	5	.276	.280	.249
T Martinez	5.08	73	9	0	17	49	38	54	2	0	.328	.439	.241
M Bellhorn	4.07	63	20	0	8	30	52	112	3	0	.324	.357	.210
R Sierra	3.27	39	12	0	4	29	9	41	0	0	.265	.371	.229
J Flaherty	1.83	21	5	0	2	11	6	26	0	0	.206	.252	.165
B Crosby	3.48	27	0	1	1	6	4	14	4	1	.304	.327	.276
M Lawton	5.15	6	0	0	2	4	7	8	1	0	.263	.250	.125
R Sanchez	3.36	12	1	0	0	2	2	3	0	1	.326	.302	.279
A Phillips	2.13	6	4	0	1	4	1	13	0	0	.171	.325	.150
M Cabrera	1.19	4	0	0	0	0	0	2	0	0	.211	.211	.211
R Johnson	3.44	4	2	0	0	0	1	4	0	0	.300	.333	.222
F Escalona	5.31	4	1	0	0	2	1	4	0	0	.375	.357	.286

Let the dependent variable be the RPG statistic.
a.   Develop the best one-variable estimated regression equation.
b.   Use the methods in this section to develop the best estimated multiple regression equation for predicting a player's RPG.

Stroke

19.   Refer to exercise 14. Using age, blood pressure, whether a person is a smoker, and any interaction involving those variables, develop an estimated regression equation that can be used to predict risk. Briefly describe the process you used to develop an estimated regression equation for these data.

16.5 Multiple Regression Approach to Experimental Design

In Section 15.7 we discussed the use of dummy variables in multiple regression analysis. In this section we show how the use of dummy variables in a multiple regression equation can provide another approach to solving experimental design problems. We will demonstrate the multiple regression approach to experimental design by applying it to the Chemitech, Inc., completely randomized design introduced in Chapter 13.

Recall that Chemitech developed a new filtration system for municipal water supplies. The components for the new filtration system will be purchased from several suppliers, and Chemitech will assemble the components at its plant in Columbia, South Carolina. Three different assembly methods, referred to as methods A, B, and C, have been proposed. Managers at Chemitech want to determine which assembly method can produce the greatest number of filtration systems per week.

A random sample of 15 employees was selected, and each of the three assembly methods was randomly assigned to 5 employees. The number of units assembled by each employee is shown in Table 16.8. The sample mean number of units produced with each of the three assembly methods is as follows:

Assembly Method	Mean Number Produced
A	62
B	66
C	52

Although method B appears to result in higher production rates than either of the other methods, the issue is whether the three sample means observed are different enough for us to conclude that the means of the populations corresponding to the three methods of assembly are different.

We begin the regression approach to this problem by defining dummy variables that will be used to indicate which assembly method was used. Because the Chemitech problem has

TABLE 16.8   NUMBER OF UNITS PRODUCED BY 15 WORKERS

	Method	
A	**B**	**C**
58	58	48
64	69	57
55	71	59
66	64	47
67	68	49

TABLE 16.9 DUMMY VARIABLES FOR THE CHEMITECH EXPERIMENT

A	B	
1	0	Observation is associated with assembly method A
0	1	Observation is associated with assembly method B
0	0	Observation is associated with assembly method C

three assembly methods or treatments, we need two dummy variables. In general, if the factor being investigated involves k distinct levels or treatments, we need to define $k - 1$ dummy variables. For the Chemitech experiment we define dummy variables A and B as shown in Table 16.9.

We can use the dummy variables to relate the number of units produced per week, y, to the method of assembly the employee uses.

$$E(y) = \text{Expected value of the number of units produced per week}$$
$$= \beta_0 + \beta_1 A + \beta_2 B$$

Thus, if we are interested in the expected value of the number of units assembled per week for an employee who uses method C, our procedure for assigning numerical values to the dummy variables would result in setting $A = B = 0$. The multiple regression equation then reduces to

$$E(y) = \beta_0 + \beta_1(0) + \beta_2(0) = \beta_0$$

We can interpret β_0 as the expected value of the number of units assembled per week for an employee who uses method C. In other words, β_0 is the mean number of units assembled per week using method C.

Next let us consider the forms of the multiple regression equation for each of the other methods. For method A the values of the dummy variables are $A = 1$ and $B = 0$, and

$$E(y) = \beta_0 + \beta_1(1) + \beta_2(0) = \beta_0 + \beta_1$$

For method B we set $A = 0$ and $B = 1$, and

$$E(y) = \beta_0 + \beta_1(0) + \beta_2(1) = \beta_0 + \beta_2$$

We see that $\beta_0 + \beta_1$ represents the mean number of units assembled per week using method A, and $\beta_0 + \beta_2$ represents the mean number of units assembled per week using method B.

We now want to estimate the coefficients β_0, β_1, and β_2 and hence develop an estimate of the mean number of units assembled per week for each method. Table 16.10 shows the sample data, consisting of 15 observations of A, B, and y. Figure 16.18 shows the corresponding Minitab multiple regression output. We see that the estimates of β_0, β_1, and β_2 are $b_0 = 52$, $b_1 = 10$, and $b_2 = 14$. Thus, the best estimate of the mean number of units assembled per week for each assembly method is as follows:

Assembly Method	Prediction of $E(y)$
A	$b_0 + b_1 = 52 + 10 = 62$
B	$b_0 = 52 + 14 = 66$
C	$b_0 = 52$

TABLE 16.10 INPUT DATA FOR THE CHEMITECH COMPLETELY RANDOMIZED DESIGN

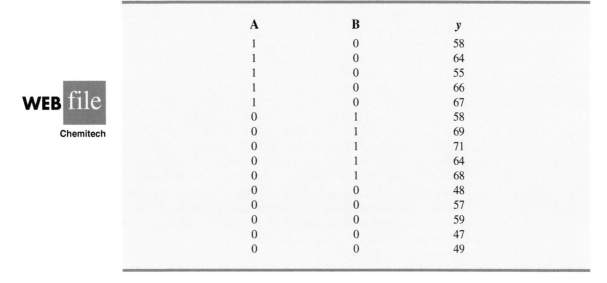

A	B	y
1	0	58
1	0	64
1	0	55
1	0	66
1	0	67
0	1	58
0	1	69
0	1	71
0	1	64
0	1	68
0	0	48
0	0	57
0	0	59
0	0	47
0	0	49

WEB file

Chemitech

Note that the estimate of the mean number of units produced with each of the three assembly methods obtained from the regression analysis is the same as the sample mean shown previously.

Now let us see how we can use the output from the multiple regression analysis to perform the ANOVA test on the difference among the means for the three plants. First, we observe that if the means do not differ

$$E(y) \text{ for method A} - E(y) \text{ for method C} = 0$$
$$E(y) \text{ for method B} - E(y) \text{ for method C} = 0$$

FIGURE 16.18 MULTIPLE REGRESSION OUTPUT FOR THE CHEMITECH COMPLETELY RANDOMIZED DESIGN

```
The regression equation is
y = 52.0 + 10.0 A + 14.0 B

Predictor      Coef   SE Coef       T      P
Constant     52.000     2.380   21.84  0.000
A            10.000     3.367    2.97  0.012
B            14.000     3.367    4.16  0.001

S = 5.32291    R-Sq = 60.5%    R-Sq(adj) = 53.9%

Analysis of Variance

SOURCE           DF       SS      MS      F      P
Regression        2   520.00  260.00   9.18  0.004
Residual Error   12   340.00   28.33
Total            14   860.00
```

Because β_0 equals $E(y)$ for method C and $\beta_0 + \beta_1$ equals $E(y)$ for method A, the first difference is equal to $(\beta_0 + \beta_1) - \beta_0 = \beta_1$. Moreover, because $\beta_0 + \beta_2$ equals $E(y)$ for method B, the second difference is equal to $(\beta_0 + \beta_2) - \beta_0 = \beta_2$. We would conclude that the three methods do not differ if $\beta_1 = 0$ and $\beta_2 = 0$. Hence, the null hypothesis for a test for difference of means can be stated as

$$H_0 : \beta_1 = \beta_2 = 0$$

Suppose the level of significance is $\alpha = .05$. Recall that to test this type of null hypothesis about the significance of the regression relationship we use the F test for overall significance. The Minitab output in Figure 16.18 shows that the p-value corresponding to $F = 9.18$ is .004. Because the p-value $= .004 < \alpha = .05$, we reject $H_0 : \beta_1 = \beta_2 = 0$ and conclude that the means for the three assembly methods are not the same. Because the F test shows that the multiple regression relationship is significant, a t test can be conducted to determine the significance of the individual parameters, β_1 and β_2. Using $\alpha = .05$, the p-values of .012 and .001 on the Minitab output indicate that we can reject $H_0 : \beta_1 = 0$ and $H_0 : \beta_2 = 0$. Hence, both parameters are statistically significant. Thus, we can also conclude that the means for methods A and C are different and that the means for methods B and C are different.

Exercises

Methods

20. Consider a completely randomized design involving four treatments: A, B, C, and D. Write a multiple regression equation that can be used to analyze these data. Define all variables.

21. Write a multiple regression equation that can be used to analyze the data for a randomized block design involving three treatments and two blocks. Define all variables.

22. Write a multiple regression equation that can be used to analyze the data for a two-factorial design with two levels for factor A and three levels for factor B. Define all variables.

Applications

23. The Jacobs Chemical Company wants to estimate the mean time (minutes) required to mix a batch of material on machines produced by three different manufacturers. To limit the cost of testing, four batches of material were mixed on machines produced by each of the three manufacturers. The times needed to mix the material follow.

Manufacturer 1	Manufacturer 2	Manufacturer 3
20	28	20
26	26	19
24	31	23
22	27	22

a. Write a multiple regression equation that can be used to analyze the data.
b. What are the best estimates of the coefficients in your regression equation?

c. In terms of the regression equation coefficients, what hypotheses must we test to see whether the mean time to mix a batch of material is the same for all three manufacturers?

d. For an $\alpha = .05$ level of significance, what conclusion should be drawn?

24. Four different paints are advertised as having the same drying time. To check the manufacturers' claims, five samples were tested for each of the paints. The time in minutes until the paint was dry enough for a second coat to be applied was recorded for each sample. The data obtained follow.

Paint 1	Paint 2	Paint 3	Paint 4
128	144	133	150
137	133	143	142
135	142	137	135
124	146	136	140
141	130	131	153

a. Use $\alpha = .05$ to test for any significant differences in mean drying time among the paints.

b. What is your estimate of the mean drying time for paint 2? How is it obtained from the computer output?

25. An automobile dealer conducted a test to determine whether the time needed to complete a minor engine tune-up depends on whether a computerized engine analyzer or an electronic analyzer is used. Because tune-up time varies among compact, intermediate, and full-sized cars, the three types of cars were used as blocks in the experiment. The data (time in minutes) obtained follow.

		Car		
		Compact	Intermediate	Full Size
Analyzer	Computerized	50	55	63
	Electronic	42	44	46

Use $\alpha = .05$ to test for any significant differences.

26. A mail-order catalog firm designed a factorial experiment to test the effect of the size of a magazine advertisement and the advertisement design on the number (in thousands) of catalog requests received. Three advertising designs and two sizes of advertisements were considered. The following data were obtained. Test for any significant effects due to type of design, size of advertisement, or interaction. Use $\alpha = .05$.

		Size of Advertisement	
		Small	Large
Design	A	8	12
		12	8
	B	22	26
		14	30
	C	10	18
		18	14

16.6 Autocorrelation and the Durbin–Watson Test

Often, the data used for regression studies in business and economics are collected over time. It is not uncommon for the value of y at time t, denoted by y_t, to be related to the value of y at previous time periods. In such cases, we say **autocorrelation** (also called **serial correlation**) is present in the data. If the value of y in time period t is related to its value in time period $t - 1$, first-order autocorrelation is present. If the value of y in time period t is related to the value of y in time period $t - 2$, second-order autocorrelation is present, and so on.

One of the assumptions of the regression model is the error terms are independent. However, when autocorrelation is present, this assumption is violated. In the case of first-order autocorrelation, the error at time t, denoted ϵ_t, will be related to the error at time period $t - 1$, denoted ϵ_{t-1}. Two cases of first-order autocorrelation are illustrated in Figure 16.19. Panel A is the case of positive autocorrelation; panel B is the case of negative autocorrelation. With positive autocorrelation we expect a positive residual in one period to be followed by a positive residual in the next period, a negative residual in one period to be followed by a negative residual in the next period, and so on. With negative autocorrelation, we expect a positive residual in one period to be followed by a negative residual in the next period, then a positive residual, and so on.

When autocorrelation is present, serious errors can be made in performing tests of statistical significance based upon the assumed regression model. It is therefore important to be able to detect autocorrelation and take corrective action. We will show how the Durbin-Watson statistic can be used to detect first-order autocorrelation.

Suppose the values of ϵ are not independent but are related in the following manner:

$$\epsilon_t = \rho\epsilon_{t-1} + z_t \tag{16.16}$$

where ρ is a parameter with an absolute value less than one and z_t is a normally and independently distributed random variable with a mean of zero and a variance of σ^2. From equation (16.16) we see that if $\rho = 0$, the error terms are not related, and each has a mean of zero and a variance of σ^2. In this case, there is no autocorrelation and the regression assumptions

FIGURE 16.19   TWO DATA SETS WITH FIRST-ORDER AUTOCORRELATION

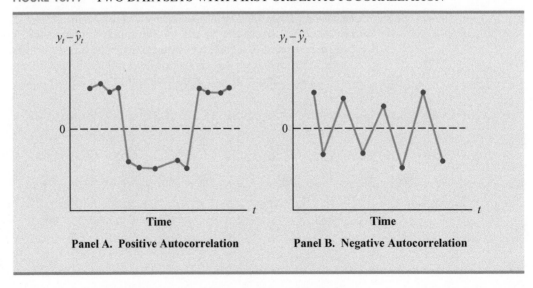

Panel A. Positive Autocorrelation

Panel B. Negative Autocorrelation

are satisfied. If $\rho > 0$, we have positive autocorrelation; if $\rho < 0$, we have negative autocorrelation. In either of these cases, the regression assumptions about the error term are violated.

The **Durbin-Watson test** for autocorrelation uses the residuals to determine whether $\rho = 0$. To simplify the notation for the Durbin-Watson statistic, we denote the ith residual by $e_i = y_i - \hat{y}_i$. The Durbin-Watson test statistic is computed as follows.

DURBIN-WATSON TEST STATISTIC

$$d = \frac{\sum_{t=2}^{n}(e_t - e_{t-1})^2}{\sum_{t=1}^{n}e_t^2} \tag{16.17}$$

If successive values of the residuals are close together (positive autocorrelation), the value of the Durbin-Watson test statistic will be small. If successive values of the residuals are far apart (negative autocorrelation), the value of the Durbin-Watson statistic will be large.

The Durbin-Watson test statistic ranges in value from zero to four, with a value of two indicating no autocorrelation is present. Durbin and Watson developed tables that can be used to determine when their test statistic indicates the presence of autocorrelation. Table 16.11 shows lower and upper bounds (d_L and d_U) for hypothesis tests using $\alpha = .05$; n denotes the number of observations. The null hypothesis to be tested is always that there is no autocorrelation.

$$H_0: \rho = 0$$

The alternative hypothesis to test for positive autocorrelation is

$$H_a: \rho > 0$$

TABLE 16.11   CRITICAL VALUES FOR THE DURBIN-WATSON TEST FOR AUTOCORRELATION

Note: Entries in the table are the critical values for a one-tailed Durbin-Watson test for autocorrelation. For a two-tailed test, the level of significance is doubled.

Significance Points of d_L and d_U: $\alpha = .05$
Number of Independent Variables

	1		2		3		4		5	
n^*	d_L	d_U	d_L	d_U	d_L	d_U	d_L	d_U	d_L	d_U
15	1.08	1.36	.95	1.54	.82	1.75	.69	1.97	.56	2.21
20	1.20	1.41	1.10	1.54	1.00	1.68	.90	1.83	.79	1.99
25	1.29	1.45	1.21	1.55	1.12	1.66	1.04	1.77	.95	1.89
30	1.35	1.49	1.28	1.57	1.21	1.65	1.14	1.74	1.07	1.83
40	1.44	1.54	1.39	1.60	1.34	1.66	1.29	1.72	1.23	1.79
50	1.50	1.59	1.46	1.63	1.42	1.67	1.38	1.72	1.34	1.77
70	1.58	1.64	1.55	1.67	1.52	1.70	1.49	1.74	1.46	1.77
100	1.65	1.69	1.63	1.72	1.61	1.74	1.59	1.76	1.57	1.78

*Interpolate linearly for intermediate n values.

FIGURE 16.20   HYPOTHESIS TEST FOR AUTOCORRELATION USING
THE DURBIN-WATSON TEST

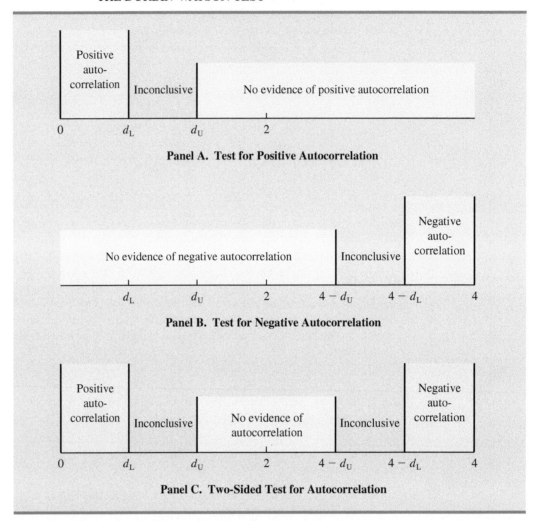

The alternative hypothesis to test for negative autocorrelation is

$$H_a: \rho < 0$$

A two-sided test is also possible. In this case the alternative hypothesis is

$$H_a: \rho \neq 0$$

Figure 16.20 shows how the values of d_L and d_U in Table 16.11 are used to test for autocorrelation. Panel A illustrates the test for positive autocorrelation. If $d < d_L$, we conclude that positive autocorrelation is present. If $d_L \leq d \leq d_U$, we say the test is inconclusive. If $d > d_U$, we conclude that there is no evidence of positive autocorrelation.

Panel B illustrates the test for negative autocorrelation. If $d > 4 - d_L$, we conclude that negative autocorrelation is present. If $4 - d_U \leq d \leq 4 - d_L$, we say the test is inconclusive. If $d < 4 - d_U$, we conclude that there is no evidence of negative autocorrelation.

Panel C illustrates the two-sided test. If $d < d_{\text{L}}$ or $d > 4 - d_{\text{L}}$, we reject H_0 and conclude that autocorrelation is present. If $d_{\text{L}} \leq d \leq d_{\text{U}}$ or $4 - d_{\text{U}} \leq d \leq 4 - d_{\text{L}}$, we say the test is inconclusive. If $d_{\text{U}} < d < 4 - d_{\text{U}}$, we conclude that there is no evidence of autocorrelation.

If significant autocorrelation is identified, we should investigate whether we omitted one or more key independent variables that have time-ordered effects on the dependent variable. If no such variables can be identified, including an independent variable that measures the time of the observation (for instance, the value of this variable could be one for the first observation, two for the second observation, and so on) will sometimes eliminate or reduce the autocorrelation. When these attempts to reduce or remove autocorrelation do not work, transformations on the dependent or independent variables can prove helpful; a discussion of such transformations can be found in more advanced texts on regression analysis.

Note that the Durbin-Watson tables list the smallest sample size as 15. The reason is that the test is generally inconclusive for smaller sample sizes; in fact, many statisticians believe the sample size should be at least 50 for the test to produce worthwhile results.

Exercises

Applications

27. The following data show the daily closing prices (in dollars per share) for a stock.

ClosingPrice

Date	Price ($)
Nov. 3	82.87
Nov. 4	83.00
Nov. 7	83.61
Nov. 8	83.15
Nov. 9	82.84
Nov. 10	83.99
Nov. 11	84.55
Nov. 14	84.36
Nov. 15	85.53
Nov. 16	86.54
Nov. 17	86.89
Nov. 18	87.77
Nov. 21	87.29
Nov. 22	87.99
Nov. 23	88.80
Nov. 25	88.80
Nov. 28	89.11
Nov. 29	89.10
Nov. 30	88.90
Dec. 1	89.21

a. Define the independent variable Period, where Period = 1 corresponds to the data for November 3, Period = 2 corresponds to the data for November 4, and so on. Develop the estimated regression equation that can be used to predict the closing price given the value of Period.

b. At the .05 level of significance, test for any positive autocorrelation in the data.

28. Refer to the Cravens data set in Table 16.5. In Section 16.3 we showed that the estimated regression equation involving Accounts, AdvExp, Poten, and Share had an adjusted coefficient

of determination of 88.1%. Use the .05 level of significance and apply the Durbin-Watson test to determine whether positive autocorrelation is present.

Summary

In this chapter we discussed several concepts used by model builders to help identify the best estimated regression equation. First, we introduced the concept of a general linear model to show how the methods discussed in Chapters 14 and 15 could be extended to handle curvilinear relationships and interaction effects. Then we discussed how transformations involving the dependent variable could be used to account for problems such as nonconstant variance in the error term.

In many applications of regression analysis, a large number of independent variables are considered. We presented a general approach based on an F statistic for adding or deleting variables from a regression model. We then introduced a larger problem involving 25 observations and eight independent variables. We saw that one issue encountered in solving larger problems is finding the best subset of the independent variables. To help in that task, we discussed several variable selection procedures: stepwise regression, forward selection, backward elimination, and best-subsets regression.

In Section 16.5, we extended the discussion of how multiple regression models could be developed to provide another approach for solving analysis of variance and experimental design problems. The chapter concluded with an application of residual analysis to show the Durbin-Watson test for autocorrelation.

Glossary

General linear model A model of the form $y = \beta_0 + \beta_1 z_1 + \beta_2 z_2 + \cdots + \beta_p z_p + \epsilon$, where each of the independent variables $z_j (j = 1, 2, \ldots, p)$ is a function of $x_1, x_2, \ldots, x_k$, the variables for which data have been collected.

Interaction The effect of two independent variables acting together.

Variable selection procedures Methods for selecting a subset of the independent variables for a regression model.

Autocorrelation Correlation in the errors that arises when the error terms at successive points in time are related.

Serial correlation Same as autocorrelation.

Durbin-Watson test A test to determine whether first-order autocorrelation is present.

Key Formulas

General Linear Model

$$y = \beta_0 + \beta_1 z_1 + \beta_2 z_2 + \cdots + \beta_p z_p + \epsilon \qquad (16.1)$$

F Test Statistic for Adding or Deleting $p - q$ Variables

$$F = \frac{\dfrac{\text{SSE}(x_1, x_2, \ldots, x_q) - \text{SSE}(x_1, x_2, \ldots, x_q, x_{q+1}, \ldots, x_p)}{p - q}}{\dfrac{\text{SSE}(x_1, x_2, \ldots, x_q, x_{q+1}, \ldots, x_p)}{n - p - 1}} \qquad (16.13)$$

First-Order Autocorrelation

$$\epsilon_t = \rho\epsilon_{t-1} + z_t \tag{16.16}$$

Durbin-Watson Test Statistic

$$d = \frac{\sum\limits_{t=2}^{n}(e_t - e_{t-1})^2}{\sum\limits_{t=1}^{n} e_t^2} \tag{16.17}$$

Supplementary Exercises

CorporateBonds

29. A sample containing years to maturity and yield (%) for 40 corporate bonds is contained in the data file named CorporateBonds (*Barron's,* April 2, 2012).
    a. Develop a scatter diagram of the data using x = years to maturity as the independent variable. Does a simple linear regression model appear to be appropriate?
    b. Develop an estimated regression equation with x = years to maturity and x^2 as the independent variables.
    c. As an alternative to fitting a second-order model, fit a model using the natural logarithm of price as the independent variable; that is, $\hat{y} = b_0 + b_1\ln(x)$. Does the estimated regression using the natural logarithm of x provide a better fit than the estimated regression developed in part (b)? Explain.

30. *Consumer Reports* tested 19 different brands and models of road, fitness, and comfort bikes. Road bikes are designed for long road trips; fitness bikes are designed for regular workouts or daily commutes; and comfort bikes are designed for leisure rides on typically flat roads. The following data show the type, weight (lb.), and price ($) for the 19 bicycles tested (*Consumer Reports* website, February 2009).

Bikes

Brand and Model	Type	Weight	Price($)
Klein RÃªve v	Road	20	1800
Giant OCR Composite 3	Road	22	1800
Giant OCR 1	Road	22	1000
Specialized Roubaix	Road	21	1300
Trek Pilot 2.1	Road	21	1320
Cannondale Synapse 4	Road	21	1050
LeMond Poprad	Road	22	1350
Raleigh Cadent 1.0	Road	24	650
Giant FCR3	Fitness	23	630
Schwinn Super Sport GS	Fitness	23	700
Fuji Absolute 2.0	Fitness	24	700
Jamis Coda Comp	Fitness	26	830
Cannondale Road Warrior 400	Fitness	25	700
Schwinn Sierra GS	Comfort	31	340
Mongoose Switchback SX	Comfort	32	280
Giant Sedona DX	Comfort	32	360
Jamis Explorer 4.0	Comfort	35	600
Diamondback Wildwood Deluxe	Comfort	34	350
Specialized Crossroads Sport	Comfort	31	330

    a. Develop a scatter diagram with weight as the independent variable and price as the dependent variable. Does a simple linear regression model appear to be appropriate?
    b. Develop an estimated multiple regression equation with x = weight and x^2 as the two independent variables.

c. Use the following dummy variables to develop an estimated regression equation that can be used to predict the price given the type of bike: Type_Fitness = 1 if the bike is a fitness bike, 0 otherwise; and Type_Comfort = 1 if the bike is a comfort bike; 0 otherwise. Compare the results obtained to the results obtained in part (b).

d. To account for possible interaction between the type of bike and the weight of the bike, develop a new estimated regression equation that can be used to predict the price of the bike given the type, the weight of the bike, and any interaction between weight and each of the dummy variables defined in part (c). What estimated regression equation appears to be the best predictor of price? Explain.

31. A study investigated the relationship between audit delay (Delay), the length of time from a company's fiscal year-end to the date of the auditor's report, and variables that describe the client and the auditor. Some of the independent variables that were included in this study follow.

Industry A dummy variable coded 1 if the firm was an industrial company or 0 if the firm was a bank, savings and loan, or insurance company.

Public A dummy variable coded 1 if the company was traded on an organized exchange or over the counter; otherwise coded 0.

Quality A measure of overall quality of internal controls, as judged by the auditor, on a five-point scale ranging from "virtually none" (1) to "excellent" (5).

Finished A measure ranging from 1 to 4, as judged by the auditor, where 1 indicates "all work performed subsequent to year-end" and 4 indicates "most work performed prior to year-end."

A sample of 40 companies provided the following data.

Audit

Delay	Industry	Public	Quality	Finished
62	0	0	3	1
45	0	1	3	3
54	0	0	2	2
71	0	1	1	2
91	0	0	1	1
62	0	0	4	4
61	0	0	3	2
69	0	1	5	2
80	0	0	1	1
52	0	0	5	3
47	0	0	3	2
65	0	1	2	3
60	0	0	1	3
81	1	0	1	2
73	1	0	2	2
89	1	0	2	1
71	1	0	5	4
76	1	0	2	2
68	1	0	1	2
68	1	0	5	2
86	1	0	2	2
76	1	1	3	1
67	1	0	2	3
57	1	0	4	2
55	1	1	3	2
54	1	0	5	2
69	1	0	3	3
82	1	0	5	1
94	1	0	1	1

Delay	Industry	Public	Quality	Finished
74	1	1	5	2
75	1	1	4	3
69	1	0	2	2
71	1	0	4	4
79	1	0	5	2
80	1	0	1	4
91	1	0	4	1
92	1	0	1	4
46	1	1	4	3
72	1	0	5	2
85	1	0	5	1

    a. Develop the estimated regression equation using all of the independent variables.
    b. Did the estimated regression equation developed in part (a) provide a good fit? Explain.
    c. Develop a scatter diagram showing Delay as a function of Finished. What does this scatter diagram indicate about the relationship between Delay and Finished?
    d. On the basis of your observations about the relationship between Delay and Finished, develop an alternative estimated regression equation to the one developed in (a) to explain as much of the variability in Delay as possible.

32. Refer to the data in exercise 31. Consider a model in which only Industry is used to predict Delay. At a .01 level of significance, test for any positive autocorrelation in the data.

33. Refer to the data in exercise 31.
    a. Develop an estimated regression equation that can be used to predict Delay by using Industry and Quality.
    b. Plot the residuals obtained from the estimated regression equation developed in part (a) as a function of the order in which the data are presented. Does any autocorrelation appear to be present in the data? Explain.
    c. At the .05 level of significance, test for any positive autocorrelation in the data.

34. A study was conducted to investigate browsing activity by shoppers. Shoppers were classified as nonbrowsers, light browsers, and heavy browsers. For each shopper in the study, a measure was obtained to determine how comfortable the shopper was in the store. Higher scores indicated greater comfort. Assume that the following data are from this study. Use a .05 level of significance to test for differences in comfort levels among the three types of browsers.

Browsing

Nonbrowser	Light Browser	Heavy Browser
4	5	5
5	6	7
6	5	5
3	4	7
3	7	4
4	4	6
5	6	5
4	5	7

CarMileage

35. The Department of Energy and the U.S. Environmental Protection Agency's *2012 Fuel Economy Guide* provides fuel efficiency data for 2012 model year cars and trucks (Department of Energy website, April 16, 2012). The file named CarMileage provides a portion of the data for 316 cars. The column labeled Size identifies the size of the car (Compact, Midsize, and Large) and the column labeled Hwy MPG shows the fuel efficiency rating for highway driving in terms of miles per gallon. Use $\alpha = .05$ and test for any significant difference in the mean fuel efficiency rating for highway driving among the three sizes of cars.

Case Problem 1   Analysis of PGA Tour Statistics

The Professional Golfers Association (PGA) maintains data on performance and earnings for members of the PGA Tour. Based on total earnings in PGA Tour events, the top 125 players are exempt for the following season. Making the top 125 money list is important because a player who is "exempt" has qualified to be a full-time member of the PGA Tour for the following season.

Scoring average is generally considered the most important statistic in terms of success on the PGA Tour. To investigate the relationship between scoring average and variables such as driving distance, driving accuracy, greens in regulation, sand saves, and average putts per round, year-end performance data for the 125 players who had the highest total earnings in PGA Tour events for 2008 are contained in the file named PGATour (PGA Tour website, 2009). Each row of the data set corresponds to a PGA Tour player, and the data have been sorted based upon total earnings. Descriptions for the variables in the data set follow.

Money	Total earnings in PGA Tour events.
Scoring Average	The average number of strokes per completed round.
DrDist (Driving Distance)	DrDist is the average number of yards per measured drive. On the PGA Tour driving distance is measured on two holes per round. Care is taken to select two holes which face in opposite directions to counteract the effect of wind. Drives are measured to the point at which they come to rest regardless of whether they are in the fairway or not.
DrAccu (Driving Accuracy)	The percentage of time a tee shot comes to rest in the fairway (regardless of club). Driving accuracy is measured on every hole, excluding par 3's.
GIR (Greens in Regulation)	The percentage of time a player was able to hit the green in regulation. A green is considered hit in regulation if any portion of the ball is touching the putting surface after the GIR stroke has been taken. The GIR stroke is determined by subtracting 2 from par (1st stroke on a par 3, 2nd on a par 4, 3rd on a par 5). In other words, a green is considered hit in regulation if the player has reached the putting surface in par minus two strokes.
Sand Saves	The percentage of time a player was able to get "up and down" once in a greenside sand bunker (regardless of score). "Up and down" indicates it took the player 2 shots or less to put the ball in the hole from a greenside sand bunker.
PPR (Putts per Round)	The average number of putts per round.
Scrambling	The percentage of time a player missed the green in regulation but still made par or better.
Bounce Back	The percentage of time a player is over par on a hole and then under par on the following hole. In other words, it is the percentage of holes with a bogey or worse followed on the next hole with a birdie or better.

Managerial Report

Suppose that you have been hired by the commissioner of the PGA Tour to analyze the data for a presentation to be made at the annual PGA Tour meeting. The commissioner has asked whether it would be possible to use these data to determine the performance measures that are the best predictors of a player's average score. Use the methods presented in this and previous chapters to analyze the data. Prepare a report for the PGA Tour commissioner that summarizes your analysis, including key statistical results, conclusions, and recommendations. Include any appropriate technical material in an appendix.

Case Problem 2 Rating Wines from the Piedmont Region of Italy

WineRatings

Wine Spectator magazine contains articles and reviews on every aspect of the wine industry, including ratings of wine from around the world. In a recent issue they reviewed and scored 475 wines from the Piedmont region of Italy using a 100-point scale (*Wine Spectator,* April 30, 2011). The following table shows how the *Wine Spectator* score each wine received is used to rate each wine as being classic, outstanding, very good, good, mediocre, or not recommended.

Score	Rating
95–100	Classic: a great wine
90–94	Outstanding: a wine of superior character and style
85–89	Very good: a wine with special qualities
80–84	Good: a solid, well-made wine
75–79	Mediocre: a drinkable wine that may have minor flaws
below 75	Not Recommended

A key question for most consumers is whether paying more for a bottle of wine will result in a better wine. To investigate this question for wines from the Piedmont region we selected a random sample of 100 of the 475 wines that *Wine Spectator* reviewed. The data, contained in the file named WineRatings, shows the price ($), the *Wine Spectator* score, and the rating for each wine.

Managerial Report

1. Develop a table that shows the number of wines that were classified as classic, outstanding, very good, good, mediocre, and not recommended and the average price. Does there appear to be any relationship between the price of the wine and the *Wine Spectator* rating? Are there any other aspects of your initial summary of the data that stand out?
2. Develop a scatter diagram with price on the horizontal axis and the *Wine Spectator* score on the vertical axis. Does the relationship between price and score appear to be linear?
3. Using linear regression, develop an estimated regression equation that can be used to predict the score given the price of the wine.
4. Using a second-order model, develop an estimated regression equation that can be used to predict the score given the price of the wine.
5. Compare the results from fitting a linear model and fitting a second-order model.
6. As an alternative to fitting a second-order model, fit a model using the natural logarithm of price as the independent variable. Compare the results with the second-order model.
7. Based upon your analysis, would you say that spending more for a bottle of wine will provide a better wine?
8. Suppose that you want to spend a maximum of $30 for a bottle of wine. In this case, will spending closer to your upper limit for price result in a better wine than a much lower price?

Appendix 16.1   Variable Selection Procedures with Minitab

Cravens

In Section 16.4 we discussed the use of variable selection procedures in solving multiple regression problems. In Figure 16.16 we showed the Minitab stepwise regression output for the Cravens data, and in Figure 16.17 we showed the Minitab best-subsets output. In this appendix we describe the steps required to generate the output in both of these figures, as well as the steps required to use the forward selection and backward elimination procedures. First, the data in Table 16.5 must be entered in a Minitab worksheet. The values of Sales, Time, Poten, AdvExp, Share, Change, Accounts, Work, and Rating are entered into columns C1–C9 of a Minitab worksheet.

Using Minitab's Stepwise Procedure

The following steps can be used to produce the Minitab stepwise regression output for the Cravens data.

> **Step 1.** Select the **Stat** menu
> **Step 2.** Select the **Regression** menu
> **Step 3.** Choose **Stepwise**
> **Step 4.** When the **Stepwise Regression** dialog box appears:
> > Enter Sales in the **Response** box
> > Enter Time, Poten, AdvExp, Share, Change, Accounts, Work, and Rating in the **Predictors** box
> > Select the **Methods** button
> **Step 5.** When the **Stepwise-Methods** dialog box appears:
> > Select **Stepwise (forward and backward)**
> > Enter .05 in the **Alpha to enter** box
> > Enter .05 in the **Alpha to remove** box
> > Click **OK**
> **Step 6.** When the **Stepwise Regression** dialog box reappears:
> > Click **OK**

Using Minitab's Forward Selection Procedure

To use Minitab's forward selection procedure, we simply modify step 5 in Minitab's stepwise regression procedure as shown here:

> **Step 5.** When the **Stepwise-Methods** dialog box appears:
> > Select **Forward selection**
> > Enter .05 in the **Alpha to enter** box
> > Click **OK**

Using Minitab's Backward Elimination Procedure

To use Minitab's backward elimination procedure, we simply modify step 5 in Minitab's stepwise regression procedure as shown here:

> **Step 5.** When the **Stepwise-Methods** dialog box appears:
> > Select **Backward elimination**
> > Enter .05 in the **Alpha to remove** box
> > Click **OK**

Using Minitab's Best-Subsets Procedure

The following steps can be used to produce the Minitab best-subsets regression output for the Craven data.

> **Step 1.** Select the **Stat** menu
> **Step 2.** Select the **Regression** menu
> **Step 3.** Choose **Best Subsets**
> **Step 4.** When the **Best Subsets Regression** dialog box appears:
> > Enter Sales in the **Response** box
> > Enter Time, Poten, AdvExp, Share, Change, Accounts, Work, and Rating in the **Predictors** box
> > Click **OK**

Appendix 16.2 Variable Selection Procedures Using StatTools

Cravens

In this appendix we show how StatTools can be used to perform three variable selection procedures: stepwise regression, forward selection, and backward elimination. First, we show how StatTools can provide the stepwise regression output for the Cravens problem.

Begin by using the Data Set Manager to create a StatTools data set for these data using the procedure described in the appendix in Chapter 1. The following steps describe how StatTools can be used to provide the stepwise regression results.

> **Step 1.** Click the **StatTools** tab on the Ribbon
> **Step 2.** In the **Analyses** group, click **Regression and Classification**
> **Step 3.** Choose the **Regression** option
> **Step 4.** When the StatTools-Regression dialog box appears:
> > Select **Stepwise** in the **Regression Type** box
> > In the **Variables** section:
> > > Click the **Format** button and select **Unstacked**
> > > In the column labeled **D** select **Sales**
> > > In the column labeled **I** select **Time, Poten, AdvExp, Share, Change, Accounts, Work,** and **Rating**
> > In the **Parameters** section:
> > > Select **Use p-Values**
> > > Enter .05 in the **p-Value to Enter** box
> > > Enter .05 in the **p-Value to Leave** box
> > In the **Advance Options** section, select **Include Detailed Step Information**
> > Click **OK**

The stepwise regression output for the Cravens problem will appear.

The StatTools-Regression dialog box contains a number of more advanced options for developing prediction interval estimates and producing residual plots. The StatTools Help facility provides information on using all these options. StatTools can also be used to perform the forward selection and backward elimination procedures. The steps required are very similar to the steps for the stepwise procedure. The major difference is that in step 4 you would select either Forward or Backward in the Regression Type box. If you choose Forward, you would enter a value in the p-Value to Enter box and if you choose Backward you would enter a value the p-Value to Leave box.

CHAPTER 17

Time Series Analysis and Forecasting

CONTENTS

STATISTICS IN PRACTICE:
NEVADA OCCUPATIONAL
HEALTH CLINIC

17.1 TIME SERIES PATTERNS
Horizontal Pattern
Trend Pattern
Seasonal Pattern
Trend and Seasonal Pattern
Cyclical Pattern
Selecting a Forecasting Method

17.2 FORECAST ACCURACY

17.3 MOVING AVERAGES AND
EXPONENTIAL SMOOTHING
Moving Averages
Weighted Moving Averages
Exponential Smoothing

17.4 TREND PROJECTION
Linear Trend Regression
Holt's Linear Exponential
Smoothing
Nonlinear Trend Regression

17.5 SEASONALITY AND TREND
Seasonality Without Trend
Seasonality and Trend
Models Based on Monthly Data

17.6 TIME SERIES
DECOMPOSITION
Calculating the Seasonal Indexes
Deseasonalizing the Time Series
Using the Deseasonalized Time
Series to Identify Trend
Seasonal Adjustments
Models Based on Monthly Data
Cyclical Component

NEVADA OCCUPATIONAL HEALTH CLINIC*
SPARKS, NEVADA

Nevada Occupational Health Clinic is a privately owned medical clinic in Sparks, Nevada. The clinic specializes in industrial medicine. Operating at the same site for more than 20 years, the clinic had been in a rapid growth phase. Monthly billings increased from $57,000 to more than $300,000 in 26 months, when the main clinic building burned to the ground.

The clinic's insurance policy covered physical property and equipment as well as loss of income due to the interruption of regular business operations. Settling the property insurance claim was a relatively straightforward matter of determining the value of the physical property and equipment lost during the fire. However, determining the value of the income lost during the seven months that it took to rebuild the clinic was a complicated matter involving negotiations between the business owners and the insurance company. No preestablished rules could help calculate "what would have happened" to the clinic's billings if the fire had not occurred. To estimate the lost income, the clinic used a forecasting method to project the growth in business that would have been realized during the seven-month lost-business period. The actual history of billings prior to the fire provided the basis for a forecasting model with linear trend

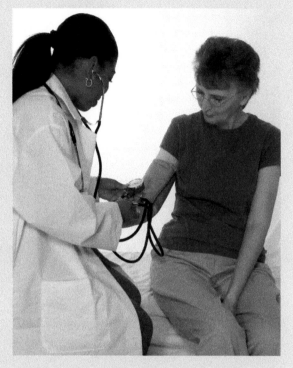

A physician checks a patient's blood pressure at the Nevada Occupational Health Clinic. © Bob Pardue–Medical Lifestyle/Alamy.

and seasonal components as discussed in this chapter. This forecasting model enabled the clinic to establish an accurate estimate of the loss, which was eventually accepted by the insurance company.

---

*The authors are indebted to Bard Betz, Director of Operations, and Curtis Brauer, Executive Administrative Assistant, Nevada Occupational Health Clinic, for providing this Statistics in Practice.

A forecast is simply a prediction of what will happen in the future. Managers must learn to accept that regardless of the technique used, they will not be able to develop perfect forecasts.

The purpose of this chapter is to provide an introduction to time series analysis and forecasting. Suppose we are asked to provide quarterly forecasts of sales for one of our company's products over the coming one-year period. Production schedules, raw material purchasing, inventory policies, and sales quotas will all be affected by the quarterly forecasts we provide. Consequently, poor forecasts may result in poor planning and increased costs for the company. How should we go about providing the quarterly sales forecasts? Good judgment, intuition, and an awareness of the state of the economy may give us a rough idea or "feeling" of what is likely to happen in the future, but converting that feeling into a number that can be used as next year's sales forecast is difficult.

Forecasting methods can be classified as qualitative or quantitative. Qualitative methods generally involve the use of expert judgment to develop forecasts. Such methods are appropriate when historical data on the variable being forecast are either not applicable or unavailable. Quantitative forecasting methods can be used when (1) past information about the variable being forecast is available, (2) the information can be quantified, and (3) it is reasonable to assume that the pattern of the past will continue into the future. In such cases, a forecast can be developed using a time series method or a causal method. We will focus exclusively on quantitative forecasting methods in this chapter.

If the historical data are restricted to past values of the variable to be forecast, the forecasting procedure is called a *time series method* and the historical data are referred to as a time series. The objective of time series analysis is to discover a pattern in the historical data or time series and then extrapolate the pattern into the future; the forecast is based solely on past values of the variable and/or on past forecast errors.

Causal forecasting methods are based on the assumption that the variable we are forecasting has a cause-effect relationship with one or more other variables. In the discussion of regression analysis in Chapters 14, 15, and 16, we showed how one or more independent variables could be used to predict the value of a single dependent variable. Looking at regression analysis as a forecasting tool, we can view the time series value that we want to forecast as the dependent variable. Hence, if we can identify a good set of related independent, or explanatory, variables, we may be able to develop an estimated regression equation for predicting or forecasting the time series. For instance, the sales for many products are influenced by advertising expenditures, so regression analysis may be used to develop an equation showing how sales and advertising are related. Once the advertising budget for the next period is determined, we could substitute this value into the equation to develop a prediction or forecast of the sales volume for that period. Note that if a time series method were used to develop the forecast, advertising expenditures would not be considered; that is, a time series method would base the forecast solely on past sales.

By treating time as the independent variable and the time series as a dependent variable, regression analysis can also be used as a time series method. To help differentiate the application of regression analysis in these two cases, we use the terms *cross-sectional regression* and *time series regression*. Thus, time series regression refers to the use of regression analysis when the independent variable is time. Because our focus in this chapter is on time series methods, we leave the discussion of the application of regression analysis as a causal forecasting method to more advanced texts on forecasting.

17.1 Time Series Patterns

Gasoline

A **time series** is a sequence of observations on a variable measured at successive points in time or over successive periods of time. The measurements may be taken every hour, day, week, month, or year, or at any other regular interval.[1] The pattern of the data is an important factor in understanding how the time series has behaved in the past. If such behavior can be expected to continue in the future, we can use the past pattern to guide us in selecting an appropriate forecasting method.

To identify the underlying pattern in the data, a useful first step is to construct a **time series plot**. A time series plot is a graphical presentation of the relationship between time and the time series variable; time is on the horizontal axis and the time series values are shown on the vertical axis. Let us review some of the common types of data patterns that can be identified when examining a time series plot.

Horizontal Pattern

A **horizontal pattern** exists when the data fluctuate around a constant mean. To illustrate a time series with a horizontal pattern, consider the 12 weeks of data in Table 17.1. These data

TABLE 17.1

GASOLINE SALES TIME SERIES

Week	Sales (1000s of gallons)
1	17
2	21
3	19
4	23
5	18
6	16
7	20
8	18
9	22
10	20
11	15
12	22

[1]We limit our discussion to time series in which the values of the series are recorded at equal intervals. Cases in which the observations are made at unequal intervals are beyond the scope of this text.

FIGURE 17.1   GASOLINE SALES TIME SERIES PLOT

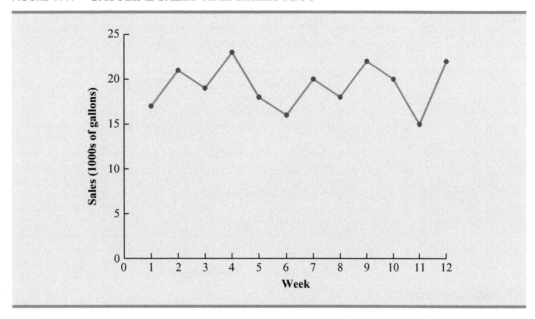

GasolineRevised

TABLE 17.2

GASOLINE SALES
TIME SERIES
AFTER OBTAINING
THE CONTRACT
WITH THE
VERMONT
STATE POLICE

Week	Sales (1000s of gallons)
1	17
2	21
3	19
4	23
5	18
6	16
7	20
8	18
9	22
10	20
11	15
12	22
13	31
14	34
15	31
16	33
17	28
18	32
19	30
20	29
21	34
22	33

show the number of gallons of gasoline sold by a gasoline distributor in Bennington, Vermont, over the past 12 weeks. The average value or mean for this time series is 19.25 or 19,250 gallons per week. Figure 17.1 shows a time series plot for these data. Note how the data fluctuate around the sample mean of 19,250 gallons. Although random variability is present, we would say that these data follow a horizontal pattern.

The term **stationary time series**[2] is used to denote a time series whose statistical properties are independent of time. In particular this means that

1. The process generating the data has a constant mean.
2. The variability of the time series is constant over time.

A time series plot for a stationary time series will always exhibit a horizontal pattern. But simply observing a horizontal pattern is not sufficient evidence to conclude that the time series is stationary. More advanced texts on forecasting discuss procedures for determining if a time series is stationary and provide methods for transforming a time series that is not stationary into a stationary series.

Changes in business conditions can often result in a time series that has a horizontal pattern shifting to a new level. For instance, suppose the gasoline distributor signs a contract with the Vermont State Police to provide gasoline for state police cars located in southern Vermont. With this new contract, the distributor expects to see a major increase in weekly sales starting in week 13. Table 17.2 shows the number of gallons of gasoline sold for the original time series and for the 10 weeks after signing the new contract. Figure 17.2 shows the corresponding time series plot. Note the increased level of the time series beginning in week 13. This change in the level of the time series makes it more difficult to choose an appropriate forecasting method. Selecting a forecasting method that adapts well to changes in the level of a time series is an important consideration in many practical applications.

[2]For a formal definition of stationary see G. E. P., Box, G. M. Jenkins, and G. C. Reinsell, *Time Series Analysis: Forecasting and Control*, 3rd ed. Englewood Cliffs, NJ: Prentice Hall, 1994, p. 23.

FIGURE 17.2 GASOLINE SALES TIME SERIES PLOT AFTER OBTAINING THE
CONTRACT WITH THE VERMONT STATE POLICE

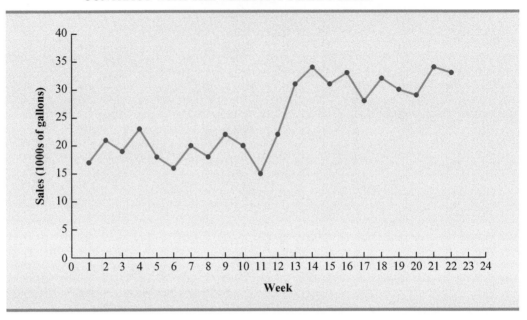

Trend Pattern

Bicycle

TABLE 17.3

BICYCLE SALES
TIME SERIES

Year	Sales (1000s)
1	21.6
2	22.9
3	25.5
4	21.9
5	23.9
6	27.5
7	31.5
8	29.7
9	28.6
10	31.4

Although time series data generally exhibit random fluctuations, a time series may also show gradual shifts or movements to relatively higher or lower values over a longer period of time. If a time series plot exhibits this type of behavior, we say that a **trend pattern** exists. A trend is usually the result of long-term factors such as population increases or decreases, changing demographic characteristics of the population, technology, and/or consumer preferences.

To illustrate a time series with a trend pattern, consider the time series of bicycle sales for a particular manufacturer over the past 10 years, as shown in Table 17.3 and Figure 17.3. Note that 21,600 bicycles were sold in year one, 22,900 were sold in year two, and so on. In year 10, the most recent year, 31,400 bicycles were sold. Visual inspection of the time series plot shows some up and down movement over the past 10 years, but the time series also seems to have a systematically increasing or upward trend.

The trend for the bicycle sales time series appears to be linear and increasing over time, but sometimes a trend can be described better by other types of patterns. For instance, the data in Table 17.4 and the corresponding time series plot in Figure 17.4 show the sales for a cholesterol drug since the company won FDA approval for it 10 years ago. The time series increases in a nonlinear fashion; that is, the rate of change of revenue does not increase by a constant amount from one year to the next. In fact, the revenue appears to be growing in an exponential fashion. Exponential relationships such as this are appropriate when the percentage change from one period to the next is relatively constant.

Seasonal Pattern

The trend of a time series can be identified by analyzing multiyear movements in historical data. Seasonal patterns are recognized by seeing the same repeating patterns over successive periods of time. For example, a manufacturer of swimming pools expects low sales activity in the fall and winter months, with peak sales in the spring and summer months. Manufacturers of snow removal equipment and heavy clothing, however, expect just the

FIGURE 17.3   BICYCLE SALES TIME SERIES PLOT

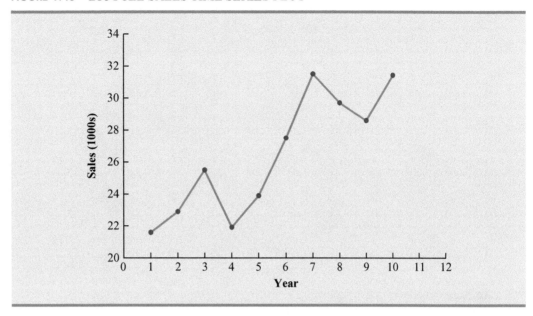

Cholesterol

TABLE 17.4

CHOLESTEROL
REVENUE
TIME SERIES
($MILLIONS)

Year	Revenue
1	23.1
2	21.3
3	27.4
4	34.6
5	33.8
6	43.2
7	59.5
8	64.4
9	74.2
10	99.3

opposite yearly pattern. Not surprisingly, the pattern for a time series plot that exhibits a repeating pattern over a one-year period due to seasonal influences is called a **seasonal pattern**. While we generally think of seasonal movement in a time series as occurring within one year, time series data can also exhibit seasonal patterns of less than one year in duration. For example, daily traffic volume shows within-the-day "seasonal" behavior, with peak levels occurring during rush hours, moderate flow during the rest of the day and early evening, and light flow from midnight to early morning.

As an example of a seasonal pattern, consider the number of umbrellas sold at a clothing store over the past five years. Table 17.5 shows the time series and Figure 17.5 shows the corresponding time series plot. The time series plot does not indicate any long-term trend in sales. In fact, unless you look carefully at the data, you might conclude that the data follow a horizontal pattern. But closer inspection of the time series plot reveals a regular pattern in the data. That is, the first and third quarters have moderate sales, the second quarter has the highest sales, and the fourth quarter tends to have the lowest sales volume. Thus, we would conclude that a quarterly seasonal pattern is present.

Trend and Seasonal Pattern

Some time series include a combination of a trend and seasonal pattern. For instance, the data in Table 17.6 and the corresponding time series plot in Figure 17.6 show television set sales for a particular manufacturer over the past four years. Clearly, an increasing trend is present. But, Figure 17.6 also indicates that sales are lowest in the second quarter of each year and increase in quarters 3 and 4. Thus, we conclude that a seasonal pattern also exists for television set sales. In such cases we need to use a forecasting method that has the capability to deal with both trend and seasonality.

Cyclical Pattern

A **cyclical pattern** exists if the time series plot shows an alternating sequence of points below and above the trend line lasting more than one year. Many economic time series exhibit

FIGURE 17.4   CHOLESTEROL REVENUE TIMES SERIES PLOT ($MILLIONS)

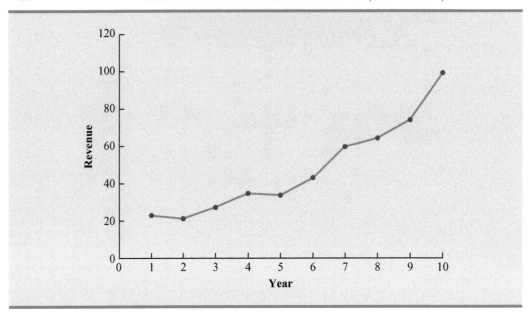

TABLE 17.5   UMBRELLA SALES TIME SERIES

WEB file

Umbrella

Year	Quarter	Sales
1	1	125
	2	153
	3	106
	4	88
2	1	118
	2	161
	3	133
	4	102
3	1	138
	2	144
	3	113
	4	80
4	1	109
	2	137
	3	125
	4	109
5	1	130
	2	165
	3	128
	4	96

cyclical behavior with regular runs of observations below and above the trend line. Often, the cyclical component of a time series is due to multiyear business cycles. For example, periods of moderate inflation followed by periods of rapid inflation can lead to time series that alternate below and above a generally increasing trend line (e.g., a time series for housing costs). Business cycles are extremely difficult, if not impossible, to forecast. As a

FIGURE 17.5   UMBRELLA SALES TIME SERIES PLOT

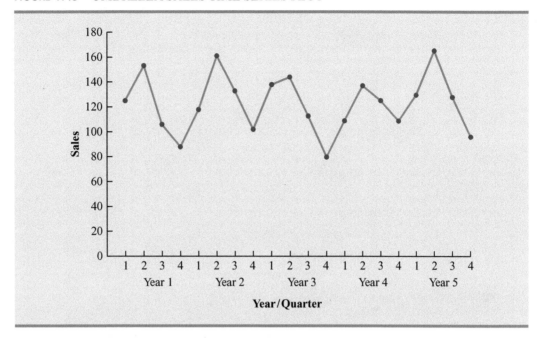

TABLE 17.6   QUARTERLY TELEVISION SET SALES TIME SERIES

TVSales

Year	Quarter	Sales (1000s)
1	1	4.8
	2	4.1
	3	6.0
	4	6.5
2	1	5.8
	2	5.2
	3	6.8
	4	7.4
3	1	6.0
	2	5.6
	3	7.5
	4	7.8
4	1	6.3
	2	5.9
	3	8.0
	4	8.4

result, cyclical effects are often combined with long-term trend effects and referred to as trend-cycle effects. In this chapter we do not deal with cyclical effects that may be present in the time series.

Selecting a Forecasting Method

The underlying pattern in the time series is an important factor in selecting a forecasting method. Thus, a time series plot should be one of the first things developed when trying to determine which forecasting method to use. If we see a horizontal pattern, then we need to

FIGURE 17.6   QUARTERLY TELEVISION SET SALES TIME SERIES PLOT

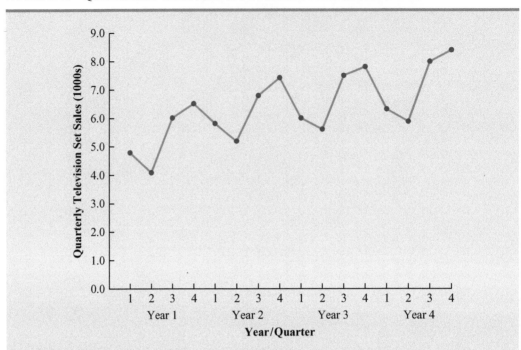

select a method appropriate for this type of pattern. Similarly, if we observe a trend in the data, then we need to use a forecasting method that has the capability to handle trend effectively. The next two sections illustrate methods that can be used in situations where the underlying pattern is horizontal; in other words, no trend or seasonal effects are present. We then consider methods appropriate when trend and/or seasonality are present in the data.

Forecast Accuracy

In this section we begin by developing forecasts for the gasoline time series shown in Table 17.1 using the simplest of all the forecasting methods: an approach that uses the most recent week's sales volume as the forecast for the next week. For instance, the distributor sold 17 thousand gallons of gasoline in week 1; this value is used as the forecast for week 2. Next, we use 21, the actual value of sales in week 2, as the forecast for week 3, and so on. The forecasts obtained for the historical data using this method are shown in Table 17.7 in the column labeled Forecast. Because of its simplicity, this method is often referred to as a *naive* forecasting method.

How accurate are the forecasts obtained using this *naive* forecasting method? To answer this question we will introduce several measures of forecast accuracy. These measures are used to determine how well a particular forecasting method is able to reproduce the time series data that are already available. By selecting the method that has the best accuracy for the data already known, we hope to increase the likelihood that we will obtain better forecasts for future time periods.

The key concept associated with measuring forecast accuracy is **forecast error**, defined as

$$\text{Forecast Error} = \text{Actual Value} - \text{Forecast}$$

TABLE 17.7   COMPUTING FORECASTS AND MEASURES OF FORECAST ACCURACY USING THE MOST RECENT VALUE AS THE FORECAST FOR THE NEXT PERIOD

Week	Time Series Value	Forecast	Forecast Error	Absolute Value of Forecast Error	Squared Forecast Error	Percentage Error	Absolute Value of Percentage Error
1	17						
2	21	17	4	4	16	19.05	19.05
3	19	21	−2	2	4	−10.53	10.53
4	23	19	4	4	16	17.39	17.39
5	18	23	−5	5	25	−27.78	27.78
6	16	18	−2	2	4	−12.50	12.50
7	20	16	4	4	16	20.00	20.00
8	18	20	−2	2	4	−11.11	11.11
9	22	18	4	4	16	18.18	18.18
10	20	22	−2	2	4	−10.00	10.00
11	15	20	−5	5	25	−33.33	33.33
12	22	15	7	7	49	31.82	31.82
		Totals	5	41	179	1.19	211.69

For instance, because the distributor actually sold 21 thousand gallons of gasoline in week 2 and the forecast, using the sales volume in week 1, was 17 thousand gallons, the forecast error in week 2 is

$$\text{Forecast Error in week 2} = 21 - 17 = 4$$

The fact that the forecast error is positive indicates that in week 2 the forecasting method underestimated the actual value of sales. Next, we use 21, the actual value of sales in week 2, as the forecast for week 3. Since the actual value of sales in week 3 is 19, the forecast error for week 3 is $19 - 21 = -2$. In this case, the negative forecast error indicates that in week 3 the forecast overestimated the actual value. Thus, the forecast error may be positive or negative, depending on whether the forecast is too low or too high. A complete summary of the forecast errors for this naive forecasting method is shown in Table 17.7 in the column labeled Forecast Error.

In regression analysis, a residual is defined as the difference between the observed value of the dependent variable and the estimated value. The forecast errors are analogous to the residuals in regression analysis.

A simple measure of forecast accuracy is the mean or average of the forecast errors. Table 17.7 shows that the sum of the forecast errors for the gasoline sales time series is 5; thus, the mean or average forecast error is 5/11 = .45. Note that although the gasoline time series consists of 12 values, to compute the mean error we divided the sum of the forecast errors by 11 because there are only 11 forecast errors. Because the mean forecast error is positive, the method is underforecasting; in other words, the observed values tend to be greater than the forecasted values. Because positive and negative forecast errors tend to offset one another, the mean error is likely to be small; thus, the mean error is not a very useful measure of forecast accuracy.

The **mean absolute error**, denoted MAE, is a measure of forecast accuracy that avoids the problem of positive and negative forecast errors offsetting one another. As you might expect given its name, MAE is the average of the absolute values of the forecast errors. Table 17.7 shows that the sum of the absolute values of the forecast errors is 41; thus,

$$\text{MAE} = \text{average of the absolute value of forecast errors} = \frac{41}{11} = 3.73$$

In regression analysis the mean square error (MSE) is the residual sum of squares divided by its degrees of freedom. In forecasting, MSE is the average of the sum of squared forecast errors.

Another measure that avoids the problem of positive and negative forecast errors offsetting each other is obtained by computing the average of the squared forecast errors. This measure of forecast accuracy, referred to as the **mean squared error**, is denoted MSE. From Table 17.7, the sum of the squared errors is 179; hence,

$$\text{MSE} = \text{average of the sum of squared forecast errors} = \frac{179}{11} = 16.27$$

The size of MAE and MSE depends upon the scale of the data. As a result, it is difficult to make comparisons for different time intervals, such as comparing a method of forecasting monthly gasoline sales to a method of forecasting weekly sales, or to make comparisons across different time series. To make comparisons like these we need to work with relative or percentage error measures. The **mean absolute percentage error**, denoted MAPE, is such a measure. To compute MAPE we must first compute the percentage error for each forecast. For example, the percentage error corresponding to the forecast of 17 in week 2 is computed by dividing the forecast error in week 2 by the actual value in week 2 and multiplying the result by 100. For week 2 the percentage error is computed as follows:

$$\text{Percentage error for week 2} = \frac{4}{21}(100) = 19.05\%$$

Thus, the forecast error for week 2 is 19.05% of the observed value in week 2. A complete summary of the percentage errors is shown in Table 17.7 in the column labeled Percentage Error. In the next column, we show the absolute value of the percentage error.

Table 17.7 shows that the sum of the absolute values of the percentage errors is 211.69; thus,

$$\text{MAPE} = \text{average of the absolute value of percentage forecast errors} = \frac{211.69}{11} = 19.24\%$$

Summarizing, using the naive (most recent observation) forecasting method, we obtained the following measures of forecast accuracy:

$$\text{MAE} = 3.73$$
$$\text{MSE} = 16.27$$
$$\text{MAPE} = 19.24\%$$

These measures of forecast accuracy simply measure how well the forecasting method is able to forecast historical values of the time series. Now, suppose we want to forecast sales for a future time period, such as week 13. In this case the forecast for week 13 is 22, the actual value of the time series in week 12. Is this an accurate estimate of sales for week 13? Unfortunately, there is no way to address the issue of accuracy associated with forecasts for future time periods. But, if we select a forecasting method that works well for the historical data, and we think that the historical pattern will continue into the future, we should obtain results that will ultimately be shown to be good.

Before closing this section, let's consider another method for forecasting the gasoline sales time series in Table 17.1. Suppose we use the average of all the historical data available as the forecast for the next period. We begin by developing a forecast for week 2. Since there is only one historical value available prior to week 2, the forecast for week 2 is just the time series value in week 1; thus, the forecast for week 2 is 17 thousand gallons of gasoline. To compute the forecast for week 3, we take the average of the sales values in weeks 1 and 2. Thus,

TABLE 17.8   COMPUTING FORECASTS AND MEASURES OF FORECAST ACCURACY USING THE AVERAGE OF ALL THE HISTORICAL DATA AS THE FORECAST FOR THE NEXT PERIOD

Week	Time Series Value	Forecast	Forecast Error	Absolute Value of Forecast Error	Squared Forecast Error	Percentage Error	Absolute Value of Percentage Error
1	17						
2	21	17.00	4.00	4.00	16.00	19.05	19.05
3	19	19.00	0.00	0.00	0.00	0.00	0.00
4	23	19.00	4.00	4.00	16.00	17.39	17.39
5	18	20.00	−2.00	2.00	4.00	−11.11	11.11
6	16	19.60	−3.60	3.60	12.96	−22.50	22.50
7	20	19.00	1.00	1.00	1.00	5.00	5.00
8	18	19.14	−1.14	1.14	1.31	−6.35	6.35
9	22	19.00	3.00	3.00	9.00	13.64	13.64
10	20	19.33	0.67	0.67	0.44	3.33	3.33
11	15	19.40	−4.40	4.40	19.36	−29.33	29.33
12	22	19.00	3.00	3.00	9.00	13.64	13.64
		Totals	4.53	26.81	89.07	2.76	141.34

$$\text{Forecast for week 3} = \frac{17 + 21}{2} = 19$$

Similarly, the forecast for week 4 is

$$\text{Forecast for week 4} = \frac{17 + 21 + 19}{3} = 19$$

The forecasts obtained using this method for the gasoline time series are shown in Table 17.8 in the column labeled Forecast. Using the results shown in Table 17.8, we obtained the following values of MAE, MSE, and MAPE:

$$\text{MAE} = \frac{26.81}{11} = 2.44$$

$$\text{MSE} = \frac{89.07}{11} = 8.10$$

$$\text{MAPE} = \frac{141.34}{11} = 12.85\%$$

We can now compare the accuracy of the two forecasting methods we have considered in this section by comparing the values of MAE, MSE, and MAPE for each method.

	Naive Method	Average of Past Values
MAE	3.73	2.44
MSE	16.27	8.10
MAPE	19.24%	12.85%

For every measure, the average of past values provides more accurate forecasts than using the most recent observation as the forecast for the next period. In general, if the underlying time series is stationary, the average of all the historical data will always provide the best results.

But suppose that the underlying time series is not stationary. In Section 17.1 we mentioned that changes in business conditions can often result in a time series that has a horizontal pattern shifting to a new level. We discussed a situation in which the gasoline distributor signed a contract with the Vermont State Police to provide gasoline for state police cars located in southern Vermont. Table 17.2 shows the number of gallons of gasoline sold for the original time series and the 10 weeks after signing the new contract, and Figure 17.2 shows the corresponding time series plot. Note the change in level in week 13 for the resulting time series. When a shift to a new level like this occurs, it takes a long time for the forecasting method that uses the average of all the historical data to adjust to the new level of the time series. But, in this case, the simple naive method adjusts very rapidly to the change in level because it uses the most recent observation available as the forecast.

Measures of forecast accuracy are important factors in comparing different forecasting methods, but we have to be careful not to rely upon them too heavily. Good judgment and knowledge about business conditions that might affect the forecast also have to be carefully considered when selecting a method. And historical forecast accuracy is not the only consideration, especially if the time series is likely to change in the future.

In the next section we will introduce more sophisticated methods for developing forecasts for a time series that exhibits a horizontal pattern. Using the measures of forecast accuracy developed here, we will be able to determine if such methods provide more accurate forecasts than we obtained using the simple approaches illustrated in this section. The methods that we will introduce also have the advantage of adapting well in situations where the time series changes to a new level. The ability of a forecasting method to adapt quickly to changes in level is an important consideration, especially in short-term forecasting situations.

Exercises

Methods

1. Consider the following time series data.

Week	1	2	3	4	5	6
Value	18	13	16	11	17	14

   Using the naive method (most recent value) as the forecast for the next week, compute the following measures of forecast accuracy.
   a. Mean absolute error.
   b. Mean squared error.
   c. Mean absolute percentage error.
   d. What is the forecast for week 7?

2. Refer to the time series data in exercise 1. Using the average of all the historical data as a forecast for the next period, compute the following measures of forecast accuracy.
   a. Mean absolute error.
   b. Mean squared error.
   c. Mean absolute percentage error.
   d. What is the forecast for week 7?

3. Exercises 1 and 2 used different forecasting methods. Which method appears to provide the more accurate forecasts for the historical data? Explain.

4. Consider the following time series data.

Month	1	2	3	4	5	6	7
Value	24	13	20	12	19	23	15

a. Compute MSE using the most recent value as the forecast for the next period. What is the forecast for month 8?
b. Compute MSE using the average of all the data available as the forecast for the next period. What is the forecast for month 8?
c. Which method appears to provide the better forecast?

17.3   Moving Averages and Exponential Smoothing

In this section we discuss three forecasting methods that are appropriate for a time series with a horizontal pattern: moving averages, weighted moving averages, and exponential smoothing. These methods also adapt well to changes in the level of a horizontal pattern such as we saw with the extended gasoline sales time series (Table 17.2 and Figure 17.2). However, without modification they are not appropriate when significant trend, cyclical, or seasonal effects are present. Because the objective of each of these methods is to "smooth out" the random fluctuations in the time series, they are referred to as smoothing methods. These methods are easy to use and generally provide a high level of accuracy for short-range forecasts, such as a forecast for the next time period.

Moving Averages

The **moving averages** method uses the average of the most recent k data values in the time series as the forecast for the next period. Mathematically, a moving average forecast of order k is as follows:

MOVING AVERAGE FORECAST OF ORDER k

$$F_{t+1} = \frac{\sum (\text{most recent } k \text{ data values})}{k} = \frac{Y_t + Y_{t-1} + \dots + Y_{t-k+1}}{k} \quad \textbf{(17.1)}$$

where

$$F_{t+1} = \text{forecast of the times series for period } t + 1$$
$$Y_t = \text{actual value of the time series in period } t$$

The term *moving* is used because every time a new observation becomes available for the time series, it replaces the oldest observation in the equation and a new average is computed. As a result, the average will change, or move, as new observations become available.

To illustrate the moving averages method, let us return to the gasoline sales data in Table 17.1 and Figure 17.1. The time series plot in Figure 17.1 indicates that the gasoline sales time series has a horizontal pattern. Thus, the smoothing methods of this section are applicable.

To use moving averages to forecast a time series, we must first select the order, or number of time series values, to be included in the moving average. If only the most recent values of the time series are considered relevant, a small value of k is preferred. If more past values are considered relevant, then a larger value of k is better. As mentioned earlier, a time series with a horizontal pattern can shift to a new level over time. A moving average will adapt to the new level of the series and resume providing good forecasts in k periods. Thus, a smaller value of k will track shifts in a time series more quickly. But larger values of k will be more effective in smoothing out the random fluctuations over time. So managerial judgment based on an understanding of the behavior of a time series is helpful in choosing a good value for k.

To illustrate how moving averages can be used to forecast gasoline sales, we will use a three-week moving average ($k = 3$). We begin by computing the forecast of sales in week 4 using the average of the time series values in weeks 1–3.

$$F_4 = \text{average of weeks 1–3} = \frac{17 + 21 + 19}{3} = 19$$

Thus, the moving average forecast of sales in week 4 is 19 or 19,000 gallons of gasoline. Because the actual value observed in week 4 is 23, the forecast error in week 4 is $23 - 19 = 4$.

Next, we compute the forecast of sales in week 5 by averaging the time series values in weeks 2–4.

$$F_5 = \text{average of weeks 2–4} = \frac{21 + 19 + 23}{3} = 21$$

Hence, the forecast of sales in week 5 is 21 and the error associated with this forecast is $18 - 21 = -3$. A complete summary of the three-week moving average forecasts for the gasoline sales time series is provided in Table 17.9. Figure 17.7 shows the original time series plot and the three-week moving average forecasts. Note how the graph of the moving average forecasts has tended to smooth out the random fluctuations in the time series.

TABLE 17.9   SUMMARY OF THREE-WEEK MOVING AVERAGE CALCULATIONS

Week	Time Series Value	Forecast	Forecast Error	Absolute Value of Forecast Error	Squared Forecast Error	Percentage Error	Absolute Value of Percentage Error
1	17						
2	21						
3	19						
4	23	19	4	4	16	17.39	17.39
5	18	21	−3	3	9	−16.67	16.67
6	16	20	−4	4	16	−25.00	25.00
7	20	19	1	1	1	5.00	5.00
8	18	18	0	0	0	0.00	0.00
9	22	18	4	4	16	18.18	18.18
10	20	20	0	0	0	0.00	0.00
11	15	20	−5	5	25	−33.33	33.33
12	22	19	3	3	9	13.64	13.64
		Totals	0	24	92	−20.79	129.21

FIGURE 17.7 GASOLINE SALES TIME SERIES PLOT AND THREE-WEEK MOVING AVERAGE FORECASTS

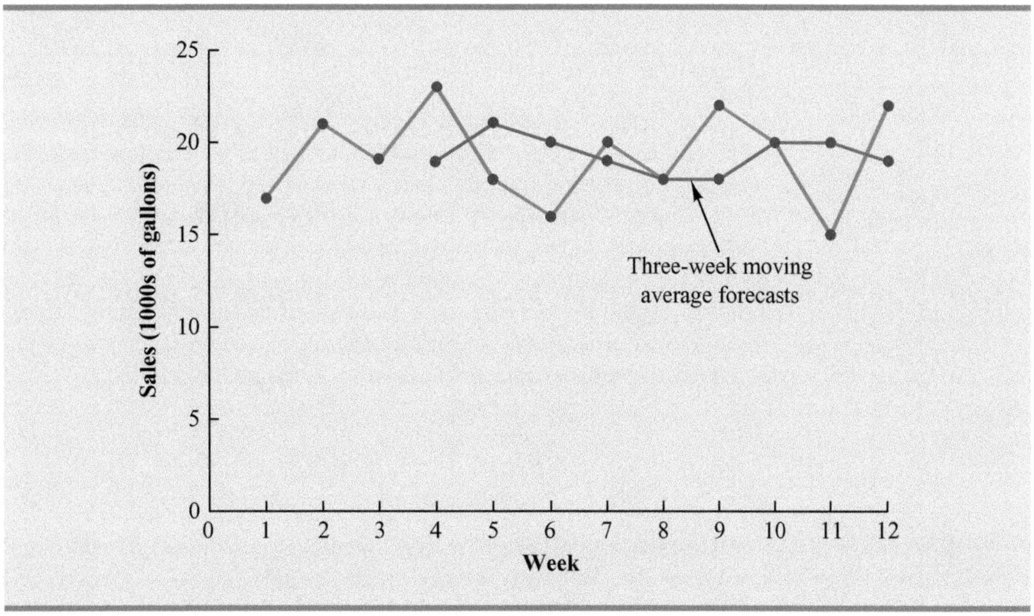

To forecast sales in week 13, the next time period in the future, we simply compute the average of the time series values in weeks 10, 11, and 12.

$$F_{13} = \text{average of weeks } 10\text{–}12 = \frac{20 + 15 + 22}{3} = 19$$

Thus, the forecast for week 13 is 19 or 19,000 gallons of gasoline.

Forecast accuracy In Section 17.2 we discussed three measures of forecast accuracy: MAE, MSE, and MAPE. Using the three-week moving average calculations in Table 17.9, the values for these three measures of forecast accuracy are

$$\text{MAE} = \frac{24}{9} = 2.67$$

$$\text{MSE} = \frac{92}{9} = 10.22$$

$$\text{MAPE} = \frac{129.21}{9} = 14.36\%$$

In situations where you need to compare forecasting methods for different time periods, such as comparing a forecast of weekly sales to a forecast of monthly sales, relative measures such as MAPE are preferred.

In Section 17.2 we also showed that using the most recent observation as the forecast for the next week (a moving average of order $k = 1$) resulted in values of MAE = 3.73, MSE = 16.27, and MAPE = 19.24%. Thus, in each case the three-week moving average approach provided more accurate forecasts than simply using the most recent observation as the forecast.

To determine if a moving average with a different order k can provide more accurate forecasts, we recommend using trial and error to determine the value of k that minimizes MSE. For the gasoline sales time series, it can be shown that the minimum value of MSE corresponds to a moving average of order $k = 6$ with MSE = 6.79. If we are willing to assume that the order of the moving average that is best for the historical data will also be best for future values of the time series, the most accurate moving average forecasts of gasoline sales can be obtained using a moving average of order $k = 6$.

Weighted Moving Averages

A moving average forecast of order $k = 3$ is just a special case of the weighted moving averages method in which each weight is equal to 1/3.

In the moving averages method, each observation in the moving average calculation receives the same weight. One variation, known as **weighted moving averages**, involves selecting a different weight for each data value and then computing a weighted average of the most recent k values as the forecast. In most cases, the most recent observation receives the most weight, and the weight decreases for older data values. Let us use the gasoline sales time series to illustrate the computation of a weighted three-week moving average. We assign a weight of 3/6 to the most recent observation, a weight of 2/6 to the second most recent observation, and a weight of 1/6 to the third most recent observation. Using this weighted average, our forecast for week 4 is computed as follows:

$$\text{Forecast for week 4} = \tfrac{1}{6}(17) + \tfrac{2}{6}(21) + \tfrac{3}{6}(19) = 19.33$$

Note that for the weighted moving average method the sum of the weights is equal to 1.

Forecast accuracy To use the weighted moving averages method, we must first select the number of data values to be included in the weighted moving average and then choose weights for each of the data values. In general, if we believe that the recent past is a better predictor of the future than the distant past, larger weights should be given to the more recent observations. However, when the time series is highly variable, selecting approximately equal weights for the data values may be best. The only requirement in selecting the weights is that their sum must equal 1. To determine whether one particular combination of number of data values and weights provides a more accurate forecast than another combination, we recommend using MSE as the measure of forecast accuracy. That is, if we assume that the combination that is best for the past will also be best for the future, we would use the combination of number of data values and weights that minimizes MSE for the historical time series to forecast the next value in the time series.

Exponential Smoothing

There are a number of exponential smoothing procedures. The method presented here is often referred to as single exponential smoothing. In the next section we show how an exponential smoothing method that uses two smoothing constants can be used to forecast a time series with a linear trend.

Exponential smoothing also uses a weighted average of past time series values as a forecast; it is a special case of the weighted moving averages method in which we select only one weight—the weight for the most recent observation. The weights for the other data values are computed automatically and become smaller as the observations move farther into the past. The exponential smoothing equation follows.

EXPONENTIAL SMOOTHING FORECAST

$$F_{t+1} = \alpha Y_t + (1 - \alpha)F_t \tag{17.2}$$

where

F_{t+1} = forecast of the time series for period $t + 1$
Y_t = actual value of the time series in period t
F_t = forecast of the time series for period t
α = smoothing constant $(0 \le \alpha \le 1)$

Equation (17.2) shows that the forecast for period $t + 1$ is a weighted average of the actual value in period t and the forecast for period t. The weight given to the actual value in period t is the **smoothing constant** α and the weight given to the forecast in period t is $1 - \alpha$. It turns out that the exponential smoothing forecast for any period is actually a weighted average of *all the previous actual values* of the time series. Let us illustrate by working with a time series involving only three periods of data: Y_1, Y_2, and Y_3.

To initiate the calculations, we let F_1 equal the actual value of the time series in period 1; that is, $F_1 = Y_1$. Hence, the forecast for period 2 is

$$\begin{aligned} F_2 &= \alpha Y_1 + (1 - \alpha)F_1 \\ &= \alpha Y_1 + (1 - \alpha)Y_1 \\ &= Y_1 \end{aligned}$$

We see that the exponential smoothing forecast for period 2 is equal to the actual value of the time series in period 1.

The forecast for period 3 is

$$F_3 = \alpha Y_2 + (1 - \alpha)F_2 = \alpha Y_2 + (1 - \alpha)Y_1$$

Finally, substituting this expression for F_3 in the expression for F_4, we obtain

$$\begin{aligned} F_4 &= \alpha Y_3 + (1 - \alpha)F_3 \\ &= \alpha Y_3 + (1 - \alpha)[\alpha Y_2 + (1 - \alpha)Y_1] \\ &= \alpha Y_3 + \alpha(1 - \alpha)Y_2 + (1 - \alpha)^2 Y_1 \end{aligned}$$

The term exponential smoothing comes from the exponential nature of the weighting scheme for the historical values.

We now see that F_4 is a weighted average of the first three time series values. The sum of the coefficients, or weights, for Y_1, Y_2, and Y_3 equals 1. A similar argument can be made to show that, in general, any forecast F_{t+1} is a weighted average of all the previous time series values.

Despite the fact that exponential smoothing provides a forecast that is a weighted average of all past observations, all past data do not need to be saved to compute the forecast for the next period. In fact, equation (17.2) shows that once the value for the smoothing constant α is selected, only two pieces of information are needed to compute the forecast: Y_t, the actual value of the time series in period t, and F_t, the forecast for period t.

To illustrate the exponential smoothing approach, let us again consider the gasoline sales time series in Table 17.1 and Figure 17.1. As indicated previously, to start the calculations we set the exponential smoothing forecast for period 2 equal to the actual value of the time series in period 1. Thus, with $Y_1 = 17$, we set $F_2 = 17$ to initiate the computations. Referring to the time series data in Table 17.1, we find an actual time series value in period 2 of $Y_2 = 21$. Thus, period 2 has a forecast error of $21 - 17 = 4$.

Continuing with the exponential smoothing computations using a smoothing constant of $\alpha = .2$, we obtain the following forecast for period 3:

$$F_3 = .2Y_2 + .8F_2 = .2(21) + .8(17) = 17.8$$

Once the actual time series value in period 3, $Y_3 = 19$, is known, we can generate a forecast for period 4 as follows:

$$F_4 = .2Y_3 + .8F_3 = .2(19) + .8(17.8) = 18.04$$

Continuing the exponential smoothing calculations, we obtain the weekly forecast values shown in Table 17.10. Note that we have not shown an exponential smoothing forecast

TABLE 17.10 SUMMARY OF THE EXPONENTIAL SMOOTHING FORECASTS
AND FORECAST ERRORS FOR THE GASOLINE SALES TIME SERIES
WITH SMOOTHING CONSTANT $\alpha = .2$

Week	Time Series Value	Forecast	Forecast Error	Squared Forecast Error
1	17			
2	21	17.00	4.00	16.00
3	19	17.80	1.20	1.44
4	23	18.04	4.96	24.60
5	18	19.03	−1.03	1.06
6	16	18.83	−2.83	8.01
7	20	18.26	1.74	3.03
8	18	18.61	−0.61	0.37
9	22	18.49	3.51	12.32
10	20	19.19	0.81	0.66
11	15	19.35	−4.35	18.92
12	22	18.48	3.52	12.39
		Totals	10.92	98.80

or a forecast error for week 1 because no forecast was made. For week 12, we have $Y_{12} = 22$ and $F_{12} = 18.48$. We can we use this information to generate a forecast for week 13.

$$F_{13} = .2Y_{12} + .8F_{12} = .2(22) + .8(18.48) = 19.18$$

Thus, the exponential smoothing forecast of the amount sold in week 13 is 19.18, or 19,180 gallons of gasoline. With this forecast, the firm can make plans and decisions accordingly.

Figure 17.8 shows the time series plot of the actual and forecast time series values. Note in particular how the forecasts "smooth out" the irregular or random fluctuations in the time series.

Forecast accuracy In the preceding exponential smoothing calculations, we used a smoothing constant of $\alpha = .2$. Although any value of α between 0 and 1 is acceptable, some values will yield better forecasts than others. Insight into choosing a good value for α can be obtained by rewriting the basic exponential smoothing model as follows:

$$F_{t+1} = \alpha Y_t + (1 - \alpha)F_t$$
$$F_{t+1} = \alpha Y_t + F_t - \alpha F_t$$
$$F_{t+1} = F_t + \alpha(Y_t - F_t) \tag{17.3}$$

Thus, the new forecast F_{t+1} is equal to the previous forecast F_t plus an adjustment, which is the smoothing constant α times the most recent forecast error, $Y_t - F_t$. That is, the forecast in period $t + 1$ is obtained by adjusting the forecast in period t by a fraction of the forecast error. If the time series contains substantial random variability, a small value of the smoothing constant is preferred. The reason for this choice is that if much of the forecast error is due to random variability, we do not want to overreact and adjust the forecasts too quickly. For a time series with relatively little random variability, forecast errors are more likely to represent a change in the level of the series. Thus, larger values of the smoothing

FIGURE 17.8   ACTUAL AND FORECAST GASOLINE SALES TIME SERIES
WITH SMOOTHING CONSTANT $\alpha = .2$

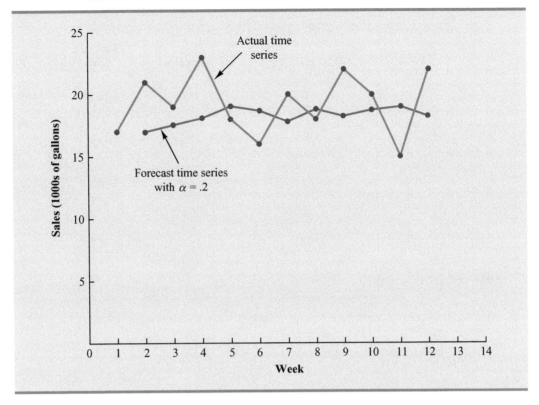

constant provide the advantage of quickly adjusting the forecasts; this allows the forecasts to react more quickly to changing conditions.

The criterion we will use to determine a desirable value for the smoothing constant α is the same as the criterion we proposed for determining the order or number of periods of data to include in the moving averages calculation. That is, we choose the value of α that minimizes the MSE. A summary of the MSE calculations for the exponential smoothing forecast of gasoline sales with $\alpha = .2$ is shown in Table 17.10. Note that there is one less squared error term than the number of time periods because we had no past values with which to make a forecast for period 1. The value of the sum of squared forecast errors is 98.80; hence MSE = 98.80/11 = 8.98. Would a different value of α provide better results in terms of a lower MSE value? Perhaps the most straightforward way to answer this question is simply to try another value for α. We will then compare its mean squared error with the MSE value of 8.98 obtained by using a smoothing constant of $\alpha = .2$.

The exponential smoothing results with $\alpha = .3$ are shown in Table 17.11. The value of the sum of squared forecast errors is 102.83; hence MSE = 102.83/11 = 9.35. With MSE = 9.35, we see that, for the current data set, a smoothing constant of $\alpha = .3$ results in less forecast accuracy than a smoothing constant of $\alpha = .2$. Thus, we would be inclined to prefer the original smoothing constant of $\alpha = .2$. Using a trial-and-error calculation with other values of α, we can find a "good" value for the smoothing constant. This value can be used in the exponential smoothing model to provide forecasts for the future. At a later date, after new time series observations are obtained, we analyze the newly collected time series data to determine whether the smoothing constant should be revised to provide better forecasting results.

TABLE 17.11   SUMMARY OF THE EXPONENTIAL SMOOTHING FORECASTS AND
FORECAST ERRORS FOR THE GASOLINE SALES TIME SERIES WITH
SMOOTHING CONSTANT $\alpha = .3$

Week	Time Series Value	Forecast	Forecast Error	Squared Forecast Error
1	17			
2	21	17.00	4.00	16.00
3	19	18.20	0.80	0.64
4	23	18.44	4.56	20.79
5	18	19.81	−1.81	3.28
6	16	19.27	−3.27	10.69
7	20	18.29	1.71	2.92
8	18	18.80	−0.80	0.64
9	22	18.56	3.44	11.83
10	20	19.59	0.41	0.17
11	15	19.71	−4.71	22.18
12	22	18.30	3.70	13.69
		Totals	8.03	102.83

NOTES AND COMMENTS

1. Spreadsheet packages are an effective aid in choosing a good value of α for exponential smoothing. With the time series data and the forecasting formulas in a spreadsheet, you can experiment with different values of α and choose the value that provides the smallest forecast error using one or more of the measures of forecast accuracy (MAE, MSE, or MAPE).

2. We presented the moving average and exponential smoothing methods in the context of a stationary time series. These methods can also be used to forecast a nonstationary time series which shifts in level but exhibits no trend or seasonality. Moving averages with small values of k adapt more quickly than moving averages with larger values of k. Exponential smoothing models with smoothing constants closer to one adapt more quickly than models with smaller values of the smoothing constant.

Exercises

Methods

5. Consider the following time series data.

Week	1	2	3	4	5	6
Value	18	13	16	11	17	14

a. Construct a time series plot. What type of pattern exists in the data?

b. Develop the three-week moving average forecasts for this time series. Compute MSE and a forecast for week 7.

c. Use $\alpha = .2$ to compute the exponential smoothing forecasts for the time series. Compute MSE and a forecast for week 7.

    d.   Compare the three-week moving average approach with the exponential smoothing approach using $\alpha = .2$. Which appears to provide more accurate forecasts based on MSE? Explain.

    e.   Use a smoothing constant of $\alpha = .4$ to compute the exponential smoothing forecasts. Does a smoothing constant of .2 or .4 appear to provide more accurate forecasts based on MSE? Explain.

6.   Consider the following time series data.

Month	1	2	3	4	5	6	7
Value	24	13	20	12	19	23	15

   Construct a time series plot. What type of pattern exists in the data?

    a.   Develop the three-week moving average forecasts for this time series. Compute MSE and a forecast for week 8.

    b.   Use $\alpha = .2$ to compute the exponential smoothing forecasts for the time series. Compute MSE and a forecast for week 8.

    c.   Compare the three-week moving average approach with the exponential smoothing approach using $\alpha = .2$. Which appears to provide more accurate forecasts based on MSE?

    d.   Use a smoothing constant of $\alpha = .4$ to compute the exponential smoothing forecasts. Does a smoothing constant of .2 or .4 appear to provide more accurate forecasts based on MSE? Explain.

WEB file

Gasoline

7.   Refer to the gasoline sales time series data in Table 17.1.

    a.   Compute four-week and five-week moving averages for the time series.

    b.   Compute the MSE for the four-week and five-week moving average forecasts.

    c.   What appears to be the best number of weeks of past data (three, four, or five) to use in the moving average computation? Recall that MSE for the three-week moving average is 10.22.

WEB file

Gasoline

8.   Refer again to the gasoline sales time series data in Table 17.1.

    a.   Using a weight of 1/2 for the most recent observation, 1/3 for the second most recent observation, and 1/6 for third most recent observation, compute a three-week weighted moving average for the time series.

    b.   Compute the MSE for the weighted moving average in part (a). Do you prefer this weighted moving average to the unweighted moving average? Remember that the MSE for the unweighted moving average is 10.22.

    c.   Suppose you are allowed to choose any weights as long as they sum to 1. Could you always find a set of weights that would make the MSE at least as small for a weighted moving average than for an unweighted moving average? Why or why not?

WEB file

Gasoline

9.   With the gasoline time series data from Table 17.1, show the exponential smoothing forecasts using $\alpha = .1$.

    a.   Applying the MSE measure of forecast accuracy, would you prefer a smoothing constant of $\alpha = .1$ or $\alpha = .2$ for the gasoline sales time series?

    b.   Are the results the same if you apply MAE as the measure of accuracy?

    c.   What are the results if MAPE is used?

10.   With a smoothing constant of $\alpha = .2$, equation (17.2) shows that the forecast for week 13 of the gasoline sales data from Table 17.1 is given by $F_{13} = .2Y_{12} + .8F_{12}$. However, the forecast for week 12 is given by $F_{12} = .2Y_{11} + .8F_{11}$. Thus, we could combine these two results to show that the forecast for week 13 can be written

$$F_{13} = .2Y_{12} + .8(.2Y_{11} + .8F_{11}) = .2Y_{12} + .16Y_{11} + .64Y_{11} + .64F_{11}$$

    a.   Making use of the fact that $F_{11} = .2Y_{10} + .8F_{10}$ (and similarly for F_{10} and F_9), continue to expand the expression for F_{13} until it is written in terms of the past data values Y_{12}, Y_{11}, Y_{10}, Y_9, Y_8, and the forecast for period 8.

    b.   Refer to the coefficients or weights for the past values Y_{12}, Y_{11}, Y_{10}, Y_9, Y_8. What observation can you make about how exponential smoothing weights past data values in arriving at new forecasts? Compare this weighting pattern with the weighting pattern of the moving averages method.

Applications

11.   For the Hawkins Company, the monthly percentages of all shipments received on time over the past 12 months are 80, 82, 84, 83, 83, 84, 85, 84, 82, 83, 84, and 83.
    a.   Construct a time series plot. What type of pattern exists in the data?
    b.   Compare the three-month moving average approach with the exponential smoothing approach for $\alpha = .2$. Which provides more accurate forecasts using MSE as the measure of forecast accuracy?
    c.   What is the forecast for next month?

12.   Corporate triple-A bond interest rates for 12 consecutive months follow.

      9.5   9.3   9.4   9.6   9.8   9.7   9.8   10.5   9.9   9.7   9.6   9.6

    a.   Construct a time series plot. What type of pattern exists in the data?
    b.   Develop three-month and four-month moving averages for this time series. Does the three-month or four-month moving average provide more accurate forecasts based on MSE? Explain.
    c.   What is the moving average forecast for the next month?

13.   The values of Alabama building contracts (in $ millions) for a 12-month period follow.

      240   350   230   260   280   320   220   310   240   310   240   230

    a.   Construct a time series plot. What type of pattern exists in the data?
    b.   Compare the three-month moving average approach with the exponential smoothing forecast using $\alpha = .2$. Which provides more accurate forecasts based on MSE?
    c.   What is the forecast for the next month?

14.   The following time series shows the sales of a particular product over the past 12 months.

ProductSales

Month	Sales	Month	Sales
1	105	7	145
2	135	8	140
3	120	9	100
4	105	10	80
5	90	11	100
6	120	12	110

    a.   Construct a time series plot. What type of pattern exists in the data?
    b.   Use $\alpha = .3$ to compute the exponential smoothing forecasts for the time series.
    c.   Use a smoothing constant of $\alpha = .5$ to compute the exponential smoothing forecasts. Does a smoothing constant of .3 or .5 appear to provide more accurate forecasts based on MSE?

15.   Ten weeks of data on the Commodity Futures Index are 7.35, 7.40, 7.55, 7.56, 7.60, 7.52, 7.52, 7.70, 7.62, and 7.55.
    a.   Construct a time series plot. What type of pattern exists in the data?
    b.   Compute the exponential smoothing forecasts for $\alpha = .2$.
    c.   Compute the exponential smoothing forecasts for $\alpha = .3$.
    d.   Which exponential smoothing constant provides more accurate forecasts based on MSE? Forecast week 11.

16. The U.S. Census Bureau tracks the median price for new home sales by month of year. The median prices for April for the years 1990 to 2011 follow (U.S. Census Bureau website, April 16, 2012).

HomePrices

Year	Price ($1000s)	Year	Price ($1000s)
1990	130.0	2001	175.2
1991	121.0	2002	187.1
1992	120.0	2003	189.5
1993	127.0	2004	222.3
1994	129.0	2005	236.3
1995	134.0	2006	257.0
1996	140.0	2007	242.5
1997	150.0	2008	246.4
1998	148.0	2009	219.2
1999	159.9	2010	208.3
2000	162.6	2011	224.7

a. Construct a time series plot. Comment on any pattern you observe. Discuss some of the factors that may have resulted in this time series plot.
b. Given the time series plot in part (a), do you think the forecasting methods developed in this section are appropriate for this time series? Explain.
c. To forecast a value for April 2012, how much of the past data would you use? Explain.

(17.4) Trend Projection

We present three forecasting methods in this section that are appropriate for time series exhibiting a trend pattern. First, we show how simple linear regression can be used to forecast a time series with a linear trend. We then illustrate how to develop forecasts using Holt's linear exponential smoothing, an extension of single exponential smoothing that uses two smoothing constants: one to account for the level of the time series and a second to account for the linear trend in the data. Finally, we show how the curve-fitting capability of regression analysis can also be used to forecast time series with a curvilinear or nonlinear trend.

Bicycle

Linear Trend Regression

TABLE 17.12

BICYCLE SALES TIME SERIES

Year	Sales (1000s)
1	21.6
2	22.9
3	25.5
4	21.9
5	23.9
6	27.5
7	31.5
8	29.7
9	28.6
10	31.4

In Section 17.1 we used the bicycle sales time series in Table 17.3 and Figure 17.3 to illustrate a time series with a trend pattern. Let us now use this time series to illustrate how simple linear regression can be used to forecast a time series with a linear trend. The data for the bicycle time series are repeated in Table 17.12 and Figure 17.9.

Although the time series plot in Figure 17.9 shows some up and down movement over the past 10 years, we might agree that the linear trend line shown in Figure 17.10 provides a reasonable approximation of the long-run movement in the series. We can use the methods of simple linear regression (see Chapter 14) to develop such a linear trend line for the bicycle sales time series.

In Chapter 14, the estimated regression equation describing a straight-line relationship between an independent variable x and a dependent variable y is written as

$$\hat{y} = b_0 + b_1 x$$

FIGURE 17.9   BICYCLE SALES TIME SERIES PLOT

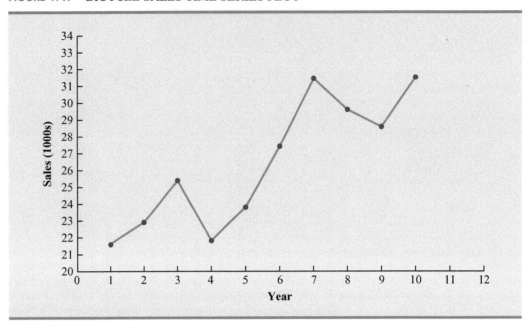

FIGURE 17.10   TREND REPRESENTED BY A LINEAR FUNCTION FOR THE BICYCLE SALES TIME SERIES

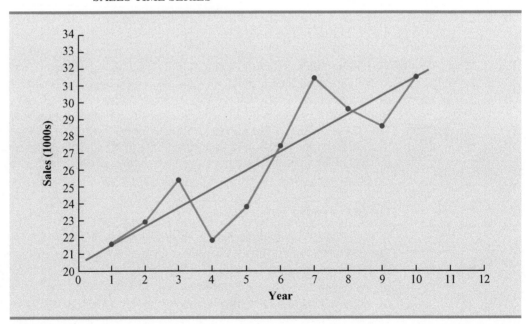

where $\hat{y}$ is the estimated or predicted value of y. To emphasize the fact that in forecasting the independent variable is time, we will replace x with t and $\hat{y}$ with T_t to emphasize that we are estimating the trend for a time series. Thus, for estimating the linear trend in a time series we will use the following estimated regression equation.

LINEAR TREND EQUATION

$$T_t = b_0 + b_1 t \qquad (17.4)$$

where

$$T_t = \text{linear trend forecast in period } t$$
$$b_0 = \text{intercept of the linear trend line}$$
$$b_1 = \text{slope of the linear trend line}$$
$$t = \text{time period}$$

In equation (17.4), the time variable begins at $t = 1$ corresponding to the first time series observation (year 1 for the bicycle sales time series) and continues until $t = n$ corresponding to the most recent time series observation (year 10 for the bicycle sales time series). Thus, for the bicycle sales time series $t = 1$ corresponds to the oldest time series value and $t = 10$ corresponds to the most recent year.

Formulas for computing the estimated regression coefficients (b_1 and b_0) in equation (17.4) follow.

COMPUTING THE SLOPE AND INTERCEPT FOR A LINEAR TREND*

$$b_1 = \frac{\sum_{t=1}^{n}(t - \bar{t})(Y_t - \bar{Y})}{\sum_{t=1}^{n}(t - \bar{t})^2} \qquad (17.5)$$

$$b_0 = \bar{Y} - b_1\bar{t} \qquad (17.6)$$

where

$$Y_t = \text{value of the time series in period } t$$
$$n = \text{number of time periods (number of observations)}$$
$$\bar{Y} = \text{average value of the time series}$$
$$\bar{t} = \text{average value of } t$$

---

*An alternate formula for b_1 is

$$b_1 = \frac{\sum_{t=1}^{n} t Y_t - \left(\sum_{t=1}^{n} t \sum_{t=1}^{n} Y_t\right)/n}{\sum_{t=1}^{n} t^2 - \left(\sum_{t=1}^{n} t\right)^2/n}$$

This form of equation (17.5) is often recommended when using a calculator to compute b_1.

To compute the linear trend equation for the bicycle sales time series, we begin the calculations by computing $\bar{t}$ and $\bar{Y}$ using the information in Table 17.12.

$$\bar{t} = \frac{\sum_{t=1}^{n} t}{n} = \frac{55}{10} = 5.5$$

$$\bar{Y} = \frac{\sum_{t=1}^{n} Y_t}{n} = \frac{264.5}{10} = 26.45$$

TABLE 17.13 SUMMARY OF LINEAR TREND CALCULATIONS FOR THE BICYCLE SALES TIME SERIES

t	Y_t	$t - \bar{t}$	$Y_t - \bar{Y}$	$(t - \bar{t})(Y_t - \bar{Y})$	$(t - \bar{t})^2$
1	21.6	−4.5	−4.85	21.825	20.25
2	22.9	−3.5	−3.55	12.425	12.25
3	25.5	−2.5	−0.95	2.375	6.25
4	21.9	−1.5	−4.55	6.825	2.25
5	23.9	−0.5	−2.55	1.275	0.25
6	27.5	0.5	1.05	0.525	0.25
7	31.5	1.5	5.05	7.575	2.25
8	29.7	2.5	3.25	8.125	6.25
9	28.6	3.5	2.15	7.525	12.25
10	31.4	4.5	4.95	22.275	20.25
Totals 55	264.5			90.750	82.50

Using these values, and the information in Table 17.13, we can compute the slope and intercept of the trend line for the bicycle sales time series.

$$b_1 = \frac{\sum_{t=1}^{n}(t - \bar{t})(Y_t - \bar{Y})}{\sum_{t=1}^{n}(t - \bar{t})^2} = \frac{90.75}{82.5} = 1.1$$

$$b_0 = \bar{Y} - b_1\bar{t} = 26.45 - 1.1(5.5) = 20.4$$

Therefore, the linear trend equation is

$$T_t = 20.4 + 1.1t$$

The slope of 1.1 indicates that over the past 10 years the firm experienced an average growth in sales of about 1100 units per year. If we assume that the past 10-year trend in sales is a good indicator of the future, this trend equation can be used to develop forecasts for future time periods. For example, substituting $t = 11$ into the equation yields next year's trend projection or forecast, T_{11}.

$$T_{11} = 20.4 + 1.1(11) = 32.5$$

Thus, using trend projection, we would forecast sales of 32,500 bicycles next year.

To compute the accuracy associated with the trend projection forecasting method, we will use the MSE. Table 17.14 shows the computation of the sum of squared errors for the bicycle sales time series. Thus, for the bicycle sales time series,

$$\text{MSE} = \frac{\sum_{t=1}^{n}(Y_t - F_t)^2}{n} = \frac{30.7}{10} = 3.07$$

Because linear trend regression in forecasting uses the same regression analysis procedure introduced in Chapter 14, we can use the standard regression analysis procedures in Minitab or Excel to perform the calculations. Figure 17.11 shows the computer output for the bicycle sales time series obtained using Minitab's regression analysis module.

TABLE 17.14   SUMMARY OF THE LINEAR TREND FORECASTS AND FORECAST
ERRORS FOR THE BICYCLE SALES TIME SERIES

Year	Sales (1000s) Y_t	Forecast T_t	Forecast Error	Squared Forecast Error
1	21.6	21.5	0.1	0.01
2	22.9	22.6	0.3	0.09
3	25.5	23.7	1.8	3.24
4	21.9	24.8	−2.9	8.41
5	23.9	25.9	−2.0	4.00
6	27.5	27.0	0.5	0.25
7	31.5	28.1	3.4	11.56
8	29.7	29.2	0.5	0.25
9	28.6	30.3	−1.7	2.89
10	31.4	31.4	0.0	0.00
			Total	30.70

In Figure 17.11 the value of MSE in the ANOVA table is

$$\text{MSE} = \frac{\text{Sum of Squares Due to Error}}{\text{Degrees of Freedom}} = \frac{30.7}{8} = 3.837$$

MSD in Minitab's Trend Analysis output is the mean squared deviation, the average of the squared forecast errors.

This value of MSE differs from the value of MSE that we computed previously because the sum of squared errors is divided by 8 instead of 10; thus, MSE in the regression output is not the average of the squared forecast errors. Most forecasting packages, however, compute MSE by taking the average of the squared errors. Thus, when using time series packages to develop a trend equation, the value of MSE that is reported may differ slightly from the value you would obtain using a general regression approach. For instance, in Figure 17.12, we show the graphical portion of the computer output obtained using Minitab's Trend Analysis time series procedure. Note that MSD = 3.07 is the average of the squared forecast errors.

FIGURE 17.11   MINITAB REGRESSION OUTPUT FOR THE BICYCLE SALES
TIME SERIES

```
The regression equation is
Y = 20.4 + 1.10 t

Predictor     Coef     SE Coef       T        p
Constant    20.400       1.338    15.24    0.000
t            1.1000      0.2157     5.10    0.001

S = 1.95895    R-sq = 76.5%    R-sq(adj) = 73.5%

Analysis of Variance

SOURCE          DF         SS       MS        F        p
Regression       1     99.825   99.825    26.01    0.001
Residual Error   8     30.700    3.837
Total            9    130.525
```

FIGURE 17.12   MINITAB TIME SERIES LINEAR TREND ANALYSIS OUTPUT
FOR THE BICYCLE SALES TIME SERIES

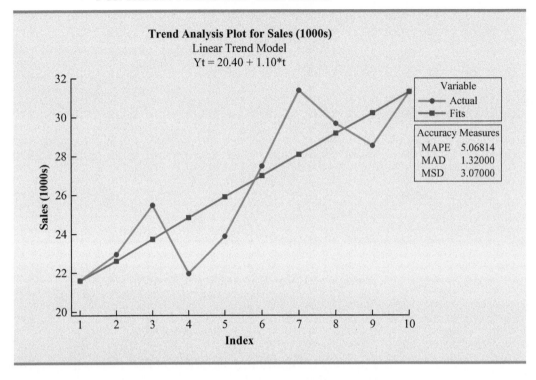

Holt's Linear Exponential Smoothing

Charles Holt developed a version of exponential smoothing that can be used to forecast a time
series with a linear trend. Recall that the exponential smoothing procedure discussed in Section 17.3 uses the smoothing constant α to "smooth out" the randomness or irregular fluctuations in a time series; and, forecasts for time period $t + 1$ are obtained using the equation

*Holt's linear exponential
smoothing is often called
double exponential
smoothing.*

$$F_{t+1} = \alpha Y_t + (1 - \alpha)F_t$$

Forecasts for Holt's **linear exponential smoothing** method are obtained using two smoothing constants, α and β, and three equations.

EQUATIONS FOR HOLT'S LINEAR EXPONENTIAL SMOOTHING

$$L_t = \alpha Y_t + (1 - \alpha)(L_{t-1} + b_{t-1}) \tag{17.7}$$
$$b_t = \beta(L_t - L_{t-1}) + (1 - \beta)\, b_{t-1} \tag{17.8}$$
$$F_{t+k} = L_t + b_t\, k \tag{17.9}$$

where

L_t = estimate of the level of the time series in period t

b_t = estimate of the slope of the time series in period t

α = smoothing constant for the level of the time series

β = smoothing constant for the slope of the time series
F_{t+k} = forecast for k periods ahead
k = the number of periods ahead to be forecast

Let us apply Holt's method to the bicycle sales time series in Table 17.12 using $\alpha = .1$ and $\beta = .2$. To get the method started, we need values for L_1, the estimate of the level of the time series in year 1, and b_1, the estimate of the slope of the time series in year 1. A commonly used approach is to set $L_1 = Y_1$ and $b_1 = Y_2 - Y_1$. Using this startup procedure, we obtain

$$L_1 = Y_1 = 21.6$$
$$b_1 = Y_2 - Y_1 = 22.9 - 21.6 = 1.3$$

Using equation (17.9) with $k = 1$, the forecast of sales in year 2 is $F_2 = L_1 + b_1 = 21.6 + 1.3(1) = 22.9$. Then we move on using equations (17.7) to (17.9) to compute estimates of the level and trend for year 2 as well as a forecast for year 3.

First we use equation (17.7) and the smoothing constant $\alpha = .1$ to compute an estimate of the level of the time series in year 2.

$$L_2 = .1(22.9) + .9(21.6 + 1.3) = 22.9$$

Note that $21.6 + 1.3$ is the forecast of sales for year 2. Thus, the estimate of the level of the time series in year 2 obtained using equation (17.7) is simply a weighted average of the observed value in year 2 (using a weight of $\alpha = .1$) and the forecast for year 2 (using a weight of $1 - \alpha = 1 - .1 = .9$). In general, large values of α place more weight on the observed value (Y_t) whereas smaller values place more weight on the forecasted value ($L_{t-1} + b_{t-1}$).

Next we use equation (17.8) and the smoothing constant $\beta = .2$ to compute an estimate of the slope of the time series in year 2.

$$b_2 = .2(22.9 - 21.6) + (1 - .2)(1.3) = 1.3$$

The estimate the slope of the time series in year 2 is a weighted average of the difference in the estimated level of the time series between year 2 and year 1 (using a weight of $\beta = .2$) and the estimate of the slope in year 1 (using a weight of $1 - \beta = 1 - .2 = .8$). In general, higher values of β place more weight on the difference between the estimated levels, whereas smaller values place more weight on the estimate of the slope from the last period.

Using the estimates of L_2 and b_2 just obtained, the forecast of sales for year 3 is computed using equation (17.9):

$$F_3 = L_2 + b_2 = 22.9 + 1.3(1) = 24.2$$

The other calculations are made in a similar manner and are shown in Table 17.15. The sum of the squared forecast errors is 39.678; hence MSE = 39.678/9 = 4.41.

Will different values for the smoothing constants α and β provide more accurate forecasts? To answer this question we would have to try different combinations of α and β to determine if a combination can be found that will provide a value of MSE lower than 4.41, the value we obtained using smoothing constants $\alpha = .1$ and $\beta = .2$. Searching for good values of α and β can be done by trial and error or using more advanced statistical software packages that have an option for selecting the optimal set of smoothing constants.

TABLE 17.15 SUMMARY CALCULATIONS FOR HOLT'S LINEAR EXPONENTIAL SMOOTHING FOR THE BICYCLE SALES TIME SERIES USING $\alpha = .1$ AND $\beta = .2$

Year	Sales (1000s) Y_t	Estimated Level L_t	Estimated Trend b_t	Forecast F_t	Forecast Error	Squared Forecast Error
1	21.6	21.600	1.300			
2	22.9	22.900	1.300	22.900	0.000	0.000
3	25.5	24.330	1.326	24.200	1.300	1.690
4	21.9	25.280	1.251	25.656	−3.756	14.108
5	23.9	26.268	1.198	26.531	−2.631	6.924
6	27.5	27.470	1.199	27.466	0.034	0.001
7	31.5	28.952	1.256	28.669	2.831	8.016
8	29.7	30.157	1.245	30.207	−0.507	0.257
9	28.6	31.122	1.189	31.402	−2.802	7.851
10	31.4	32.220	1.171	32.311	−0.911	0.830
					Total	39.678

Note that the estimate of the level of the time series in year 10 is $L_1 = 32.220$ and the estimate of the slope in year 10 is $b_1 = 1.171$. If we assume that the past 10-year trend in sales is a good indicator of the future, equation (17.9) can be used to develop forecasts for future time periods. For example, substituting $t = 11$ into equation (17.9) yields next year's trend projection or forecast, F_{11}.

$$F_{11} = L_{10} + b_{10}(1) = 32.220 + 1.171 = 33.391$$

Thus, using Holt's linear exponential smoothing we would forecast sales of 33,391 bicycles next year.

Nonlinear Trend Regression

WEB file

Cholesterol

TABLE 17.16

CHOLESTEROL REVENUE TIME SERIES ($MILLIONS)

Year (t)	Revenue ($millions)
1	23.1
2	21.3
3	27.4
4	34.6
5	33.8
6	43.2
7	59.5
8	64.4
9	74.2
10	99.3

The use of a linear function to model trend is common. However, as we discussed previously, sometimes time series have a curvilinear or nonlinear trend. As an example, consider the annual revenue in millions of dollars for a cholesterol drug for the first 10 years of sales. Table 17.16 shows the time series and Figure 17.13 shows the corresponding time series plot. For instance, revenue in year 1 was $23.1 million; revenue in year 2 was $21.3 million; and so on. The time series plot indicates an overall increasing or upward trend. But, unlike the bicycle sales time series, a linear trend does not appear to be appropriate. Instead, a curvilinear function appears to be needed to model the long-term trend.

Quadratic trend equation A variety of nonlinear functions can be used to develop an estimate of the trend for the cholesterol time series. For instance, consider the following quadratic trend equation:

$$T_t = b_0 + b_1 t + b_2 t^2 \qquad \textbf{(17.10)}$$

For the cholesterol time series, $t = 1$ corresponds to year 1, $t = 2$ corresponds to year 2, and so on.

The general linear model discussed in Section 16.1 can be used to compute the values of b_0, b_1, and b_2. There are two independent variables, year and year squared, and the dependent variable is the sales revenue in millions of dollars. Thus, the first observation is 1,

FIGURE 17.13 CHOLESTEROL REVENUE TIMES SERIES PLOT ($MILLIONS)

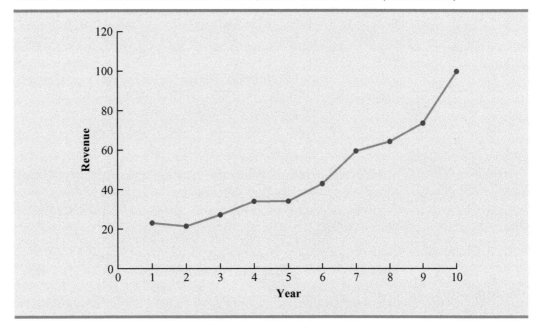

1, 23.1; the second observation is 2, 4, 21.3; the third observation is 3, 9, 27.4; and so on. Figure 17.14 shows the Minitab multiple regression output for the quadratic trend model; the estimated regression equation is

$$\text{Revenue (\$millions)} = 24.2 - 2.11 \text{ Year } + 0.922 \text{ YearSq}$$

where

$$\text{Year} = 1, 2, 3, \ldots, 10$$
$$\text{YearSq} = 1, 4, 9, \ldots, 100$$

FIGURE 17.14 MINITAB QUADRATIC TREND REGRESSION OUTPUT FOR THE BICYCLE SALES TIME SERIES

```
The regression equation is
Revenue = 24.2 - 2.11 Year + 0.922 YearSq

Predictor     Coef    SE Coef       T       p
Constant    24.182      4.676    5.17   0.001
Year        -2.106      1.953   -1.08   0.317
YearSq      0.9216     0.1730    5.33   0.001


S = 3.97578   R-Sq = 98.1%   R-Sq(adj) = 97.6%


Analysis of Variance

SOURCE            DF       SS      MS       F       p
Regression         2   5770.1  2885.1  182.52   0.000
Residual Error     7    110.6    15.8
Total              9   5880.8
```

Using the standard multiple regression procedure requires us to compute the values for year squared as a second independent variable. Alternatively, we can use Minitab's Time Series—Trend Analysis procedure to provide the same results. It does not require developing values for year squared and is easier to use. We recommend using this approach when solving exercises involving using quadratic trends.

Exponential trend equation Another alternative that can be used to model the non-linear pattern exhibited by the cholesterol time series is to fit an exponential model to the data. For instance, consider the following exponential trend equation:

$$T_t = b_0(b_1)^t \tag{17.11}$$

To better understand this exponential trend equation, suppose $b_0 = 20$ and $b_1 = 1.2$. Then, for $t = 1$, $T_1 = 20(1.2)^1 = 24$; for $t = 2$, $T_2 = 20(1.2)^2 = 28.8$; and for $t = 3$, $T_3 = 20(1.2)^3 = 34.56$. Note that T_t is not increasing by a constant amount as in the case of the linear trend model, but by a constant percentage; the percentage increase is 20%.

Minitab has the capability in its time series module to compute an exponential trend equation and it can then be used for forecasting. Unfortunately, Excel does not have this capability. But, in Section 16.1, we do describe how, by taking logarithms of the terms in equation (17.11), the general linear model methodology can be used to compute an exponential trend equation.

Minitab's time series module is quite easy to use to develop an exponential trend equation. There is no need to deal with logarithms and use regression analysis to compute the exponential trend equation. In Figure 17.15, we show the graphical portion of the computer output obtained using Minitab's Trend Analysis time series procedure to fit an exponential trend equation.

FIGURE 17.15 MINITAB TIME SERIES EXPONENTIAL GROWTH TREND ANALYSIS OUTPUT FOR THE CHOLESTEROL SALES TIME SERIES

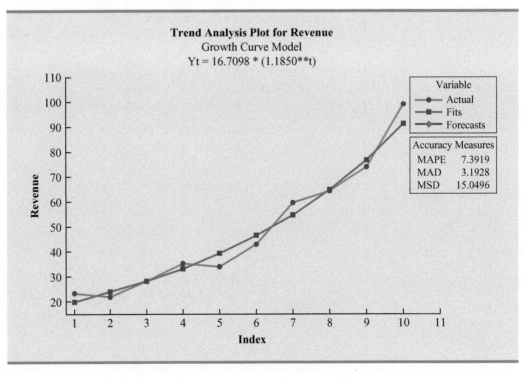

NOTES AND COMMENTS

Linear trend regression is based upon finding the estimated regression equation that minimizes the sum of squared forecast errors and therefore MSE. So, we would expect linear trend regression to outperform Holt's linear exponential smoothing in terms of MSE. For example, for the bicycle sales time series, the value of MSE using linear trend regression is 3.07 as compared to a value of 3.97 using Holt's linear exponential smoothing. Linear trend regression also provides a more accurate forecast using the MAE measure of forecast accuracy; for the bicycle sales time series, linear trend regression results in a value of MAE of 1.32 versus a value of 1.67 using Holt's linear method. However, based on MAPE, Holt's linear exponential smoothing (MAPE = 5.07%) outperforms linear trend regression (6.42%). Hence, for the bicycle sales time series, deciding which method provides the more accurate forecasts depends upon which measure of forecast accuracy is used.

Exercises

Methods

17. Consider the following time series data.

t	1	2	3	4	5
Y_t	6	11	9	14	15

   a. Construct a time series plot. What type of pattern exists in the data?
   b. Develop the linear trend equation for this time series.
   c. What is the forecast for $t = 6$?

18. Refer to the time series in exercise 17. Use Holt's linear exponential smoothing method with $\alpha = .3$ and $\beta = .5$ to develop a forecast for $t = 6$.

19. Consider the following time series.

t	1	2	3	4	5	6	7
Y_t	120	110	100	96	94	92	88

   a. Construct a time series plot. What type of pattern exists in the data?
   b. Develop the linear trend equation for this time series.
   c. What is the forecast for $t = 8$?

20. Consider the following time series.

t	1	2	3	4	5	6	7
Y_t	82	60	44	35	30	29	35

   a. Construct a time series plot. What type of pattern exists in the data?
   b. Using Minitab or Excel, develop the quadratic trend equation for the time series.
   c. What is the forecast for $t = 8$?

21. The general fund budget for the state of Kentucky for 1988 (Period 1) to 2011 (Period 24) follows (*Northern Kentucky Enquirer,* January 18, 2012).

KYBudget

Year	Period	Budget ($billions)	Year	Period	Budget ($billions)
1988	1	3.03	2000	13	6.48
1989	2	3.29	2001	14	6.65
1990	3	3.56	2002	15	6.56
1991	4	4.31	2003	16	6.78
1992	5	4.36	2004	17	6.98
1993	6	4.51	2005	18	7.65
1994	7	4.65	2006	19	8.38
1995	8	5.15	2007	20	8.57
1996	9	5.34	2008	21	8.66
1997	10	5.66	2009	22	8.43
1998	11	6.01	2010	23	8.23
1999	12	6.20	2011	24	8.76

a.   Construct a time series plot. What type of pattern exists in the data?
b.   Develop a linear trend equation for this time series.
c.   What is the forecast for 2012?

22.   The Seneca Children's Fund (SCF) is a local charity that runs a summer camp for disadvantaged children. The fund's board of directors has been working very hard in recent years to decrease the amount of overhead expenses, a major factor in how charities are rated by independent agencies. The following data show the percentage of the money SCF has raised that was spent on administrative and fund-raising expenses for 2006–2012.

Year	Period (t)	Expense (%)
2006	1	13.9
2007	2	12.2
2008	3	10.5
2009	4	10.4
2010	5	11.5
2011	6	10.0
2012	7	8.5

a.   Construct a time series plot. What type of pattern exists in the data?
b.   Develop the linear trend equation for this time series.
c.   Forecast the percentage of administrative expenses for 2013.
d.   If SCF can maintain their current trend in reducing administrative expenses, how long will it take them to achieve a level of 5% or less?

23.   The president of a small manufacturing firm is concerned about the continual increase in manufacturing costs over the past several years. The following figures provide a time series of the cost per unit for the firm's leading product over the past eight years.

Year	Cost/Unit ($)	Year	Cost/Unit ($)
1	20.00	5	26.60
2	24.50	6	30.00
3	28.20	7	31.00
4	27.50	8	36.00

a.   Construct a time series plot. What type of pattern exists in the data?
b.   Develop the linear trend equation for this time series.
c.   What is the average cost increase that the firm has been realizing per year?
d.   Compute an estimate of the cost/unit for next year.

24. FRED® (Federal Reserve Economic Data), a database of more than 3000 U.S. economic time series, contains historical data on foreign exchange rates. The following data show the foreign exchange rate for the United States and China (Federal Reserve Bank of St.Louis website). The units for Rate are the number of Chinese yuan to one U.S. dollar.

ExchangeRate

Year	Month	Rate
2007	October	7.5019
2007	November	7.4210
2007	December	7.3682
2008	January	7.2405
2008	February	7.1644
2008	March	7.0722
2008	April	6.9997
2008	May	6.9725
2008	June	6.8993
2008	July	6.8355

a. Construct a time series plot. Does a linear trend appear to be present?
b. Using Minitab or Excel, develop the linear trend equation for this time series.
c. Use the trend equation to forecast the exchange rate for August 2008.
d. Would you feel comfortable using the trend equation to forecast the exchange rate for December 2008?

25. Automobile unit sales at B. J. Scott Motors, Inc., provided the following 10-year time series.

Year	Sales	Year	Sales
1	400	6	260
2	390	7	300
3	320	8	320
4	340	9	340
5	270	10	370

a. Construct a time series plot. Comment on the appropriateness of a linear trend.
b. Using Minitab or Excel, develop a quadratic trend equation that can be used to forecast sales.
c. Using the trend equation developed in part (b), forecast sales in year 11.
d. Suggest an alternative to using a quadratic trend equation to forecast sales. Explain.

26. Giovanni Food Products produces and sells frozen pizzas to public schools throughout the eastern United States. Using a very aggressive marketing strategy they have been able to increase their annual revenue by approximately $10 million over the past 10 years. But increased competition has slowed their growth rate in the past few years. The annual revenue, in millions of dollars, for the previous 10 years is shown.

Pasta

Year	Revenue
1	8.53
2	10.84
3	12.98
4	14.11
5	16.31
6	17.21
7	18.37
8	18.45
9	18.40
10	18.43

a. Construct a time series plot. Comment on the appropriateness of a linear trend.
b. Using Minitab or Excel, develop a quadratic trend equation that can be used to forecast revenue.
c. Using the trend equation developed in part (b), forecast revenue in year 11.

27. The number of users of Facebook from 2004 through 2011 follows (Facebook website, April 16, 2012).

WEB file

Facebook

Year	Period	Users (Millions)
2004	1	1
2005	2	6
2006	3	12
2007	4	58
2008	5	145
2009	6	360
2010	7	608
2011	8	845

a. Construct a time series plot. What type of pattern exists?
b. Using Minitab or Excel, develop a quadratic trend equation.

(17.5) Seasonality and Trend

In this section we show how to develop forecasts for a time series that has a seasonal pattern. To the extent that seasonality exists, we need to incorporate it into our forecasting models to ensure accurate forecasts. We begin by considering a seasonal time series with no trend and then discuss how to model seasonality with trend.

WEB file

Umbrella

Seasonality Without Trend

As an example, consider the number of umbrellas sold at a clothing store over the past five years. Table 17.17 shows the time series and Figure 17.16 shows the corresponding time series plot. The time series plot does not indicate any long-term trend in sales. In fact, unless you look carefully at the data, you might conclude that the data follow a horizontal pattern and that single exponential smoothing could be used to forecast sales. But closer inspection of the time series plot reveals a pattern in the data. That is, the first and third quarters have moderate sales, the second quarter has the highest sales, and the fourth quarter tends to be the lowest quarter in terms of sales volume. Thus, we would conclude that a quarterly seasonal pattern is present.

In Chapter 15 we showed how dummy variables can be used to deal with categorical independent variables in a multiple regression model. We can use the same approach to model a time series with a seasonal pattern by treating the season as a categorical variable. Recall that when a categorical variable has k levels, $k - 1$ dummy variables are required. So, if there are four seasons, we need three dummy variables. For instance, in the umbrella sales time series season is a categorical variable with four levels: quarter 1, quarter 2, quarter 3, and quarter 4. Thus, to model the seasonal effects in the umbrella time series we need $4 - 1 = 3$ dummy variables. The three dummy variables can be coded as follows:

$$Qtr1 = \begin{cases} 1 \text{ if Quarter 1} \\ 0 \text{ otherwise} \end{cases} \quad Qtr2 = \begin{cases} 1 \text{ if Quarter 2} \\ 0 \text{ otherwise} \end{cases} \quad Qtr3 = \begin{cases} 1 \text{ if Quarter 3} \\ 0 \text{ otherwise} \end{cases}$$

TABLE 17.17

UMBRELLA SALES TIME SERIES

Year	Quarter	Sales
1	1	125
	2	153
	3	106
	4	88
2	1	118
	2	161
	3	133
	4	102
3	1	138
	2	144
	3	113
	4	80
4	1	109
	2	137
	3	125
	4	109
5	1	130
	2	165
	3	128
	4	96

FIGURE 17.16   UMBRELLA SALES TIME SERIES PLOT

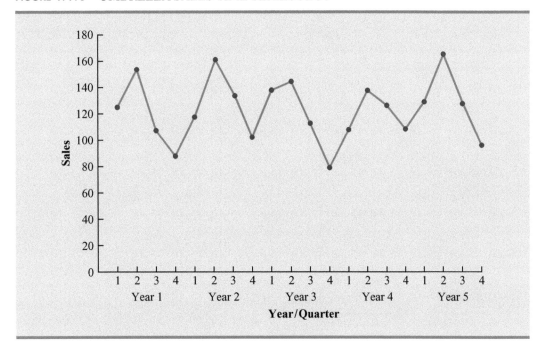

Using $\hat{Y}$ to denote the estimated or forecasted value of sales, the general form of the estimated regression equation relating the number of umbrellas sold to the quarter the sales take place follows:

$$\hat{Y} = b_0 + b_1 \text{ Qtr1} + b_2 \text{ Qtr2} + b_3 \text{ Qtr3}$$

Table 17.18 is the umbrella sales time series with the coded values of the dummy variables shown. Using the data in Table 17.18 and Minitab's regression procedure, we obtained the computer output shown in Figure 17.17. The estimated multiple regression equation obtained is

$$\text{Sales} = 95.0 + 29.0 \text{ Qtr1} + 57.0 \text{ Qtr2} + 26.0 \text{ Qtr3}$$

We can use this equation to forecast quarterly sales for next year.

Quarter 1: Sales = 95.0 + 29.0(1) + 57.0(0) + 26.0(0) = 124
Quarter 2: Sales = 95.0 + 29.0(0) + 57.0(1) + 26.0(0) = 152
Quarter 3: Sales = 95.0 + 29.0(0) + 57.0(0) + 26.0(1) = 121
Quarter 4: Sales = 95.0 + 29.0(0) + 57.0(1) + 26.0(0) = 95

It is interesting to note that we could have obtained the quarterly forecasts for next year simply by computing the average number of umbrellas sold in each quarter, as shown in the following table.

Year	Quarter 1	Quarter 2	Quarter 3	Quarter 4
1	125	153	106	88
2	118	161	133	102
3	138	144	113	80
4	109	137	125	109
5	130	165	128	96
Average	124	152	121	95

TABLE 17.18 UMBRELLA SALES TIME SERIES WITH DUMMY VARIABLES

Year	Quarter	Qtr1	Qtr2	Qtr3	Sales
1	1	1	0	0	125
	2	0	1	0	153
	3	0	0	1	106
	4	0	0	0	88
2	1	1	0	0	118
	2	0	1	0	161
	3	0	0	1	133
	4	0	0	0	102
3	1	1	0	0	138
	2	0	1	0	144
	3	0	0	1	113
	4	0	0	0	80
4	1	1	0	0	109
	2	0	1	0	137
	3	0	0	1	125
	4	0	0	0	109
5	1	1	0	0	130
	2	0	1	0	165
	3	0	0	1	128
	4	0	0	0	96

Nonetheless, the regression output shown in Figure 17.17 provides additional information that can be used to assess the accuracy of the forecast and determine the significance of the results. And, for more complex types of problem situations, such as dealing with a time series that has both trend and seasonal effects, this simple averaging approach will not work.

Seasonality and Trend

TVSales

Let us now extend the regression approach to include situations where the time series contains both a seasonal effect and a linear trend by showing how to forecast the quarterly television set sales time series introduced in Section 17.1. The data for the television set time series are shown in Table 17.19. The time series plot in Figure 17.18 indicates that sales are lowest in the second quarter of each year and increase in quarters 3 and 4. Thus, we conclude that a seasonal pattern exists for television set sales. But the time series also has an upward linear trend that will need to be accounted for in order to develop accurate forecasts of quarterly sales. This is easily handled by combining the dummy variable approach for

TABLE 17.19

TELEVISION SET SALES TIME SERIES

Year	Quarter	Sales (1000s)
1	1	4.8
	2	4.1
	3	6.0
	4	6.5
2	1	5.8
	2	5.2
	3	6.8
	4	7.4
3	1	6.0
	2	5.6
	3	7.5
	4	7.8
4	1	6.3
	2	5.9
	3	8.0
	4	8.4

FIGURE 17.17 MINITAB REGRESSION OUTPUT FOR THE UMBRELLA SALES TIME SERIES

```
The regression equation is
Sales = 95.0 + 29.0 Qtr1 + 57.0 Qtr2 + 26.0 Qtr3

Predictor    Coef    SE Coef      T       P
Constant    95.000    5.065    18.76   0.000
Qtr1        29.000    7.162     4.05   0.001
Qtr2        57.000    7.162     7.96   0.000
Qtr3        26.000    7.162     3.63   0.002
```

FIGURE 17.18 TELEVISION SET SALES TIME SERIES PLOT

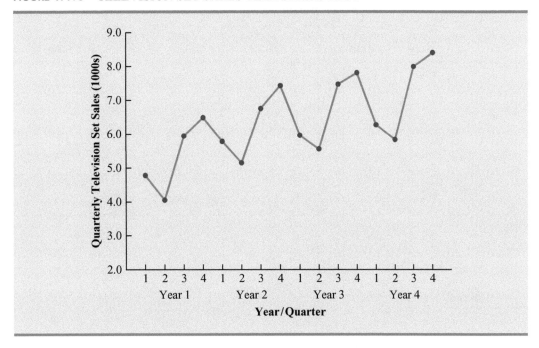

seasonality with the time series regression approach we discussed in Section 17.3 for handling linear trend.

The general form of the estimated multiple regression equation for modeling both the quarterly seasonal effects and the linear trend in the television set time series is as follows:

$$\hat{Y}_t = b_0 + b_1 \text{ Qtr1} + b_2 \text{ Qtr2} + b_3 \text{ Qtr3} + b_4 t$$

where

$\hat{Y}_t$ = estimate or forecast of sales in period t

Qtr1 = 1 if time period t corresponds to the first quarter of the year; 0 otherwise

Qtr2 = 1 if time period t corresponds to the second quarter of the year; 0 otherwise

Qtr3 = 1 if time period t corresponds to the third quarter of the year; 0 otherwise

t = time period

Table 17.20 is the revised television set sales time series that includes the coded values of the dummy variables and the time period t. Using the data in Table 17.20, and Minitab's regression procedure, we obtained the computer output shown in Figure 17.19. The estimated multiple regression equation is

$$\text{Sales} = 6.07 - 1.36 \text{ Qtr1} - 2.03 \text{ Qtr2} - .304 \text{ Qtr3} + .146t \qquad \textbf{(17.12)}$$

We can now use equation (17.12) to forecast quarterly sales for next year. Next year is year 5 for the television set sales time series; that is, time periods 17, 18, 19, and 20.

Forecast for Time Period 17 (Quarter 1 in Year 5)

$$\text{Sales} = 6.07 - 1.36(1) - 2.03(0) - .304(0) + .146(17) = 7.19$$

Forecast for Time Period 18 (Quarter 2 in Year 5)

$$\text{Sales} = 6.07 - 1.36(0) - 2.03(1) - .304(0) + .146(18) = 6.67$$

TABLE 17.20 TELEVISION SET SALES TIME SERIES WITH DUMMY VARIABLES AND TIME PERIOD

Year	Quarter	Qtr1	Qtr2	Qtr3	Period	Sales (1000s)
1	1	1	0	0	1	4.8
	2	0	1	0	2	4.1
	3	0	0	1	3	6.0
	4	0	0	0	4	6.5
2	1	1	0	0	5	5.8
	2	0	1	0	6	5.2
	3	0	0	1	7	6.8
	4	0	0	0	8	7.4
3	1	1	0	0	9	6.0
	2	0	1	0	10	5.6
	3	0	0	1	11	7.5
	4	0	0	0	12	7.8
4	1	1	0	0	13	6.3
	2	0	1	0	14	5.9
	3	0	0	1	15	8.0
	4	0	0	0	16	8.4

Forecast for Time Period 19 (Quarter 3 in Year 5)

$$\text{Sales} = 6.07 - 1.36(0) - 2.03(0) - .304(1) + .146(19) = 8.54$$

Forecast for Time Period 20 (Quarter 4 in Year 5)

$$\text{Sales} = 6.07 - 1.36(0) - 2.03(0) - .304(0) + .146(20) = 8.99$$

Thus, accounting for the seasonal effects and the linear trend in television set sales, the estimates of quarterly sales in year 5 are 7190, 6670, 8540, and 8990.

The dummy variables in the estimated multiple regression equation actually provide four estimated multiple regression equations, one for each quarter. For instance, if time period t corresponds to quarter 1, the estimate of quarterly sales is

$$\text{Quarter 1: Sales} = 6.07 - 1.36(1) - 2.03(0) - .304(0) + .146t = 4.71 + .146t$$

FIGURE 17.19 MINITAB REGRESSION OUTPUT FOR THE UMBRELLA SALES TIME SERIES

```
The regression equation is
Sales (1000s) = 6.07 - 1.36 Qtr1 - 2.03 Qtr2 - 0.304
                Qtr3 + 0.146 Period

Predictor     Coef   SE Coef       T      P
Constant    6.0688    0.1625   37.35  0.000
Qtr1       -1.3631    0.1575   -8.66  0.000
Qtr2       -2.0337    0.1551  -13.11  0.000
Qtr3       -0.3044    0.1537   -1.98  0.073
Period     0.14562   0.01211   12.02  0.000
```

Similarly, if time period t corresponds to quarters 2, 3, and 4, the estimates of quarterly sales are

Quarter 2: Sales = 6.07 − 1.36(0) − 2.03(1) − .304(0) + .146t = 4.04 + .146t
Quarter 3: Sales = 6.07 − 1.36(0) − 2.03(0) − .304(1) + .146t = 5.77 + .146t
Quarter 4: Sales = 6.07 − 1.36(0) − 2.03(0) − .304(0) + .146t = 6.07 + .146t

The slope of the trend line for each quarterly forecast equation is .146, indicating a growth in sales of about 146 sets per quarter. The only difference in the four equations is that they have different intercepts. For instance, the intercept for the quarter 1 equation is 4.71 and the intercept for the quarter 4 equation is 6.07. Thus, sales in quarter 1 are 4.71 − 6.07 = −1.36 or 1360 sets less than in quarter 4. In other words, the estimated regression coefficient for Qtr1 in equation (17.12) provides an estimate of the difference in sales between quarter 1 and quarter 4. Similar interpretations can be provided for −2.03, the estimated regression coefficient for dummy variable Qtr2, and −.304, the estimated regression coefficient for dummy variable Qtr3.

Models Based on Monthly Data

Whenever a categorical variable such as season has k levels, $k − 1$ dummy variables are required.

In the preceding television set sales example, we showed how dummy variables can be used to account for the quarterly seasonal effects in the time series. Because there were 4 levels for the categorical variable season, 3 dummy variables were required. However, many businesses use monthly rather than quarterly forecasts. For monthly data, season is a categorical variable with 12 levels and thus $12 − 1 = 11$ dummy variables are required. For example, the 11 dummy variables could be coded as follows:

$$\text{Month1} = \begin{cases} 1 \text{ if January} \\ 0 \text{ otherwise} \end{cases}$$

$$\text{Month2} = \begin{cases} 1 \text{ if February} \\ 0 \text{ otherwise} \end{cases}$$

.

.

.

$$\text{Month11} = \begin{cases} 1 \text{ if November} \\ 0 \text{ otherwise} \end{cases}$$

Other than this change, the multiple regression approach for handling seasonality remains the same.

Exercises

Methods

28.   Consider the following time series.

Quarter	Year 1	Year 2	Year 3
1	71	68	62
2	49	41	51
3	58	60	53
4	78	81	72

a. Construct a time series plot. What type of pattern exists in the data?
b. Use the following dummy variables to develop an estimated regression equation to account for seasonal effects in the data: Qtr1 = 1 if Quarter 1, 0 otherwise; Qtr2 = 1 if Quarter 2, 0 otherwise; Qtr3 = 1 if Quarter 3, 0 otherwise.
c. Compute the quarterly forecasts for next year.

29. Consider the following time series data.

Quarter	Year 1	Year 2	Year 3
1	4	6	7
2	2	3	6
3	3	5	6
4	5	7	8

a. Construct a time series plot. What type of pattern exists in the data?
b. Use the following dummy variables to develop an estimated regression equation to account for any seasonal and linear trend effects in the data: Qtr1 = 1 if Quarter 1, 0 otherwise; Qtr2 = 1 if Quarter 2, 0 otherwise; Qtr3 = 1 if Quarter 3, 0 otherwise.
c. Compute the quarterly forecasts for next year.

Applications

30. The quarterly sales data (number of copies sold) for a college textbook over the past three years follow.

Quarter	Year 1	Year 2	Year 3
1	1690	1800	1850
2	940	900	1100
3	2625	2900	2930
4	2500	2360	2615

a. Construct a time series plot. What type of pattern exists in the data?
b. Use the following dummy variables to develop an estimated regression equation to account for any seasonal effects in the data: Qtr1 = 1 if Quarter 1, 0 otherwise; Qtr2 = 1 if Quarter 2, 0 otherwise; Qtr3 = 1 if Quarter 3, 0 otherwise.
c. Compute the quarterly forecasts for next year.
d. Let t = 1 to refer to the observation in quarter 1 of year 1; t = 2 to refer to the observation in quarter 2 of year 1; . . . and t = 12 to refer to the observation in quarter 4 of year 3. Using the dummy variables defined in part (b) and t, develop an estimated regression equation to account for seasonal effects and any linear trend in the time series. Based upon the seasonal effects in the data and linear trend, compute the quarterly forecasts for next year.

31. Air pollution control specialists in southern California monitor the amount of ozone, carbon dioxide, and nitrogen dioxide in the air on an hourly basis. The hourly time series data exhibit seasonality, with the levels of pollutants showing patterns that vary over the hours in the day. On July 15, 16, and 17, the following levels of nitrogen dioxide were observed for the 12 hours from 6:00 A.M. to 6:00 P.M.

July 15:	25	28	35	50	60	60	40	35	30	25	25	20
July 16:	28	30	35	48	60	65	50	40	35	25	20	20
July 17:	35	42	45	70	72	75	60	45	40	25	25	25

a. Construct a time series plot. What type of pattern exists in the data?

b. Use the following dummy variables to develop an estimated regression equation to account for the seasonal effects in the data.

> Hour1 = 1 if the reading was made between 6:00 A.M. and 7:00 A.M.;
> 0 otherwise
> Hour2 = 1 if if the reading was made between 7:00 A.M. and 8:00 A.M.;
> 0 otherwise
>
> .
> .
> .
>
> Hour11 = 1 if the reading was made between 4:00 P.M. and 5:00 P.M.,
> 0 otherwise.

Note that when the values of the 11 dummy variables are equal to 0, the observation corresponds to the 5:00 P.M. to 6:00 P.M. hour.

c. Using the estimated regression equation developed in part (a), compute estimates of the levels of nitrogen dioxide for July 18.

d. Let $t = 1$ to refer to the observation in hour 1 on July 15; $t = 2$ to refer to the observation in hour 2 of July 15; . . . and $t = 36$ to refer to the observation in hour 12 of July 17. Using the dummy variables defined in part (b) and t, develop an estimated regression equation to account for seasonal effects and any linear trend in the time series. Based upon the seasonal effects in the data and linear trend, compute estimates of the levels of nitrogen dioxide for July 18.

32. South Shore Construction builds permanent docks and seawalls along the southern shore of Long Island, New York. Although the firm has been in business only five years, revenue has increased from $308,000 in the first year of operation to $1,084,000 in the most recent year. The following data show the quarterly sales revenue in thousands of dollars.

Quarter	Year 1	Year 2	Year 3	Year 4	Year 5
1	20	37	75	92	176
2	100	136	155	202	282
3	175	245	326	384	445
4	13	26	48	82	181

a. Construct a time series plot. What type of pattern exists in the data?

b. Use the following dummy variables to develop an estimated regression equation to account for seasonal effects in the data. Qtr1 = 1 if Quarter 1, 0 otherwise; Qtr2 = 1 if Quarter 2, 0 otherwise; Qtr3 = 1 if Quarter 3, 0 otherwise. Based only on the seasonal effects in the data, compute estimates of quarterly sales for year 6.

c. Let Period = 1 to refer to the observation in quarter 1 of year 1; Period = 2 to refer to the observation in quarter 2 of year 1; . . . and Period = 20 to refer to the observation in quarter 4 of year 5. Using the dummy variables defined in part (b) and Period, develop an estimated regression equation to account for seasonal effects and any linear trend in the time series. Based upon the seasonal effects in the data and linear trend, compute estimates of quarterly sales for year 6.

33. Electric power consumption is measured in kilowatt-hours (kWh). The local utility company offers an interrupt program whereby commercial customers that participate receive favorable rates but must agree to cut back consumption if the utility requests them to do so. Timko Products has agreed to cut back consumption from noon to 8:00 P.M. on Thursday. To determine Timko's savings, the utility must estimate Timko's normal power usage for this period of time. Data on Timko's electric power consumption for the previous 72 hours are shown below.

Power

Time Period	Monday	Tuesday	Wednesday	Thursday
12–4 A.M.	—	19,281	31,209	27,330
4–8 A.M	—	33,195	37,014	32,715
8–12 noon	—	99,516	119,968	152,465
12–4 P.M.	124,299	123,666	156,033	
4–8 P.M.	113,545	111,717	128,889	
8–12 midnight	41,300	48,112	73,923	

a. Construct a time series plot. What type of pattern exists in the data?
b. Use the following dummy variables to develop an estimated regression equation to account for any seasonal effects in the data.

  Time1 = 1 for time period 12–4 A.M.; 0 otherwise
  Time2 = 1 for time period 4–8 A.M; 0 otherwise
  Time3 = 1 for time period 8–12 noon; 0 otherwise
  Time4 = 1 for time period 12–4 P.M; 0 otherwise
  Time5 = 1 for time period 4–8 P.M; 0 otherwise

c. Use the estimated regression equation developed in part (b) to estimate Timko's normal usage over the period of interrupted service.
d. Let Period = 1 to refer to the observation for Monday in the time period 12–4 P.M.; Period = 2 to refer to the observation for Monday in the time period 4–8 P.M; . . . and Period = 18 to refer to the observation for Thursday in the time period 8–12 noon. Using the dummy variables defined in part (b) and Period, develop an estimated regression equation to account for seasonal effects and any linear trend in the time series.
e. Using the estimated regression equation developed in part (d), estimate Timko's normal usage over the period of interrupted service.

34. Three years of monthly lawn-maintenance expenses ($) for a six-unit apartment house in southern Florida follow.

AptExp

Month	Year 1	Year 2	Year 3
January	170	180	195
February	180	205	210
March	205	215	230
April	230	245	280
May	240	265	290
June	315	330	390
July	360	400	420
August	290	335	330
September	240	260	290
October	240	270	295
November	230	255	280
December	195	220	250

a. Construct a time series plot. What type of pattern exists in the data?
b. Develop an estimated regression equation that can be used to account for any seasonal and linear trend effects in the data. Use the following dummy variables to account for the seasonal effects in the data: Jan = 1 if January, 0 otherwise; Feb = 1 if February, 0 otherwise; Mar = 1 if March, 0 otherwise; . . . Nov = 1 if November, 0 otherwise. Note that using this coding method, when all the 11 dummy variables are 0, the observation corresponds to an expense in December.
c. Compute the monthly forecasts for next year based upon both trend and seasonal effects.

17.6 Time Series Decomposition

In this section we turn our attention to what is called **time series decomposition**. Time series decomposition can be used to separate or decompose a time series into seasonal, trend, and irregular components. While this method can be used for forecasting, its primary applicability is to get a better understanding of the time series. Many business and economic time series are maintained and published by government agencies such as the Census Bureau and the Bureau of Labor Statistics. These agencies use time series decomposition to create deseasonalized time series.

Understanding what is really going on with a time series often depends upon the use of deseasonalized data. For instance, we might be interested in learning whether electrical power consumption is increasing in our area. Suppose we learn that electric power consumption in September is down 3% from the previous month. Care must be exercised in using such information, because whenever a seasonal influence is present, such comparisons may be misleading if the data have not been deseasonalized. The fact that electric power consumption is down 3% from August to September might be only the seasonal effect associated with a decrease in the use of air conditioning and not because of a long-term decline in the use of electric power. Indeed, after adjusting for the seasonal effect, we might even find that the use of electric power increased. Many other time series, such as unemployment statistics, home sales, and retail sales, are subject to strong seasonal influences. It is important to deseasonalize such data before making a judgment about any long-term trend.

Time series decomposition methods assume that Y_t, the actual time series value at period t, is a function of three components: a trend component; a seasonal component; and an irregular or error component. How these three components are combined to generate the observed values of the time series depends upon whether we assume the relationship is best described by an additive or a multiplicative model.

An **additive decomposition model** takes the following form:

$$Y_t = \text{Trend}_t + \text{Seasonal}_t + \text{Irregular}_t \qquad \textbf{(17.13)}$$

where

$$\text{Trend}_t = \text{trend value at time period } t$$
$$\text{Seasonal}_t = \text{seasonal value at time period } t$$
$$\text{Irregular}_t = \text{irregular value at time period } t$$

The irregular component corresponds to the error term ε in the simple linear regression model we discussed in Chapter 14.

In an additive model the values for the three components are simply added together to obtain the actual time series value Y_t. The irregular or error component accounts for the variability in the time series that cannot be explained by the trend and seasonal components.

An additive model is appropriate in situations where the seasonal fluctuations do not depend upon the level of the time series. The regression model for incorporating seasonal and trend effects in Section 17.5 is an additive model. If the sizes of the seasonal fluctuations in earlier time periods are about the same as the sizes of the seasonal fluctuations in later time periods, an additive model is appropriate. However, if the seasonal fluctuations change over time, growing larger as the sales volume increases because of a long-term linear trend, then a multiplicative model should be used. Many business and economic time series follow this pattern.

A **multiplicative decomposition model** takes the following form:

$$Y_t = \text{Trend}_t \times \text{Seasonal}_t \times \text{Irregular}_t \qquad \textbf{(17.14)}$$

where

$$\text{Trend}_t = \text{trend value at time period } t$$
$$\text{Seasonal}_t = \text{seasonal index at time period } t$$
$$\text{Irregular}_t = \text{irregular index at time period } t$$

The Census Bureau uses a multiplicative model in conjunction with its methodology for deseasonalizing time series.

In this model, the trend and seasonal and irregular components are multiplied to give the value of the time series. Trend is measured in units of the item being forecast. However, the seasonal and irregular components are measured in relative terms, with values above 1.00 indicating effects above the trend and values below 1.00 indicating effects below the trend.

Because this is the method most often used in practice, we will restrict our discussion of time series decomposition to showing how to develop estimates of the trend and seasonal components for a multiplicative model. As an illustration we will work with the quarterly television set sales time series introduced in Section 17.5; the quarterly sales data are shown in Table 17.19 and the corresponding time series plot is presented in Figure 17.18. After demonstrating how to decompose a time series using the multiplicative model, we will show how the seasonal indices and trend component can be recombined to develop a forecast.

Calculating the Seasonal Indexes

Figure 17.18 indicates that sales are lowest in the second quarter of each year and increase in quarters 3 and 4. Thus, we conclude that a seasonal pattern exists for the television set sales time series. The computational procedure used to identify each quarter's seasonal influence begins by computing a moving average to remove the combined seasonal and irregular effects from the data, leaving us with a time series that contains only trend and any remaining random variation not removed by the moving average calculations.

Because we are working with a quarterly series, we will use four data values in each moving average. The moving average calculation for the first four quarters of the television set sales data is

$$\text{First moving average} = \frac{4.8 + 4.1 + 6.0 + 6.5}{4} = \frac{21.4}{4} = 5.35$$

Note that the moving average calculation for the first four quarters yields the average quarterly sales over year 1 of the time series. Continuing the moving average calculations, we next add the 5.8 value for the first quarter of year 2 and drop the 4.8 for the first quarter of year 1. Thus, the second moving average is

$$\text{Second moving average} = \frac{4.1 + 6.0 + 6.5 + 5.8}{4} = \frac{22.4}{4} = 5.60$$

Similarly, the third moving average calculation is $(6.0 + 6.5 + 5.8 + 5.2)/4 = 5.875$.

Before we proceed with the moving average calculations for the entire time series, let us return to the first moving average calculation, which resulted in a value of 5.35. The 5.35 value is the average quarterly sales volume for year 1. As we look back at the calculation of the 5.35 value, associating 5.35 with the "middle" of the moving average group makes sense. Note, however, that with four quarters in the moving average, there is no middle period. The 5.35 value really corresponds to period 2.5, the last half of quarter 2 and the first half of quarter 3. Similarly, if we go to the next moving average value of 5.60, the middle period corresponds to period 3.5, the last half of quarter 3 and the first half of quarter 4.

The two moving average values we computed do not correspond directly to the original quarters of the time series. We can resolve this difficulty by computing the average of the two moving averages. Since the center of the first moving average is period 2.5 (half a period or quarter early) and the center of the second moving average is period 3.5 (half a period or quarter late), the average of the two moving averages is centered at quarter 3, exactly where it should be. This moving average is referred to as a *centered moving average*. Thus, the centered moving average for period 3 is (5.35 + 5.60)/2 = 5.475. Similarly, the centered moving average value for period 4 is (5.60 + 5.875)/2 = 5.738. Table 17.21 shows a complete summary of the moving average and centered moving average calculations for the television set sales data.

What do the centered moving averages in Table 17.21 tell us about this time series? Figure 17.20 shows a time series plot of the actual time series values and the centered moving average values. Note particularly how the centered moving average values tend to "smooth out" both the seasonal and irregular fluctuations in the time series. The centered moving averages represent the trend in the data and any random variation that was not removed by using moving averages to smooth the data.

Previously we showed that the multiplicative decomposition model is

$$Y_t = \text{Trend}_t \times \text{Seasonal}_t \times \text{Irregular}_t$$

TABLE 17.21 CENTERED MOVING AVERAGE CALCULATIONS FOR THE TELEVISION SET SALES TIME SERIES

Year	Quarter	Sales (1000s)	Four-Quarter Moving Average	Centered Moving Average
1	1	4.8		
1	2	4.1		
			5.350	
1	3	6.0		5.475
			5.600	
1	4	6.5		5.738
			5.875	
2	1	5.8		5.975
			6.075	
2	2	5.2		6.188
			6.300	
2	3	6.8		6.325
			6.350	
2	4	7.4		6.400
			6.450	
3	1	6.0		6.538
			6.625	
3	2	5.6		6.675
			6.725	
3	3	7.5		6.763
			6.800	
3	4	7.8		6.838
			6.875	
4	1	6.3		6.938
			7.000	
4	2	5.9		7.075
			7.150	
4	3	8.0		
4	4	8.4		

FIGURE 17.20   QUARTERLY TELEVISION SET SALES TIME SERIES AND CENTERED MOVING AVERAGE

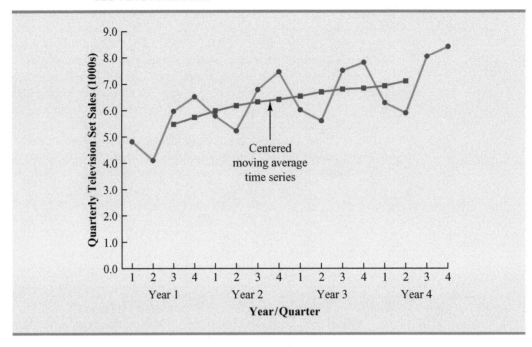

By dividing each side of this equation by the trend component T_t, we can identify the combined seasonal-irregular effect in the time series.

The seasonal-irregular values are often referred to as the de-trended values of the time series.

$$\frac{Y_t}{\text{Trend}_t} = \frac{\text{Trend}_t \times \text{Seasonal}_t \times \text{Irregular}_t}{\text{Trend}_t} = \text{Seasonal}_t \times \text{Irregular}_t$$

For example, the third quarter of year 1 shows a trend value of 5.475 (the centered moving average). So 6.0/5.475 = 1.096 is the combined seasonal-irregular value. Table 17.22 summarizes the seasonal-irregular values for the entire time series.

Consider the seasonal-irregular values for the third quarter: 1.096, 1.075, and 1.109. Seasonal-irregular values greater than 1.00 indicate effects above the trend estimate and values below 1.00 indicate effects below the trend estimate. Thus, the three seasonal-irregular values for quarter 3 show an above-average effect in the third quarter. Since the year-to-year fluctuations in the seasonal-irregular values are primarily due to random error, we can average the computed values to eliminate the irregular influence and obtain an estimate of the third-quarter seasonal influence.

$$\text{Seasonal effect of quarter 3} = \frac{1.096 + 1.075 + 1.109}{3} = 1.09$$

We refer to 1.09 as the *seasonal index* for the third quarter. Table 17.23 summarizes the calculations involved in computing the seasonal indexes for the television set sales time series. The seasonal indexes for the four quarters are .93, .84, 1.09, and 1.14.

Interpretation of the seasonal indexes in Table 17.23 provides some insight about the seasonal component in television set sales. The best sales quarter is the fourth quarter, with sales averaging 14% above the trend estimate. The worst, or slowest, sales quarter is the second quarter; its seasonal index of .84 shows that the sales average is 16% below the trend estimate. The seasonal component corresponds clearly to the intuitive expectation that television viewing interest and thus television purchase patterns tend to peak in the

TABLE 17.22 SEASONAL IRREGULAR VALUES FOR THE TELEVISION SET SALES TIME SERIES

Year	Quarter	Sales (1000s)	Centered Moving Average	Seasonal-Irregular Value
1	1	4.8		
1	2	4.1		
1	3	6.0	5.475	1.096
1	4	6.5	5.738	1.133
2	1	5.8	5.975	0.971
2	2	5.2	6.188	0.840
2	3	6.8	6.325	1.075
2	4	7.4	6.400	1.156
3	1	6.0	6.538	0.918
3	2	5.6	6.675	0.839
3	3	7.5	6.763	1.109
3	4	7.8	6.838	1.141
4	1	6.3	6.938	0.908
4	2	5.9	7.075	0.834
4	3	8.0		
4	4	8.4		

TABLE 17.23 SEASONAL INDEX CALCULATIONS FOR THE TELEVISION SET SALES TIME SERIES

Quarter	Seasonal-Irregular Values			Seasonal Index
1	0.971	0.918	0.908	0.93
2	0.840	0.839	0.834	0.84
3	1.096	1.075	1.109	1.09
4	1.133	1.156	1.141	1.14

fourth quarter because of the coming winter season and reduction in outdoor activities. The low second-quarter sales reflect the reduced interest in television viewing due to the spring and presummer activities of potential customers.

One final adjustment is sometimes necessary in obtaining the seasonal indexes. Because the multiplicative model requires that the average seasonal index equal 1.00, the sum of the four seasonal indexes in Table 17.23 must equal 4.00. In other words, the seasonal effects must even out over the year. The average of the seasonal indexes in our example is equal to 1.00, and hence this type of adjustment is not necessary. In other cases, a slight adjustment may be necessary. To make the adjustment, multiply each seasonal index by the number of seasons divided by the sum of the unadjusted seasonal indexes. For instance, for quarterly data, multiply each seasonal index by 4/(sum of the unadjusted seasonal indexes). Some of the exercises will require this adjustment to obtain the appropriate seasonal indexes.

Deseasonalizing the Time Series

A time series that has had the seasonal effects removed is referred to as a **deseasonalized time series**, and the process of using the seasonal indexes to remove the seasonal effects from a time series is referred to as deseasonalizing the time series. Using a multiplicative

TABLE 17.24   DESEASONALIZED VALUES FOR THE TELEVISION SET SALES TIME SERIES

Year	Quarter	Time Period	Sales (1000s)	Seasonal Index	Deseasonalized Sales
1	1	1	4.8	0.93	5.16
	2	2	4.1	0.84	4.88
	3	3	6.0	1.09	5.50
	4	4	6.5	1.14	5.70
2	1	5	5.8	0.93	6.24
	2	6	5.2	0.84	6.19
	3	7	6.8	1.09	6.24
	4	8	7.4	1.14	6.49
3	1	9	6.0	0.93	6.45
	2	10	5.6	0.84	6.67
	3	11	7.5	1.09	6.88
	4	12	7.8	1.14	6.84
4	1	13	6.3	0.93	6.77
	2	14	5.9	0.84	7.02
	3	15	8.0	1.09	7.34
	4	16	8.4	1.14	7.37

Economic time series adjusted for seasonal variations are often reported in publications such as the Survey of Current Business, The Wall Street Journal, *and* BusinessWeek.

decomposition model, we deseasonalize a time series by dividing each observation by its corresponding seasonal index. The multiplicative decomposition model is

$$Y_t = \text{Trend}_t \times \text{Seasonal}_t \times \text{Irregular}_t$$

So, when we divide each time series observation (Y_t) by its corresponding seasonal index, the resulting data show only trend and random variability (the irregular component). The deseasonalized time series for television set sales is summarized in Table 17.24. A graph of the deseasonalized time series is shown in Figure 17.21.

FIGURE 17.21   DESEASONALIZED TELEVISION SET SALES TIME SERIES

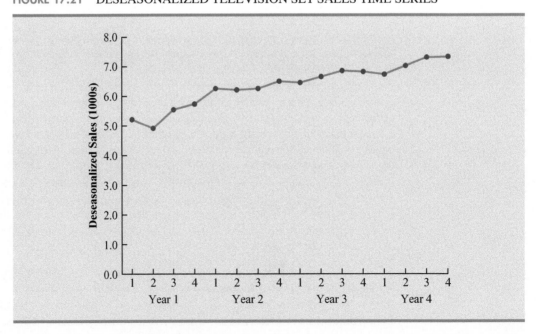

Using the Deseasonalized Time Series to Identify Trend

The graph of the deseasonalized television set sales time series shown in Figure 17.21 appears to have an upward linear trend. To identify this trend, we will fit a linear trend equation to the deseasonalized time series using the same method shown in Section 17.4. The only difference is that we will be fitting a trend line to the deseasonalized data instead of the original data.

Recall that for a linear trend the estimated regression equation can be written as

$$T_t = b_0 + b_1 t$$

where

$$T_t = \text{linear trend forecast in period } t$$
$$b_0 = \text{intercept of the linear trend line}$$
$$b_1 = \text{slope of the trend line}$$
$$t = \text{time period}$$

In Section 17.4 we provided formulas for computing the values of b_0 and b_1. To fit a linear trend line to the deseasonalized data in Table 17.24, the only change is that the deseasonalized time series values are used instead of the observed values Y_t in computing b_0 and b_1.

Figure 17.22 shows the computer output obtained using Minitab's regression analysis procedure to estimate the trend line for the deseasonalized television set time series. The estimated linear trend equation is

$$\text{Deseasonalized Sales} = 5.10 + 0.148t$$

The slope of 0.148 indicates that over the past 16 quarters, the firm averaged a deseasonalized growth in sales of about 148 sets per quarter. If we assume that the past 16-quarter trend in sales data is a reasonably good indicator of the future, this equation can be used to develop a trend projection for future quarters. For example, substituting $t = 17$ into the equation yields next quarter's deseasonalized trend projection, T_{17}.

$$T_{17} = 5.10 + 0.148(17) = 7.616$$

FIGURE 17.22 MINITAB REGRESSION OUTPUT FOR THE DESEASONALIZED TELEVISION SET SALES TIME SERIES

```
The regression equation is
Deseasonalized Sales = 5.10 + 0.148 Period

Predictor      Coef   SE Coef        T       P
Constant     5.1050    0.1133    45.07   0.000
Period       0.14760   0.01171   12.60   0.000

S = 0.215985    R-Sq = 91.9%    R-Sq(adj) = 91.3%

Analysis of Variance

Source           DF       SS       MS       F       P
Regression        1   7.4068   7.4068  158.78   0.000
Residual Error   14   0.6531   0.0466
Total            15   8.0599
```

TABLE 17.25   QUARTERLY FORECASTS FOR THE TELEVISION SET SALES TIME SERIES

Year	Quarter	Deseasonalized Trend Forecast	Seasonal Index	Quarterly Forecast
5	1	7616	0.93	(7616)(0.93) = 7083
	2	7764	0.84	(7764)(0.84) = 6522
	3	7912	1.09	(7912)(1.09) = 8624
	4	8060	1.14	(8060)(1.14) = 9188

Thus, using the deseasonalized data, the linear trend forecast for next quarter (period 17) is 7616 television sets. Similarly, the deseasonalized trend forecasts for the next three quarters (periods 18, 19, and 20) are 7764, 7912, and 8060 television sets, respectively.

Seasonal Adjustments

The final step in developing the forecast when both trend and seasonal components are present is to use the seasonal indexes to adjust the deseasonalized trend projections. Returning to the television set sales example, we have a deseasonalized trend projection for the next four quarters. Now we must adjust the forecast for the seasonal effect. The seasonal index for the first quarter of year 5 ($t = 17$) is 0.93, so we obtain the quarterly forecast by multiplying the deseasonalized forecast based on trend ($T_{17} = 7616$) by the seasonal index (0.93). Thus, the forecast for the next quarter is 7616(0.93) = 7083. Table 17.25 shows the quarterly forecast for quarters 17 through 20. The high-volume fourth quarter has a 9188-unit forecast, and the low-volume second quarter has a 6522-unit forecast.

Models Based on Monthly Data

In the preceding television set sales example, we used quarterly data to illustrate the computation of seasonal indexes. However, many businesses use monthly rather than quarterly forecasts. In such cases, the procedures introduced in this section can be applied with minor modifications. First, a 12-month moving average replaces the four-quarter moving average; second, 12 monthly seasonal indexes, rather than four quarterly seasonal indexes, must be computed. Other than these changes, the computational and forecasting procedures are identical.

Cyclical Component

Mathematically, the multiplicative model of equation (17.14) can be expanded to include a cyclical component.

$$Y_t = \text{Trend}_t \times \text{Cyclical}_t \times \text{Seasonal}_t \times \text{Irregular}_t \qquad \text{(17.15)}$$

The cyclical component, like the seasonal component, is expressed as a percentage of trend. As mentioned in Section 17.1, this component is attributable to multiyear cycles in the time series. It is analogous to the seasonal component, but over a longer period of time. However, because of the length of time involved, obtaining enough relevant data to estimate the cyclical component is often difficult. Another difficulty is that cycles usually vary in length. Because it is so difficult to identify and/or separate cyclical effects from long-term trend effects, in practice these effects are often combined and referred to as a combined trend-cycle component. We leave further discussion of the cyclical component to specialized texts on forecasting methods.

NOTES AND COMMENTS

1. There are a number of different approaches to computing the seasonal indexes. In this section each seasonal index was computed by averaging the corresponding seasonal-irregular values. Another approach, and the one used by Minitab, is to use the median of the seasonal-irregular values as the seasonal index.

2. Calendar adjustments are often made before deseasonalizing a time series. For example, if a time series consists of monthly sales values, the value for February sales may be less than for another month simply because there are fewer days in February. To account for this factor, we would first divide each month's sales value by the number of days in the month to obtain a daily average. Since the average number of days in a month is approximately $365/12 = 30.4167$, we then multiply the daily averages by 30.4167 to obtain adjusted monthly values. For the examples and exercises in this chapter, you can assume that any required calendar adjustments have already been made.

Exercises

Methods

35. Consider the following time series data.

Quarter	Year 1	Year 2	Year 3
1	4	6	7
2	2	3	6
3	3	5	6
4	5	7	8

a. Construct a time series plot. What type of pattern exists in the data?
b. Show the four-quarter and centered moving average values for this time series.
c. Compute seasonal indexes and adjusted seasonal indexes for the four quarters.

36. Refer to exercise 35.
a. Deseasonalize the time series using the adjusted seasonal indexes computed in part (c) of exercise 35.
b. Using Minitab or Excel, compute the linear trend regression equation for the deseasonalized data.
c. Compute the deseasonalized quarterly trend forecast for Year 4.
d. Use the seasonal indexes to adjust the deseasonalized trend forecasts computed in part (c).

Applications

37. The quarterly sales data (number of copies sold) for a college textbook over the past three years follow.

TextSales

Quarter	Year 1	Year 2	Year 3
1	1690	1800	1850
2	940	900	1100
3	2625	2900	2930
4	2500	2360	2615

a. Construct a time series plot. What type of pattern exists in the data?
b. Show the four-quarter and centered moving average values for this time series.
c. Compute the seasonal and adjusted seasonal indexes for the four quarters.
d. When does the publisher have the largest seasonal index? Does this result appear reasonable? Explain.
e. Deseasonalize the time series.
f. Compute the linear trend equation for the deseasonalized data and forecast sales using the linear trend equation.
g. Adjust the linear trend forecasts using the adjusted seasonal indexes computed in part (c).

38. Three years of monthly lawn-maintenance expenses ($) for a six-unit apartment house in southern Florida follow.

WEB file

AptExp

Month	Year 1	Year 2	Year 3
January	170	180	195
February	180	205	210
March	205	215	230
April	230	245	280
May	240	265	290
June	315	330	390
July	360	400	420
August	290	335	330
September	240	260	290
October	240	270	295
November	230	255	280
December	195	220	250

a. Construct a time series plot. What type of pattern exists in the data?
b. Identify the monthly seasonal indexes for the three years of lawn-maintenance expenses for the apartment house in southern Florida as given here. Use a 12-month moving average calculation.
c. Deseasonalize the time series.
d. Compute the linear trend equation for the deseasonalized data.
e. Compute the deseasonalized trend forecasts and then adjust the trend forecasts using the seasonal indexes to provide a forecast for monthly expenses in year 4.

39. Air pollution control specialists in southern California monitor the amount of ozone, carbon dioxide, and nitrogen dioxide in the air on an hourly basis. The hourly time series data exhibit seasonality, with the levels of pollutants showing patterns over the hours in the day. On July 15, 16, and 17, the following levels of nitrogen dioxide were observed in the downtown area for the 12 hours from 6:00 A.M. to 6:00 P.M.

WEB file

Pollution

July 15:	25	28	35	50	60	60	40	35	30	25	25	20
July 16:	28	30	35	48	60	65	50	40	35	25	20	20
July 17:	35	42	45	70	72	75	60	45	40	25	25	25

a. Construct a time series plot. What type of pattern exists in the data?
b. Identify the hourly seasonal indexes for the 12 readings each day.
c. Deseasonalize the time series.
d. Using Minitab or Excel, compute the linear trend equation for the deseasonalized data.
e. Compute the deseasonalized trend forecasts for the 12 hours for July 18 and then adjust the trend forecasts using the seasonal indexes computed in part (b).

40. Electric power consumption is measured in kilowatt-hours (kWh). The local utility company offers an interrupt program whereby commercial customers that participate receive favorable rates but must agree to cut back consumption if the utility requests them to do so. Timko

Products cut back consumption at 12:00 noon Thursday. To assess the savings, the utility must estimate Timko's usage without the interrupt. The period of interrupted service was from noon to 8:00 P.M. Data on electric power consumption for the previous 72 hours are available.

Power

Time Period	Monday	Tuesday	Wednesday	Thursday
12–4 A.M.	—	19,281	31,209	27,330
4–8 A.M	—	33,195	37,014	32,715
8–12 noon	—	99,516	119,968	152,465
12–4 P.M.	124,299	123,666	156,033	
4–8 P.M.	113,545	111,717	128,889	
8–12 midnight	41,300	48,112	73,923	

a. Is there a seasonal effect over the 24-hour period?
b. Compute seasonal indexes for the six 4-hour periods.
c. Use trend adjusted for seasonal indexes to estimate Timko's normal usage over the period of interrupted service.

Summary

This chapter provided an introduction to the basic methods of time series analysis and forecasting. First, we showed that the underlying pattern in the time series can often be identified by constructing a time series plot. Several types of data patterns can be distinguished, including a horizontal pattern, a trend pattern, and a seasonal pattern. The forecasting methods we have discussed are based on which of these patterns are present in the time series.

For a time series with a horizontal pattern, we showed how moving averages and exponential smoothing can be used to develop a forecast. The moving averages method consists of computing an average of past data values and then using that average as the forecast for the next period. In the exponential smoothing method, a weighted average of past time series values is used to compute a forecast. These methods also adapt well when a horizontal pattern shifts to a different level and resumes a horizontal pattern.

An important factor in determining what forecasting method to use involves the accuracy of the method. We discussed three measures of forecast accuracy: mean absolute error (MAE), mean squared error (MSE), and mean absolute percentage error (MAPE). Each of these measures is designed to determine how well a particular forecasting method is able to reproduce the time series data that are already available. By selecting a method that has the best accuracy for the data already known, we hope to increase the likelihood that we will obtain better forecasts for future time periods.

For time series that have only a long-term linear trend, we showed how simple time series regression can be used to make trend projections. We also discussed how an extension of single exponential smoothing, referred to as Holt's linear exponential smoothing, can be used to forecast a time series with a linear trend. For a time series with a curvilinear or nonlinear trend, we showed how multiple regression can be used to fit a quadratic trend equation or an exponential trend equation to the data.

For a time series with a seasonal pattern, we showed how the use of dummy variables in a multiple regression model can be used to develop an estimated regression equation with seasonal effects. We then extended the regression approach to include situations where the time series contains both a seasonal and a linear trend effect by showing how to combine the dummy variable approach for handling seasonality with the time series regression approach for handling linear trend.

In the last section of the chapter we showed how time series decomposition can be used to separate or decompose a time series into seasonal and trend components and then to deseasonalize the time series. We showed how to compute seasonal indexes for a multiplicative model, how to use the seasonal indexes to deseasonalize the time series, and how to use regression analysis on the deseasonalized data to estimate the trend component. The final step in developing a forecast when both trend and seasonal components are present is to use the seasonal indexes to adjust the trend projections.

Glossary

Time series A sequence of observations on a variable measured at successive points in time or over successive periods of time.

Time series plot A graphical presentation of the relationship between time and the time series variable. Time is shown on the horizontal axis and the time series values are shown on the verical axis.

Horizontal pattern A horizontal pattern exists when the data fluctuate around a constant mean.

Stationary time series A time series whose statistical properties are indepepndent of time. For a stationary time series the process generating the data has a constant mean and the variability of the time series is constant over time.

Trend pattern A trend pattern exists if the time series plot shows gradual shifts or movements to relatively higher or lower values over a longer period of time.

Seasonal pattern A seasonal pattern exists if the time series plot exhibits a repeating pattern over successive periods. The successive periods are often one-year intervals, which is where the name seasonal pattern comes from.

Cyclical pattern A cyclical pattern exists if the time series plot shows an alternating sequence of points below and above the trend line lasting more than one year.

Forecast error The difference between the actual time series value and the forecast.

Mean absolute error (MAE) The average of the absolute values of the forecast errors.

Mean squared error (MSE) The average of the sum of squared forecast errors.

Mean absolute percentage error (MAPE) The average of the absolute values of the percentage forecast errors.

Moving averages A forecasting method that uses the average of the most recent k data values in the time series as the forecast for the next period.

Weighted moving averages A forecasting method that involves selecting a different weight for the most recent k data values values in the time series and then computing a weighted average of the values. The sum of the weights must equal one.

Exponential smoothing A forecasting method that uses a weighted average of past time series values as the forecast; it is a special case of the weighted moving averages method in which we select only one weight—the weight for the most recent observation.

Smoothing constant A parameter of the exponential smoothing model that provides the weight given to the most recent time series value in the calculation of the forecast value.

Linear exponential smoothing An extension of single exponential smoothing that uses two smoothing constants to enable forecasts to be developed for a time series with a linear trend.

Time series decompostition A time series method that is used to separate or decompose a time series into seasonal and trend components.

Additive decomposition model In an additive decomposition model the actual time series value at time period t is obtained by adding the values of a trend component, a seasonal component, and an irregular component.

Multiplicative decomposition model In a multiplicative decomposition model the actual time series value at time period t is obtained by multiplying the values of a trend component, a seasonal component, and an irregular component.

Deseasonalized time series A time series from which the effect of season has been removed by dividing each original time series observation by the corresponding seasonal index.

Key Formulas

Moving Average Forecast of Order k

$$F_{t+1} = \frac{\sum(\text{most recent } k \text{ data values})}{k} \tag{17.1}$$

Exponential Smoothing Forecast

$$F_{t+1} = \alpha Y_t + (1 - \alpha) F_t \tag{17.2}$$

Linear Trend Equation

$$T_t = b_0 + b_1 t \tag{17.4}$$

where

$$b_1 = \frac{\sum_{t=1}^{n}(t - \bar{t})(Y_t - \bar{Y})}{\sum_{t=1}^{n}(t - \bar{t})^2} \tag{17.5}$$

$$b_0 = \bar{Y} - b_1 \bar{t} \tag{17.6}$$

Holt's Linear Exponential Smoothing

$$L_t = \alpha Y_t + (1 - \alpha)(L_{t-1} + b_{t-1}) \tag{17.7}$$
$$b_t = \beta(L_t - L_{t-1}) + (1 - \beta) b_{t-1} \tag{17.8}$$
$$F_{t+k} = L_t + b_t k \tag{17.9}$$

Quadratic Trend Equation

$$T_t = b_0 + b_1 t + b_2 t^2 \tag{17.10}$$

Exponential Trend Equation

$$T_t = b_0(b_1)^t \tag{17.11}$$

Additive Decomposition Model

$$Y_t = \text{Trend}_t + \text{Seasonal}_t + \text{Irregular}_t \tag{17.13}$$

Multiplicative Decomposition Model

$$Y_t = \text{Trend}_t \times \text{Seasonal}_t \times \text{Irregular}_t \tag{17.14}$$

Supplementary Exercises

41. The weekly demand (in cases) for a particular brand of automatic dishwasher detergent for a chain of grocery stores located in Columbus, Ohio, follows.

WEB file

Dishwasher

Week	Demand	Week	Demand
1	22	6	24
2	18	7	20
3	23	8	19
4	21	9	18
5	17	10	21

    a.   Construct a time series plot. What type of pattern exists in the data?

    b.   Use a three-week moving average to develop a forecast for week 11.

    c.   Use exponential smoothing with a smoothing constant of $\alpha = .2$ to develop a forecast for week 11.

    d.   Which of the two methods do you prefer? Why?

42.   The following table reports the percentage of stocks in a portfolio for nine quarters from 2010 to 2012.

WEB file

Portfolio

Quarter	Stock %
1st—2010	29.8
2nd—2010	31.0
3rd—2010	29.9
4th—2010	30.1
1st—2011	32.2
2nd—2011	31.5
3rd—2011	32.0
4th—2011	31.9
1st—2012	30.0

    a.   Construct a time series plot. What type of pattern exists in the data?

    b.   Use exponential smoothing to forecast this time series. Consider smoothing constants of $\alpha = .2, .3$, and $.4$. What value of the smoothing constant provides the most accurate forecasts?

    c.   What is the forecast of the percentage of stocks in a typical portfolio for the second quarter of 2009?

43.   United Dairies, Inc., supplies milk to several independent grocers throughout Dade County, Florida. Managers at United Dairies want to develop a forecast of the number of half-gallons of milk sold per week. Sales data for the past 12 weeks follow.

WEB file

UDFMilk

Week	Sales	Week	Sales
1	2750	7	3300
2	3100	8	3100
3	3250	9	2950
4	2800	10	3000
5	2900	11	3200
6	3050	12	3150

    a.   Construct a time series plot. What type of pattern exists in the data?

    b.   Use exponential smoothing withf $\alpha = .4$ to develop a forecast of demand for week 13.

44.   To avoid a monthly service fee in an interest-bearing checking account, customers must maintain a minimum average daily balance. Bankrate's 2008 survey of 249 banks and thrifts in the top 25 metropolitan areas showed that you need to maintain an average balance of $3,462 to avoid a monthly service fee. With an average fee of $11.97 and an average interest rate of only 0.24 percent, customers with interest-bearing checking accounts

are not getting much value for basically providing the bank with a line of credit equal to the average monthly balance required to avoid the monthly service fee (Bankrate website, October 27, 2008). The following table shows the minimum average balance required to avoid paying a monthly service fee from 2001–2008.

Year	Balance ($)
2001	2435
2002	2593
2003	2258
2004	2087
2005	2294
2006	2660
2007	3317
2008	3462

a. Construct a time series plot. What type of pattern exists in the data?
b. Using Minitab or Excel, develop a linear trend equation for the time series. Compute an estimate of the average balance required to avoid a monthly service fee for 2009.
c. Using Minitab or Excel, develop a quadratic trend equation for the time series. Compute an estimate of the average balance required to avoid a monthly service fee for 2009.
d. Using MSE, which approach provides the most accurate forecasts for the historical data?
e. For these data would you recommend that the forecast for 2009 be developed using the linear trend equation or the quadratic trend equation? Explain.

45. The Garden Avenue Seven sells CDs of its musical performances. The following table reports sales (in units) for the past 18 months. The group's manager wants an accurate method for forecasting future sales.

WEB file

CDSales

Month	Sales	Month	Sales	Month	Sales
1	293	7	381	13	549
2	283	8	431	14	544
3	322	9	424	15	601
4	355	10	433	16	587
5	346	11	470	17	644
6	379	12	481	18	660

a. Construct a time series plot. What type of pattern exists in the data?
b. Use exponential smoothing with $\alpha = .3, .4,$ and $.5$. Which value of α provides the most accurate forecasts?
c. Use trend projection to provide a forecast. What is the value of MSE?
d. Which method of forecasting would you recommend to the manager? Why?

46. The Mayfair Department Store in Davenport, Iowa, is trying to determine the amount of sales lost while it was shut down during July and August because of damage caused by the Mississippi River flood. Sales data for January through June follow.

Month	Sales ($1000s)	Month	Sales ($1000s)
January	185.72	April	210.36
February	167.84	May	255.57
March	205.11	June	261.19

a. Use exponential smoothing, with $\alpha = .4$, to develop a forecast for July and August. (*Hint*: Use the forecast for July as the actual sales in July in developing the August forecast.) Comment on the use of exponential smoothing for forecasts more than one period into the future.

b. Use trend projection to forecast sales for July and August.

c. Mayfair's insurance company proposed a settlement based on lost sales of $240,000 in July and August. Is this amount fair? If not, what amount would you recommend as a counteroffer?

47. Canton Supplies, Inc., is a service firm that employs approximately 100 individuals. Managers of Canton Supplies are concerned about meeting monthly cash obligations and want to develop a forecast of monthly cash requirements. Because of a recent change in operating policy, only the past seven months of data that follow are considered to be relevant.

Month	1	2	3	4	5	6	7
Cash Required ($1000s)	205	212	218	224	230	240	246

a. Construct a time series plot. What type of pattern exists in the data?

b. Use Holt's linear exponential smoothing with $\alpha = .6$ and $\beta = .4$ to forecast cash requirements for each of the next two months.

c. Using Minitab or Excel, develop a linear trend equation to forecast cash requirements for each of the next two months.

d. Would you recommend using Holt's linear exponential smoothing with $\alpha = .6$ and $\beta = .4$ to forecast cash requirements for each of the next two months or the linear trend equation? Explain.

48. The Costello Music Company has been in business for five years. During that time, sales of pianos increased from 12 units in the first year to 76 units in the most recent year. Fred Costello, the firm's owner, wants to develop a forecast of piano sales for the coming year. The historical data follow.

Year	1	2	3	4	5
Sales	12	28	34	50	76

a. Construct a time series plot. What type of pattern exists in the data?

b. Develop the linear trend equation for the time series. What is the average increase in sales that the firm has been realizing per year?

c. Forecast sales for years 6 and 7.

49. Consider the Costello Music Company problem in exercise 48. The quarterly sales data follow.

WEB file

PianoSales

Year	Quarter 1	Quarter 2	Quarter 3	Quarter 4	Total Yearly Sales
1	4	2	1	5	12
2	6	4	4	14	28
3	10	3	5	16	34
4	12	9	7	22	50
5	18	10	13	35	76

a. Use the following dummy variables to develop an estimated regression equation to account for any seasonal and linear trend effects in the data: Qtr1 = 1 if Quarter 1, 0 otherwise; Qtr2 = 1 if Quarter 2, 0 otherwise; and Qtr3 = 1 if Quarter 3, 0 otherwise.

b. Compute the quarterly forecasts for next year.

50. Refer to the Costello Music Company problem in exercise 49.

a. Using time series decomposition, compute the seasonal indexes for the four quarters.

b. When does Costello Music experience the largest seasonal effect? Does this result appear reasonable? Explain.

51. Refer to the Costello Music Company time series in exercise 49.
   a. Deseasonalize the data and use the deseasonalized time series to identify the trend.
   b. Use the results of part (a) to develop a quarterly forecast for next year based on trend.
   c. Use the seasonal indexes developed in exercise 50 to adjust the forecasts developed in part (b) to account for the effect of season.

52. Hudson Marine has been an authorized dealer for C&D marine radios for the past seven years. The following table reports the number of radios sold each year.

Year	1	2	3	4	5	6	7
Number Sold	35	50	75	90	105	110	130

   a. Construct a time series plot. Does a linear trend appear to be present?
   b. Using Minitab or Excel, develop a linear trend equation for this time series.
   c. Use the linear trend equation developed in part (b) to develop a forecast for annual sales in year 8.

53. Refer to the Hudson Marine problem in exercise 52. Suppose the quarterly sales values for the seven years of historical data are as follows.

WEB file

HudsonMarine

Year	Quarter 1	Quarter 2	Quarter 3	Quarter 4	Total Yearly Sales
1	6	15	10	4	35
2	10	18	15	7	50
3	14	26	23	12	75
4	19	28	25	18	90
5	22	34	28	21	105
6	24	36	30	20	110
7	28	40	35	27	130

   a. Use the following dummy variables to develop an estimated regression equation to account for any season and linear trend effects in the data: Qtr1 $= 1$ if Quarter 1, 0 otherwise; Qtr2 $= 1$ if Quarter 2, 0 otherwise; and Qtr3 $= 1$ if Quarter 3, 0 otherwise.
   b. Compute the quarterly forecasts for next year.

54. Refer to the Hudson Marine problem in exercise 53.
   a. Compute the centered moving average values for this time series.
   b. Construct a time series plot that also shows the centered moving average and original time series on the same graph. Discuss the differences between the original time series plot and the centered moving average time series.
   c. Compute the seasonal indexes for the four quarters.
   d. When does Hudson Marine experience the largest seasonal effect? Does this result seem reasonable? Explain.

55. Refer to the Hudson Marine data in exercise 53.
   a. Deseasonalize the data and use the deseasonalized time series to identify the trend.
   b. Use the results of part (a) to develop a quarterly forecast for next year based on trend.
   c. Use the seasonal indexes developed in exercise 54 to adjust the forecasts developed in part (b) to account for the effect of season.

Case Problem 1   Forecasting Food and Beverage Sales

The Vintage Restaurant, on Captiva Island near Fort Myers, Florida, is owned and operated by Karen Payne. The restaurant just completed its third year of operation. Since opening her restaurant, Karen has sought to establish a reputation for the Vintage as a high-quality dining establishment that specializes in fresh seafood. Through the efforts of Karen and her staff, her restaurant has become one of the best and fastest growing restaurants on the island.

TABLE 17.26   FOOD AND BEVERAGE SALES FOR THE VINTAGE
RESTAURANT ($1000s)

Month	First Year	Second Year	Third Year
January	242	263	282
February	235	238	255
March	232	247	265
April	178	193	205
May	184	193	210
June	140	149	160
July	145	157	166
August	152	161	174
September	110	122	126
October	130	130	148
November	152	167	173
December	206	230	235

To better plan for future growth of the restaurant, Karen needs to develop a system that will enable her to forecast food and beverage sales by month for up to one year in advance. Table 17.26 shows the value of food and beverage sales ($1000s) for the first three years of operation.

Managerial Report

Perform an analysis of the sales data for the Vintage Restaurant. Prepare a report for Karen that summarizes your findings, forecasts, and recommendations. Include the following:

1. A time series plot. Comment on the underlying pattern in the time series.
2. An analysis of the seasonality of the data. Indicate the seasonal indexes for each month, and comment on the high and low seasonal sales months. Do the seasonal indexes make intuitive sense? Discuss.
3. Deseasonalize the time series. Does there appear to be any trend in the deseasonalized time series?
4. Using the time series decomposition method, forecast sales for January through December of the fourth year.
5. Using the dummy variable regression approach, forecast sales for January through December of the fourth year.
6. Provide summary tables of your calculations and any graphs in the appendix of your report.

Assume that January sales for the fourth year turn out to be $295,000. What was your forecast error? If this error is large, Karen may be puzzled about the difference between your forecast and the actual sales value. What can you do to resolve her uncertainty in the forecasting procedure?

Case Problem 2   Forecasting Lost Sales

The Carlson Department Store suffered heavy damage when a hurricane struck on August 31. The store was closed for four months (September through December), and Carlson is now involved in a dispute with its insurance company about the amount of lost sales during the time the store was closed. Two key issues must be resolved: (1) the amount of sales Carlson would have made if the hurricane had not struck and (2) whether Carlson is entitled to any compensation for excess sales due to increased business activity after the storm. More than

TABLE 17.27   SALES FOR CARLSON DEPARTMENT STORE ($MILLIONS)

CarlsonSales

Month	Year 1	Year 2	Year 3	Year 4	Year 5
January		1.45	2.31	2.31	2.56
February		1.80	1.89	1.99	2.28
March		2.03	2.02	2.42	2.69
April		1.99	2.23	2.45	2.48
May		2.32	2.39	2.57	2.73
June		2.20	2.14	2.42	2.37
July		2.13	2.27	2.40	2.31
August		2.43	2.21	2.50	2.23
September	1.71	1.90	1.89	2.09	
October	1.90	2.13	2.29	2.54	
November	2.74	2.56	2.83	2.97	
December	4.20	4.16	4.04	4.35	

$8 billion in federal disaster relief and insurance money came into the county, resulting in increased sales at department stores and numerous other businesses.

Table 17.27 gives Carlson's sales data for the 48 months preceding the storm. Table 17.28 reports total sales for the 48 months preceding the storm for all department stores in the county, as well as the total sales in the county for the four months the Carlson Department Store was closed. Carlson's managers asked you to analyze these data and develop estimates of the lost sales at the Carlson Department Store for the months of September through December. They also asked you to determine whether a case can be made for excess storm-related sales during the same period. If such a case can be made, Carlson is entitled to compensation for excess sales it would have earned in addition to ordinary sales.

Managerial Report

Prepare a report for the managers of the Carlson Department Store that summarizes your findings, forecasts, and recommendations. Include the following:

1. An estimate of sales for Carlson Department Store had there been no hurricane.
2. An estimate of countywide department store sales had there been no hurricane.
3. An estimate of lost sales for the Carlson Department Store for September through December.

TABLE 17.28   DEPARTMENT STORE SALES FOR THE COUNTY ($MILLIONS)

CountySales

Month	Year 1	Year 2	Year 3	Year 4	Year 5
January		46.80	46.80	43.80	48.00
February		48.00	48.60	45.60	51.60
March		60.00	59.40	57.60	57.60
April		57.60	58.20	53.40	58.20
May		61.80	60.60	56.40	60.00
June		58.20	55.20	52.80	57.00
July		56.40	51.00	54.00	57.60
August		63.00	58.80	60.60	61.80
September	55.80	57.60	49.80	47.40	69.00
October	56.40	53.40	54.60	54.60	75.00
November	71.40	71.40	65.40	67.80	85.20
December	117.60	114.00	102.00	100.20	121.80

In addition, use the countywide actual department stores sales for September through December and the estimate in part (2) to make a case for or against excess storm-related sales.

Appendix 17.1 Forecasting with Minitab

In this appendix we show how Minitab can be used to develop forecasts using the following forecasting methods: moving averages, exponential smoothing, trend projection, Holt's linear exponential smoothing, and time series decomposition.

Moving Averages

To show how Minitab can be used to develop forecasts using the moving averages method, we will develop a forecast for the gasoline sales time series in Table 17.1 and Figure 17.1. The sales data for the 12 weeks are entered into column 2 of the worksheet. The following steps can be used to produce a three-week moving average forecast for week 13.

Step 1. Select the **Stat** menu
Step 2. Choose **Time Series**
Step 3. Choose **Moving Average**
Step 4. When the Moving Average dialog box appears:
  Enter C2 in the **Variable** box
  Enter 3 in the **MA length** box
  Select **Generate forecasts**
  Enter 1 in the **Number of forecasts** box
  Enter 12 in the **Starting from origin** box
  Click **OK**

Measures of forecast accuracy and the forecast for week 13 are shown in the session window. The mean absolute error is labeled MAD and the mean squared error is labeled MSD in the Minitab output.

Exponential Smoothing

To show how Minitab can be used to develop an exponential smoothing forecast, we will again develop a forecast of sales in week 13 for the gasoline sales time series in Table 17.1 and Figure 17.1. The sales data for the 12 weeks are entered into column 2 of the worksheet. The following steps can be used to produce a forecast for week 13 using a smoothing constant of $\alpha = .2$.

Step 1. Select the **Stat** menu
Step 2. Choose **Time Series**
Step 3. Choose **Single Exp Smoothing**
Step 4. When the Single Exponential Smoothing dialog box appears:
  Enter C2 in the **Variable** box
  Select the **Use** option for the Weight to Use in Smoothing
  Enter 0.2 in the Use box
  Select **Generate forecasts**
  Enter 1 in the **Number of forecasts** box
  Enter 12 in the **Starting from origin** box
  Select **Options**
Step 5. When the Single Exponential Smoothing-Options dialog box appears:
  Enter 1 in the **Use average of first K observations** box
  Click **OK**
Step 6. When the Single Exponential Smoothing dialog box appears:
  Click **OK**

Measures of forecast accuracy and the exponential smoothing forecast for week 13 are shown in the session window. The mean absolute error is labeled MAD and the mean squared error is labeled MSD in the Minitab output.*

Trend Projection

WEB file

Bicycle

To show how Minitab can be used for trend projection, we develop a forecast for the bicycle sales time series in Table 17.3 and Figure 17.3. The year numbers are entered into column 1 and the sales data are entered into column 2 of the worksheet. The following steps can be used to produce a forecast for year 11 using trend projection.

Step 1. Select the **Stat** menu
Step 2. Choose **Time Series**
Step 3. Choose **Trend Analysis**
Step 4. When the Trend Analysis dialog box appears:
  Enter C2 in the **Variable** box
  Choose **Linear** for the Model Type
  Select **Generate forecasts**
  Enter 1 in the **Number of forecasts** box
  Enter 10 in the **Starting from origin** box
  Click **OK**

The equation for linear trend, measures of forecast accuracy, and the forecast for the next year are shown in the session window. The mean absolute error is labeled MAD and the mean square error is labeled MSD in the Minitab output. To generate forecasts for a quadratic or exponential trend select **Quadratic** of **Exponential growth** instead of **Linear** in step 4.

Holt's Linear Exponential Smoothing

WEB file

Bicycle

To show how Minitab can be used to develop forecasts using Holt's linear exponential smoothing method, we develop a forecast for the bicycle sales time series in Table 17.3 and Figure 17.3. In Minitab, Holt's linear exponential smoothing method is referred to as Double Exponential Smoothing. The year numbers are entered into column 1 and the sales data are entered into column 2 of the worksheet. The following steps can be used to forecast sales in year 11 using Holt's linear exponential smoothing with $\alpha = .1$ and $\beta = .2$.

Step 1. Select the **Stat** menu
Step 2. Choose **Time Series**
Step 3. Choose **Double Exp Smoothing**
Step 4. When the Double Exponential Smoothing dialog box appears:
  Enter C2 in the **Variable** box
  Select the **Use** option for the Weights to Use in Smoothing
  Enter .1 in the **level** box
  Enter .2 in the **trend** box
  Select **Generate forecasts**
  Enter 1 in the **Number of forecasts** box
  Enter 10 in the **Starting from origin** box
  Click **OK**

---

*The value of MSD computed by Minitab is not the same as the value of MSE that we computed in Section 17.3. Minitab uses a forecast of 17 for week 1 and computes MSD using all 12 weeks of data. In Section 17.3 we compute MSE using only the data for weeks 2 through 12, because we had no past values with which to make a forecast for week 1.

Measures of forecast accuracy and Holt's linear exponential smoothing forecast for year 11 are shown in the session window. The mean absolute error is labeled MAD and the mean square error is labeled MSD in the Minitab output.

Time Series Decomposition

TVSales

To show how Minitab can be used to forecast a time series with trend and seasonality using time series decomposition, we develop a forecast for the television set sales time series in Table 17.6 and Figure 17.6. In Minitab, the user has the option of either a multiplicative or additive decomposition model. We will illustrate how to use the multiplicative approach as described in section 17.6. The year numbers are entered into column 1, the quarter values are entered into column 2, and the sales data are entered into column 3 of the worksheet. The following steps can be used to produce a forecast for the next quarter.

Step 1. Select the **Stat** menu
Step 2. Choose **Time Series**
Step 3. Choose **Decomposition**
Step 4. When the Decomposition dialog box appears:
        Enter C3 in the **Variable** box
        Enter 4 in the **Season Length** box
        Select **Multiplicative** for Method Type
        Select **Trend plus Seasonal** for Model Components
        Select **Generate forecasts**
        Enter 1 in the **Number of forecasts** box
        Enter 16 in the **Starting from origin** box
        Click **OK**

The seasonal indexes,[†] measures of forecast accuracy, and the forecast for the next quarter are shown in the session window. The mean absolute error is labeled MAD and the mean square error is labeled MSD in the Minitab output.

Appendix 17.2   Forecasting with Excel

In this appendix we show how Excel can be used to develop forecasts using three forecasting methods: moving averages, exponential smoothing, and trend projection.

Moving Averages

Gasoline

To show how Excel can be used to develop forecasts using the moving averages method, we will develop a forecast for the gasoline sales time series in Table 17.1 and Figure 17.1. The sales data for the 12 weeks are entered into worksheet rows 2 through 13 of column B. The following steps can be used to produce a three-week moving average.

Step 1. Click the **Data** tab on the Ribbon
Step 2. In the **Analysis** group, click **Data Analysis**
Step 3. Choose **Moving Average** from the list of Analysis Tools
Step 4. When the Moving Average dialog box appears:
        Enter B2:B13 in the **Input Range** box
        Enter 3 in the **Interval** box
        Enter C2 in the **Output Range** box
        Click **OK**

[†]The results differ slightly from the results shown in Table 17.12 because Minitab computes the seasonal indexes using the median of the seasonal-irregular values.

The three-week moving averages will appear in column C of the worksheet. The forecast for week 4 appears next to the sales value for week 3, and so on. Forecasts for periods of other length can be computed easily by entering a different value in the **Interval** box.

Exponential Smoothing

Gasoline

To show how Excel can be used for exponential smoothing, we again develop a forecast for the gasoline sales time series in Table 17.1 and Figure 17.1. The sales data for the 12 weeks are entered into worksheet rows 2 through 13 of column B. The following steps can be used to produce a forecast using a smoothing constant of $\alpha = .2$.

Step 1. Click the **Data** tab on the Ribbon
Step 2. In the **Analysis** group, click **Data Analysis**
Step 3. Choose **Exponential Smoothing** from the list of Analysis Tools
Step 4. When the Exponential Smoothing dialog box appears:
  Enter B2:B13 in the **Input Range** box
  Enter .8 in the **Damping factor** box
  Enter C2 in the **Output Range** box
  Click **OK**

The exponential smoothing forecasts will appear in column C of the worksheet. Note that the value we entered in the Damping factor box is $1 - \alpha$; forecasts for other smoothing constants can be computed easily by entering a different value for $1 - \alpha$ in the Damping factor box.

Trend Projection

Bicycle

To show how Excel can be used for trend projection, we develop a forecast for the bicycle sales time series in Table 17.3 and Figure 17.3. The data, with appropriate labels in row 1, are entered into worksheet rows 1 through 11 of columns A and B. The following steps can be used to produce a forecast for year 11 by trend projection.

Step 1. Select an empty cell in the worksheet
Step 2. Select the **Formulas** tab on the Ribbon
Step 3. In the **Function Library** group, click **Insert** Function
Step 4. When the Insert Function dialog box appears:
  Choose **Statistical** in the Or select a category box
  Choose **Forecast** in the Select a function box
Step 5. When the Forecast Arguments dialog box appears:
  Enter 11 in the **x** box
  Enter B2:B11 in the **Known y's** box
  Enter A2:A11 in the **Known x's** box
  Click **OK**

The forecast for year 11, in this case 32.5, will appear in the cell selected in step 1.

Appendix 17.3   Forecasting Using StatTools

In this appendix we show how StatTools can be used to develop forecasts using three forecasting methods: moving averages, exponential smoothing, and Holt's linear exponential smoothing.

Moving Averages

To show how StatTools can be used to develop forecasts using the moving averages method we will develop a forecast for the gasoline sales time series in Table 17.1 and Figure 17.1. Begin by using the Data Set Manager to create a StatTools data set for these data using the procedure described in the appendix in Chapter 1. The following steps will generate a three-week moving average forecast for week 13.

Step 1. Click the **StatTools** tab on the Ribbon
Step 2. In the **Analyses Group**, click **Time Series and Forecasting**
Step 3. Choose the **Forecast** option
Step 4. When the StatTools-Forecast dialog box appears:
    In the **Variables** section, select **Sales**
    Select the **Forecast Settings** tab
      In the **Method** section, select **Moving Average**
      In the Parameters section, enter 3 in the **Span** box
    Select the **Time Scale** tab
      In the **Seasonal Period** section, select **None**
      In the **Label Style** section, select **Integer**
    Click **OK**

The following output will appear: three measures of forecast accuracy; time series plots showing the original data, the forecasts, and the forecast errors; and a table showing the forecasts and forecast errors. Note that StatTools uses the term "Mean Abs Err" to identify the value of MAE; "Root Mean Sq Err" to identify the square root of the value of MSE; and "Mean Abs Per% Err" to identify the value of MAPE.

Exponential Smoothing

WEB file

Gasoline

To show how StatTools can be used to develop an exponential smoothing forecast, we will again develop a forecast of sales in week 13 for the gasoline time series shown in Table 17.1 and Figure 17.1. Begin by using the Data Set Manager to create a StatTools data set for these data using the procedure described in the appendix in Chapter 1. The following steps will produce a forecast using a smoothing constant of $\alpha = .2$.

Step 1. Click the **StatTools** tab on the Ribbon
Step 2. In the **Analyses Group**, click **Time Series and Forecasting**
Step 3. Choose the **Forecast** option
Step 4. When the StatTools-Forecast dialog box appears:
    In the **Variables** section, select **Sales**
    Select the **Forecast Settings** tab
      In the **Method** section, select **Exponential Smoothing (Simple)**
      Remove the check mark in the **Optimize Parameters** box
      In the Parameters section, enter .2 in the **Level (a)** box
    Select the Time Scale tab
      In the **Seasonal Period** section, select **None**
      In the **Label Style** section, select **Integer**
    Click **OK**

The following output will appear: three measures of forecast accuracy; time series plots showing the original data, the forecasts, and the forecast errors; and a table showing the forecasts and forecast errors. Note that StatTools uses the term "Mean Abs Err" to identify the value of MAE; "Root Mean Sq Err" to identify the square root of the value of MSE; and "Mean Abs Per% Err" to identify the value of MAPE.

Holt's Linear Exponential Smoothing

WEB file

Bicycle

To show how StatTools can be used for trend projection, we develop a forecast for the bicycle sales time series in Table 17.3 and Figure 17.3 using Holt's linear exponential smoothing. Begin by using the Data Set Manager to create a StatTools data set for these data using the procedure described in the appendix in Chapter 1. The following steps will produce a forecast using smoothing constants of $\alpha = .1$ and $\beta = .2$.

Step 1. Click the **StatTools** tab on the Ribbon

Step 2. In the **Analyses Group**, click **Time Series and Forecasting**

Step 3. Choose the **Forecast** option

Step 4. When the StatTools-Forecast dialog box appears:

    In the **Variables** section, select **Sales**

    Select the **Forecast Settings** tab

      In the **Method** section, select **Exponential Smoothing (Holt's)**

      Remove the check mark in the **Optimize Parameters** box

      In the Parameters section, enter .1 in the **Level (a)** box

      In the Parameters section, enter .2 in the **Trend (b)** box

    Select the Time Scale tab

      In the **Seasonal Period** section, select **None**

      In the **Label Style** section, select **Integer**

    Click **OK**

The following output will appear: three measures of forecast accuracy; time series plots showing the original data, the forecasts, and the forecast errors; and a table showing the forecasts and forecast errors. Note that StatTools uses the term "Mean Abs Err" to identify the value of MAE; "Root Mean Sq Err" to identify the square root of the of MSE; and "Mean Abs Per% Err" to identify the value of MAPE. The StatTools output differs slightly from the results shown in Section 17.4 because StatTools uses a different approach to compute the estimate of the slope in period 1. With larger data sets the choice of startup values is not critical.

Appendix B: Tables

TABLE 1 CUMULATIVE PROBABILITIES FOR THE STANDARD NORMAL DISTRIBUTION

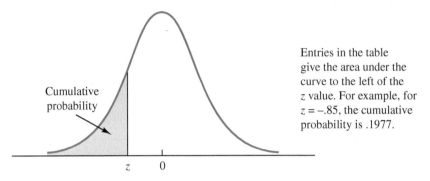

Cumulative probability

Entries in the table give the area under the curve to the left of the z value. For example, for z = −.85, the cumulative probability is .1977.

z	.00	.01	.02	.03	.04	.05	.06	.07	.08	.09
−3.0	.0013	.0013	.0013	.0012	.0012	.0011	.0011	.0011	.0010	.0010
−2.9	.0019	.0018	.0018	.0017	.0016	.0016	.0015	.0015	.0014	.0014
−2.8	.0026	.0025	.0024	.0023	.0023	.0022	.0021	.0021	.0020	.0019
−2.7	.0035	.0034	.0033	.0032	.0031	.0030	.0029	.0028	.0027	.0026
−2.6	.0047	.0045	.0044	.0043	.0041	.0040	.0039	.0038	.0037	.0036
−2.5	.0062	.0060	.0059	.0057	.0055	.0054	.0052	.0051	.0049	.0048
−2.4	.0082	.0080	.0078	.0075	.0073	.0071	.0069	.0068	.0066	.0064
−2.3	.0107	.0104	.0102	.0099	.0096	.0094	.0091	.0089	.0087	.0084
−2.2	.0139	.0136	.0132	.0129	.0125	.0122	.0119	.0116	.0113	.0110
−2.1	.0179	.0174	.0170	.0166	.0162	.0158	.0154	.0150	.0146	.0143
−2.0	.0228	.0222	.0217	.0212	.0207	.0202	.0197	.0192	.0188	.0183
−1.9	.0287	.0281	.0274	.0268	.0262	.0256	.0250	.0244	.0239	.0233
−1.8	.0359	.0351	.0344	.0336	.0329	.0322	.0314	.0307	.0301	.0294
−1.7	.0446	.0436	.0427	.0418	.0409	.0401	.0392	.0384	.0375	.0367
−1.6	.0548	.0537	.0526	.0516	.0505	.0495	.0485	.0475	.0465	.0455
−1.5	.0668	.0655	.0643	.0630	.0618	.0606	.0594	.0582	.0571	.0559
−1.4	.0808	.0793	.0778	.0764	.0749	.0735	.0721	.0708	.0694	.0681
−1.3	.0968	.0951	.0934	.0918	.0901	.0885	.0869	.0853	.0838	.0823
−1.2	.1151	.1131	.1112	.1093	.1075	.1056	.1038	.1020	.1003	.0985
−1.1	.1357	.1335	.1314	.1292	.1271	.1251	.1230	.1210	.1190	.1170
−1.0	.1587	.1562	.1539	.1515	.1492	.1469	.1446	.1423	.1401	.1379
−.9	.1841	.1814	.1788	.1762	.1736	.1711	.1685	.1660	.1635	.1611
−.8	.2119	.2090	.2061	.2033	.2005	.1977	.1949	.1922	.1894	.1867
−.7	.2420	.2389	.2358	.2327	.2296	.2266	.2236	.2206	.2177	.2148
−.6	.2743	.2709	.2676	.2643	.2611	.2578	.2546	.2514	.2483	.2451
−.5	.3085	.3050	.3015	.2981	.2946	.2912	.2877	.2843	.2810	.2776
−.4	.3446	.3409	.3372	.3336	.3300	.3264	.3228	.3192	.3156	.3121
−.3	.3821	.3783	.3745	.3707	.3669	.3632	.3594	.3557	.3520	.3483
−.2	.4207	.4168	.4129	.4090	.4052	.4013	.3974	.3936	.3897	.3859
−.1	.4602	.4562	.4522	.4483	.4443	.4404	.4364	.4325	.4286	.4247
−.0	.5000	.4960	.4920	.4880	.4840	.4801	.4761	.4721	.4681	.4641

TABLE 1   CUMULATIVE PROBABILITIES FOR THE STANDARD NORMAL
DISTRIBUTION (*Continued*)

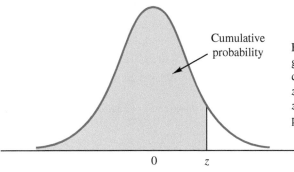

Cumulative
probability

Entries in the table
give the area under the
curve to the left of the
z value. For example, for
z = 1.25, the cumulative
probability is .8944.

z	.00	.01	.02	.03	.04	.05	.06	.07	.08	.09
.0	.5000	.5040	.5080	.5120	.5160	.5199	.5239	.5279	.5319	.5359
.1	.5398	.5438	.5478	.5517	.5557	.5596	.5636	.5675	.5714	.5753
.2	.5793	.5832	.5871	.5910	.5948	.5987	.6026	.6064	.6103	.6141
.3	.6179	.6217	.6255	.6293	.6331	.6368	.6406	.6443	.6480	.6517
.4	.6554	.6591	.6628	.6664	.6700	.6736	.6772	.6808	.6844	.6879
.5	.6915	.6950	.6985	.7019	.7054	.7088	.7123	.7157	.7190	.7224
.6	.7257	.7291	.7324	.7357	.7389	.7422	.7454	.7486	.7517	.7549
.7	.7580	.7611	.7642	.7673	.7704	.7734	.7764	.7794	.7823	.7852
.8	.7881	.7910	.7939	.7967	.7995	.8023	.8051	.8078	.8106	.8133
.9	.8159	.8186	.8212	.8238	.8264	.8289	.8315	.8340	.8365	.8389
1.0	.8413	.8438	.8461	.8485	.8508	.8531	.8554	.8577	.8599	.8621
1.1	.8643	.8665	.8686	.8708	.8729	.8749	.8770	.8790	.8810	.8830
1.2	.8849	.8869	.8888	.8907	.8925	.8944	.8962	.8980	.8997	.9015
1.3	.9032	.9049	.9066	.9082	.9099	.9115	.9131	.9147	.9162	.9177
1.4	.9192	.9207	.9222	.9236	.9251	.9265	.9279	.9292	.9306	.9319
1.5	.9332	.9345	.9357	.9370	.9382	.9394	.9406	.9418	.9429	.9441
1.6	.9452	.9463	.9474	.9484	.9495	.9505	.9515	.9525	.9535	.9545
1.7	.9554	.9564	.9573	.9582	.9591	.9599	.9608	.9616	.9625	.9633
1.8	.9641	.9649	.9656	.9664	.9671	.9678	.9686	.9693	.9699	.9706
1.9	.9713	.9719	.9726	.9732	.9738	.9744	.9750	.9756	.9761	.9767
2.0	.9772	.9778	.9783	.9788	.9793	.9798	.9803	.9808	.9812	.9817
2.1	.9821	.9826	.9830	.9834	.9838	.9842	.9846	.9850	.9854	.9857
2.2	.9861	.9864	.9868	.9871	.9875	.9878	.9881	.9884	.9887	.9890
2.3	.9893	.9896	.9898	.9901	.9904	.9906	.9909	.9911	.9913	.9916
2.4	.9918	.9920	.9922	.9925	.9927	.9929	.9931	.9932	.9934	.9936
2.5	.9938	.9940	.9941	.9943	.9945	.9946	.9948	.9949	.9951	.9952
2.6	.9953	.9955	.9956	.9957	.9959	.9960	.9961	.9962	.9963	.9964
2.7	.9965	.9966	.9967	.9968	.9969	.9970	.9971	.9972	.9973	.9974
2.8	.9974	.9975	.9976	.9977	.9977	.9978	.9979	.9979	.9980	.9981
2.9	.9981	.9982	.9982	.9983	.9984	.9984	.9985	.9985	.9986	.9986
3.0	.9987	.9987	.9987	.9988	.9988	.9989	.9989	.9989	.9990	.9990

TABLE 2 *t* DISTRIBUTION

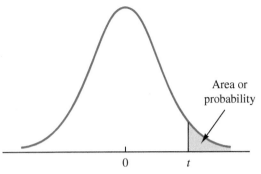

Area or probability

Entries in the table give *t* values for an area or probability in the upper tail of the *t* distribution. For example, with 10 degrees of freedom and a .05 area in the upper tail, $t_{.05} = 1.812$.

Degrees of Freedom	Area in Upper Tail					
	.20	.10	.05	.025	.01	.005
1	1.376	3.078	6.314	12.706	31.821	63.656
2	1.061	1.886	2.920	4.303	6.965	9.925
3	.978	1.638	2.353	3.182	4.541	5.841
4	.941	1.533	2.132	2.776	3.747	4.604
5	.920	1.476	2.015	2.571	3.365	4.032
6	.906	1.440	1.943	2.447	3.143	3.707
7	.896	1.415	1.895	2.365	2.998	3.499
8	.889	1.397	1.860	2.306	2.896	3.355
9	.883	1.383	1.833	2.262	2.821	3.250
10	.879	1.372	1.812	2.228	2.764	3.169
11	.876	1.363	1.796	2.201	2.718	3.106
12	.873	1.356	1.782	2.179	2.681	3.055
13	.870	1.350	1.771	2.160	2.650	3.012
14	.868	1.345	1.761	2.145	2.624	2.977
15	.866	1.341	1.753	2.131	2.602	2.947
16	.865	1.337	1.746	2.120	2.583	2.921
17	.863	1.333	1.740	2.110	2.567	2.898
18	.862	1.330	1.734	2.101	2.552	2.878
19	.861	1.328	1.729	2.093	2.539	2.861
20	.860	1.325	1.725	2.086	2.528	2.845
21	.859	1.323	1.721	2.080	2.518	2.831
22	.858	1.321	1.717	2.074	2.508	2.819
23	.858	1.319	1.714	2.069	2.500	2.807
24	.857	1.318	1.711	2.064	2.492	2.797
25	.856	1.316	1.708	2.060	2.485	2.787
26	.856	1.315	1.706	2.056	2.479	2.779
27	.855	1.314	1.703	2.052	2.473	2.771
28	.855	1.313	1.701	2.048	2.467	2.763
29	.854	1.311	1.699	2.045	2.462	2.756
30	.854	1.310	1.697	2.042	2.457	2.750
31	.853	1.309	1.696	2.040	2.453	2.744
32	.853	1.309	1.694	2.037	2.449	2.738
33	.853	1.308	1.692	2.035	2.445	2.733
34	.852	1.307	1.691	2.032	2.441	2.728

TABLE 2 t DISTRIBUTION (*Continued*)

Degrees of Freedom	Area in Upper Tail					
	.20	**.10**	**.05**	**.025**	**.01**	**.005**
35	.852	1.306	1.690	2.030	2.438	2.724
36	.852	1.306	1.688	2.028	2.434	2.719
37	.851	1.305	1.687	2.026	2.431	2.715
38	.851	1.304	1.686	2.024	2.429	2.712
39	.851	1.304	1.685	2.023	2.426	2.708
40	.851	1.303	1.684	2.021	2.423	2.704
41	.850	1.303	1.683	2.020	2.421	2.701
42	.850	1.302	1.682	2.018	2.418	2.698
43	.850	1.302	1.681	2.017	2.416	2.695
44	.850	1.301	1.680	2.015	2.414	2.692
45	.850	1.301	1.679	2.014	2.412	2.690
46	.850	1.300	1.679	2.013	2.410	2.687
47	.849	1.300	1.678	2.012	2.408	2.685
48	.849	1.299	1.677	2.011	2.407	2.682
49	.849	1.299	1.677	2.010	2.405	2.680
50	.849	1.299	1.676	2.009	2.403	2.678
51	.849	1.298	1.675	2.008	2.402	2.676
52	.849	1.298	1.675	2.007	2.400	2.674
53	.848	1.298	1.674	2.006	2.399	2.672
54	.848	1.297	1.674	2.005	2.397	2.670
55	.848	1.297	1.673	2.004	2.396	2.668
56	.848	1.297	1.673	2.003	2.395	2.667
57	.848	1.297	1.672	2.002	2.394	2.665
58	.848	1.296	1.672	2.002	2.392	2.663
59	.848	1.296	1.671	2.001	2.391	2.662
60	.848	1.296	1.671	2.000	2.390	2.660
61	.848	1.296	1.670	2.000	2.389	2.659
62	.847	1.295	1.670	1.999	2.388	2.657
63	.847	1.295	1.669	1.998	2.387	2.656
64	.847	1.295	1.669	1.998	2.386	2.655
65	.847	1.295	1.669	1.997	2.385	2.654
66	.847	1.295	1.668	1.997	2.384	2.652
67	.847	1.294	1.668	1.996	2.383	2.651
68	.847	1.294	1.668	1.995	2.382	2.650
69	.847	1.294	1.667	1.995	2.382	2.649
70	.847	1.294	1.667	1.994	2.381	2.648
71	.847	1.294	1.667	1.994	2.380	2.647
72	.847	1.293	1.666	1.993	2.379	2.646
73	.847	1.293	1.666	1.993	2.379	2.645
74	.847	1.293	1.666	1.993	2.378	2.644
75	.846	1.293	1.665	1.992	2.377	2.643
76	.846	1.293	1.665	1.992	2.376	2.642
77	.846	1.293	1.665	1.991	2.376	2.641
78	.846	1.292	1.665	1.991	2.375	2.640
79	.846	1.292	1.664	1.990	2.374	2.639

TABLE 2   *t* DISTRIBUTION (*Continued*)

Degrees of Freedom	Area in Upper Tail					
	.20	**.10**	**.05**	**.025**	**.01**	**.005**
80	.846	1.292	1.664	1.990	2.374	2.639
81	.846	1.292	1.664	1.990	2.373	2.638
82	.846	1.292	1.664	1.989	2.373	2.637
83	.846	1.292	1.663	1.989	2.372	2.636
84	.846	1.292	1.663	1.989	2.372	2.636
85	.846	1.292	1.663	1.988	2.371	2.635
86	.846	1.291	1.663	1.988	2.370	2.634
87	.846	1.291	1.663	1.988	2.370	2.634
88	.846	1.291	1.662	1.987	2.369	2.633
89	.846	1.291	1.662	1.987	2.369	2.632
90	.846	1.291	1.662	1.987	2.368	2.632
91	.846	1.291	1.662	1.986	2.368	2.631
92	.846	1.291	1.662	1.986	2.368	2.630
93	.846	1.291	1.661	1.986	2.367	2.630
94	.845	1.291	1.661	1.986	2.367	2.629
95	.845	1.291	1.661	1.985	2.366	2.629
96	.845	1.290	1.661	1.985	2.366	2.628
97	.845	1.290	1.661	1.985	2.365	2.627
98	.845	1.290	1.661	1.984	2.365	2.627
99	.845	1.290	1.660	1.984	2.364	2.626
100	.845	1.290	1.660	1.984	2.364	2.626
∞	.842	1.282	1.645	1.960	2.326	2.576

TABLE 3   CHI-SQUARE DISTRIBUTION

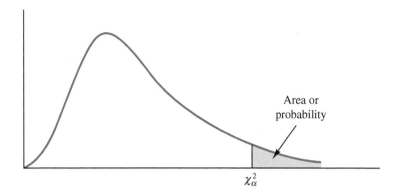

Entries in the table give χ_α^2 values, where α is the area or probability in the upper tail of the chi-square distribution. For example, with 10 degrees of freedom and a .01 area in the upper tail, $\chi_{.01}^2 = 23.209$.

Degrees of Freedom	Area in Upper Tail									
	.995	**.99**	**.975**	**.95**	**.90**	**.10**	**.05**	**.025**	**.01**	**.005**
1	.000	.000	.001	.004	.016	2.706	3.841	5.024	6.635	7.879
2	.010	.020	.051	.103	.211	4.605	5.991	7.378	9.210	10.597
3	.072	.115	.216	.352	.584	6.251	7.815	9.348	11.345	12.838
4	.207	.297	.484	.711	1.064	7.779	9.488	11.143	13.277	14.860
5	.412	.554	.831	1.145	1.610	9.236	11.070	12.832	15.086	16.750
6	.676	.872	1.237	1.635	2.204	10.645	12.592	14.449	16.812	18.548
7	.989	1.239	1.690	2.167	2.833	12.017	14.067	16.013	18.475	20.278
8	1.344	1.647	2.180	2.733	3.490	13.362	15.507	17.535	20.090	21.955
9	1.735	2.088	2.700	3.325	4.168	14.684	16.919	19.023	21.666	23.589
10	2.156	2.558	3.247	3.940	4.865	15.987	18.307	20.483	23.209	25.188
11	2.603	3.053	3.816	4.575	5.578	17.275	19.675	21.920	24.725	26.757
12	3.074	3.571	4.404	5.226	6.304	18.549	21.026	23.337	26.217	28.300
13	3.565	4.107	5.009	5.892	7.041	19.812	22.362	24.736	27.688	29.819
14	4.075	4.660	5.629	6.571	7.790	21.064	23.685	26.119	29.141	31.319
15	4.601	5.229	6.262	7.261	8.547	22.307	24.996	27.488	30.578	32.801
16	5.142	5.812	6.908	7.962	9.312	23.542	26.296	28.845	32.000	34.267
17	5.697	6.408	7.564	8.672	10.085	24.769	27.587	30.191	33.409	35.718
18	6.265	7.015	8.231	9.390	10.865	25.989	28.869	31.526	34.805	37.156
19	6.844	7.633	8.907	10.117	11.651	27.204	30.144	32.852	36.191	38.582
20	7.434	8.260	9.591	10.851	12.443	28.412	31.410	34.170	37.566	39.997
21	8.034	8.897	10.283	11.591	13.240	29.615	32.671	35.479	38.932	41.401
22	8.643	9.542	10.982	12.338	14.041	30.813	33.924	36.781	40.289	42.796
23	9.260	10.196	11.689	13.091	14.848	32.007	35.172	38.076	41.638	44.181
24	9.886	10.856	12.401	13.848	15.659	33.196	36.415	39.364	42.980	45.558
25	10.520	11.524	13.120	14.611	16.473	34.382	37.652	40.646	44.314	46.928
26	11.160	12.198	13.844	15.379	17.292	35.563	38.885	41.923	45.642	48.290
27	11.808	12.878	14.573	16.151	18.114	36.741	40.113	43.195	46.963	49.645
28	12.461	13.565	15.308	16.928	18.939	37.916	41.337	44.461	48.278	50.994
29	13.121	14.256	16.047	17.708	19.768	39.087	42.557	45.722	49.588	52.335

TABLE 3   CHI-SQUARE DISTRIBUTION (*Continued*)

Degrees of Freedom	Area in Upper Tail									
	.995	**.99**	**.975**	**.95**	**.90**	**.10**	**.05**	**.025**	**.01**	**.005**
30	13.787	14.953	16.791	18.493	20.599	40.256	43.773	46.979	50.892	53.672
35	17.192	18.509	20.569	22.465	24.797	46.059	49.802	53.203	57.342	60.275
40	20.707	22.164	24.433	26.509	29.051	51.805	55.758	59.342	63.691	66.766
45	24.311	25.901	28.366	30.612	33.350	57.505	61.656	65.410	69.957	73.166
50	27.991	29.707	32.357	34.764	37.689	63.167	67.505	71.420	76.154	79.490
55	31.735	33.571	36.398	38.958	42.060	68.796	73.311	77.380	82.292	85.749
60	35.534	37.485	40.482	43.188	46.459	74.397	79.082	83.298	88.379	91.952
65	39.383	41.444	44.603	47.450	50.883	79.973	84.821	89.177	94.422	98.105
70	43.275	45.442	48.758	51.739	55.329	85.527	90.531	95.023	100.425	104.215
75	47.206	49.475	52.942	56.054	59.795	91.061	96.217	100.839	106.393	110.285
80	51.172	53.540	57.153	60.391	64.278	96.578	101.879	106.629	112.329	116.321
85	55.170	57.634	61.389	64.749	68.777	102.079	107.522	112.393	118.236	122.324
90	59.196	61.754	65.647	69.126	73.291	107.565	113.145	118.136	124.116	128.299
95	63.250	65.898	69.925	73.520	77.818	113.038	118.752	123.858	129.973	134.247
100	67.328	70.065	74.222	77.929	82.358	118.498	124.342	129.561	135.807	140.170

TABLE 4 F DISTRIBUTION

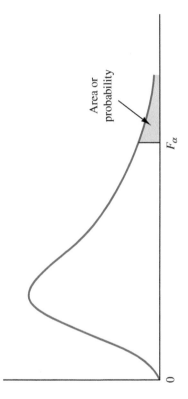

Entries in the table give F_α values, where α is the area or probability in the upper tail of the F distribution. For example, with 4 numerator degrees of freedom, 8 denominator degrees of freedom, and a .05 area in the upper tail, $F_{.05} = 3.84$.

Denominator Degrees of Freedom	Area in Upper Tail	Numerator Degrees of Freedom																	
		1	2	3	4	5	6	7	8	9	10	15	20	25	30	40	60	100	1000
1	.10	39.86	49.50	53.59	55.83	57.24	58.20	58.91	59.44	59.86	60.19	61.22	61.74	62.05	62.26	62.53	62.79	63.01	63.30
	.05	161.45	199.50	215.71	224.58	230.16	233.99	236.77	238.88	240.54	241.88	245.95	248.02	249.26	250.10	251.14	252.20	253.04	254.19
	.025	647.79	799.48	864.15	899.60	921.83	937.11	948.20	956.64	963.28	968.63	984.87	993.08	998.09	1001.40	1005.60	1009.79	1013.16	1017.76
	.01	4052.18	4999.34	5403.53	5624.26	5763.96	5858.95	5928.33	5980.95	6022.40	6055.93	6156.97	6208.66	6239.86	6260.35	6286.43	6312.97	6333.92	6362.80
2	.10	8.53	9.00	9.16	9.24	9.29	9.33	9.35	9.37	9.38	9.39	9.42	9.44	9.45	9.46	9.47	9.47	9.48	9.49
	.05	18.51	19.00	19.16	19.25	19.30	19.33	19.35	19.37	19.38	19.40	19.43	19.45	19.46	19.46	19.47	19.48	19.49	19.49
	.025	38.51	39.00	39.17	39.25	39.30	39.33	39.36	39.37	39.39	39.40	39.43	39.45	39.46	39.46	39.47	39.48	39.49	39.50
	.01	98.50	99.00	99.16	99.25	99.30	99.33	99.36	99.38	99.39	99.40	99.43	99.45	99.46	99.47	99.48	99.48	99.49	99.50
3	.10	5.54	5.46	5.39	5.34	5.31	5.28	5.27	5.25	5.24	5.23	5.20	5.18	5.17	5.17	5.16	5.15	5.14	5.13
	.05	10.13	9.55	9.28	9.12	9.01	8.94	8.89	8.85	8.81	8.79	8.70	8.66	8.63	8.62	8.59	8.57	8.55	8.53
	.025	17.44	16.04	15.44	15.10	14.88	14.73	14.62	14.54	14.47	14.42	14.25	14.17	14.12	14.08	14.04	13.99	13.96	13.91
	.01	34.12	30.82	29.46	28.71	28.24	27.91	27.67	27.49	27.34	27.23	26.87	26.69	26.58	26.50	26.41	26.32	26.24	26.14
4	.10	4.54	4.32	4.19	4.11	4.05	4.01	3.98	3.95	3.94	3.92	3.87	3.84	3.83	3.82	3.80	3.79	3.78	3.76
	.05	7.71	6.94	6.59	6.39	6.26	6.16	6.09	6.04	6.00	5.96	5.86	5.80	5.77	5.75	5.72	5.69	5.66	5.63
	.025	12.22	10.65	9.98	9.60	9.36	9.20	9.07	8.98	8.90	8.84	8.66	8.56	8.50	8.46	8.41	8.36	8.32	8.26
	.01	21.20	18.00	16.69	15.98	15.52	15.21	14.98	14.80	14.66	14.55	14.20	14.02	13.91	13.84	13.75	13.65	13.58	13.47
5	.10	4.06	3.78	3.62	3.52	3.45	3.40	3.37	3.34	3.32	3.30	3.324	3.21	3.19	3.17	3.16	3.14	3.13	3.11
	.05	6.61.	5.79	5.41	5.19	5.05	4.95	4.88	4.82	4.77	4.74	4.62	4.56	4.52	4.50	4.46	4.43	4.41	4.37
	.025	10.01	8.43	7.76	7.39	7.15	6.98	6.85	6.76	6.68	6.62	6.43	6.33	6.27	6.23	6.18	6.12	6.08	6.02
	.01	16.26	13.27	12.06	11.39	10.97	10.67	10.46	10.29	10.16	10.05	9.72	9.55	9.45	9.38	9.29	9.20	9.13	9.03

TABLE 4 *F* DISTRIBUTION (*Continued*)

		Numerator Degrees of Freedom																	
Denominator Degrees of Freedom	Area in Upper Tail	1	2	3	4	5	6	7	8	9	10	15	20	25	30	40	60	100	1000
6	.10	3.78	3.46	3.29	3.18	3.11	3.05	3.01	2.98	2.96	2.94	2.87	2.84	2.81	2.80	2.78	2.76	2.75	2.72
	.05	5.99	5.14	4.76	4.53	4.39	4.28	4.21	4.15	4.10	4.06	3.94	3.87	3.83	3.81	3.77	3.74	3.71	3.67
	.025	8.81	7.26	6.60	6.23	5.99	5.82	5.70	5.60	5.52	5.46	5.27	5.17	5.11	5.07	5.01	4.96	4.92	4.86
	.01	13.75	10.92	9.78	9.15	8.75	8.47	8.26	8.10	7.98	7.87	7.56	7.40	7.30	7.23	7.14	7.06	6.99	6.89
7	.10	3.59	3.26	3.07	2.96	2.88	2.83	2.78	2.75	2.72	2.70	2.63	2.59	2.57	2.56	2.54	2.51	2.50	2.47
	.05	5.59	4.74	4.35	4.12	3.97	3.87	3.79	3.73	3.68	3.64	3.51	3.44	3.40	3.38	3.34	3.30	3.27	3.23
	.025	8.07	6.54	5.89	5.52	5.29	5.12	4.99	4.90	4.82	4.76	4.57	4.47	4.40	4.36	4.31	4.25	4.21	4.15
	.01	12.25	9.55	8.45	7.85	7.46	7.19	6.99	6.84	6.72	6.62	6.31	6.16	6.06	5.99	5.91	5.82	5.75	5.66
8	.10	3.46	3.11	2.92	2.81	2.73	2.67	2.62	2.59	2.56	2.54	2.46	2.42	2.40	2.38	2.36	2.34	2.32	2.30
	.05	5.32	4.46	4.07	3.84	3.69	3.58	3.50	3.44	3.39	3.35	3.22	3.15	3.11	3.08	3.04	3.01	2.97	2.93
	.025	7.57	6.06	5.42	5.05	4.82	4.65	4.53	4.43	4.36	4.30	4.10	4.00	3.94	3.89	3.84	3.78	3.74	3.68
	.01	11.26	8.65	7.59	7.01	6.63	6.37	6.18	6.03	5.91	5.81	5.52	5.36	5.26	5.20	5.12	5.03	4.96	4.87
9	.10	3.36	3.01	2.81	2.69	2.61	2.55	2.51	2.47	2.44	2.42	2.34	2.30	2.27	2.25	2.23	2.21	2.19	2.16
	.05	5.12	4.26	3.86	3.63	3.48	3.37	3.29	3.23	3.18	3.14	3.01	2.94	2.89	2.86	2.83	2.79	2.76	2.71
	.025	7.21	5.71	5.08	4.72	4.48	4.32	4.20	4.10	4.03	3.96	3.77	3.67	3.60	3.56	3.51	3.45	3.40	3.34
	.01	10.56	8.02	6.99	6.42	6.06	5.80	5.61	5.47	5.35	5.26	4.96	4.81	4.71	4.65	4.57	4.48	4.41	4.32
10	.10	3.29	2.92	2.73	2.61	2.52	2.46	2.41	2.38	2.35	2.32	2.24	2.20	2.17	2.16	2.13	2.11	2.09	2.06
	.05	4.96	4.10	3.71	3.48	3.33	3.22	3.14	3.07	3.02	2.98	2.85	2.77	2.73	2.70	2.66	2.62	2.59	2.54
	.025	6.55	5.46	4.83	4.47	4.24	4.07	3.95	3.85	3.78	3.72	3.52	3.42	3.35	3.31	3.26	3.20	3.15	3.09
	.01	10.04	7.56	6.55	5.99	5.64	5.39	5.20	5.06	4.94	4.85	4.56	4.41	4.31	4.25	4.17	4.08	4.01	3.92
11	.10	3.23	2.86	2.66	2.54	2.45	2.39	2.34	2.30	2.27	2.25	2.17	2.12	2.10	2.08	2.05	2.03	2.01	1.98
	.05	4.84	3.98	3.59	3.36	3.20	3.09	3.01	2.95	2.90	2.85	2.72	2.65	2.60	2.57	2.53	2.49	2.46	2.41
	.025	6.72	5.26	4.63	4.28	4.04	3.88	3.76	3.66	3.59	3.53	3.33	3.23	3.16	3.12	3.06	3.00	2.96	2.89
	.01	9.65	7.21	6.22	5.67	5.32	5.07	4.89	4.74	4.63	4.54	4.25	4.10	4.01	3.94	3.86	3.78	3.71	3.61
12	.10	3.18	2.81	2.61	2.48	2.39	2.33	2.28	2.24	2.21	2.19	2.10	2.06	2.03	2.01	1.99	1.96	1.94	1.91
	.05	4.75	3.89	3.49	3.26	3.11	3.00	2.91	2.85	2.80	2.75	2.62	2.54	2.50	2.47	2.43	2.38	2.35	2.30
	.025	6.55	5.10	4.47	4.12	3.89	3.73	3.61	3.51	3.44	3.37	3.18	3.07	3.01	2.96	2.91	2.85	2.80	2.73
	.01	9.33	6.93	5.95	5.41	5.06	4.82	4.64	4.50	4.39	4.30	4.01	3.86	3.76	3.70	3.62	3.54	3.47	3.37
13	.10	3.14	2.76	2.56	2.43	2.35	2.28	2.23	2.20	2.16	2.14	2.05	2.01	1.98	1.96	1.93	1.90	1.88	1.85
	.05	4.67	3.81	3.41	3.18	3.03	2.92	2.83	2.77	2.71	2.67	2.53	2.46	2.41	2.38	2.34	2.30	2.26	2.21
	.025	6.41	4.97	4.35	4.00	3.77	3.60	3.48	3.39	3.31	3.25	3.05	2.95	2.88	2.84	2.78	2.72	2.67	2.60
	.01	9.07	6.70	5.74	5.21	4.86	4.62	4.44	4.30	4.19	4.10	3.82	3.66	3.57	3.51	3.43	3.34	3.27	3.18
14	.10	3.10	2.73	2.52	2.39	2.31	2.24	2.19	2.15	2.12	2.10	2.01	1.96	1.93	1.91	1.89	1.86	1.83	1.80
	.05	4.60	3.74	3.34	3.11	2.96	2.85	2.76	2.70	2.65	2.60	2.46	2.39	2.34	2.31	2.27	2.22	2.19	2.14
	.025	6.30	4.86	4.24	3.89	3.66	3.50	3.38	3.29	3.21	3.15	2.95	2.84	2.78	2.73	2.67	2.61	2.56	2.50
	.01	8.86	6.51	5.56	5.04	4.69	4.46	4.28	4.14	4.03	3.94	3.66	3.51	3.41	3.35	3.27	3.18	3.11	3.02
15	.10	3.07	2.70	2.49	2.36	2.27	2.21	2.16	2.12	2.09	2.06	1.97	1.92	1.89	1.87	1.85	1.82	1.79	1.76
	.05	4.54	3.68	3.29	3.06	2.90	2.79	2.71	2.64	2.59	2.54	2.40	2.33	2.28	2.25	2.20	2.16	2.12	2.07
	.025	6.20	4.77	4.15	3.80	3.58	3.41	3.29	3.20	3.12	3.06	2.86	2.76	2.69	2.64	2.59	2.52	2.47	2.40
	.01	8.68	6.36	5.42	4.89	4.56	4.32	4.14	4.00	3.89	3.80	3.52	3.37	3.28	3.21	3.13	3.05	2.98	2.88

Denominator Degrees of Freedom	Area in Upper Tail	Numerator Degrees of Freedom																	
		1	2	3	4	5	6	7	8	9	10	15	20	25	30	40	60	100	1000
16	.10	3.05	2.67	2.46	2.33	2.24	2.18	2.13	2.09	2.06	2.03	1.94	1.89	1.86	1.84	1.81	1.78	1.76	1.72
	.05	4.49	3.63	3.24	3.01	2.85	2.74	2.66	2.59	2.54	2.49	2.35	2.28	2.23	2.19	2.15	2.11	2.07	2.02
	.025	6.12	4.69	4.08	3.73	3.50	3.34	3.22	3.12	3.05	2.99	2.79	2.68	2.61	2.57	2.51	2.45	2.40	2.32
	.01	8.53	6.23	5.29	4.77	4.44	4.20	4.03	3.89	3.78	3.69	3.41	3.26	3.16	3.10	3.02	2.93	2.86	2.76
17	.10	3.03	2.64	2.44	2.31	2.22	2.15	2.10	2.06	2.03	2.00	1.91	1.86	1.83	1.81	1.78	1.75	1.73	1.69
	.05	4.45	3.59	3.20	2.96	2.81	2.70	2.61	2.55	2.49	2.45	2.31	2.23	2.18	2.15	2.10	2.06	2.02	1.97
	.025	6.04	4.62	4.01	3.66	3.44	3.28	3.16	3.06	2.98	2.92	2.72	2.62	2.55	2.50	2.44	2.38	2.33	2.26
	.01	8.40	6.11	5.19	4.67	4.34	4.10	3.93	3.79	3.68	3.59	3.31	3.16	3.07	3.00	2.92	2.83	2.76	2.66
18	.10	3.01	2.62	2.42	2.29	2.20	2.13	2.08	2.04	2.00	1.98	1.89	1.84	1.80	1.78	1.75	1.72	1.70	1.66
	.05	4.41	3.55	3.16	2.93	2.77	2.66	2.58	2.51	2.46	2.41	2.27	2.19	2.14	2.11	2.06	2.02	1.98	1.92
	.025	5.98	4.56	3.95	3.61	3.38	3.22	3.10	3.01	2.93	2.87	2.67	2.56	2.49	2.44	2.38	2.32	2.27	2.20
	.01	8.29	6.01	5.09	4.58	4.25	4.01	3.84	3.71	3.60	3.51	3.23	3.08	2.98	2.92	2.84	2.75	2.68	2.58
19	.10	2.99	2.61	2.40	2.27	2.18	2.11	2.06	2.02	1.98	1.96	1.86	1.81	1.78	1.76	1.73	1.70	1.67	1.64
	.05	4.38	3.52	3.13	2.90	2.74	2.63	2.54	2.48	2.42	2.38	2.23	2.16	2.11	2.07	2.03	1.98	1.94	1.88
	.025	5.92	4.51	3.90	3.56	3.33	3.17	3.05	2.96	2.88	2.82	2.62	2.51	2.44	2.39	2.33	2.27	2.22	2.14
	.01	8.18	5.93	5.01	4.50	4.17	3.94	3.77	3.63	3.52	3.43	3.15	3.00	2.91	2.84	2.76	2.67	2.60	2.50
20	.10	2.97	2.59	2.38	2.25	2.16	2.09	2.04	2.00	1.96	1.94	1.84	1.79	1.76	1.74	1.71	1.68	1.65	1.61
	.05	4.35	3.49	3.10	2.87	2.71	2.60	2.51	2.45	2.39	2.35	2.20	2.12	2.07	2.04	1.99	1.95	1.91	1.85
	.025	5.87	4.46	3.86	3.51	3.29	3.13	3.01	2.91	2.84	2.77	2.57	2.46	2.40	2.35	2.29	2.22	2.17	2.09
	.01	8.10	5.85	4.94	4.43	4.10	3.87	3.70	3.56	3.46	3.37	3.09	2.94	2.84	2.78	2.69	2.61	2.54	2.43
21	.10	2.96	2.57	2.36	2.23	2.14	2.08	2.02	1.98	1.95	1.92	1.83	1.78	1.74	1.72	1.69	1.66	1.63	1.59
	.05	4.32	3.47	3.07	2.84	2.68	2.57	2.49	2.42	2.37	2.32	2.18	2.10	2.05	2.01	1.96	1.92	1.88	1.82
	.025	5.83	4.42	3.82	3.48	3.25	3.09	2.97	2.87	2.80	2.73	2.53	2.42	2.36	2.31	2.25	2.18	2.13	2.05
	.01	8.02	5.78	4.87	4.37	4.04	3.81	3.64	3.51	3.40	3.31	3.03	2.88	2.79	2.72	2.64	2.55	2.48	2.37
22	.10	2.95	2.56	2.35	2.22	2.13	2.06	2.01	1.97	1.93	1.90	1.81	1.76	1.73	1.70	1.67	1.64	1.61	1.57
	.05	4.30	3.44	3.05	2.82	2.66	2.55	2.46	2.40	2.34	2.30	2.15	2.07	2.02	1.98	1.94	1.89	1.85	1.79
	.025	5.79	4.38	3.78	3.44	3.22	3.05	2.93	2.84	2.76	2.70	2.50	2.39	2.32	2.27	2.21	2.14	2.09	2.01
	.01	7.95	5.72	4.82	4.31	3.99	3.76	3.59	3.45	3.35	3.26	2.98	2.83	2.73	2.67	2.58	2.50	2.42	2.32
23	.10	2.94	2.55	2.34	2.21	2.11	2.05	1.99	1.95	1.92	1.89	1.80	1.74	1.71	1.69	1.66	1.62	1.59	1.55
	.05	4.28	3.42	3.03	2.80	2.64	2.53	2.44	2.37	2.32	2.27	2.13	2.05	2.00	1.96	1.91	1.86	1.82	1.76
	.025	5.75	4.35	3.75	3.41	3.18	3.02	2.90	2.81	2.73	2.67	2.47	2.36	2.29	2.24	2.18	2.11	2.06	1.98
	.01	7.88	5.66	4.76	4.26	3.94	3.71	3.54	3.41	3.30	3.21	2.93	2.78	2.69	2.62	2.54	2.45	2.37	2.27
24	.10	2.93	2.54	2.33	2.19	2.10	2.04	1.98	1.94	1.91	1.88	1.78	1.73	1.70	1.67	1.64	1.61	1.58	1.54
	.05	4.26	3.40	3.01	2.78	2.62	2.51	2.42	2.36	2.30	2.25	2.11	2.03	1.97	1.94	1.89	1.84	1.80	1.74
	.025	5.72	4.32	3.72	3.38	3.15	2.99	2.87	2.78	2.70	2.64	2.44	2.33	2.26	2.21	2.15	2.08	2.02	1.94
	.01	7.82	5.61	4.72	4.22	3.90	3.67	3.50	3.36	3.26	3.17	2.89	2.74	2.64	2.58	2.49	2.40	2.33	2.22

TABLE 4 *F* DISTRIBUTION (*Continued*)

Denominator Degrees of Freedom	Area in Upper Tail	Numerator Degrees of Freedom																	
		1	2	3	4	5	6	7	8	9	10	15	20	25	30	40	60	100	1000
25	.10	2.92	2.53	2.32	2.18	2.09	2.02	1.97	1.93	1.89	1.87	1.77	1.72	1.68	1.66	1.63	1.59	1.56	1.52
	.05	4.24	3.39	2.99	2.76	2.60	2.49	2.40	2.34	2.28	2.24	2.09	2.01	1.96	1.92	1.87	1.82	1.78	1.72
	.025	5.69	4.29	3.69	3.35	3.13	2.97	2.85	2.75	2.68	2.61	2.41	2.30	2.23	2.18	2.12	2.05	2.00	1.91
	.01	7.77	5.57	4.68	4.18	3.85	3.63	3.46	3.32	3.22	3.13	2.85	2.70	2.60	2.54	2.45	2.36	2.29	2.18
26	.10	2.91	2.52	2.31	2.17	2.08	2.01	1.96	1.92	1.88	1.86	1.76	1.71	1.67	1.65	1.61	1.58	1.55	1.51
	.05	4.23	3.37	2.98	2.74	2.59	2.47	2.39	2.32	2.27	2.22	2.07	1.99	1.94	1.90	1.85	1.80	1.76	1.70
	.025	5.66	4.27	3.67	3.33	3.10	2.94	2.82	2.73	2.65	2.59	2.39	2.28	2.21	2.16	2.09	2.03	1.97	1.89
	.01	7.72	5.53	4.64	4.14	3.82	3.59	3.42	3.29	3.18	3.09	2.81	2.66	2.57	2.50	2.42	2.33	2.25	2.14
27	.10	2.90	2.51	2.30	2.17	2.07	2.00	1.95	1.91	1.87	1.85	1.75	1.70	1.66	1.64	1.60	1.57	1.54	1.50
	.05	4.21	3.35	2.96	2.73	2.57	2.46	2.37	2.31	2.25	2.20	2.06	1.97	1.92	1.88	1.84	1.79	1.74	1.68
	.025	5.63	4.24	3.65	3.31	3.08	2.92	2.80	2.71	2.63	2.57	2.36	2.25	2.18	2.13	2.07	2.00	1.94	1.86
	.01	7.68	5.49	4.60	4.11	3.78	3.56	3.39	3.26	3.15	3.06	2.78	2.63	2.54	2.47	2.38	2.29	2.22	2.11
28	.10	2.89	2.50	2.29	2.16	2.06	2.00	1.94	1.90	1.87	1.84	1.74	1.69	1.65	1.63	1.59	1.56	1.53	1.48
	.05	4.20	3.34	2.95	2.71	2.56	2.45	2.36	2.29	2.24	2.19	2.04	1.96	1.91	1.87	1.82	1.77	1.73	1.66
	.025	5.61	4.22	3.63	3.29	3.06	2.90	2.78	2.69	2.61	2.55	2.34	2.23	2.16	2.11	2.05	1.98	1.92	1.84
	.01	7.64	5.45	4.57	4.07	3.75	3.53	3.36	3.23	3.12	3.03	2.75	2.60	2.51	2.44	2.35	2.26	2.19	2.08
29	.10	2.89	2.50	2.28	2.15	2.06	1.99	1.93	1.89	1.86	1.83	1.73	1.68	1.64	1.62	1.58	1.55	1.52	1.47
	.05	4.18	3.33	2.93	2.70	2.55	2.43	2.35	2.28	2.22	2.18	2.03	1.94	1.89	1.85	1.81	1.75	1.71	1.65
	.025	5.59	4.20	3.61	3.27	3.04	2.88	2.76	2.67	2.59	2.53	2.32	2.21	2.14	2.09	2.03	1.96	1.90	1.82
	.01	7.60	5.42	4.54	4.04	3.73	3.50	3.33	3.20	3.09	3.00	2.73	2.57	2.48	2.41	2.33	2.23	2.16	2.05
30	.10	2.88	2.49	2.28	2.14	2.05	1.98	1.93	1.88	1.85	1.82	1.72	1.67	1.63	1.61	1.57	1.54	1.51	1.46
	.05	4.17	3.32	2.92	2.69	2.53	2.42	2.33	2.27	2.21	2.16	2.01	1.93	1.88	1.84	1.79	1.74	1.70	1.63
	.025	5.57	4.18	3.59	3.25	3.03	2.87	2.75	2.65	2.57	2.51	2.31	2.20	2.12	2.07	2.01	1.94	1.88	1.80
	.01	7.56	5.39	4.51	4.02	3.70	3.47	3.30	3.17	3.07	2.98	2.70	2.55	2.45	2.39	2.30	2.21	2.13	2.02
40	.10	2.84	2.44	2.23	2.09	2.00	1.93	1.87	1.83	1.79	1.76	1.66	1.61	1.57	1.54	1.51	1.47	1.43	1.38
	.05	4.08	3.23	2.84	2.61	2.45	2.34	2.25	2.18	2.12	2.08	1.92	1.84	1.78	1.74	1.69	1.64	1.59	1.52
	.025	5.42	4.05	3.46	3.13	2.90	2.74	2.62	2.53	2.45	2.39	2.18	2.07	1.99	1.94	1.88	1.80	1.74	1.65
	.01	7.31	5.18	4.31	3.83	3.51	3.29	3.12	2.99	2.89	2.80	2.52	2.37	2.27	2.20	2.11	2.02	1.94	1.82
60	.10	2.79	2.39	2.18	2.04	1.95	1.87	1.82	1.77	1.74	1.71	1.60	1.54	1.50	1.48	1.44	1.40	1.36	1.30
	.05	4.00	3.15	2.76	2.53	2.37	2.25	2.17	2.10	2.04	1.99	1.84	1.75	1.69	1.65	1.59	1.53	1.48	1.40
	.025	5.29	3.93	3.34	3.01	2.79	2.63	2.51	2.41	2.33	2.27	2.06	1.94	1.87	1.82	1.74	1.67	1.60	1.49
	.01	7.08	4.98	4.13	3.65	3.34	3.12	2.95	2.82	2.72	2.63	2.35	2.20	2.10	2.03	1.94	1.84	1.75	1.62
100	.10	2.76	2.36	2.14	2.00	1.91	1.83	1.78	1.73	1.69	1.66	1.56	1.49	1.45	1.42	1.38	1.34	1.29	1.22
	.05	3.94	3.09	2.70	2.46	2.31	2.19	2.10	2.03	1.97	1.93	1.77	1.68	1.62	1.57	1.52	1.45	1.39	1.30
	.025	5.18	3.83	3.25	2.92	2.70	2.54	2.42	2.32	2.24	2.18	1.97	1.85	1.77	1.71	1.64	1.56	1.48	1.36
	.01	6.90	4.82	3.98	3.51	3.21	2.99	2.82	2.69	2.59	2.50	2.22	2.07	1.97	1.89	1.80	1.69	1.60	1.45
1000	.10	2.71	2.31	2.09	1.95	1.85	1.78	1.72	1.68	1.64	1.61	1.49	1.43	1.38	1.35	1.30	1.25	1.20	1.08
	.05	3.85	3.00	2.61	2.38	2.22	2.11	2.02	1.95	1.89	1.84	1.68	1.58	1.52	1.47	1.41	1.33	1.26	1.11
	.025	5.04	3.70	3.13	2.80	2.58	2.42	2.30	2.20	2.13	2.06	1.85	1.72	1.64	1.58	1.50	1.41	1.32	1.13
	.01	6.66	4.63	3.80	3.34	3.04	2.82	2.66	2.53	2.43	2.34	2.06	1.90	1.79	1.72	1.61	1.50	1.38	1.16

Chapter 8

2. Use $\bar{x} \pm z_{\alpha/2}(\sigma/\sqrt{n})$
  a. $32 \pm 1.645(6/\sqrt{50})$
    32 ± 1.4; 30.6 to 33.4
  b. $32 \pm 1.96(6/\sqrt{50})$
    32 ± 1.66; 30.34 to 33.66
  c. $32 \pm 2.576(6/\sqrt{50})$
    32 ± 2.19; 29.81 to 34.19

4. 54

5. a. With 99% confidence $z_{\alpha/2} = z_{.005} = 2.576$
    Margin of Error $= 2.576\,\sigma/\sqrt{n} = 2.576\,(6/\sqrt{64}) = 1.93$
  b. Confidence Interval: 21.52 ± 1.93 or 19.59 to 23.45

6. 8.1 to 8.9

8. a. Population is at least approximately normal
  b. 3.41
  c. 4.48

10. a. \$113,638 to \$124,672
  b. \$112,581 to \$125,729
  c. \$110,515 to \$127,795
  d. Width increases as confidence level increases

12. a. 2.179
  b. -1.676
  c. 2.457
  d. -1.708 and 1.708
  e. -2.014 and 2.014

13. a. $\bar{x} = \dfrac{\Sigma x_i}{n} = \dfrac{80}{8} = 10$

  b. $s = \sqrt{\dfrac{\Sigma(x_i - \bar{x})^2}{n-1}} = \sqrt{\dfrac{84}{7}} = 3.464$

c. $t_{.025}\left(\dfrac{s}{\sqrt{n}}\right) = 2.365\left(\dfrac{3.46}{\sqrt{8}}\right) = 2.9$

d. $\bar{x} \pm t_{.025}\left(\dfrac{s}{\sqrt{n}}\right)$

10 ± 2.9 (7.1 to 12.9)

14. a. 21.5 to 23.5
  b. 21.3 to 23.7
  c. 20.9 to 24.1
  d. A larger margin of error and a wider interval

15. $\bar{x} \pm t_{a/2}(s/\sqrt{n})$

90% confidence: $df = 64$ and $t_{.05} = 1.669$

$19.5 \pm 1.669\left(\dfrac{5.2}{\sqrt{65}}\right)$

19.5 ± 1.08 or (18.42 to 20.58)
95% confidence: $df = 64$ and $t_{.025} = 1.998$

$19.5 \pm 1.998\left(\dfrac{5.2}{\sqrt{65}}\right)$

19.5 ± 1.29 or (18.21 to 20.79)

16. a. 9.7063, 7.9805
  b. 7.1536 to 12.2590
  c. 3.8854, 1.6194
  d. 3.3674 to 4.4034

18. a. 22 weeks
  b. 3.8020
  c. 18.20 to 25.80
  d. Larger n next time

20. $\bar{x} = 22$; 21.48 to 22.52

22. a. $9,269 to $12,541
  b. 1523
  c. 4,748,714, $34 million

24. a. Planning value of $\sigma = \dfrac{\text{Range}}{4} = \dfrac{36}{4} = 9$

  b. $n = \dfrac{z_{.025}^2\sigma^2}{E^2} = \dfrac{(1.96)^2(9)^2}{(3)^2} = 34.57$; use $n = 35$

  c. $n = \dfrac{(1.96)^2(9)^2}{(2)^2} = 77.79$; use $n = 78$

25. a. Use $n = \dfrac{z_{a/2}^2\sigma^2}{E^2}$

  $n = \dfrac{(1.96)^2(6.84)^2}{(1.5)^2} = 79.88$; use $n = 80$

  b. $n = \dfrac{(1.645)^2(6.84)^2}{(2)^2} = 31.65$; use $n = 32$

26. a. 25
  b. 49
  c. 97

28. a. 328
  b. 465
  c. 803
  d. n gets larger; no to 99% confidence

30. 1537

31. a. $\bar{p} = \dfrac{100}{400} = .25$

  b. $\sqrt{\dfrac{\bar{p}(1-\bar{p})}{n}} = \sqrt{\dfrac{.25(.75)}{400}} = .0217$

  c. $\bar{p} \pm z_{.025}\sqrt{\dfrac{\bar{p}(1-\bar{p})}{n}}$

  $.25 \pm 1.96(.0217)$
  $.25 \pm .0424$; .2076 to .2924

32. a. .6733 to .7267
  b. .6682 to .7318

34. 1068

35. a. $\bar{p} = \dfrac{1760}{2000} = .88$

  b. Margin of error

  $z_{.05} = \sqrt{\dfrac{\bar{p}(1-\bar{p})}{n}} = 1.645\sqrt{\dfrac{.88(1-.88)}{2000}} = .0120$

  c. Confidence interval
    $.88 \pm .0120$ or .868 to .892

  d. Margin of error

  $z_{.05} = \sqrt{\dfrac{\bar{p}(1-\bar{p})}{n}} = 1.96\sqrt{\dfrac{.88(1-.88)}{2000}} = .0142$

  95% confidence interval
    $.88 \pm .0142$ or .8658 to .8942

36. a. .23
  b. .1716 to .2884

38. a. .1790
  b. .0738, .5682 to .7158
  c. 354

39. a. $n = \dfrac{z_{.025}^2 p^*(1-p^*)}{E^2} = \dfrac{(1.96)^2(.156)(1-.156)}{(.03)^2}$
    $= 562$

  b. $n = \dfrac{z_{.005}^2 p^*(1-p^*)}{E^2} = \dfrac{(2.576)^2(.156)(1-.156)}{(.03)^2}$
    $= 970.77$; use 971

40. .0346 (.4854 to .5546)

42. a. .0442
  b. 601, 1068, 2401, 9604

44. a. 4.00
  b. $29.77 to $37.77

46. a. 122
  b. $1751 to $1995
  c. $172, 316 million
  d. Less than $1873

48. a. 14 minutes
  b. 13.38 to 14.62
  c. 32 per day
  d. Staff reduction

50. 37

52. 176

54. a. .5420
  b. .0508
  c. .4912 to .5928

56. a. .8273
  b. .7957 to .8589

58. a. 1267
  b. 1509

60. a. .3101
  b. .2898 to .3304
  c. 8219; no, this sample size is unnecessarily large

Chapter 9

2. a. H_0: $\mu \leq 14$
    H_a: $\mu > 14$
  b. No evidence that the new plan increases sales
  c. The research hypothesis $\mu > 14$ is supported; the new plan increases sales

4. a. H_0: $\mu \geq 220$
    H_a: $\mu < 220$
  b. Cannot conclude proposed method reduces cost.
  c. Can conclude proposed method reduces cost.

5. a. Conclude that the population mean monthly cost of electricity in the Chicago neighborhood is greater than $104 and hence higher than in the comparable neighborhood in Cincinnati
  b. The Type I error is rejecting H_0 when it is true; this error occurs if the researcher concludes that the population mean monthly cost of electricity is greater than $104 in the Chicago neighborhood when the population mean cost is actually less than or equal to $104
  c. The Type II error is accepting H_0 when it is false; this error occurs if the researcher concludes that the population mean monthly cost for the Chicago neighborhood is less than or equal to $104 when it is not

6. a. H_0: $\mu \leq 1$
    H_a: $\mu > 1$
  b. Claiming $\mu > 1$ when it is not true
  c. Claiming $\mu \leq 1$ when it is not true

8. a. H_0: $\mu \geq 220$
    H_a: $\mu < 220$
  b. Claiming $\mu < 220$ when it is not true
  c. Claiming $\mu \geq 220$ when it is not true

10. a. $z = \dfrac{\bar{x} - \mu_0}{\sigma/\sqrt{n}} = \dfrac{26.4 - 25}{6/\sqrt{40}} = 1.48$
  b. Using normal table with $z = 1.48$: p-value = $1.0000 - .9306 = .0694$
  c. p-value $> .01$, do not reject H_0
  d. Reject H_0 if $z \geq 2.33$
    $1.48 < 2.33$, do not reject H_0

11. a. $z = \dfrac{\bar{x} - \mu_0}{\sigma/\sqrt{n}} = \dfrac{14.15 - 15}{3/\sqrt{50}} = -2.00$
  b. p-value = $2(.0228) = .0456$
  c. p-value $\leq .05$, reject H_0

  d. Reject H_0 if $z \leq -1.96$ or $z \geq 1.96$
    $-2.00 \leq -1.96$, reject H_0

12. a. .1056; do not reject H_0
  b. .0062; reject H_0
  c. ≈ 0; reject H_0
  d. .7967; do not reject H_0

14. a. .3844; do not reject H_0
  b. .0074; reject H_0
  c. .0836; do not reject H_0

15. a. H_0: $\mu \geq 1056$
    H_a: $\mu < 1056$
  b. $z = \dfrac{\bar{x} - \mu_0}{\sigma/\sqrt{n}} = \dfrac{910 - 1056}{1600/\sqrt{400}} = -1.83$
    p-value = .0336
  c. p-value $\leq .05$, reject H_0; the mean refund of "last-minute" filers is less than $1056
  d. Reject H_0 if $z \leq -1.645$
    $-1.83 \leq -1.645$; reject H_0

16. a. H_0: $\mu \leq 3173$
    H_a: $\mu > 3173$
  b. .0207
  c. Reject H_0, conclude mean credit card balance for undergraduate student has increased

18. a. H_0: $\mu = 4.1$
    H_a: $\mu \neq 4.1$
  b. -2.21, .0272
  c. Reject H_0; return for Mid-Cap Growth Funds differs from that for U.S. Diversified Funds

20. a. H_0: $\mu \geq 32.79$
    H_a: $\mu < 32.79$
  b. -2.73
  c. .0032
  d. Reject H_0; conclude the mean monthly Internet bill is less in the southern state

22. a. H_0: $\mu = 8$
    H_a: $\mu \neq 8$
  b. .1706
  c. Do not reject H_0; we cannot conclude the mean waiting time differs from 8 minutes
  d. 7.83 to 8.97; yes

24. a. $t = \dfrac{\bar{x} - \mu_0}{s/\sqrt{n}} = \dfrac{17 - 18}{4.5/\sqrt{48}} = -1.54$
  b. Degrees of freedom = $n - 1 = 47$
    Area in lower tail is between .05 and .10
    p-value (two-tail) is between .10 and .20
    Exact p-value = .1303
  c. p-value $> .05$; do not reject H_0
  d. With $df = 47$, $t_{.025} = 2.012$
    Reject H_0 if $t \leq -2.012$ or $t \geq 2.012$
    $t = -1.54$; do not reject H_0

26. a. Between .02 and .05; exact p-value = .0397; reject H_0
  b. Between .01 and .02; exact p-value = .0125; reject H_0
  c. Between .10 and .20; exact p-value = .1285; do not reject H_0

27. a. $H_0: \mu \geq 238$
   $H_a: \mu < 238$

   b. $t = \dfrac{\bar{x} - \mu_0}{s/\sqrt{n}} = \dfrac{231 - 238}{80/\sqrt{100}} = -.88$

   Degrees of freedom $= n - 1 = 99$
   p-value is between .10 and .20
   Exact p-value $= .1905$

   c. p-value $> .05$; do not reject H_0
   Cannot conclude mean weekly benefit in Virginia is less than the national mean

   d. $df = 99$, $t_{.05} = -1.66$
   Reject H_0 if $t \leq -1.66$
   $-.88 > -1.66$; do not reject H_0

28. a. $H_0: \mu \geq 9$
   $H_a: \mu < 9$

   b. Between .005 and .01
   Exact p-value $= .0072$

   c. Reject H_0; mean tenure of a CEO is less than 9 years

30. a. $H_0: \mu = 6.4$
   $H_a: \mu \neq 6.4$

   b. Between .10 and .20
   Exact p-value $= .1268$

   c. Do not reject H_0; cannot conclude that the group consensus is wrong

32. a. $H_0: \mu = 10{,}192$
   $H_a: \mu \neq 10{,}192$

   b. Between .02 and .05
   Exact p-value $= .0304$

   c. Reject H_0; mean price at dealership differs from national mean price

34. a. $H_0: \mu = 2$
   $H_a: \mu \neq 2$

   b. 2.2

   c. .516

   d. Between .20 and .40
   Exact p-value $= .2535$

   e. Do not reject H_0; no reason to change from 2 hours for cost estimating

36. a. $z = \dfrac{\bar{p} - p_0}{\sqrt{\dfrac{p_0(1 - p_0)}{n}}} = \dfrac{.68 - .75}{\sqrt{\dfrac{.75(1 - .75)}{300}}} = -2.80$

   p-value $= .0026$
   p-value $\leq .05$; reject H_0

   b. $z = \dfrac{.72 - .75}{\sqrt{\dfrac{.75(1 - .75)}{300}}} = -1.20$

   p-value $= .1151$
   p-value $> .05$; do not reject H_0

   c. $z = \dfrac{.70 - .75}{\sqrt{\dfrac{.75(1 - .75)}{300}}} = -2.00$

p-value $= .0228$
p-value $\leq .05$; reject H_0

   d. $z = \dfrac{.77 - .75}{\sqrt{\dfrac{.75(1 - .75)}{300}}} = .80$

   p-value $= .7881$
   p-value $> .05$; do not reject H_0

38. a. $H_0: p = .64$
   $H_a: p \neq .64$

   b. $\bar{p} = 52/100 = .52$

   $z = \dfrac{\bar{p} - p_0}{\sqrt{\dfrac{p_0(1 - p_0)}{n}}} = \dfrac{.52 - .64}{\sqrt{\dfrac{.64(1 - .64)}{100}}} = -2.50$

   p-value $= 2(.0062) = .0124$

   c. p-value $\leq .05$; reject H_0
   Proportion differs from the reported .64

   d. Yes, because $\bar{p} = .52$ indicates that fewer believe the supermarket brand is as good as the name brand

40. a. 21

   b. $H_0: p \geq .46$
   $H_a: p < .46$
   p-value $\approx .0436$

   c. Yes, .0436

42. a. $\bar{p} = .15$

   b. .0718 to .2282

   c. The return rate for the Houston store is different than the national average

44. a. $H_0: p \leq .51$
   $H_a: p > .51$

   b. $\bar{p} = .58$, p-value $= .0026$

   c. Reject H_0; people working the night shift get drowsy more often

46.

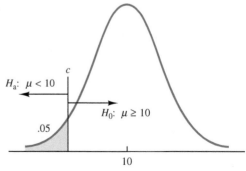

$c = 10 - 1.645(5/\sqrt{120}) = 9.25$
Reject H_0 if $\bar{x} \leq 9.25$

   a. When $\mu = 9$,

   $z = \dfrac{9.25 - 9}{5/\sqrt{120}} = .55$

   $P(\text{Reject } H_0) = (1.0000 - .7088) = .2912$

   b. Type II error

c. When $\mu = 8$,

$$z = \frac{9.25 - 8}{5/\sqrt{120}} = 2.74$$

$$\beta = (1.0000 - .9969) = .0031$$

48. a. Concluding $\mu \leq 15$ when it is not true
   b. .2676
   c. .0179

49. a. $H_0: \mu \geq 25$
   $H_a: \mu < 25$
   Reject H_0 if $z \leq -2.05$

$$z = \frac{\bar{x} - \mu_0}{\sigma/\sqrt{n}} = \frac{\bar{x} - 25}{3/\sqrt{30}} = -2.05$$

   Solve for $\bar{x} = 23.88$
   Decision Rule: Accept H_0 if $\bar{x} > 23.88$
   Reject H_0 if $\bar{x} \leq 23.88$

   b. For $\mu = 23$,

$$z = \frac{23.88 - 23}{3/\sqrt{30}} = 1.61$$

$$\beta = 1.0000 - .9463 = .0537$$

   c. For $\mu = 24$,

$$z = \frac{23.88 - 24}{3/\sqrt{30}} = -.22$$

$$\beta = 1.0000 - .4129 = .5871$$

   d. The Type II error cannot be made in this case; note that when $\mu = 25.5$, H_0 is true; the Type II error can only be made when H_0 is false

50. a. Concluding $\mu = 28$ when it is not true
   b. .0853, .6179, .6179, .0853
   c. .9147

52. .1151, .0015
   Increasing n reduces β

54. $n = \dfrac{(z_\alpha + z_\beta)^2 \sigma^2}{(\mu_0 - \mu_a)^2} = \dfrac{(1.645 + 1.28)^2 (5)^2}{(10 - 9)^2} = 214$

56. 109

57. At $\mu_0 = 400$, $\alpha = .02$; $z_{.02} = 2.05$
   At $\mu_a = 385$, $\beta = .10$; $z_{.10} = 1.28$
   With $\sigma = 30$,

$$n = \frac{(z_\alpha + z_\beta)^2 \sigma^2}{(\mu_0 - \mu_a)^2} = \frac{(2.05 + 1.28)^2 (30)^2}{(400 - 385)^2} = 44.4 \text{ or } 45$$

58. 324

60. a. $H_0: \mu = 16$
   $H_a: \mu \neq 16$
   b. .0286; reject H_0
   Readjust line
   c. .2186; do not reject H_0
   Continue operation
   d. $z = 2.19$; reject H_0
   $z = -1.23$; do not reject H_0
   Yes, same conclusion

62. a. $H_0: \mu \leq 119,155$
   $H_a: \mu > 119,155$

b. .0047
c. Reject H_0; mean annual income for theatergoers in Bay Area is higher

64. $t = -1.05$
   p-value between .20 and .40
   Exact p-value $= .2999$
   Do not reject H_0; there is no evidence to conclude that the age at which women had their first child has changed

66. $t = 2.26$
   p-value between .01 and .025
   Exact p-value $= .0155$
   Reject H_0; mean cost is greater than $125,000

68. a. $H_0: p \leq .80$
   $H_a: p > .80$
   Conclude that airline travelers feel security will be improved
   b. Cannot reject H_0; mandatory use is not recommended

70. a. $H_0: p \leq .80$
   $H_a: p > .80$
   b. .84
   c. .0418
   d. Reject H_0; more than 80% of customers are satisfied with service of home agents

72. $H_0: p \geq .90$
   $H_a: p < .90$
   p-value $= .0808$
   Do not reject H_0; claim of at least 90% cannot be rejected

74. a. $H_0: \mu \leq 72$
   $H_a: \mu > 72$
   b. .2912
   c. .7939
   d. 0, because H_0 is true

76. a. 45
   b. .0192, .2358, .7291, .7291, .2358, .0192

d. $\hat{y} = 68 - 3x$

e. 38

4. a.

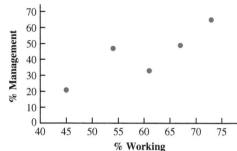

b. There appears to be a positive linear relationship between the percentage of women working in the five companies (x) and the percentage of management jobs held by women in that company (y)

c. Many different straight lines can be drawn to provide a linear approximation of the relationship between x and y; in part (d) we will determine the equation of a straight line that "best" represents the relationship according to the least squares criterion

d. $\bar{x} = \dfrac{\Sigma x_i}{n} = \dfrac{300}{5} = 60$ $\bar{y} = \dfrac{\Sigma y_i}{n} = \dfrac{215}{5} = 43$

$\Sigma(x_i - \bar{x})(y_i - \bar{y}) = 624$ $\Sigma(x_i - \bar{x})^2 = 480$

$b_1 = \dfrac{\Sigma(x_i - \bar{x})(y_i - \bar{y})}{\Sigma(x_i - \bar{x})^2} = \dfrac{624}{480} = 1.3$

$b_0 = \bar{y} - b_1\bar{x} = 43 - 1.3(60) = -35$

$\hat{y} = -35 + 1.3x$

e. $\hat{y} = -35 + 1.3x = -35 + 1.3(60) = 43\%$

6. c. $\hat{y} = -70.391 + 17.175x$

e. 43.8 or approximately 44%

8. c. $\hat{y} = .2046 + .9077x$

e. 3.29 or approximately 3.3

10. c. $\hat{y} = -167.81 + 2.7149x$

e. Yes

12. c. $\hat{y} = 17.49 + 1.0334x$

d. \$150

14. c. $\hat{y} = 37.1217 + .51758x$

d. 73

15. a. $\hat{y}_i = .2 + 2.6x_i$ and $\bar{y} = 8$

x_i	y_i	$\hat{y}_i$	$y_i - \hat{y}_i$	$(y_i - \hat{y}_i)^2$	$y_i - \bar{y}$	$(y_i - \bar{y})^2$
1	3	2.8	.2	.04	−5	25
2	7	5.4	1.6	2.56	−1	1
3	5	8.0	−3.0	9.00	−3	9
4	11	10.6	.4	.16	3	9
5	14	13.2	.8	.64	6	36
				SSE = 12.40		SST = 80

$SSR = SST - SSE = 80 - 12.4 = 67.6$

Chapter 14

1. a.

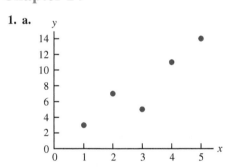

b. There appears to be a positive linear relationship between x and y

c. Many different straight lines can be drawn to provide a linear approximation of the relationship between x and y; in part (d) we will determine the equation of a straight line that "best" represents the relationship according to the least squares criterion

d. Summations needed to compute the slope and y-intercept:

$\bar{x} = \dfrac{\Sigma x_i}{n} = \dfrac{15}{5} = 3$, $\bar{y} = \dfrac{\Sigma y_i}{n} = \dfrac{40}{5} = 8$,

$\Sigma(x_i - \bar{x})(y_i - \bar{y}) = 26$, $\Sigma(x_i - \bar{x})^2 = 10$

$b_1 = \dfrac{\Sigma(x_i - \bar{x})(y_i - \bar{y})}{\Sigma(x_i - \bar{x})^2} = \dfrac{26}{10} = 2.6$

$b_0 = \bar{y} - b_1\bar{x} = 8 - (2.6)(3) = 0.2$

$\hat{y} = 0.2 - 2.6x$

e. $\hat{y} = .2 + 2.6x = .2 + 2.6(4) = 10.6$

2. b. There appears to be a negative linear relationship between x and y

b. $r^2 = \dfrac{\text{SSR}}{\text{SST}} = \dfrac{67.6}{80} = .845$

The least squares line provided a good fit; 84.5% of the variability in y has been explained by the least squares line

c. $r_{xy} = \sqrt{.845} = +.9192$

16. a. SSE = 230, SST = 1850, SSR = 1620

b. $r^2 = .876$

c. $r_{xy} = -.936$

18. a. $\bar{x} = \Sigma x_i/n = 600/6 = 100$ $\bar{y} = \Sigma y_i/n = 330/6 = 55$

SST $= \Sigma(y_i - \bar{y})^2 = 1800$ SSE $= \Sigma(y_i - \hat{y}_i)^2 = 287.624$

SSR $=$ SST $-$ SSR $= 1800 - 287.624 = 1512.376$

b. $r^2 = \dfrac{\text{SSR}}{\text{SST}} = \dfrac{1512.376}{1800} = .84$

c. $r = \sqrt{r^2} = \sqrt{.84} = .917$

20. a. $\hat{y} = 28{,}574 - 1439x$

b. $r^2 = .864$

c. $6989

22. a. .77

b. Yes

c. $r_{xy} = +.88$, strong

23. a. $s^2 = \text{MSE} = \dfrac{\text{SSE}}{n-2} = \dfrac{12.4}{3} = 4.133$

b. $s = \sqrt{\text{MSE}} = \sqrt{4.133} = 2.033$

c. $\Sigma(x_i - \bar{x})^2 = 10$

$$s_{b_1} = \dfrac{s}{\sqrt{\Sigma(x_i - \bar{x})^2}} = \dfrac{2.033}{\sqrt{10}} = .643$$

d. $t = \dfrac{b_1 - \beta_1}{s_{b_1}} = \dfrac{2.6 - 0}{.643} = 4.044$

From the t table (3 degrees of freedom), area in tail is between .01 and .025

p-value is between .02 and .05

Using Excel or Minitab, the p-value corresponding to $t = 4.04$ is .0272

Because p-value $\leq \alpha$, we reject H_0: $\beta_1 = 0$

e. MSR $= \dfrac{\text{SSR}}{1} = 67.6$

$$F = \dfrac{\text{MSR}}{\text{MSE}} = \dfrac{67.6}{4.133} = 16.36$$

From the F table (1 numerator degree of freedom and 3 denominator), p-value is between .025 and .05

Using Excel or Minitab, the p-value corresponding to $F = 16.36$ is .0272

Because p-value $\leq \alpha$, we reject H_0: $\beta_1 = 0$

Source of Variation	Sum of Squares	Degrees of Freedom	Mean Square	F	p-value
Regression	67.6	1	67.6	16.36	.0272
Error	12.4	3	4.133		
Total	80	4			

24. a. 76.6667

b. 8.7560

c. .6526

d. Significant; p-value = .0193

e. Significant; p-value = .0193

26. a. In the statement of exercise 18, $\hat{y} = 23.194 + .318x$

In solving exercise 18, we found SSE = 287.624

$s^2 = \text{MSE} = \text{SSE}/(n-2) = 287.624/4 = 71.906$

$s = \sqrt{\text{MSE}} = \sqrt{71.906} = 8.4797$

$\Sigma(x - \bar{x})^2 = 14{,}950$

$$s_{b_1} = \dfrac{s}{\sqrt{\Sigma(x-\bar{x})^2}} = \dfrac{8.4797}{\sqrt{14{,}950}} = .0694$$

$$t = \dfrac{b_1}{s_{b_1}} = \dfrac{.318}{.0694} = 4.58$$

Using t table (4 degrees of freedom), area in tail is between .005 and .01

p-value is between .01 and .02

Using Excel, the p-value corresponding to $t = 4.58$ is .010

Because p-value $\leq \alpha$, we reject H_0: $\beta_1 = 0$; there is a significant relationship between price and overall score

b. In exercise 18 we found SSR = 1512.376

MSR = SSR/1 = 1512.376/1 = 1512.376

$F = $ MSR/MSE $= 1512.376/71.906 = 21.03$

Using F table (1 degree of freedom numerator and 4 denominator), p-value is between .025 and .01

Using Excel, the p-value corresponding to $F = 11.74$ is .010

Because p-value $\leq \alpha$, we reject H_0: $\beta_1 = 0$

c.

Source of Variation	Sum of Squares	Degrees of Freedom	Mean Square	F	p-value
Regression	1512.376	1	1512.376	21.03	.010
Error	287.624	4	71.906		
Total	1800	5			

28. They are related; p-value = .000

30. Significant; p-value = .0042

32. a. $s = 2.033$

$\bar{x} = 3$, $\Sigma(x_i - \bar{x})^2 = 10$

$$s_{\hat{y}*} = s\sqrt{\dfrac{1}{n} + \dfrac{(x* - \bar{x})^2}{\Sigma(x_i - \bar{x})^2}}$$

$$= 2.033\sqrt{\dfrac{1}{5} + \dfrac{(4-3)^2}{10}} = 1.11$$

b. $\hat{y}* = .2 + 2.6x* = .2 + 2.6(4) = 10.6$

$\hat{y}* \pm t_{\alpha/2}s_{\hat{y}*}$

$10.6 \pm 3.182(1.11)$

10.6 ± 3.53, or 7.07 to 14.13

c. $s_{\text{pred}} = s\sqrt{1 + \dfrac{1}{n} + \dfrac{(x^* - \bar{x})^2}{\Sigma(x_i - \bar{x})^2}}$

$= 2.033\sqrt{1 + \dfrac{1}{5} + \dfrac{(4 - 3)^2}{10}} = 2.32$

d. $\hat{y}^* \pm t_{\alpha/2}s_{\text{pred}}$

$10.6 \pm 3.182(2.32)$

10.6 ± 7.38, or 3.22 to 17.98

34. Confidence interval: 8.65 to 21.15

Prediction interval: -4.50 to 41.30

35. a. $\hat{y}^* = 2090.5 + 581.1x^* = 2090.5 + 581.1(3) = 3833.8$

b. $s = \sqrt{\text{MSE}} = \sqrt{21,284} = 145.89$

$\bar{x} = 3.2, \Sigma(x_i - \bar{x})^2 = 0.74$

$s_{\hat{y}^*} = s\sqrt{\dfrac{1}{n} + \dfrac{(x^* - \bar{x})^2}{\Sigma(x_i - \bar{x})^2}}$

$= 145.89\sqrt{\dfrac{1}{6} + \dfrac{(3 - 3.2)^2}{0.74}} = 68.54$

$\hat{y}^* \pm t_{\alpha/2}s_{\hat{y}^*}$

$3833.8 \pm 2.776(68.54) = 3833.8 \pm 190.27$

or \$3643.53 to \$4024.07

c. $s_{\text{pred}} = s\sqrt{1 + \dfrac{1}{n} + \dfrac{(x^* - \bar{x})^2}{\Sigma(x_i - \bar{x})^2}}$

$= 145.89\sqrt{1 + \dfrac{1}{6} + \dfrac{(3 - 3.2)^2}{0.74}} = 161.19$

$\hat{y}^* \pm t_{\alpha/2}s_{\text{pred}}$

$3833.8 \pm 2.776(161.19) = 3833.8 \pm 447.46$

or \$3386.34 to \$4281.26

d. As expected, the prediction interval is much wider than the confidence interval. This is due to the fact that it is more difficult to predict the starting salary for one new student with a GPA of 3.0 than it is to estimate the mean for all students with a GPA of 3.0.

36. a. \$112,190 to \$119,810

b. \$104,710 to \$127,290

38. a. \$5046.67

b. \$3815.10 to \$6278.24

c. Not out of line

40. a. 9

b. $\hat{y} = 20.0 + 7.21x$

c. 1.3626

d. $\text{SSE} = \text{SST} - \text{SSR} = 51,984.1 - 41,587.3 = 10,396.8$

$\text{MSE} = 10,396.8/7 = 1485.3$

$F = \dfrac{\text{MSR}}{\text{MSE}} = \dfrac{41,587.3}{1485.3} = 28.0$

From the F table (1 numerator degree of freedom and 7 denominator), p-value is less than .01

Using Excel or Minitab, the p-value corresponding to $F = 28.0$ is .0011

Because p-value $\leq \alpha = .05$, we reject H_0: $\beta_1 = 0$

e. $\hat{y} = 20.0 + 7.21(50) = 380.5$, or \$380,500

42. a. $\hat{y} = 80.0 + 50.0x$

b. 30

c. Significant; p-value $= .000$

d. \$680,000

44. b. Yes

c. $\hat{y} = 2044.38 - 28.35$ weight

d. Significant; p-value $= .000$

e. .774; a good fit

45. a. $\bar{x} = \dfrac{\Sigma x_i}{n} = \dfrac{70}{5} = 14, \bar{y} = \dfrac{\Sigma y_i}{n} = \dfrac{76}{5} = 15.2,$

$\Sigma(x_i - \bar{x})(y_i - \bar{y}) = 200, \Sigma(x_i - \bar{x})^2 = 126$

$b_1 = \dfrac{\Sigma(x_i - \bar{x})(y_i - \bar{y})}{\Sigma(x_i - \bar{x})^2} = \dfrac{200}{126} = 1.5873$

$b_0 = \bar{y} - b_1\bar{x} = 15.2 - (1.5873)(14) = -7.0222$

$\hat{y} = -7.02 + 1.59x$

b.

x_i	y_i	$\hat{y}_i$	$y_i - \hat{y}_i$
6	6	2.52	3.48
11	8	10.47	-2.47
15	12	16.83	-4.83
18	20	21.60	-1.60
20	30	24.78	5.22

c.

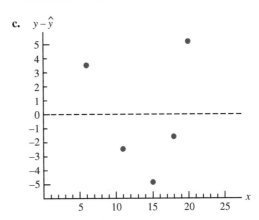

With only five observations, it is difficult to determine whether the assumptions are satisfied; however, the plot does suggest curvature in the residuals, which would indicate that the error term assumptions are not satisfied; the scatter diagram for these data also indicates that the underlying relationship between x and y may be curvilinear

d. $s^2 = 23.78$

$h_i = \dfrac{1}{n} + \dfrac{(x_i - \bar{x})^2}{\Sigma(x_i - \bar{x})^2} = \dfrac{1}{5} + \dfrac{(x_i - 14)^2}{126}$

x_i	h_i	$s_{y_i - \hat{y}_i}$	$y_i - \hat{y}_i$	Standardized Residuals
6	.7079	2.64	3.48	1.32
11	.2714	4.16	-2.47	-.59
15	.2079	4.34	-4.83	-1.11
18	.3270	4.00	-1.60	-.40
20	.4857	3.50	5.22	1.49

e. The plot of the standardized residuals against $\hat{y}$ has the same shape as the original residual plot; as stated in part (c), the curvature observed indicates that the assumptions regarding the error term may not be satisfied

46. a. $\hat{y} = 2.32 + .64x$

    b. No; the variance appears to increase for larger values of x

47. a. Let x = advertising expenditures and y = revenue

$$\hat{y} = 29.4 + 1.55x$$

    b. SST = 1002, SSE = 310.28, SSR = 691.72

$$MSR = \frac{SSR}{1} = 691.72$$

$$MSE = \frac{SSE}{n-2} = \frac{310.28}{5} = 62.0554$$

$$F = \frac{MSR}{MSE} = \frac{691.72}{62.0554} = 11.15$$

From the F table (1 numerator degree of freedom and 5 denominator), p-value is between .01 and .025

Using Excel or Minitab, p-value = .0206

Because p-value $\le \alpha = .05$, we conclude that the two variables are related

    c.

x_i	y_i	$\hat{y}_i = 29.40 + 1.55x_i$	$y_i - \hat{y}_i$
1	19	30.95	−11.95
2	32	32.50	−.50
4	44	35.60	8.40
6	40	38.70	1.30
10	52	44.90	7.10
14	53	51.10	1.90
20	54	60.40	−6.40

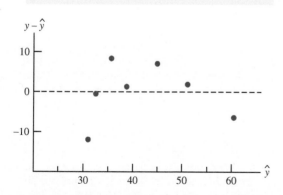

    d. The residual plot leads us to question the assumption of a linear relationship between x and y; even though the relationship is significant at the $\alpha = .05$ level, it would be extremely dangerous to extrapolate beyond the range of the data

48. b. Yes

50. a. Using Minitab, we obtained the estimated regression equation $\hat{y} = 66.1 + .402x$; a portion of the Minitab

output is shown in Figure D14.50; the fitted values and standardized residuals are shown:

x_i	y_i	$\hat{y}_i$	Standardized Residuals
135	145	120.41	2.11
110	100	110.35	−1.08
130	120	118.40	.14
145	120	124.43	−.38
175	130	136.50	−.78
160	130	130.47	−.04
120	110	114.38	−.41

    b.

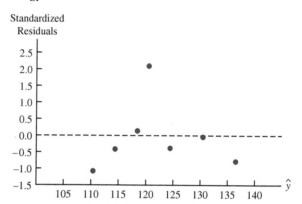

The standardized residual plot indicates that the observation $x = 135$, $y = 145$ may be an outlier; note that this observation has a standardized residual of 2.11

    c. The scatter diagram is shown:

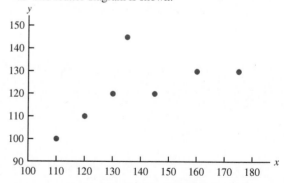

The scatter diagram also indicates that the observation $x = 135$, $y = 145$ may be an outlier; the implication is that for simple linear regression outliers can be identified by looking at the scatter diagram

52. b. $\hat{y} = 91.0 - 0.917x$

    b. Smithsonian Institution: outlier
American Cancer Society: influential observation

54. b. Value = −252 + 5.83 Revenue

    c. There are five unusual observations (9, 19, 21, 22, and 32).

58. b. $\hat{y} = -669 + .157$ DJIA
   c. Significant; p-value $= .001$
   d. $r^2 = .949$; excellent fit

60. b. GR(%) $= 25.4 + .285$ RR(%)
   c. Significant; p-value $= .000$
   d. No; $r^2 = .449$
   e. Yes
   f. Yes

62. a. $\hat{y} = 22.2 - .148x$
   b. Significant relationship; p-value $= .028$
   c. Good fit; $r^2 = .739$
   d. 12.294 to 17.271

64. a. $\hat{y} = 220 + 132x$

   b. Significant; p-value $= .000$
   c. $r^2 = .873$; very good fit
   d. \$559.50 to \$933.90

66. a. Market beta $= .95$
   b. Significant; p-value $= .029$
   c. $r^2 = .470$; not a good fit
   d. Xerox has a higher risk

68. b. There appears to be a negative linear relationship between the two variables
   c. $\hat{y} = 16.5 - .0588$ Miles
   d. Significant; p-value $= .000$
   e. $r^2 = .539$; reasonably good fit
   g. approximately \$13,000; no

FIGURE D14.50

```
The regression equation is
Y = 66.1 + 0.402 X

Predictor      Coef      SE Coef       T        p
Constant      66.10        32.06     2.06    0.094
X            0.4023       0.2276     1.77    0.137

S = 12.62      R-sq = 38.5%      R-sq(adj) = 26.1%

Analysis of Variance

SOURCE             DF         SS        MS       F        p
Regression          1      497.2     497.2    3.12    0.137
Residual Error      5      795.7     159.1
Total               6     1292.9

Unusual Observations
Obs      X         Y        Fit    SE Fit    Residual    St Resid
  1    135    145.00     120.42      4.87       24.58        2.11R

   R denotes an observation with a large standardized residual
```

Chapter 15

2. a. The estimated regression equation is
   $\hat{y} = 45.06 + 1.94x_1$
   An estimate of y when $x_1 = 45$ is
   $\hat{y} = 45.06 + 1.94(45) = 132.36$
   b. The estimated regression equation is
   $\hat{y} = 85.22 + 4.32x_2$
   An estimate of y when $x_2 = 15$ is
   $\hat{y} = 85.22 + 4.32(15) = 150.02$
   c. The estimated regression equation is
   $\hat{y} = -18.37 + 2.01x_1 + 4.74x_2$
   An estimate of y when $x_1 = 45$ and $x_2 = 15$ is
   $\hat{y} = -18.37 + 2.01(45) + 4.74(15) = 143.18$

4. a. \$255,000

5. a. The Minitab output is shown in Figure D15.5a
   b. The Minitab output is shown in Figure D15.5b
   c. It is 1.60 in part (a) and 2.29 in part (b); in part (a) the coefficient is an estimate of the change in revenue due to a one-unit change in television advertising expenditures; in part (b) it represents an estimate of the change in revenue due to a one-unit change in television advertising expenditures when the amount of newspaper advertising is held constant
   d. Revenue $= 83.2 + 2.29(3.5) + 1.30(1.8) = 93.56$ or \$93,560

FIGURE D15.5a

```
The regression equation is
Revenue = 88.6 + 1.60 TVAdv


Predictor        Coef     SE Coef          T          p
Constant       88.638       1.582      56.02      0.000
TVAdv          1.6039      0.4778       3.36      0.015


S = 1.215     R-sq = 65.3%      R-sq(adj) = 59.5%

Analysis of Variance


SOURCE             DF          SS          MS          F          p
Regression          1      16.640      16.640      11.27     0.015
Residual Error      6       8.860       1.477
Total               7      25.500
```

FIGURE D15.5b

```
The regression equation is
Revenue = 83.2 + 2.29 TVAdv + 1.30 NewsAdv


Predictor        Coef     SE Coef          T          p
Constant       83.230       1.574      52.88      0.000
TVAdv          2.2902      0.3041       7.53      0.001
NewsAdv        1.3010      0.3207       4.06      0.010


S = 0.6426    R-sq = 91.9%      R-sq(adj) = 88.7%

Analysis of Variance


SOURCE             DF          SS          MS          F          p
Regression          2      23.435      11.718      28.38     0.002
Residual Error      5       2.065       0.413
Total               7      25.500
```

6. a. Win% = −58.8 + 16.4 Yds/Att
b. Win% = 97.5 − 1600 Int/Att
c. Win% = −5.8 + 12.9 Yds/Att − 1084 Int/Att
d. 35%

8. a. Overall = 69.3 + .235 Shore Excursions
b. Overall = 45.2 + .253 Shore Excursions
        + .248 Food/Dining
c. 87.76 or approximately 88.

10. a. R/IP = .676 − .284 SO/IP
b. R/IP = .308 + 1.35 HR/IP
c. R/IP = .537 − .248 SO/IP + 1.03 HR/IP
d. .48
e. Suggestion does not make sense

12. a. $R^2 = \dfrac{\text{SSR}}{\text{SST}} = \dfrac{14{,}052.2}{15{,}182.9} = .926$

b. $R_a^2 = 1 - (1 - R^2)\dfrac{n - 1}{n - p - 1}$

$= 1 - (1 - .926)\dfrac{10 - 1}{10 - 2 - 1} = .905$

c. Yes; after adjusting for the number of independent variables in the model, we see that 90.5% of the variability in y has been accounted for

14. a. .75
b. .68

15. a. $R^2 = \dfrac{\text{SSR}}{\text{SST}} = \dfrac{23.435}{25.5} = .919$

$R_a^2 = 1 - (1 - R^2)\dfrac{n - 1}{n - p - 1}$

$= 1 - (1 - .919)\dfrac{8 - 1}{8 - 2 - 1} = .887$

b. Multiple regression analysis is preferred because both R^2 and R_a^2 show an increased percentage of the variability of y explained when both independent variables are used

16. a. No, $R^2 = .577$

b. Better fit with multiple regression

18. a. $R^2 = .563$, $R_a^2 = .512$

b. The fit is not very good

19. a. $\text{MSR} = \dfrac{\text{SSR}}{p} = \dfrac{6216.375}{2} = 3108.188$

$\text{MSE} = \dfrac{\text{SSE}}{n - p - 1} = \dfrac{507.75}{10 - 2 - 1} = 72.536$

b. $F = \dfrac{\text{MSR}}{\text{MSE}} = \dfrac{3108.188}{72.536} = 42.85$

From the F table (2 numerator degrees of freedom and 7 denominator), p-value is less than .01

Using Excel or Minitab the p-value corresponding to $F = 42.85$ is .0001

Because p-value $\leq \alpha$, the overall model is significant

c. $t = \dfrac{b_1}{s_{b_1}} = \dfrac{.5906}{.0813} = 7.26$

p-value $= .0002$

Because p-value $\leq \alpha$, β_1 is significant

d. $t = \dfrac{b_2}{s_{b_2}} = \dfrac{.4980}{.0567} = 8.78$

p-value $= .0001$

Because p-value $\leq \alpha$, β_2 is significant

20. a. Significant; p-value $= .000$

b. Significant; p-value $= .000$

c. Significant; p-value $= .002$

22. a. SSE $= 4000$, $s^2 = 571.43$, MSR $= 6000$

b. Significant; p-value $= .008$

23. a. $F = 28.38$

p-value $= .002$

Because p-value $\leq \alpha$, there is a significant relationship

b. $t = 7.53$

p-value $= .001$

Because p-value $\leq \alpha$, β_1 is significant and x_1 should not be dropped from the model

c. $t = 4.06$

p-value $= .010$

Because p-value $\leq \alpha$, β_2 is significant and x_2 should not be dropped from the model

24. a. $\hat{y} = -.682 + .0498\,\text{Revenue} + .0147\,\%\,\text{Wins}$

b. Significant; p-value $= .001$

c. Revenue is significant; p-value $= .001$
%Wins is significant; p-value $= .025$

26. a. Significant; p-value $= .001$

b. All significant; p-values are all $< \alpha = .05$

28. a. Using Minitab, the 95% confidence interval is 132.16 to 154.16

b. Using Minitab, the 95% prediction interval is 111.13 at 175.18

29. a. See Minitab output in Figure D15.5b.

$\hat{y} = 83.23 + 2.29(3.5) + 1.30(1.8) = 93.555$ or $\$93,555$

b. Minitab results: 92.840 to 94.335, or $\$92,840$ to $\$94,335$

c. Minitab results: 91.774 to 95.401, or $\$91,774$ to $\$95,401$

30. a. 46.758 to 50.646

b. 44.815 to 52.589

32. a. $E(y) = \beta_0 + \beta_1 x_1 + \beta_2 x_2$

where $x_2 = \begin{cases} 0 \text{ if level 1} \\ 1 \text{ if level 2} \end{cases}$

b. $E(y) = \beta_0 + \beta_1 x_1 + \beta_2(0) = \beta_0 + \beta_1 x_1$

c. $E(y) = \beta_0 + \beta_1 x_1 + \beta_2(1) = \beta_0 + \beta_1 x_1 + \beta_2$

d. $\beta_2 = E(y \mid \text{level 2}) - E(y \mid \text{level 1})$

β_1 is the change in $E(y)$ for a 1-unit change in x_1 holding x_2 constant

34. a. $\$15,300$

b. $\hat{y} = 10.1 - 4.2(2) + 6.8(8) + 15.3(0) = 56.1$
Sales prediction: $\$56,100$

c. $\hat{y} = 10.1 - 4.2(1) + 6.8(3) + 15.3(1) = 41.6$
Sales prediction: $\$41,600$

36. a. $\hat{y} = 1.86 + 0.291\,\text{Months} + 1.10\,\text{Type} - 0.609\,\text{Person}$

b. Significant; p-value $= .002$

c. Person is not significant; p-value $= .167$

38. a. $\hat{y} = -91.8 + 1.08\,\text{Age} + .252\,\text{Pressure} + 8.74\,\text{Smoker}$

b. Significant; p-value $= .01$

c. 95% prediction interval is 21.35 to 47.18 or a probability of .2135 to .4718; quit smoking and begin some type of treatment to reduce his blood pressure

39. a. The Minitab output is shown in Figure D15.39

b. Minitab provides the following values:

x_i	y_i	$\hat{y}_i$	Standardized Residual
1	3	2.8	.16
2	7	5.4	.94
3	5	8.0	-1.65
4	11	10.6	.24
5	14	13.2	.62

FIGURE D15.39

```
The regression equation is
Y = 0.20 + 2.60 X

Predictor       Coef     SE Coef        T        p
Constant       0.200       2.132     0.09    0.931
X             2.6000      0.6429     4.04    0.027

S = 2.033      R-sq = 84.5%      R-sq(adj) = 79.3%

Analysis of Variance
SOURCE            DF         SS         MS       F       p
Regression         1     67.600     67.600   16.35   0.027
Residual Error     3     12.400      4.133
Total              4     80.000
```

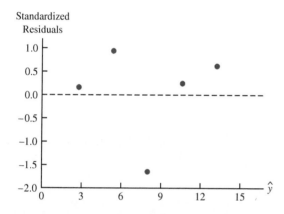

The point (3, 5) does not appear to follow the trend of the remaining data; however, the value of the standardized residual for this point, -1.65, is not large enough for us to conclude that (3, 5) is an outlier

c. Minitab provides the following values:

x_i	y_i	Studentized Deleted Residual
1	3	.13
2	7	.91
3	5	−4.42
4	11	.19
5	14	.54

$t_{.025} = 4.303$ ($n - p - 2 = 5 - 1 - 2 = 2$ degrees of freedom)

Because the studentized deleted residual for (3, 5) is $-4.42 < -4.303$, we conclude that the 3rd observation is an outlier

40. a. $\hat{y} = -53.3 + 3.11x$

b. $-1.94, -.12, 1.79, .40, -1.90$; no

c. $.38, .28, .22, .20, .92$; no

d. $.60, .00, .26, .03, 11.09$; yes, the fifth observation

41. a. The Minitab output appears in Figure D15.5b; the estimated regression equation is

Revenue $= 83.2 + 2.29$ TVAdv $+ 1.30$ NewsAdv

b. Minitab provides the following values:

$\hat{y}_i$	Standardized Residual	$\hat{y}_i$	Standardized Residual
96.63	−1.62	94.39	1.10
90.41	−1.08	94.24	−.40
94.34	1.22	94.42	−1.12
92.21	−.37	93.35	1.08

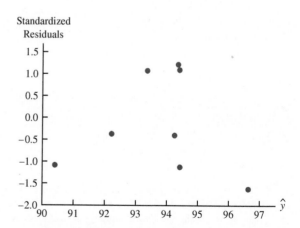

With relatively few observations, it is difficult to determine whether any of the assumptions regarding ϵ have been violated; for instance, an argument could be made that there does not appear to be any pattern in the plot; alternatively, an argument could be made that there is a curvilinear pattern in the plot

c. The values of the standardized residuals are greater than -2 and less than $+2$; thus, using this test, there are no outliers

As a further check for outliers, we used Minitab to compute the following studentized deleted residuals:

Observation	Studentized Deleted Residual	Observation	Studentized Deleted Residual
1	−2.11	5	1.13
2	−1.10	6	−.36
3	1.31	7	−1.16
4	−.33	8	1.10

$t_{.025} = 2.776$ ($n - p - 2 = 8 - 2 - 2 = 4$ degrees of freedom)

Because none of the studentized deleted residuals are less than −2.776 or greater than 2.776, we conclude that there are no outliers in the data

d. Minitab provides the following values:

Observation	h_i	D_i
1	.63	1.52
2	.65	.70
3	.30	.22
4	.23	.01
5	.26	.14
6	.14	.01
7	.66	.81
8	.13	.06

The critical leverage value is

$$\frac{3(p + 1)}{n} = \frac{3(2 + 1)}{8} = 1.125$$

Because none of the values exceed 1.125, we conclude that there are no influential observations; however, using Cook's distance measure, we see that $D_1 > 1$ (rule of thumb critical value); thus, we conclude that the first observation is influential

Final conclusion: observation 1 is an influential observation

42. b. Unusual trend
 c. No outliers
 d. Observation 2 is an influential observation

44. a. $E(y) = \dfrac{e^{\beta_0 + \beta_1 x}}{1 + e^{\beta_0 + \beta_1 x}}$
 b. Estimate of the probability that a customer who does not have a Simmons credit card will make a purchase
 c. $\hat{g}(x) = -0.9445 + 1.0245x$
 d. .28 for customers who do not have a Simmons credit card .52 for customers who have a Simmons credit card
 e. Estimated odds ratio = 2.79

46. a. $E(y) = \dfrac{e^{\beta_0 + \beta_1 x}}{1 + e^{\beta_0 + \beta_1 x}}$
 b. $E(y) = \dfrac{e^{-2.6355 + 0.22018x}}{1 + e^{-2.6355 + 0.22018x}}$
 c. Significant; p-value = .0002
 d. .39

e. $1200
f. Estimated odds ratio = 1.25

48. a. $E(y) = \dfrac{e^{\beta_0 + \beta_1 x_1 + \beta_2 x_2}}{1 + e^{\beta_0 + \beta_1 x_1 + \beta_2 x_2}}$
 b. $\hat{g}(x) = -39.4982 + 3.37449$ Wet + 1.81628 Noise
 c. .88
 d. Probability is .04

50. b. 67.39

52. a. $\hat{y} = -1.41 + .0235x_1 + .00486x_2$
 b. Significant; p-value = .0001
 c. Both significant
 d. $R^2 = .937$; $R_a^2 = 9.19$; good fit

54. a. Buy Again = −7.522 + 1.8151 Steering
 b. Yes
 c. Buy Again = −5.388 + .6899 Steering + .9113 Treadwear
 d. Significant; p-value = .001

56. a. $\hat{y} = 4.9090 + 10.4658$ FundDE + 21.6823 FundIE
 b. $R^2 = .6144$; reasonably good fit
 c. $\hat{y} = 1.1899 + 6.8969$ FundDE + 17.6800 FundIE
     + 0.0265 Net Asset Value ($)
     + 6.4564 Expense Ratio (%)
     Net Asset Value ($) is not significant and can be deleted
 d. $\hat{y} = -4.6074 + 8.1713$ FundDE + 19.5194 FundIE
     + 5.5197 Expense Ratio (%) + 5.9237 3StarRank
     + 8.2367 4StarRank + 6.6241 5StarRank
 e. 15.28%

Chapter 16

1. a. The Minitab output is shown in Figure D16.1a
 b. Because the p-value corresponding to $F = 6.85$ is .059 > α = .05, the relationship is not significant
 c.

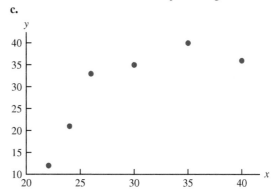

The scatter diagram suggests that a curvilinear relationship may be appropriate
 d. The Minitab output is shown in Figure D16.1d
 e. Because the p-value corresponding to $F = 25.68$ is .013 < α = .05, the relationship is significant
 f. $\hat{y} = -168.88 + 12.187(25) - .17704(25)^2 = 25.145$

FIGURE D16.1a

```
The regression equation is
Y = - 6.8 + 1.23 X

Predictor      Coef    SE Coef        T         p
Constant      -6.77      14.17    -0.48     0.658
X            1.2296     0.4697     2.62     0.059

S = 7.269      R-sq = 63.1%      R-sq(adj) = 53.9%

Analysis of Variance

SOURCE            DF        SS       MS       F        p
Regression         1    362.13   362.13    6.85    0.059
Residual Error     4    211.37    52.84
Total              5    573.50
```

FIGURE D16.1d

```
The regression equation is
Y = - 169 + 12.2 X - 0.177 XSQ

Predictor       Coef    SE Coef        T          p
Constant     -168.88      39.79    -4.74      0.024
X             12.187      2.663     4.58      0.020
XSQ         -0.17704    0.04290    -4.13      0.026

S = 3.248      R-sq = 94.5%      R-sq(adj) = 90.8%

Analysis of Variance

SOURCE            DF        SS       MS       F        p
Regression         2    541.85   270.92   25.68    0.013
Residual Error     3     31.65    10.55
Total              5    573.50
```

2. a. $\hat{y} = 9.32 + .424x$; p-value $= .117$ indicates a weak relationship between x and y
  b. $\hat{y} = -8.10 + 2.41x - .0480x^2$
   $R_a^2 = .932$; a good fit
  c. 20.965

4. a. $\hat{y} = 943 + 8.71x$
  b. Significant; p-value $= .005 < \alpha = .01$

5. a. The Minitab output is shown in Figure D16.5a
  b. Because the p-value corresponding to $F = 73.15$ is $.003 < \alpha = .01$, the relationship is significant; we would reject H_0: $\beta_1 = \beta_2 = 0$
  c. See Figure D16.5c

6. b. No, the relationship appears to be curvilinear
  c. Several possible models; e.g.,
   $\hat{y} = 2.90 - .185x + .00351x^2$

8. a. It appears that a simple linear regression model is not appropriate

  b. Price $= 33829 - 4571$ Rating $+ 154$ RatingSq
  c. logPrice $= -10.2 + 10.4$ logRating
  d. Part (c); higher percentage of variability is explained

10. a. Significant; p-value $= .000$
  b. Significant; p-value $= .000$

11. a. SSE $= 1805 - 1760 = 45$

$$F = \frac{\text{MSR}}{\text{MSE}} = \left(\frac{1760/4}{45/25}\right) = 244.44$$

Because p-value $= .000$, the relationship is significant
  b. SSE$(x_1, x_2, x_3, x_4) = 45$
  c. SSE$(x_2, x_3) = 1805 - 1705 = 100$

  d. $F = \dfrac{(100 - 45)/2}{1.8} = 15.28$

Because p-value $= .000$, x_1 and x_2 are significant

FIGURE D16.5a

```
The regression equation is
Y = 433 + 37.4 X -0.383 XSQ

Predictor          Coef      SE Coef         T        p
Constant          432.6        141.2      3.06    0.055
X                37.429        7.807      4.79    0.017
XSQ             -0.3829       0.1036     -3.70    0.034

S = 15.83      R-sq = 98.0%     R-sq(adj) = 96.7%

Analysis of Variance

SOURCE              DF          SS        MS         F        p
Regression           2       36643     18322     73.15    0.003
Residual Error       3         751       250
Total                5       37395
```

FIGURE D16.5c

```
    Fit      Stdev.Fit                95% C.I.                   95% P.I.
 1302.01        9.93        (1270.41, 1333.61)      (1242.55, 1361.47)
```

12. a. The Minitab output is shown in Figure D16.12a
b. The Minitab output is shown in Figure D16.12b

c. $F = \dfrac{[\text{SSE(reduced)} - \text{SSE(full)}]/(\text{\# extra terms})}{\text{MSE(full)}}$

$= \dfrac{(7.2998 - 4.3240)/2}{.1663} = 8.95$

The p-value associated with $F = 8.95$ (2 numerator degrees of freedom and 26 denominator) is .001; with a p-value $< \alpha = .05$, the addition of the two independent variables is significant

14. a. $\hat{y} = -111 + 1.32\,\text{Age} + .296\,\text{Pressure}$
b. $\hat{y} = -123 + 1.51\,\text{Age} + .448\,\text{Pressure} + 8.87\,\text{Smoker} - .00276\,\text{AgePress}$
c. Significant; p-value $= .000$

16. a. Weeks $= -8.9 + 1.51\,\text{Age}$
b. Weeks $= -.07 + 1.73\,\text{Age} - 2.7\,\text{Manager} - 15.1\,\text{Head} - 17.4\,\text{Sales}$
c. Same as part (b)
d. Same as part (b)
e. Weeks $= 13.1 + 1.64\,\text{Age} - 9.76\,\text{Married} - 19.4\,\text{Head} - 29.0\,\text{Manager} - 19.0\,\text{Sales}$

FIGURE D16.12a

```
The regression equation is
Scoring Avg. = 46.3 + 14.1 Putting Avg.

Predictor           Coef     SE Coef      T        p
Constant          46.277       6.026    7.68    0.000
Putting Avg.      14.103       3.356    4.20    0.000

S = 0.510596     R-Sq = 38.7%     R-Sq(adj) = 36.5%

Analysis of Variance

SOURCE              DF         SS        MS         F        p
Regression           1     4.6036    4.6036     17.66    0.0000
Residual Error      28     7.2998    0.2607
Total               29    11.9035
```

FIGURE D16.12b

```
The regression equation is
Scoring Avg. = 59.0 - 10.3 Greens in Reg.
   + 11.4 Putting Avg - 1.81 Sand Saves

Predictor              Coef     SE Coef           T         p
Constant             59.022       5.774       10.22     0.000
Greens in Reg.      -10.281       2.877       -3.57     0.001
Putting Avg.         11.413       2.760        4.14     0.000
Sand Saves          -1.8130      0.9210       -1.97     0.060

S = 0.407808      R-Sq = 63.7%      R-Sq(adj) = 59.5%

Analysis of Variance

Source             DF          SS          MS         F         p
Regression          3      7.5795      2.5265     15.19     0.000
Residual Error     26      4.3240      0.1663
Total              29     11.9035
```

18. a. RPG = −4.05 + 27.6 OBP

b. A variety of models will provide a good fit; the five-variable model identified using Minitab's Stepwise Regression procedure with Alpha-to-Enter = .10 and Alpha-to-Remove = .10 follows:

RPG = −.0909 + 32.2 OBP + .109 HR − 21.5 AVG
    + .244 3B − .0223 BB

20.

x_1	x_2	x_3	**Treatment**
0	0	0	A
1	0	0	B
0	1	0	C
0	0	1	D

$$E(y) = \beta_0 + \beta_1 x_1 + \beta_2 x_2 + \beta_3 x_3$$

22. Factor A: $x_1 = 0$ if level 1 and 1 if level 2

Factor B:

x_2	x_3	**Level**
0	0	1
1	0	2
0	1	3

$$E(y) = \beta_0 + \beta_1 x_1 + \beta_2 x_2 + \beta_3 x_1 x_2 + \beta_4 x_1 x_3$$

23. a. The dummy variables are defined as follows:

D1	**D2**	**Mfg.**
0	0	1
1	0	2
0	1	3

$$E(y) = \beta_0 + \beta_1 D1 + \beta_2 D2$$

b. The Minitab output is shown below:

```
The regression equation is
TIME = 23.0 + 5.00 D1 - 2.00 D2

Predictor            Coef     SE Coef         T        p
Constant           23.000       1.106     20.80    0.000
D1                  5.000       1.563      3.20    0.011
D2                 -2.000       1.563     -1.28    0.233

S = 2.211         R-Sq = 70.3%    R-Sq(adj) = 63.7%

Analysis of Variance

SOURCE             DF          SS          MS         F        p
Regression          2     104.000      52.000      1064    0.004
Residual Error      9      44.000       4.889
Total              11     148.000
```

c. $H_0: \beta_1 = \beta_2 = 0$

d. The p-value of .004 is less than $\alpha = .05$; therefore, we can reject H_0 and conclude that the mean time to mix a batch of material is not the same for each manufacturer

24. a. Not significant at the .05 level of significance; p-value = .093

b. 139

26. Overall significant; p-value = .029

Individually, none of the variables are significant at the .05 level of significance; a larger sample size would be helpful

28. $d = 1.60$; test is inconclusive

30. a.

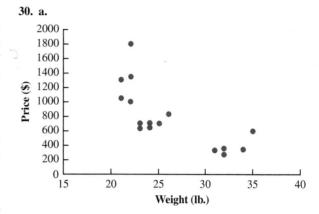

There appears to be a curvilinear relationship between weight and price

b. A portion of the Minitab output follows:

```
The regression equation is
Price = 11376 - 728 Weight + 12.0 WeightSq

Predictor    Coef    SE Coef      T        p
Constant    11376      2565     4.43    0.000
Weight      -728.3     193.7   -3.76    0.002
WeightSq    11.974     3.539    3.38    0.004

S = 242.804    R-Sq = 77.0%    R-Sq(adj) = 74.1%

Analysis of Variance

SOURCE            DF         SS        MS       F        p
Regression         2    3161747   1580874   26.82    0.000
Residual Error    16     943263     58954
Total             18    4105011
```

The results obtained support the conclusion that there is a curvilinear relationship between weight and price

c. A portion of the Minitab output follows:

```
The regression equation is
Price = 1284 - 572 Type_Fitness - 907 Type_Comfort

Predictor        Coef    SE Coef      T        p
Constant      1283.75      95.22   13.48    0.000
Type_Fitness   -571.8      153.5   -3.72    0.002
Type_Comfort   -907.1      145.5   -6.24    0.000

S = 269.328    R-Sq = 71.7%    R-Sq(adj) = 68.2%

Analysis of Variance

SOURCE            DF         SS        MS       F        p
Regression         2    2944410   1472205   20.30    0.000
Residual Error    16    1160601     72538
Total             18    4105011
```

Type of bike appears to be a significant factor in predicting price, but the estimated regression equation developed in part (b) appears to provide a slightly better fit

d. A portion of the Minitab output follows; in this output WxF denotes the interaction between the weight of the bike and the dummy variable Type_Fitness and WxC denotes the interaction between the weight of the bike and the dummy variable Type_Comfort

```
The regression equation is
Price = 5924 - 215 Weight - 6343 Type_Fitness - 7232
          Type_Comfort + 261 WxF + 266 WxC

Predictor          Coef    SE Coef       T        p
Constant           5924       1547    3.83    0.002
Weight          -214.56      71.42   -3.00    0.010
Type_Fitness      -6343       2596   -2.44    0.030
Type_Comfort      -7232       2518   -2.87    0.013
WxF               261.3      111.8    2.34    0.036
WxC              266.41      93.98    2.83    0.014


S = 224.438    R-Sq = 84.0%    R-Sq(adj) = 77.9%

Analysis of Variance

SOURCE            DF         SS        MS       F       p
Regression         5    3450170    690034   13.70   0.000
Residual Error    13     654841     50372
Total             18    4105011
```

By taking into account the type of bike, the weight, and the interaction between these two factors, this estimated regression equation provides an excellent fit

32. a. Delay = 63.0 + 11.1 Industry; no significant positive autocorrelation

34. Significant differences between comfort levels for the three types of browsers; p-value = .034

Chapter 17

1. The following table shows the calculations for parts (a), (b), and (c):

Week	Time Series Value	Forecast	Forecast Error	Absolute Value of Forecast Error	Squared Forecast Error	Percentage Error	Absolute Value of Percentage Error
1	18						
2	13	18	−5	5	25	−38.46	38.46
3	16	13	3	3	9	18.75	18.75
4	11	16	−5	5	25	−45.45	45.45
5	17	11	6	6	36	35.29	35.29
6	14	17	−3	3	9	−21.43	21.43
			Totals	22	104	−51.30	159.38

a. $MAE = \dfrac{22}{5} = 4.4$

b. $MSE = \dfrac{104}{5} = 20.8$

c. $MAPE = \dfrac{159.38}{5} = 31.88$

d. Forecast for week 7 is 14

2. The following table shows the calculations for parts (a), (b), and (c):

Week	Time Series Value	Forecast	Forecast Error	Absolute Value of Forecast Error	Squared Forecast Error	Percentage Error	Absolute Value of Percentage Error
1	18						
2	13	18.00	−5.00	5.00	25.00	−38.46	38.46
3	16	15.50	0.50	0.50	0.25	3.13	3.13
4	11	15.67	−4.67	4.67	21.81	−42.45	42.45
5	17	14.50	2.50	2.50	6.25	14.71	14.71
6	14	15.00	−1.00	1.00	1.00	−7.14	7.14
			Totals	13.67	54.31	−70.21	105.86

a. $MAE = \dfrac{13.67}{5} = 2.73$

b. $MSE = \dfrac{54.31}{5} = 10.86$

c. $MAPE = \dfrac{105.89}{5} = 21.18$

d. Forecast for week 7 is

$$\frac{18 + 13 + 16 + 11 + 17 + 14}{6} = 14.83$$

4. a. $MSE = \dfrac{363}{6} = 60.5$

Forecast for month 8 is 15

b. $MSE = \dfrac{216.72}{6} = 36.12$

Forecast for month 8 is 18

c. The average of all the previous values is better because MSE is smaller

5. a. The data appear to follow a horizontal pattern

b. Three-week moving average

Week	Time Series Value	Forecast	Forecast Error	Squared Forecast Error
1	18			
2	13			
3	16			
4	11	15.67	−4.67	21.78
5	17	13.33	3.67	13.44
6	14	14.67	−0.67	0.44
			Total	35.67

$$MSE = \frac{35.67}{3} = 11.89$$

The forecast for week 7 $= \dfrac{(11 + 17 + 14)}{3} = 14$

c. Smoothing constant $= .2$

Week	Time Series Value	Forecast	Forecast Error	Squared Forecast Error
1	18			
2	13	18.00	−5.00	25.00
3	16	17.00	−1.00	1.00
4	11	16.80	−5.80	33.64
5	17	15.64	1.36	1.85
6	14	15.91	−1.91	3.66
			Total	65.15

$$MSE = \frac{65.15}{5} = 13.03$$

The forecast for week 7 is $.2(14) + (1 - .2)15.91 = 15.53$

d. The three-week moving average provides a better forecast since it has a smaller MSE

e. Smoothing constant $= .4$

Week	Time Series Value	Forecast	Forecast Error	Squared Forecast Error
1	18			
2	13	18.00	−5.00	25.00
3	16	16.00	0.00	0.00
4	11	16.00	−5.00	25.00
5	17	14.00	3.00	9.00
6	14	15.20	−1.20	1.44
			Total	60.44

$$MSE = \frac{60.44}{5} = 12.09$$

The exponential smoothing forecast using $\alpha = .4$ provides a better forecast than the exponential smoothing forecast using $\alpha = .2$ since it has a smaller MSE

6. a. The data appear to follow a horizontal pattern

b. MSE $= \dfrac{110}{4} = 27.5$

The forecast for week 8 is 19

c. MSE $= \dfrac{252.87}{6} = 42.15$

The forecast for week 7 is 19.12

d. The three-week moving average provides a better forecast since it has a smaller MSE

e. MSE $= 39.79$

The exponential smoothing forecast using $\alpha = .4$ provides a better forecast than the exponential smoothing forecast using $\alpha = .2$ since it has a smaller MSE

8. a.

Week	4	5	6	7	8	9	10	11	12
Forecast	19.33	21.33	19.83	17.83	18.33	18.33	20.33	20.33	17.83

b. MSE $= 11.49$

Prefer the unweighted moving average here; it has a smaller MSE

c. You could always find a weighted moving average at least as good as the unweighted one; actually the unweighted moving average is a special case of the weighted ones where the weights are equal

10. b. The more recent data receive the greater weight or importance in determining the forecast; the moving averages method weights the last n data values equally in determining the forecast

12. a. The data appear to follow a horizontal pattern

b. MSE(3-Month) $= .12$
MSE(4-Month) $= .14$
Use 3-Month moving averages

c. 9.63

13. a. The data appear to follow a horizontal pattern

b.

Month	Time-Series Value	3-Month Moving Average Forecast	(Error)²	$\alpha = .2$ Forecast	(Error)²
1	240				
2	350			240.00	12100.00
3	230			262.00	1024.00
4	260	273.33	177.69	255.60	19.36
5	280	280.00	0.00	256.48	553.19
6	320	256.67	4010.69	261.18	3459.79
7	220	286.67	4444.89	272.95	2803.70
8	310	273.33	1344.69	262.36	2269.57
9	240	283.33	1877.49	271.89	1016.97
10	310	256.67	2844.09	265.51	1979.36
11	240	286.67	2178.09	274.41	1184.05
12	230	263.33	1110.89	267.53	1408.50
		Totals	17,988.52		27,818.49

MSE (3-Month) $= 17,988.52/9 = 1998.72$
MSE ($\alpha = .2$) $= 27,818.49/11 = 2528.95$

Based on the preceding MSE values, the 3-Month moving averages appear better; however, exponential smoothing was penalized by including month 2, which was difficult for any method to forecast; using only the errors for months 4 to 12, the MSE for exponential smoothing is

$$\text{MSE}(\alpha = .2) = 14{,}694.49/9 = 1632.72$$

Thus, exponential smoothing was better considering months 4 to 12

c. Using exponential smoothing,

$$F_{13} = \alpha Y_{12} + (1 - \alpha)F_{12}$$
$$= .20(230) + .80(267.53) = 260$$

14. a. The data appear to follow a horizontal pattern

b. Values for months 2–12 are as follows:

105.00   114.00   115.80   112.56   105.79   110.05
120.54   126.38   118.46   106.92   104.85

$$\text{MSE} = 510.29$$

c. Values for months 2–12 are as follows:

105.00   120.00   120.00   112.50   101.25   110.63
127.81   133.91   116.95   98.48   99.24

$$\text{MSE} = 540.55$$

Conclusion: A smoothing constant of .3 is better than a smoothing constant of .5 since the MSE is less for 0.3

16. a.

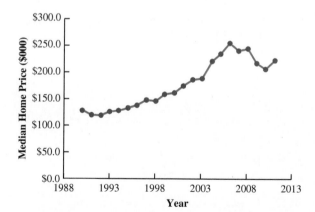

The time series plot exhibits a trend pattern; although the recession of 2008 led to a downturn in prices, the median price rose from 2010 to 2011

b. The methods discussed in this section are only applicable for a time series that has a horizontal pattern; because the time series plot exhibits a trend pattern, the methods discussed in this section are not appropriate

c. In 2003 the median price was $189,500, and in 2004 the median price was $222,300, so, it appears that the time series shifted to a new level in 2004; the time series plot using just the data for 2004 and later follows

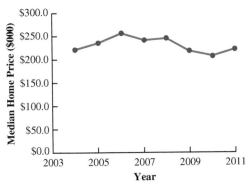

This time series plot exhibits a horizontal pattern; therefore, the methods discussed in this section are appropriate

17. a. The time series plot shows a linear trend

b. $\bar{t} = \dfrac{\sum_{t=1}^{n} t}{n} = \dfrac{15}{5} = 3$ $\bar{Y} = \dfrac{\sum_{t=1}^{n} Y_t}{n} = \dfrac{55}{5} = 11$

$\Sigma(t - \bar{t})(Y_t - \bar{Y}) = 21$ $\Sigma(t - \bar{t})^2 = 10$

$b_1 = \dfrac{\sum_{t=1}^{n}(t - \bar{t})(Y_t - \bar{Y})}{\sum_{t=1}^{n}(t - \bar{t})^2} = \dfrac{21}{10} = 2.1$

$b_0 = \bar{Y} - b_1\bar{t} = 11 - (2.1)(3) = 4.7$

$T_t = 4.7 + 2.1t$

c. $T_6 = 4.7 + 2.1(6) = 17.3$

18. Forecast for week 6 is 21.16

20. a. The time series plot exhibits a curvilinear trend
b. $T_t = 107.857 - 28.9881t + 2.65476t^2$
c. 45.86

21. a.

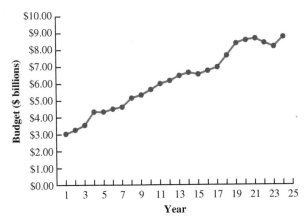

b. $\bar{t} = \dfrac{\sum_{t=1}^{n} t}{n} = \dfrac{300}{24} = 12.5$ $\bar{Y} = \dfrac{\sum_{t=1}^{n} Y_t}{n} = \dfrac{148.2}{24} = 6.175$

$\Sigma(t - \bar{t})(Y_t - \bar{Y}) = 290.86$ $\Sigma(t - \bar{t})^2 = 1150$

$b_1 = \dfrac{\sum_{t=1}^{n}(t - \bar{t})(Y_t - \bar{Y})}{\sum_{t=1}^{n}(t - \bar{t})^2} = \dfrac{290.86}{1150} = .25292$

$b_0 = \bar{Y} - b_1\bar{x} = 6.175 - (.25292)(12.5) = 3.0135$

c. $\hat{y} = 3.0135 + .25292(25) = 9.34$

Forecast for 2012 is $9.34 billion

22. a.

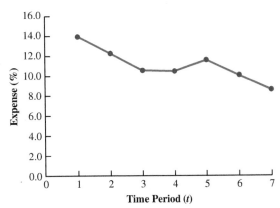

The time series plot shows a downward linear trend

b. $\bar{t} = \dfrac{\sum_{t=1}^{n} t}{n} = \dfrac{28}{7} = 4$ $\bar{Y} = \dfrac{\sum_{t=1}^{n} Y_t}{n} = \dfrac{77}{7} = 11$

$\Sigma(t - \bar{t})(Y_t - \bar{Y}) = -19.6$ $\Sigma(t - \bar{t})^2 = 28$

$b_1 = \dfrac{\sum_{t=1}^{n}(t - \bar{t})(Y_t - \bar{Y})}{\sum_{t=1}^{n}(t - \bar{t})^2} = \dfrac{-19.6}{28} = -.7$

$b_0 = \bar{Y} - b_1\bar{t} = 11 - (-.7)(4) = 13.8$

$T_t = 13.8 - .7t$

c. 2013 corresponds to time period $t = 8$, $T_8 = 13.8 - .7(8) = 8.2$

d. If SCF can continue to decrease the percentage of funds spent on administrative and fundraising by .7% per year, the forecast of expenses for 2018 is 4.70%

24. a. The time series plot shows a linear trend
b. $T_t = 7.5623 - .07541t$
c. 6.7328
d. Given the uncertainty in global market conditions, making a prediction for December using only time is not recommended

26. a. A linear trend is not appropriate
b. $T_t = 5.702 + 2.889t - 1618t^2$
c. 17.90

28. a. The time series plot shows a horizontal pattern, but there is a seasonal pattern in the data; for instance, in each year the lowest value occurs in quarter 2 and the highest value occurs in quarter 4

b. A portion of the Minitab regression output is shown;

```
The regression equation is
Value = 77.0 - 10.0 Qtr1 - 30.0
        Qtr2 - 20.0 Qtr3
```

c. The quarterly forecasts for next year are as follows:

Quarter 1 forecast = $77.0 - 10.0(1) - 30.0(0) - 20.0(0) = 67$

Quarter 2 forecast = $77.0 - 10.0(0) - 30.0(1) - 20.0(0) = 47$

Quarter 3 forecast = $77.0 - 10.0(0) - 30.0(0) - 20.0(1) = 57$

Quarter 4 forecast = $77.0 - 10.0(0) - 30.0(0) - 20.0(0) = 77$

30. a. There appears to be a seasonal pattern in the data and perhaps a moderate upward linear trend

b. A portion of the Minitab regression output follows:

```
The regression equation is
Value = 2492 - 712 Qtr1 - 1512
        Qtr2 + 327 Qtr3
```

c. The quarterly forecasts for next year are as follows:

Quarter 1 forecast is 1780
Quarter 2 forecast is 980
Quarter 3 forecast is 2819
Quarter 4 forecast is 2492

d. A portion of the Minitab regression output follows:

```
The regression equation is
Value = 2307 - 642 Qtr1 - 1465
        Qtr2 + 350 Qtr3 + 23.1 t
```

The quarterly forecasts for next year are as follows:

Quarter 1 forecast is 2058
Quarter 2 forecast is 1258
Quarter 3 forecast is 3096
Quarter 4 forecast is 2769

32. a. The time series plot shows both a linear trend and seasonal effects

b. A portion of the Minitab regression output follows:

```
The regression equation is
Revenue = 70.0 + 10.0 Qtr1 + 105
          Qtr2 + 245 Qtr3
```

Quarter 1 forecast is 80
Quarter 2 forecast is 175
Quarter 3 forecast is 315
Quarter 4 forecast is 70

c. A portion of the Minitab regression output follows

```
The regression equation is
Revenue = -70.1 + 45.0 Qtr1 + 128
          Qtr2 + 257 Qtr3 + 11.7 Period
```

Quarter 1 forecast = is 221
Quarter 2 forecast = is 315
Quarter 3 forecast = is 456
Quarter 4 forecast = is 211

34. a. The time series plot shows seasonal and linear trend effects

b. *Note:* Jan = 1 if January, 0 otherwise; Feb = 1 if February, 0 otherwise; and so on

A portion of the Minitab regression output follows:

```
The regression equation is
Expense = 175 - 18.4 Jan - 3.72 Feb +
          12.7 Mar + 45.7 Apr + 57.1
          May + 135 Jun + 181 Jul + 105
          Aug + 47.6 Sep + 50.6 Oct +
          35.3 Nov + 1.96 Period
```

c. *Note:* The next time period in the time series is Period = 37 (January of Year 4); the forecasts for January–December are 229; 246; 264; 299; 312; 392; 440; 366; 311; 316; 302; 269

35. a. The time series plot indicates a linear trend and a seasonal pattern

b.

Year	Quarter	Time Series Value	Four-Quarter Moving Average	Centered Moving Average
1	1	4		
	2	2		
			3.50	
	3	3		3.750
			4.00	
	4	5		4.125
			4.25	
2	1	6		4.500
			4.75	
	2	3		5.000
			5.25	
	3	5		5.375
			5.50	
	4	7		5.875
			6.25	
3	1	7		6.375
			6.50	
	2	6		6.625
			6.75	
	3	6		
	4	8		

c.

Year	Quarter	Time Series Value	Centered Moving Average	Seasonal-Irregular Component
1	1	4		
	2	2		
	3	3	3.750	0.800
	4	5	4.125	1.212
2	1	6	4.500	1.333
	2	3	5.000	0.600
	3	5	5.375	0.930
	4	7	5.875	1.191
3	1	7	6.375	1.098
	2	6	6.625	0.906
	3	6		
	4	8		

Quarter	Seasonal-Irregular Values		Seasonal Index	Adjusted Seasonal Index
1	1.333	1.098	1.216	1.205
2	0.600	0.906	0.752	0.746
3	0.800	0.930	0.865	0.857
4	1.212	1.191	1.201	1.191
		Total	4.036	

Adjustment for seasonal index $= \dfrac{4.000}{4.036} = 0.991$

36. a.

Year	Quarter	Deseasonalized Value
1	1	3.320
	2	2.681
	3	3.501
	4	4.198
2	1	4.979
	2	4.021
	3	5.834
	4	5.877
3	1	5.809
	2	8.043
	3	7.001
	4	6.717

b. Let Period = 1 denote the time series value in Year 1—Quarter 1; Period = 2 denote the time series value in Year 1—Quarter 2; and so on; a portion of the Minitab regression output treating Period as the independent variable and the Deseasonlized Values as the values of the dependent variable follows:

```
The regression equation is
Deseasonalized Value = 2.42 + 0.422
                       Period
```

c. The quarterly deseasonalized trend forecasts for Year 4 (Periods 13, 14, 15, and 16) are as follows:

Forecast for quarter 1 is 7.906
Forecast for quarter 2 is 8.328
Forecast for quarter 3 is 8.750
Forecast for quarter 4 is 9.172

d. Adjusting the quarterly deseasonalized trend forecasts provides the following quarterly estimates:

Forecast for quarter 1 is 9.527
Forecast for quarter 2 is 6.213
Forecast for quarter 3 is 7.499
Forecast for quarter 4 is 10.924

38. a. The time series plot shows a linear trend and seasonal effects

b. 0.71   0.78   0.83   0.97   1.02   1.30   1.50   1.23
0.98   0.99   0.93   0.79

c.

Month	Deseasonalized Expense
1	239.44
2	230.77
3	246.99
4	237.11
5	235.29
6	242.31
7	240.00
8	235.77
9	244.90
10	242.42
11	247.31
12	246.84
13	253.52
14	262.82
15	259.04
16	252.58
17	259.80
18	253.85
19	266.67
20	272.36
21	265.31
22	272.73
23	274.19
24	278.48
25	274.65
26	269.23
27	277.11
28	288.66
29	284.31
30	300.00
31	280.00
32	268.29
33	295.92
34	297.98
35	301.08
36	316.46

d. Let Period = 1 denote the time series value in January
—Year 1; Period = 2 denote the time series value in
February—Year 2; and so on; a portion of the Minitab regression output treating Period as the independent variable
and the Deseasonlized Values as the values of the dependent variable follows:

```
The regression equation is
Deseasonalized Expense = 228 + 1.96
                           Period
```

e.

Month	Monthly Forecast
January	213.37
February	235.93
March	252.69
April	297.21
May	314.53
June	403.42
July	486.42
August	386.52
September	309.88
October	314.98
November	297.71
December	254.44

40. a. The time series plot indicates a seasonal effect; power
consumption is lowest in the time period 12–4 A.M.,
steadily increases to the highest value in the 12–4 P.M.
time period, and then decreases again. There may also
be some linear trend in the data

b.

Time Period	Adjusted Seasonal Index
12–4 A.M.	0.3256
4–8 A.M.	0.4476
8–12 noon	1.3622
12–4 P.M.	1.6959
4–8 P.M.	1.4578
8–12 midnight	0.7109

c. The following Minitab output shows the results of fitting
a linear trend equation to the deseasonalized time series:

```
The regression equation is
Deseasonalized Power = 63108 + 1854 t
```

Deaseasonalized Power (t = 19) = 63,108 + 1854(19)
= 98,334

Forecast for 12–4 P.M. = 1.6959(98,334) = 166,764.63 or
approximately 166,765 kWh

Deseasonalized Power (t = 20) = 63,108 + 1854(20)
= 100,188

Forecast for 4–8 P.M. = 1.4578(100,188) = 146,054.07 or
approximately 146,054 kWh

Thus, the forecast of power consumption from noon to
8 P.M. is $166{,}765 + 146{,}054 = 312{,}819$ kWh

42. a. The time series plot indicates a horizontal pattern

b.
$$\text{MSE}(\alpha = .2) = 1.40$$
$$\text{MSE}(\alpha = .3) = 1.27$$
$$\text{MSE}(\alpha = .4) = 1.23$$

A smoothing constant of $\alpha = .4$ provides the best forecast
because it has a smaller MSE

c. 31.00

44. a. There appears to be an increasing trend in the data

b. A portion the Minitab regression output follows (*Note*:
$t = 1$ corresponds to 2001, $t = 2$ corresponds to 2002,
and so on)

```
The regression equation is
Balance($) = 1984 + 146 t
```

The forecast for 2009 $(t = 9)$ is Balance($)
$= 1984 + 146(9) = \$3298$

c. A portion of the Minitab regression output follows
(*Note*: $t = 1$ corresponds to 2001, $t = 2$ corresponds to
2002, and so on)

```
The regression equation is
Balance($) = 2924 - 419 t + 62.7 tsq
```

The forecast for 2009 $(t = 9)$ is Balance ($) = 2924 −
$419(9) + 62.7(9)^2 = \$4232$

d. The quadratic trend equation provides the best forecast
accuracy for the historical data

e. Linear trend equation

46. a. The forecast for July is 236.97
Forecast for August, using forecast for July as the actual sales in July, is 236.97
Exponential smoothing provides the same forecast for
every period in the future; this is why it is not usually
recommended for long-term forecasting

b. Using Minitab's regression procedure we obtained the
linear trend equation

$$T_t = 149.72 + 18.451t$$

Forecast for July is 278.88
Forecast for August is 297.33

c. The proposed settlement is not fair since it does not
account for the upward trend in sales; based upon trend
projection, the settlement should be based on forecasted lost sales of $278,880 in July and $297,330 in
August

48. a. The time series plot shows a linear trend

b. $T_t = -5 + 15t$
The slope of 15 indicates that the average increase in
sales is 15 pianos per year

c. 85, 100

50. a.

Quarter	Adjusted Seasonal Index
1	1.2717
2	0.6120
3	0.4978
4	1.6185

Note: Adjustment for seasonal index $= \dfrac{4}{3.8985} = 1.0260$

b. The largest effect is in quarter 4; this seems reasonable since retail sales are generally higher during October, November, and December

52. a. Yes, a linear trend pattern appears to be present

b. A portion of the Minitiab regression output follows:

```
The regression equation is
Number Sold = 22.9 + 15.5 Year
```

c. Forecast in year 8 is or approximately 147 units

54. b. The centered moving average values smooth out the time series by removing seasonal effects and some of the random variability; the centered moving average time series shows the trend in the data

c.

Quarter	Adjusted Seasonal Index
1	0.899
2	1.362
3	1.118
4	0.621

d. Hudson Marine experiences the largest seasonal increase in quarter 2; since this quarter occurs prior to the peak summer boating season, this result seems reasonable, but the largest seasonal effect is the seasonal decrease in quarter 4; this is also reasonable because of decreased boating in the fall and winter